NATURAL RESOURCE CONSERVATION

An Ecological Approach

NATURAL RESOURCE CONSERVATION

An Ecological Approach

SECOND EDITION

Oliver S. Owen Department of Biology, University of Wisconsin, Eau Claire

Macmillan Publishing Co., Inc.
New York

Collier Macmillan Publishers
London

Macmillan Publishing Co., Inc.
866 Third Avenue, New York, New York 10022

Collier-Macmillan Canada, Ltd.

Library of Congress Cataloging in Publication Data

Owen, Oliver S   (date)
    Natural resource conservation: an ecological approach.

    Includes bibliographies.
    1.   Conservation of natural resources—United States.
2.   Ecology—United States.   I.   Title.
S938.087   1975   333.7'2'0973   73-20875
ISBN 0-02-390010-5

Printing: 1 2 3 4 5 6 7 8   Year: 5 6 7 8 9 0

To my wife,

Carol

and our children

Tom, Tim, and Stephanie

May they never be denied the privilege
of hiking through a forest wilderness,
of stalking a deer, or of listening to the
dusk-chant of a whippoorwill.

Preface

I have been very gratified by the enthusiastic response the first edition of this text has received among students and teachers all over the United States. However, even before the ink was dry on the published book, I realized that there were certain important aspects of resource and environmental management that should have been given more adequate treatment. Fortunately, Macmillan, by inviting me to revise the text, has afforded me the opportunity to remedy these deficiencies. For this I am very grateful.

This is not an ordinary revision. It represents a major undertaking—virtually a complete rewriting of the book. Every chapter has either been reorganized, upgraded, or expanded. Moreover, eight entirely new chapters have been written:

Water Pollution
Noise Pollution

The Solid Waste Problem
Poisonous Substances in the Human Environment
The Energy Crisis
Nuclear Energy, Radiation, and Man
Economics and the Environment
The Future of Planet Earth

This second edition provides much more comprehensive treatment than did the original version. I feel that this second edition addresses itself much more effectively not only to the resource picture but to the whole complex of interrelated environmental problems which face America today. Many dozens of additional illustrations are included.

The author wishes to express his thanks to Charles Stewart and Joan Delaney, of Macmillan, for their cooperation and assistance. Thanks are due Judith Kneer for her expert typing of the entire manuscript and also Gerald Kneer for his diligent proofreading. I am very grateful to my brother, Earl Owen, for his suggestions. Finally, and most importantly, I affectionately acknowledge the patience, understanding, and encouragement of my wife, Carol, during the many months of writing. Without her help this second edition would never have been completed.

O. S. O.

Contents

1. Introduction   1

America in Crisis   1
History of the Conservation Movement   6
The Nixon Program   9
Progress Retarded by Governmental
Conflicts   10
Conservation Education   11
Citizen Involvement   11
Public Concern   12
Natural Resource Classification   13
Fundamental Principles of Conservation   15

2. Ecological Concepts 18

Photosynthesis 19
Organization Levels 20
Principles of Ecology 22

3. Nature of Soils 47

Soil Formation 48
Soil Properties 51
Soil Profile 59
Major Soil Groups 62

4. Depletion, Restoration, and Maintenance of Soils 69

History of Land Abuse Abroad 70
History of Land Abuse in America 73
Nature of Soil Erosion 78
Soil Erosion Control in the Rural Environment 83
Soil Conservation Service and Its Program 89
Nature of Soil Nutrients 92
Depletion of Soil Nutrients 93
Restoration of Soil Fertility 95
Soil Nutrients and Human Health 99
Projected Cropland Requirements 99
Soil Problems in the Urban-Suburban Environment 101

5. Man and Water 108

The Hydrologic Cycle 109
Water Use 113
Water Problems 114
Flood Control 121
Irrigation 131
Irrigation Problems 135

6. Water Pollution 140

Nutrients and Eutrophication 142
Oxygen-demanding Organic Wastes 149
Thermal Pollution 153
Disease-producing Organisms 158
Sediments 160

Radioactive Materials 162
Sewage Treatment and Disposal 163
Water Pollution and Industry 170
Enforcement of Pollution Laws 174
New Sources of Water 175

7. Rangelands 187

Rangeland Depletion 189
Taylor Grazing Control Act 191
Grass Plant Biology 192
Effect of Drought on Range Forage 193
Range Management 194
Range Pests and Their Control 206

8. Man and the Forest 216

The Tree: A Living Organism 217
History of Exploitation 226
U.S. Forest Service 231
Forest Management 232
Forest Conservation by Efficient Utilization 268
Meeting Future Timber Demands 270

9. Wildlife 273

History of Abuse and Depletion 274
Extinction of Wildlife 278
Biotic Potential 283
Factors Depleting Waterfowl Populations 286
Factors Depleting Deer Populations 292
Stable, Irruptive, and Cyclic Populations 297
Habitat Requirements of Wildlife 299
Animal Movements 305
Wildlife Management 308
Some Methods of Deer Management 316
Some Methods of Waterfowl Management 320

10. Freshwater Fisheries 334

The Lake Ecosystem 335
The Stream Ecosystem 340
Biotic Potential of Fish 342
Environmental Resistance Encountered by Fish 343
Fisheries Management 354

11. Man and the Ocean 378

Major Features of the Marine Ecosystem 380
Zonation of the Ocean 380
The Estuarine Ecosystem 383
Marine Food Chains and Energy Conversions 386
Marine Fish 387
Marine Shellfish 409
Marine Mammals 414

12. The Pesticide Problem 422

Causes of Pests 423
Manufacture and Use of Pesticides 423
Classification of Pesticides 425
Effect of Pests on Human Welfare 427
Cycling of Pesticides in the Ecosystem 434
Sublethal Effects of Pesticides on Wildlife 439
Effect of Ingested Pesticides on Human Health 442
Biological Control of Pests 444
Integrated Control of Pests 449
Legal Restrictions on Pesticide Use 450
Herbicides and the Ecosystem 453

13. Air Pollution 457

Evolution of the Atmosphere 458
Gases in the Unpolluted Atmosphere 458
Pollution of the Atmosphere 459
Sources of Pollution 466
Influence of Air Circulation Patterns on Pollution 469
Effects of Air Pollution on Climate 474
Effects of Air Pollution on Vegetation 477
Effects of Air Pollution on Animals 480
Effects of Air Pollution on Man 481
Cost of Air Pollution 489
Air Pollution Abatement and Control 490
The Future 501

14. Noise Pollution 504

Nature of Sound 505
Hearing Loss 507
Other Harmful Physiological Effects 508
How Can Noise Be Reduced? 510

Financial Costs of Noise Pollution Control 513
Noise Control Regulations 514
Federal Noise Control Act of 1972 515

15. The Solid Waste Problem 517

Volume of Solid Waste in America 518
Types of Solid Waste 518
Collection Methods 529
Disposal Methods 530

16. Poisonous Substances in the Human Environment 535

Mercury in the Environment 536
Lead in the Environment 541
Asbestos in the Environment 546

17. The Energy Crisis 551

Power Shortages 552
The Great Gasoline Shortage 552
What Has Caused the Energy Crisis? 554
Status of America's Traditional Energy Resources 560
Status of Energy Sources Other Than Fossil Fuels 575
Other Possible Sources of Future Energy 580
Conservation of Energy 581
Project Independence 585
Prospect 586

18. Nuclear Energy, Radiation, and Man 588

What Is Nuclear Energy? 589
The Nuclear Power Plant 591
Effects of Radiation on Human Health 598
The Breeder Reactor 600
Prospect 601

19. The Human Population Problem 604

Population Increase 605
Factors Underlying Reduced Mortality 609
Multiple Effects of Overpopulation 611
Malthusian Principle and Food Scarcity 612
Solving the Food Shortage Problem 615
What of the Future? 643

20. Economics and the Environment 648

The "Cowboy" Versus the "Spaceman" Economy   649
Methods of Pollution Control   655
Environmental Impact of Economic Growth   658
Let's Get Down to Earth   661

21. The Future of Planet Earth 666

International Commission on Environmental Quality   672
Can Man Survive?   674

Glossary 677

Index 689

1.

Introduction

To waste, to destroy, our natural resources to skin and exhaust the land instead of using it so as to increase its usefulness, will result in undermining in the days of our children the very prosperity which we ought by right to hand down to them amplified and developed.

Theodore Roosevelt,
Message to Congress, December 3, 1907

America in Crisis

America is on the sharp edge of crisis. She is degrading her natural environment. She prides herself on conquering outer space, yet after two centuries she still does not know how to manage her "inner" space here on earth. This environmental dilemma is the result of four major factors: (1) rapid population increase, (2)

Figure 1-1. *America prides herself on conquering outer space, yet after two centuries she still does not know how to manage her "inner space" here on earth.* [NASA, Photo by Astronaut Eugene A. Cernan]

pollution, (3) excessive consumption of resources, and (4) the gradual deterioration of a land ethic.

Population Increase. Demographers inform us that the population of the United States will surge upward from the 200 million of 1970 to 245 million by 1980 and 330 million by 2000. The population increase clouds the entire environmental picture and, in a sense, is the underlying cause of our present crisis.

Unless America's population surge is restrained within the very near future, even the most soundly conceived and efficiently implemented conservation practices will be to no avail. An increase in people means an increase in all types of environmental pollution. It means accelerated depletion of natural resources, most of which are already in short supply or of deteriorating quality. It means that greater numbers of people, living in overcrowded conditions, will make increasing demands on wilderness and recreation areas to "get away from it all." With each upward surge of human population, there will be a corresponding surge in the urgency and complexity of our conservation task. As Robert Heilbroner writes, "the most fearsome reality of all [is] a population that is still increasing like an uncontrollable cancer on the surface of the globe. I know of no more sobering statistic in this regard than that between [1970] and 1980 *the number of women in the most fertile age brackets, eighteen to thirty-two, will double.*" (Italics added.)

Pollution.   America, the world's most affluent nation, has also become the most effluent. We are degrading our environment with an ever-increasing variety and volume of contaminants. We are polluting lakes and streams with raw sewage, industrial wastes, radioactive materials, heat, detergents, agricultural fertilizers, and pesticides. We are releasing so many toxic materials into our immediate habitat that Rachel Carson, celebrated author of *Silent Spring,* has identified our era as the "Age of Poisons" (4). Our uncontrolled and indiscriminate use of pesticides has contaminated the entire food chain, so that all animals, including man, are affected. For example, *you, the reader, have perhaps 10 parts per million (ppm) of DDT in your tissues this very moment.* The long-term effects of such concentrations on humans are unknown. However, laboratory studies on experimental animals have shown that a concentration of 7 parts per million of DDT may have deleterious effects on heart and liver functions, and higher concentrations may interfere with reproductive processes, generate harmful mutations, and induce cancers. Many gases—including carbon monoxide, sulfur dioxide, nitrous oxide, and benzopyrenes —most of which are known to cause or contribute to respiratory ailments, are constantly being spewed into the atmosphere. Once quiet urban neighborhoods have succumbed to a noise barrage mounted by an ever-proliferating number of motor bikes, automobiles, air hammers, and trucks.

Consumption of Resources.   Although the United States has only 6 per cent of the population of the non-Communist world, it consumes 40 per cent of the total non-Communist consumption in raw materials (7). Furthermore, during the brief period since World War I (1918), Americans have consumed more of most materials than was consumed by all mankind in his previous history on earth. In his *Resources and the American Dream,* Samuel H. Ordway has suggested that many demands made on resources by the American consumer are excessive and do not contribute to human happiness in any substantial way. Americans are the most overfed, over-housed, overclothed, overmobilized, and overentertained people on earth. Our tremendous consumption of cars, summer homes, color television sets, dishwashers, air conditioners, golf carts, motorized lawn mowers, swimming pools, speed boats, water skis, and so on, certainly does not stem from need. We drive heavier and bigger automobiles than mere transportation requires. For the sake of a quick "pickup" we use high-octane gasoline and spew thousands of tons of irreplaceable lead into the atmosphere. As Harvard's John Galbraith states, "part of our food production . . . contributes not to nutrition but obesity, part of our tobacco contributes not to comfort but to carcinoma . . . part of our clothing . . . is designed not to cover nakedness but to suggest it" (7).

The high rate of consumption is, at least in part, a direct response of the people to an artificial stimulus developed with consummate skill by the want-creating industry—advertising—which is a multibillion-dollar business. On the other hand if Americans should suddenly decrease consumption of goods, the result would be economic chaos. However, there is no doubt that the high consumer demands of our affluent society have adversely affected the quality of our environment, either by using scarce resources unwisely or by increasing pollution.

It is highly questionable whether the gross national product or the sales volume of motor cars or color television sets is a valid measure of human happiness in America. In our hectic scramble for the good life, most of us have lost it. Perhaps we should heed the counsel given by Stewart Udall in *The Quiet Crisis,* "If you

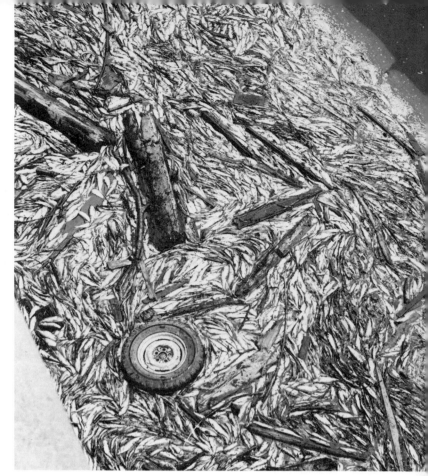

Figure 1-2. *America is polluting her lakes and streams with raw sewage, industrial wastes, radioactive materials, heat, detergents, agricultural fertilizers, and pesticides. Massive fish kills may result.* [N. Y. S. Health photo by M. Dixson]

Figure 1-3. *America is spewing large quantities of solid and gaseous contaminants into the atmosphere. Smoke from the burning of old auto batteries. South side of Houston, Texas. April 1972.* [E. P. A. Documerica—Marc St. Gil]

Figure 1-4. *As a result of the expanding population, even our wilderness is being defiled. Note the debris removed from Blue Star Spring, Yellowstone National Park.*

want inner peace, find it in solitude, not speed, and if you would find yourself, look to the land from which you came and to which you go" (16).

Deterioration of a Land Ethic. It is a curious paradox that at the same time that we have built up our standard of living we have permitted our standard of environment to deteriorate. As Aldo Leopold, eloquent spokesman for environmental quality, states in *A Sand County Almanac*, "We abuse land because we regard it as a commodity belonging to us. When we see land as a community to which we belong, we may begin to use it with love and respect" (12). In 1870 three fourths of all Americans were either farmers or members of small rural communities. They had a daily acquaintance with the age-old inter-relatedness of all aspects of the environment and the living things it supports. Today, however, most Americans are urban dwellers; they are sealed off from the land of their origin by their own constructions. There are many urbanites today who have never breathed the fragrance of spring-plowed earth, heard the drumming of a grouse, or seen the white water of rushing rapids. They have severed their connection with the land. This separation has eroded urban man's respect for the land, if it has not actually made him contemptuous of it. His aesthetic sense has degenerated to the point where he prefers the roar of a hot rod to the call of a thrush.

History of the Conservation Movement

From time to time, early in our nation's history, men with vision such as George Washington, Thomas Jefferson, Patrick Henry, Jared Elliot, and George Perkins Marsh would express their concern over resource depletion and despoilation. The greatest advances in conservation, however, have been made in this century. They have occurred in three "waves"—the first (1900–1910) under the dynamic and forceful leadership of Theodore Roosevelt and Gifford Pinchot, the second (1930's) under the aegis of Franklin D. Roosevelt; the third wave, which is yet cresting, was spearheaded by the late John F. Kennedy and persisted under the administrations of Lyndon B. Johnson and Richard M. Nixon.

The First Wave. President Theodore Roosevelt's decision to call the White House Conference of 1908 was greatly influenced by a number of important events in the several preceding decades: the enactment of several laws that regulated the manner in which the public lands (public domain) should be disposed of (including various mining laws and the Homestead Act of 1862); the deep concern of the American Association for the Advancement of Science over the exploitation and depletion of timber in the Great Lakes states, a concern that was formally presented to Congress in 1870 and again in 1890; a study of arid lands by Major J. W. Powell in the 1870's, which was instrumental in the inclusion of an irrigation section in the U.S. Geological Survey; a 1907 report by the Inland Waterways Commission, headed by Gifford Pinchot, which pointed out that the use and control of water would have an impact on other resources, such as timber, soil, wildlife, and minerals (2). In addition to these factors, there was growing apprehension in 1908 that resource mismanagement might have tragic future consequences if America's rapidly growing population reached the 200 million projected for 1950.

Invited to the White House Conference on Natural Resources were governors, congressional leaders, scientists, informed sportsmen, and foreign experts. The meeting was unique in American history. As a result of the conference a fifty-man National Conservation Commission was formed composed of scientists, statesmen, and businessmen, under the inspirational leadership of Gifford Pinchot. This com-

Figure 1-5. *President Theodore Roosevelt, outdoorsman, big-game hunter, and conservationist, at Yosemite National Park.* [*U.S. Department of Agriculture*]

6

mission eventually completed the nation's first comprehensive natural resource inventory. The White House Conference also indirectly resulted in the formation of forty-one state conservation agencies (many of which are vigorous today) by concerned governors (2, 8).

President Roosevelt employed the natural resource inventory as a basis for withdrawing 200 million acres of public lands from further settlement and entry (making it impossible for private interests to acquire them), with an eye to converting them into permanent public "reserves." Under Roosevelt 148 million acres were added to the National Forests, and 180 million acres of coal lands in the western states and Alaska and 5 million acres of phosphate-bearing lands were withdrawn from the public domain. In addition, 1.5 million acres of watershed were reserved to ensure that future development of their water-power potential would be in the public interest (2).

The Second Wave.   Franklin D. Roosevelt is a notable example of the right man in the right place at the right time. When he assumed office there was urgent need for an imaginative program in job creation (8). President Roosevelt's administration not only created employment, but in the process resolved numerous resource problems as well.

Under the Public Works Administration (PWA), created in 1933, many natural resource development programs were completed with the aid of such federal agencies as the Bureau of Reclamation and the Corps of Engineers. One program initiated by the PWA in 1934 was the Prairie States Forestry Project. Its goal was the establishment of shelter-belts of trees and shrubs along the one-hundredth meridian from the Texan Panhandle to the Canadian border of North Dakota. This project did much to eliminate the destructive effects of wind (2).

The National Resources Board, appointed by Roosevelt, completed the nation's second comprehensive natural resource inventory in 1934. In its report not only did the board cite resource problems, but it described proper remedial measures. Through the effects of this agency, as well as those of the Natural Resource Committee, which superseded it in 1935, there developed a gradual acceptance of the need to plan for future resource requirements on the basis of current resources. Most of the states also established resource planning agencies as a result of the impetus provided by the National Resources Committee.

The Civilian Conservation Corps (CCC), which functioned from 1933 to 1949, profitably engaged almost 2.5 million young men. Much of its work involved conservation projects. At its peak the Corps was organized into 2,652 camps, each with a 200-man capacity, many located in national parks and forests. The forest workers constructed fire lanes, removed fire hazards, fought forest fires, fought pests, and planted millions of trees. The park workers constructed bridges, improved access roads, and built nature trails. In addition, the Corps made lake and stream improvements and participated in flood-control projects, not only on federal lands but even on areas under county or state jurisdiction. The CCC program made outstanding contributions to the conservation of the human resource, for it resulted not only in improved health, skills, and self-respect of the enrollees, but also in decreased delinquency (2, 8).

In 1933 Roosevelt established the Soil Erosion Service. It was superseded in 1935 by the Soil Conservation Service. The time was ripe for such action. The frequent occurrence of "black blizzards" over the Dust Bowl of the Great Plains bore eloquent testimony of the condition of our soils. Not only has the SCS conducted soil conservation demonstrations to show farmers the techniques and importance of erosion control, but it has been actively engaged in basic research (8).

The establishment of the TVA in 1933 was a bold experiment, unique in conservation history, to integrate the resource development (water, soils, forests, wildlife) of an entire river basin. Although highly controversial, it has received international acclaim and has served as a model for similar projects in India and other foreign countries (8).

In 1936 President Roosevelt convened the first North American Wildlife and Resources Conference. Attended by specialists in wildlife management, interested sportsmen, and government officials, it had as its objectives (1) a survey of the wildlife resource, (2) a statement of conservation problems, and (3) techniques and policies by means of which these problems might be resolved. This conference convenes annually to this day.

Through the Wildlife Restoration Act of 1937 the states were given financial assistance in the acquisition and development of suitable lands (grassland for prairie chickens, marshland for waterfowl, and so on) for wildlife.

During World War II and the Korean War all the nation's attention and energies were focused on military victory, even at the cost of resource depletion. In the early 1950's the nation enjoyed unprecedented prosperity. It was exceedingly difficult for an affluent society to generate much enthusiasm for conservation, despite continued resource despoliation. To the man on the street, and to many congressmen, the questions of water and air pollution, soil erosion, pesticides, threatened extinction of wildlife and forest mismanagement lacked immediacy. Anyway, America's "scientific and technological know-how," which had swept her to victory on the world's battlefields, would neatly and effectively provide the remedies.

The Third Wave. The third wave of the conservation effort was initiated under the brilliant leadership of John F. Kennedy, who assumed the presidency in 1961. Kennedy convened a White House Conference in 1962, which was attended by 500 of the nation's leading conservationists. The status of America's resources was reviewed. The main features of Kennedy's natural resource program included preservation of wilderness areas, development of marine resources, reservation of remaining shorelines for public use, expansion of outdoor recreation opportunities, enhancement of freshwater supplies by desalinization, aid to metropolitan areas in solving space problems, formulation of plans for the development of the water resources of all river basins, vigorous action against all forms of pollution, encouragement of scientists and technologists to develop suitable substitutes for resource in short supply, and organization of the Youth Conservation Corps to provide the manpower required to implement much of his program (2).

The impetus given to the conservation movement by Kennedy was sustained after his assassination by his successor, Lyndon B. Johnson. During February of 1965, President Johnson stressed to Congress the urgency of preventing further environmental deterioration and restoring the environment as much as possible to its original state. Many of the bills signed by Johnson were concerned with the upgrading of human resources, control of air and water pollution, preservation of wilderness areas, and environmental beautification. The development of outdoor recreation opportunities for a burgeoning population with unparalleled mobility, leisure, and economic status was also an immediate concern.

The Nixon Program

In his State of the Union message of January, 1970, President Nixon proclaimed, "The great question of the 1970's is: Shall we surrender to our surroundings or shall we make our peace with nature and begin to make reparations for the damage we have done to our air, to our land and to our water?" The main features of his message of environmental import were:

1. A recognition that affluence could not necessarily guarantee happiness: "Our recognition of the truth that wealth and happiness are not the same require us to measure success or failure by new criteria."
2. A promise of a new program for buying wilderness and recreation areas.
3. A proposal to assist states to set and enforce clean air standards by spending $104 million for this purpose.
4. A promise to establish stricter federal auto emission standards.
5. A five-year $10 billion program to enable all municipalities to have modern municipal waste-treatment plants "in every place in America where they are needed to make our waters clean again" (15).

On the face of his message it would appear that the cause of conservation and environmental quality would be well served for the duration of Nixon's term(s) in office. After all, this was the first time in many years that a president had stressed environmental problems and their resolution in a State of the Union address. As *Time* magazine put it:

President Nixon's . . . message illustrated anew how swiftly a once radical idea can become national consensus and good politics. Only a few years ago the thought that the quality of life in America is not good enough, and that the United States is wantonly despoiling its physical environment was the concern mainly of left-wing critics, grumpy academics and dedicated conservationists well out of the mainstream of American politics. Yet . . . the President effectively moved to assume personal command of the gathering battle for a better environment (1).

However, the consensus of most Democrats in Congress and, more significantly, of most professional ecologists and conservationists was that President Nixon did not go nearly far enough in his proposed financial support of environmental quality and antipollution programs. First of all, the federal government would provide only 40 per cent of the $10 billion municipal waste treatment program; the remainder would have to be paid from state and local sources. It might be extremely difficult for communities to raise the necessary monies since their bond markets are very tight. And even if the $10 billion could be raised from combined federal-state-community sources, this would be "peanuts" compared to the sums *really required* in serious, wide-sweeping water pollution abatement. Thus University of Wisconsin ecologist David Archbald states:

In view of the federal government's own estimate that it will take $40 billion just to "clean up" Lake Erie, does the President's proposal of only a $10 billion program mean Lake Erie has been written off as a lost cause? . . . What about sources of water pollution other than municipalities, that in industry, mining, agricultural fertilizers, pesticides, erosion and animal wastes? What about solid waste disposal? (17).

Certainly one of the major accomplishments of the Nixon administration was the organization of the Environmental Protection Agency (EPA). The EPA absorbed the following environment-related responsibilities of several other federal agencies:

1. From the National Air Pollution Control Agency: research on the health effects of atmospheric contaminants; operation of air pollution monitoring networks; establishment and enforcement of air quality standards.
2. From the Federal Water Quality Administration: research on the health effects of water pollution; establishment and enforcement of water quality standards.
3. From the Department of the Interior: research on the lethal and sublethal effects of pesticides on fish, game, fur-bearers, and songbirds.
4. From the Food and Drug Administration: surveillance of pesticide residues in foods.
5. From the Environmental Control Administration: conduct of solid waste management programs.
6. From the Environmental Radiation Standard Program: responsibility for preventing radiation damage to crops, wildlife, livestock, and man as the result of bomb testing or nuclear plant operation, and so on.

The consolidation of these programs under the EPA has eliminated much duplication of effort, promoted more efficient use of available funds, and eliminated much petty inter-agency feuding over jurisdictional authority.

Just what *real* impact the Nixon administration will have on upgrading the American environment remains to be seen.

Progress Retarded by Governmental Conflicts

Early in 1970, Lee A. Du Bridge, President Nixon's science adviser, commented on the enormity of the pollution control problem and the preservation and/or improvement of environmental quality as compared with the Apollo project: "It is unfortunate, but true, that pollution is not just a technical problem, as was the case of putting man on the moon. It is as much sociological as technological. Political personalities, economic interests are involved. There is vast overlapping of authority over environment between government agencies at all levels" (3). Representative of political personality conflicts was the "tug-of-war" between Senators Edmund S. Muskie of Maine and Henry M. Jackson of Washington. In late 1969, each wished to send his own national environmental policy bill to Congress. Muskie, chairman of the Public Works Subcommittee on Air and Water Pollution, and Jackson, Interior Committee chairman, reached such an impasse in an effort to further the jurisdiction of their respective committees that action on the bill was seriously retarded, even though it was eventually enacted into law (15).

Agency conflicts may become just as intense and deleterious to environmental progress as personality differences. Nowhere are agency antagonisms more apparent than between the Departments of Agriculture and Interior. Thus, the taxpayer discovers to his amazement that his money is being used by the Department of Agriculture to pay farmers for draining wetlands at the same time that the Department of the Interior pays farmers to maintain them. On the pesticide issue these departments again are at odds. The Department of Agriculture strongly supported massive DDT applications in insect control (before the DDT "ban" in late 1969), while the Department of Interior favored restricting its employment. The Army Corps of Engineers and the Fish and Wildlife Service have frequently been in conflict—the latter criticizing dam and canal construction by the engineers as being detrimental to wildlife and aesthetics. With such heated bickering occurring at the federal level, there is little wonder that the individual citizen occasionally becomes cynical and apathetic toward environmental issues.

Conservation Education

If America is to win her environmental struggle, it is imperative that appreciation, respect, and understanding of the delicate sun-soil-water-air-organism complex be fostered at the *preschool* level. The old aphorism "as the twig is bent the tree is inclined" is pertinent. Sociologists inform us that many adult attitudes were already shaped before age six. Many European grade schools are far ahead of their American counterparts in the quality of environmental education accomplished. At the Convocation on Ecology and the Human Environment of the St. Albans School (Washington, D.C.), Admiral H. G. Rickover, U.S. Navy, remarked:

> During a visit to Switzerland for the purpose of familiarizing myself with their educational system, I was much impressed by the way ecology was taught in a one-room village school house. It was part of the curriculum through all the primary grades, being presented at first very simply—but always graphically; later, on a more complex level; and always alongside the three R's and history and government, so that the children absorb it as part of their general education. . . . I wonder, too, whether ecology, properly presented at the higher secondary school levels, might not help dissipate the tendency in contemporary thinking of regarding technology as an irresistible force with a momentum of its own that puts it beyond human direction and restraint (13).

Wisconsin's Senator Gaylord Nelson has made strenuous attempts to initiate and/or improve the quality of conservation education at the primary and secondary grade levels. According to Nelson, "Too often elementary and secondary school teachers are uncomfortable with the thought of using the outdoors as a classroom. New techniques are being devised for teacher training to help break down this barrier so the relationships between man and his artificial world and nature can be viewed as a whole" (3). In late 1969 Nelson introduced a bill that would make conservation education a required component of classroom curricula from preschool to postgraduate levels. Through this Environmental Quality Education Act the testing and upgrading of environmental teaching programs would receive federal financial support.

Citizen Involvement

Although definitely aware that their environment is deteriorating at an appalling pace, many Americans feel that somehow, some way, the government will remedy America's current environmental ills. Unfortunately, more often than not, the wheels of government, at high levels, turn slowly. But our environmental posture demands action soon—or not at all. As Archbald put it:

those who rely completely on Washington to point the way in environmental matters are abrogating their own responsibilities. Washington certainly has no monopoly on environmental brains. And often it seems doubtful it even has its share. . . . At the community level the citizenry will have to develop a deeper concern for, identify better with, and take a keener interest in programs on local environmental problems than with national programs with Washington calling the shots. In other words a community will be more inclined to do "its own environmental thing" than to do "Washington's environmental thing." Sometimes forthright action by dedicated citizens at the grassroots and community levels can make significant contributions to mending ecosystems and do it quickly (17).

Archbald describes a novel approach to environmental problems involving a nationally coordinated action program at the community level, completely emancipated from bureaucratic impediment. Named the MEC (Man-Environment Communications) Center, it has been initiated at Madison, Wisconsin, on a trial basis; if successful, other similar community centers will be established. According to Archbald, "the MEC Center will be administered by a board representing all segments of the community. Hence the center will have access to the resources and guidance of the whole community," including university researchers, industrial executives, park and recreations officials, high school teachers, sanitarians, farmers, housewives, sportsmen, and conservation groups. All pertinent reliable pollution data will be fed into the center's computer. When other MEC Centers become established they "will exchange information and maintain close communications." Thus, by pooling their pollution data and experiences, recommendations for action can be made that would be much more reliable and authoritative than if each center operated in isolation (17).

Public Concern

Americans have mounted a crescendo of concern over their nation's environmental posture. The attitude of the general public has changed drastically since 1966. As Jim Kimball, conservation writer for the Minneapolis *Tribune*, recently stated:

Only three or four years ago I was reluctant to write because it sounded like a scare campaign, that the future of man is in jeopardy—is doomed—if he does not change his ways. Now, I am reluctant to write it but for a different reason. So many people are saying it that it is repetitious. In the past five years, or even in the past three years, the thinking of a nation has changed. It must be the fastest change in history on a profound issue. Very recently people thought that a conservationist was a bird watcher, a guy who belonged to a sportsmen's club or someone who didn't take more than his limit of fish. These same people have now added entirely new words to their vocabulary —words such as *ecology, environmental science* and, most important of all, *environmental education*. . . . The activities of man have exterminated hundreds of species, but he never cared very much. Now he cares because suddenly he realizes that his number is up. He may be the next to go . . . (9).

Growing public anxiety for environmental abuse was indicated in a Gallup poll taken a few years ago for the National Wildlife Federation. It indicated that 51 per cent of the people interviewed were seriously disturbed by the gravity of pollution. A heartening development is that even Congress, at long last, is showing concern, as is reflected in the fact that the material on environment inserted by senators and congressmen in the *Congressional Record*, January–June, 1969, was exceeded only by material dealing with the Vietnam War (6).

In late 1969 Senator Nelson and California's Congressman McCloskey called for a nationwide "Environmental Teach-In," in an attempt to marshal the energies of America's college youth "to halt the accelerating pollution and destruction of the environment." There were good reasons for focusing the effort at the student level: First, over 50 per cent of our population is under twenty-five years of age; second, youth are more flexible, more adaptable than their elders, and certainly any significant abatement of our pressing environmental problems will be predicated on substantial social, technological, and cultural changes that will place great demands on such adaptability; and third, America's youth can approach the problem with greater objectivity than their parents since they were not the generation directly responsible for the present crisis.

According to Nelson and McCloskey:

> the present student generation's commitment will determine whether we reverse the present trends. Hopefully, our young people . . . will set specific goals for the 1970's, goals for a decade of national effort which will recognize that environmental quality deserves the same priorities of expenditures as did the moon-shot effort of the 1960's. More than any other issue in this country today, environmental concern cuts across generations, political parties and attitudes (3).

Natural Resource Classification

Any portion of our natural environment—such as soil, water, rangeland, forest, wildlife, minerals, or human populations—that man can utilize to promote his welfare may be identified as a *natural resource*. Natural resources vary greatly in *quantity, mutability, renewability,* and *reusability.* Because the best type of management for a given resource depends upon these characteristics, the following classification scheme [1] is presented:

I. *Inexhaustible*
  A. *Immutable.* Seemingly incapable of much adverse change through man's activities.
    1. *Atomic energy.* Vast quantities of fissionable materials available in granitic rocks.
    2. *Wind power.* The result of climatic conditions.
    3. *Precipitation.* An unlimited supply. Man, however, will very likely alter the distribution pattern in the future. Weather modification.
    4. *Water power of tides.* Resulting from sun-moon-earth relationships.
  B. *Misusable.* Little danger of complete exhaustion, but when improperly used their resource quality may be impaired.
    1. *Solar power.* The total amount received by growing plants has been reduced by air pollution caused by man.
    2. *Atmosphere.* Local and world-wide pollution because of smoke, exhaust fumes, nuclear fallout, and so on.

[1] This scheme is slightly modified from that used by Richard J. Hartesveldt, at San Jose State College, California.

3. *Waters of oceans, lakes, and streams.* All currently being polluted at increasing rates as a result of human activity.
4. *Water power of flowing streams.* The reaction of water to gravity.
5. *Scenery in its broadest sense.* Aesthetic values subject to impairment by human activities. Examples: Mt. Rainier, Blue Ridge Mountains, Oregon and Maine coastlines, Grand Canyon.

II. *Exhaustible*
   A. *Maintainable.* Those resources in which permanency is dependent upon method of use by man.
      1. *Renewable.* The living (biotic) or dynamic resources whose perpetual harvest is dependent upon proper planning and management by man. Improper use results in impairment or exhaustion with adverse socioeconomic consequences for man.
         a. *Water in place.* The quantity and quality of water in specific places of use: streams, lakes, subterranean sources.
         b. *Soil fertility.* The ability of soil to produce plant substance desirable to man. Renewing soil fertility takes time and money.
         c. *Products of the land.* Those resources grown in or dependent upon the soil.
            (1) *Agricultural products.* Vegetables, grains, fruits, fibers, and so on.
            (2) *Forests.* Source of timber and wood pulp.
            (3) *Forage land.* Sustains herds of cattle, sheep, and goats for the production of meat, milk, leather, and wool.
            (4) *Wild animals.* Deer, wolves, eagles, bluebirds, bullfrogs, spotted salamanders, sphinx moths, fireflies, and so on.
         d. *Products of lakes, streams, and impoundments.* Freshwater fish: black bass, lake trout, catfish.
         e. *Products of the ocean.* Marine fish: herring, tuna. Marine mammals: porpoises, gray whales, Pribilof fur seals.
         f. *Human powers.* Physical and spiritual.
      2. *Nonrenewable.* Once gone there is no hope of replacement.
         a. *Species of wildlife.* The passenger pigeon, great auk, and Carolina paroquet have become extinct. They represented the end products of perhaps a million years of evolution.
         b. *Specimen wilderness.* Within several human lifespans wilderness values cannot be restored even with the most dedicated program.
   B. *Nonmaintainable.* The mineral resources. Total quantity is static. Mineral resources are regarded as wasting assets. When destroyed or consumptively used, they cannot be replaced.
      1. *Reusable.* Minerals whose consumptive usage is small. Salvage or reuse potentialities are high.
         a. *Gem minerals.* Rubies, emeralds, and so on.
         b. *Nonconsumptively used metals.* Gold, platinum, and silver; some iron, copper, and aluminum. These metals can be extracted and reworked into new products: jewelry, silverware, vases, and so on.
      2. *Nonreusable.* Those minerals with a high or total consumptive use. Exhaustion is a certainty.
         a. *Fossil fuels.* When consumed, gases (potential pollutants), heat, and water are released.
         b. *Most nonmetallic minerals.* Glass sand, gypsum, salt, and so on.
         c. *Consumptively used metals.* Lead in high-octane gasoline and in paint, zinc in galvanized iron, tin in toothpaste containers, iron in cans, and so on.

Fundamental Principles of Conservation

Harmony between man's resource requirements and the resource base depends upon basic conservation principles, several of which follow. An understanding of these principles is basic to an appreciation of the conservation policy in America today. Although briefly mentioned at this time, they will form the basis of much discussion in later chapters.

1. SENSE OF INDIVIDUAL RESPONSIBILITY. Responsibility and privilege go hand in hand. The privilege of being a citizen of the world's greatest democracy is predicated upon responsibility—to government, to our fellow man, and to the natural resources upon which we depend. The history of the United States has been inexorably intertwined with the manner in which Americans have used or abused their natural resources. The farmer who employs excessive amounts of pesticides, the camper who forgets to extinguish his campfire, the trigger-happy "sportsman" who uses robins as targets to test his marksmanship, the snowmobilist who shears off tomorrow's timber—all defile not only their own resource heritage, but more important, the heritage that belongs to all Americans.

2. ROLE OF GOVERNMENTS. Our nation's resources are so extensive and the problems associated with their intelligent utilization are so complex that it is imperative that their ultimate control be a function of local, state, and federal governments rather than of private interests. State and federal governments, in particular, have at their disposal the know-how of sophisticated specialists—agronomists, hydrologists, geologists, range managers, foresters, ichthyologists, fisheries biologists, ornithologists, mammalogists, wildlife biologists, oceanographers, human ecologists, urban planners, and experts in the areas of pollution control and recreation development. Moreover, government agencies are funded for research and the implementation of research-based programs. Consequently, they are in a position to get a wide view of a given resource problem and to appraise its possible consequences. An example might be gauging the affect of unsound logging practices on the quality or abundance of other resources.

3. MULTIPLE USE OF A GIVEN RESOURCE. A cardinal conservation goal is to "ensure the greatest good for the most people over the long run." Because most resources have multiple functions, the realization of this objective involves delicate and knowledgeable management. For example, a major river may have multiple values: for the swimmer it serves as a refreshing sanctuary from summer heat; for the angler it is the habitat of game fish; for the hunter it provides breeding sites for mallards and teal; for the canoeist it presents a challenge to his skills; for the manufacturer it is an artery for the inexpensive transport of fuel and raw materials and a channel for the discharge of industrial wastes; for the farmer it is a water source for livestock and irrigation systems; for all in the area it may be harnessed to provide inexpensive electricity. It is apparent that the river cannot be all things to all people. Not all of the potential values of a great river can be realized concurrently at the same site. Thus, the interest of the duck hunter in productive waterfowl nesting grounds might conflict with the farmer's interest in irrigation water. Similarly, the interests of anglers and industrialists might be incompatible. The construction of a power dam would effectively block the progress of both canoeists and migratory salmon.

Obviously, such conflicting interests might never be resolved. It is for this reason that local, state, and federal governments have enacted legislation to regulate resource utilization in such a manner as to serve best the interests of current and future generations. As we shall see in later chapters, such legislative control is not invariably successful.

4. INVENTORIES AND PROJECTIONS OF RESOURCE USE. In their scholarly survey of future resource needs, Landsberg, Fischman, and Fisher project America's requirements to the year 2000 (11). They estimate that required cropland will increase from the 1960 figure of 368 million acres to 418 million acres by 2000, an increase of 13.5 per cent. As a result of our population growth the requisite production of paper and paperboard will zoom from 34 million short tons (1960) to 134 million short tons by 2000, an increase of 294 per cent. In 1960 many Americans sought relief from the tensions of their crowded world and paid 93 million visits to 14 million acres of national forests. By 2000 our burgeoning population will require an expanded national forest system of 57 million acres, a 307 per cent increase, in order to accommodate the expected 2,010 million visits. In 1964 New York City and other metropolitan centers along the Atlantic coast were plagued with an acute water shortage, which may be only an indication of future water problems. Water depletion from municipal use will increase 130 per cent, from 6.9 billion gallons per day (bgd) consumed in 1960 to 15.9 bgd by the year 2000. By 2000 the American people will consume 194 million tons of iron and steel, compared to only 72 million tons in 1960, an increase of 169 per cent. Fuel (electricity, coal, oil, gas) consumption will expand 142 per cent from the 3.84 quadrillion British thermal units (BTU's) used in 1960, to 9.32 quadrillion BTU's by 2000. The final projection for land requirements is the most startling. The total land area in the coterminous United States is 1,904 million acres. In 1960 America's total land requirements for all uses (cropland, rangeland, forests, recreation areas, urban land, transportation, wildlife refuges, and reservoirs) was 1,815 million acres, leaving only 89 million residual acres. However, by 2000, projected land requirements will increase 7.6 per cent to 1,954 million acres, a figure that will exceed by 50 million acres our nation's total land area (11). It is apparent that intelligent resource management is predicated upon periodic resource base inventories that are both accurate and comprehensive, such as was initiated during the administration of Theodore Roosevelt. Without such an integrated inventory-projection policy, unexpected future shortages might upset the nation's economy and cause extensive personal suffering.

5. INTERLOCKING RESOURCE RELATIONSHIPS. Over 100 years ago George Perkins Marsh observed how men had abused agricultural lands in Europe and Asia and how this abuse ultimately resulted in the deterioration of the national economy and well-being. After returning to the United States he expounded the concept that man cannot degrade one part of his environment without simultaneously affecting other parts (16). In other words, natural human environment, although infinitely complex and varied, is a dynamic, organic whole and therefore cannot be properly investigated by studying it in isolation. Today resource specialists know that Marsh was correct. For example, the removal of a block of Douglas fir, seemingly simple and conclusive in itself, may have far-reaching effects on other resources such as wildlife, fish, soil, water, rangeland, and even atmosphere and climate. The study of such inter-relationships between organisms and their environment is known as

ecology. Aldo Leopold, late professor of game management at the University of Wisconsin, was a leading and eloquent exponent of the application of ecological concepts to conservation problems. He had the discernment of a great scientist, as is evident in his description of the dynamic interplay of forces involved in the development of mature grassland soil:

> The black prairie was built by the prairie plants, a hundred distinctive species of grasses, herbs and shrubs; by the prairie fungi, insects and bacteria; by the prairie mammals and birds, all interlocked in one humming community of cooperations and competitions—one biota. This biota, through ten thousand years of living and dying, burning and growing, preying and fleeing, freezing and thawing, built that dark and bloody ground we call prairie (12).

In the next chapter we shall examine some basic ecological principles so as to provide a conceptual framework for our discussion of resource problems and the management methods by which these problems may be either mitigated or resolved.

BIBLIOGRAPHY

1. "Action for Survival" (editorial), *Progressive* (Madison, Wis.) (April 1970), 3–6.
2. Allen, Shirley W., and Justin W. Leonard. *Conserving Natural Resources.* New York: McGraw-Hill, 1966.
3. *Audubon* (January 1970).
4. Carson, Rachel. *Silent Spring.* Boston: Houghton, 1962.
5. *Christian Science Monitor* (January 20, 1970).
6. *Congressional Record.* Proceedings and Debates of the 91st Congress, Second Session. Washington, D.C. (January 19, 1970).
7. Galbraith, John Kenneth. "How Much Should a Country Consume?" in Henry Jarrett, ed., *Perspectives on Conservation: Essays on America's Natural Resources.* Baltimore: Johns Hopkins, 1958.
8. Highsmith, Richard M., Jr., J. Granville Jensen, and Robert D. Rudd. *Conservation in the United States.* Chicago: Rand McNally, 1962.
9. Kimball, Jim. Minneapolis *Tribune* (January 18, 1970).
10. Krutch, Joseph Wood. "Dropouts, Do-Gooders, and the Two Cultures," *Amer. Forests* (August 1969), 34, 35, 41.
11. Landsberg, Hans H., Leonard L. Fischman, and Joseph L. Fisher. *Resources in America's Future.* Baltimore: Johns Hopkins, 1962.
12. Leopold, Aldo. *A Sand County Almanac.* New York: Oxford U.P., 1966.
13. Rickover, Admiral H. G. "A Humanistic Technology," *Amer. Forests* (August 1969).
14. Roberts, Walter Orr. "After the Moon, the Earth!" *Science,* 167 (January 2, 1970), 11–16.
15. Trumbull, Van. "Washington Lookout," *Amer. Forests* (November 1969).
16. Udall, Stewart L. *The Quiet Crisis.* New York: Holt, 1963.
17. *Wisconsin State Journal* (February 1, 1970).

2.

Ecological Concepts

There is an old technique used in coal mines of taking a caged canary into the mine, because canaries are much more sensitive to toxic mine gases than men are. When the canary dies, it is time for the miners to leave. The analogue between the coal mine and the biosphere is clear: Man lives in a tiny portion of the total solar system, and he shares it with many other organisms spread through many interconnected ecosystems. We know much about how natural ecosystems operate and how they are interconnected. We also know that the fitness of many ecosystems is deteriorating at an alarming rate. The symptoms of this deterioration, the fish-kills, the bird-deaths, the increasing algal blooms, the replacement of high quality fish by coarse fish are all analogues to the death of the canaries in the coal mines. But the miner can get out of the mine. Man cannot leave the biosphere. (Emphasis added)

W. B. Clapham, Jr.,
Natural Ecosystems,
New York: Macmillan Publishing Co., Inc., 1973

An understanding of certain basic ecological concepts will aid in developing an appreciation of not only the problems facing the conservationist, but also the techniques, policies, and regulations by which these problems might be resolved. Among the basic topics considered in this chapter are photosynthesis, organization levels, elemental cycles, laws of thermodynamics, food chains, food webs, ecological pyramids (numbers, biomass, and energy), tolerance ranges, population growth curves, and population regulating mechanisms.

Photosynthesis

All the energy that powers life's processes can ultimately be traced back to its original source—the sun. The solar energy "flooding" the earth "totals nine million calories per square meter per day assuming 10 hours of sunshine, or more than 36 billion calories per acre per day . . ." (15).

Photosynthesis may be defined as the "process by which solar energy is utilized in the conversion of carbon dioxide and water into sugar." With a few minor exceptions this process can occur only in the presence of *chlorophyll*, a green pigment found in plants, which serves as a catalyst for the reaction. An overall equation for photosynthesis is

$$6CO_2 + 6H_2O + \text{solar energy}$$
$$\rightarrow C_6H_{12}O_6 + 6O_2 + \text{chemical energy}$$

In a sense, the solar energy is "trapped" by chlorophyll and channeled into sugar molecules in the form of chemical energy. The preceding equation is slightly misleading in that it suggests that the carbon dioxide (CO_2) combines directly with water (H_2O) to form sugar ($C_6H_{12}O_6$). In actuality, however, there are two major phases to the reaction: (1) in a process called *photolysis* the solar energy is employed to split the water molecules into hydrogen and oxygen, the latter gas escaping from the plant as a by-product; (2) in a process called *carbon dioxide fixation* the carbon dioxide combines with hydrogen to form sugar. The world's green plants fix 550 billion tons of carbon dioxide annually.

The preceding description of photosynthesis is a gross simplification of an extremely complicated process that involves at least twenty-five individual steps and that is currently the subject of intensive research. Some of the released oxygen may be utilized directly by the plant or may be diffused from the leaf through minute "breathing" pores (*stomata*) into the atmosphere, where it becomes available to other organisms. It has been estimated that if all photosynthesis ceased today, the atmospheric supply of oxygen would be exhausted in 2,000 years. All living things of course would have long since perished. There is considerable concern among some ecologists, such as Lamont Cole, of Cornell University, that the progressive contamination of the marine environment with pesticides and industrial wastes may ultimately impair the photosynthetic activity of marine algae (which currently are responsible for 70 per cent of the world's photosynthetic activity) and greatly diminish the earth's supply of atmospheric oxygen. Another harmful result would be a diminished food base for a human consumer population that might number 7 billion by the year 2000. Except for a few simple organisms such as bacteria, which can secure energy by oxidizing inorganic compounds containing sulfur or iron, every living organism from ameba to the blue whale, is dependent upon photosynthesis for survival.

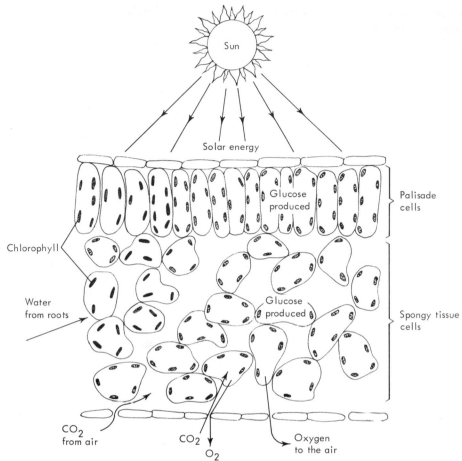

Figure 2-1. *A food factory. A cross-section of a green plant leaf showing some of the aspects of photosynthesis, the food-manufacturing process that occurs in the chloroplasts of the palisade and spongy tissue cells.*

Organization Levels

As anyone who has ever taken a course in biology knows, one of the outstanding characteristics of any living organism is its organization. In ascending order of complexity the organization levels are the following: atom, molecule, cell, tissue, organ, organ system, and organism. Although the ecologist is certainly concerned with each of these levels, most of his attention is usually focused on the supra-organismal levels—the population, community, and ecological system, or *ecosystem*. (Fig. 2-2)

POPULATION. When the layman employs the term *population* he is invariably concerned with numbers of human beings in a given locality. However, the ecologist extends the term to include any organism, human or nonhuman. Thus, he may speak of populations of white pine, black bass, or deer.

COMMUNITY. The layman employs the word *community* in reference to a town or city. The ecologist, on the other hand, would define a *community* as the "total of

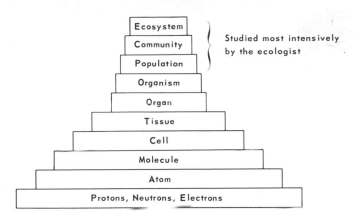

Figure 2-2. *Levels of organization. Units become less numerous but of increasing complexity when considered in a base-apex progression.*

all living organisms occupying a given locality." He might refer to the community of a woodlot, prairie, marsh, or even a rotting log or drop of pond water. The community of your backyard might embrace many thousands of individual organisms representing a great assemblage of species, from soil bacteria and earthworms to thrushes and oaks.

ECOSYSTEM. The environment of any organism is combined of both living (*biotic*) and nonliving (*abiotic*) components such as soil, air, water, and climatic factors. An ecological system, or *ecosystem*, may be defined as any portion of the biosphere in which there is a well-ordered flow of energy and materials between organisms and their environment. Although A. G. Tansley, who coined the term, restricted its application primarily to the *community* level, in recent years the concept has been extended to the levels of *population* and *organism*. Major emphasis is on the cycling of elements; the transfer, utilization, and dissipation of energy; and the rates at which these processes occur. The characteristic features of any ecosystem—whether lake, marsh, prairie, spruce forest, or city—are established and perpetuated by regulatory processes such as growth, reproduction, behavior patterns, physiological adaptations, mortality factors, and mass movements such as immigration, emigration, and migration.

Although it is convenient to consider ecosystems as separate entities, they are isolated only on the pages of ecology textbooks. In the actual world there is frequently some movement from one ecosystem to another, whether immediately adjacent or thousands of miles distant. Thus, topsoil may be blown from an Oklahoma wheat field to the Atlantic Ocean or it may be washed by spring rains into a nearby stream. Snow geese may migrate from the Canadian tundra to a Louisiana rice field. Phosphorus originating in deep marine sediments may eventually be transferred to terrestrial ecosystems as guano deposits by means of the algae-crustacean-fish-cormorant food chain.

As we shall see in later chapters, most measures applied by the conservationist involve ecosystem manipulation. Thus, prevention of winterkill of fish (resulting from oxygen-depleted water) might involve removal of snow cover from an ice-bound lake. This permits sunlight to penetrate the ice and become available to submerged aquatic plants for photosynthesis. The resultant increase in dissolved oxygen could prevent massive fish mortality. In this relatively simple example are interactions between such *nonliving* components as water, solar energy, and oxygen and the *biotic* components represented by aquatic plants, fish, and man.

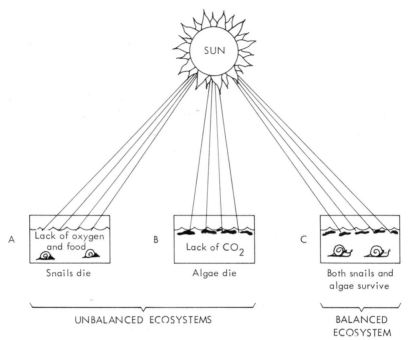

Figure 2-3. *Balanced and unbalanced ecosystems. In aquarium A, the snails die because of lack of food and oxygen. In B, the algae die from lack of the carbon dioxide necessary for photosynthesis. In C, the aquarium occupied by both snails and algae, all organisms survive. There is sufficient food and oxygen for the algae-consuming snails; the algae are able to photosynthesize because they have an adequate supply of carbon dioxide (released by the snails).* [After Amos Turk, Jonathan Turk, and Janet T. Wittes, Ecology, Pollution, Environment (Philadelphia: W.B. Saunders Company, 1972).]

Principles of Ecology

The Elemental Cycles. Roughly 92 elements occur naturally in the universe; of these about 35 to 40 are required by living organisms. These elements are continuously passing from the nonliving environment into the bodies of living organisms and back into the inanimate world in "circular" patterns known as *elemental cycles* (10, 13, 14).

THE NITROGEN CYCLE. Nitrogen, which forms about 3 per cent (by weight) of protoplasm, is an essential component of many important compounds such as

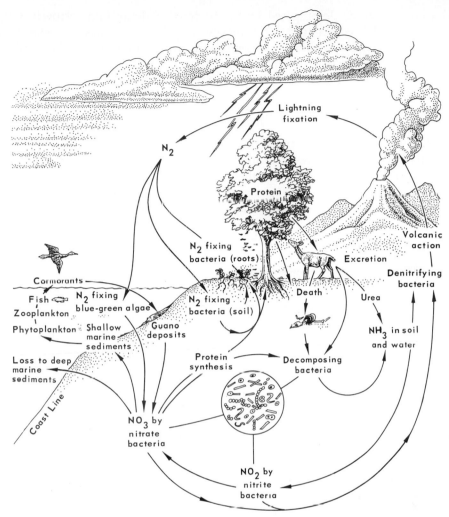

Figure 2-4. *Nitrogen cycle. Observe that nitrates which form in terrestrial ecosystems may be lost to marine ecosystems by water transport to deep ocean sediments. However, land-based nitrates washed into shallow sediments may eventually be returned to the terrestrial ecosystem via the phytoplankton-zooplankton-fish cormorant food chain.* [*Adapted from* Robert L. Smith, Ecology and Field Biology (*New York: Harper & Row, 1966*). *Used by permission of the publishers.*]

chlorophyll, hemoglobin, insulin, and DNA (deoxyribose nucleic acid), the heredity-determining molecule. Let us trace nitrogen from corn to man. Although, like man, corn is unable to utilize atmospheric nitrogen, it is able to use it as a component of soluble nitrates occurring in the soil. Corn absorbs these salts through its roots. Eventually, through a series of chemical reactions, the nitrogen is incorporated in the protein molecules distinctive to corn. When consumed by man these proteins are converted into amino acids by digestive enzymes and are built up into proteins characteristic of man. (Fig. 2-4)

The complex nitrogenous compounds occurring in animal excreta and dead plants and animals may be decomposed by the bacteria of decay into relatively simple ammonia (NH_3) compounds by a process called *ammonification*. The *nitrite bacteria* then convert the ammonia compounds into nitrite salts. A third bacterial group, the *nitrite bacteria* then transform the nitrites into nitrate salts such as potassium nitrate (KNO_3) or calcium nitrate ($Ca\ (NO_3)_2$). The conversion of ammonia compounds into nitrates is called *nitrification*. One "turn" of the nitrogen cycle would be completed when a plant absorbs soluble nitrates from the soil (9, 12, 13).

Certain kinds of soil bacteria, known as *denitrifying bacteria*, may break down ammonia compounds, nitrites and nitrates, and utilize the energy released to sustain their vital activities; in the process they release gaseous nitrogen as a by-product. This process, by means of which gaseous nitrogen is temporarily removed from the cycle and thereby made unavailable for plant or animal life, is known as *denitrification*. It is characteristic of oxygen-depleted soils. However, when soils are well aerated, these same bacteria ordinarily oxidize carbohydrates for their energy needs. It is apparent, therefore, that a farmer can to some degree maintain soil fertility by diligent tillage, for in this manner denitrification is retarded (10, 13, 14).

Research in Florida has shown that some chlorinated hydrocarbon pesticides are detrimental to the bacteria responsible for nitrification. Pesticide use, therefore, should be restricted to a minimum; for if populations of soil bacteria are greatly diminished, the nutrient cycle upon which plants, and eventually animals and men, depend would be severely disrupted (15). Paul R. Ehrlich, of Stanford University, views the phenomenon with considerable gravity. In his opinion, "our general lack of attention to the possible long range effects of these and similar subtle problems in our environment could ultimately prove to be fatal to mankind" (4).

Despite its abundance, gaseous nitrogen cannot be utilized directly by most organisms. By what means, then, is it "fixed," or brought into circulation? Nitrogen gas may be fixed by electrical discharges in the atmosphere, such as those during a thunderstorm. Volcanic eruptions represent a minor source of fixed nitrogen. However, by far the most important source is nitrogen fixation by soil and water-dwelling bacteria. Some of these occur abundantly in soil and water. However, other nitrogen-fixing bacteria live inside the roots of over 190 species of plants, including legumes (alfalfa, peas, beans, soybeans) and certain kinds of pines and alders (2). A farmer may increase the nitrogen content of a given acre eighty pounds yearly by growing legume crops! The fertility (and hence fish production) of some high altitude mountain lakes may well be dependent upon the nitrogen-replenishing activities of bacteria living in the roots of alders fringing the lake shores.

THE CARBON CYCLE. Carbon is the key element to the molecular structure of all organisms, from bacteria to man. It is an indispensable element in all the *organic* compounds characteristic of life. The principle carbon reservoir is the *atmosphere*. Six tons of carbon occur in the air column above each acre of the earth's surface. One acre of lush vegetation will remove twenty tons of carbon from the atmosphere annually. After moving into the "breathing pores" of a plant such as clover, it is combined with hydrogen to form sugar, during the process of photosynthesis. Later, when those clover leaves are consumed by an animal, say a deer, the carbon-containing organic compounds of the clover are digested and converted into deer protoplasm. When man consumes and digests venison, the digested meat is eventually transformed into human protoplasm. In all these organisms, clover, deer, and man, some carbon is released during *respiration*—a process in which the organism "burns"

Figure 2-5. *Nitrogen-fixing legume. Root system of black-eyed peas taken from a Texas farm. Note the nodules. Nitrogen-fixing bacteria are abundant in the black clay soil of this farm because peas have been grown in rotation for the past forty years.* [*Soil Conservation Service, U.S. Department of Agriculture, Photo by Morrison W. Liston*]

the organic "fuels" (carbohydrates, protein, fats) in its cells and extracts the energy in a usable form. Among plants, the carbon is released (as carbon dioxide) to the atmosphere via breathing pores, in animals such as deer and man, the carbon dioxide is exhaled from the lungs. The carbon-containing remains of dead organisms (clover, deer, man, and so on) or the wastes (feces, urine) of animals are broken down by ubiquitous bacteria and fungi, abundantly occurring in soil, air, and water. Such decomposition releases carbon into soil and air. (Researchers at the University of Notre Dame are conducting experiments with bacteria-free animals kept in sterile chambers. Although these animals—mice, rabbits, and so on—eventually grow old and die, their bodies do not decay. Hence, the carbon content of the carcasses is temporarily "taken out of circulation.")

About 300 million years ago, during the Carboniferous period, giant tree ferns and other tropical plants grew in areas now known as Pennsylvania, West Virginia, Ohio, Kentucky, Tennessee, Indiana, and Illinois. Many of these plants were buried by sediment and therefore escaped decomposition. Instead, they were eventually converted into lignite and coal. In a somewhat similar fashion, both plant and animal bodies were converted to petroleum and natural gas. The carbon in these so called fossil fuels was removed from circulation for 300 million years until industrialized man began consuming them for heat and power.

The oceans, which cover 70 per cent of the earth's surface, also serve as a reservoir. In this case the carbon is in the form of carbon dioxide, dissolved in the water. It

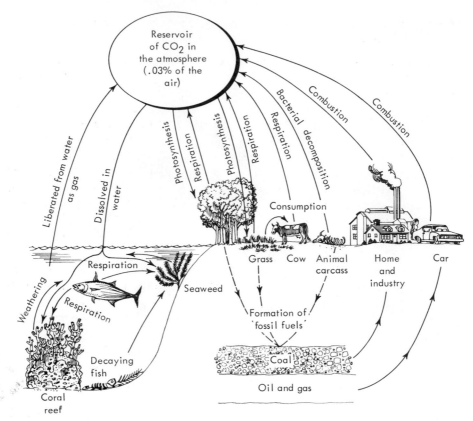

Figure 2-6. *The carbon cycle. (See text for explanation.)*

may have entered the ocean from the overlying atmosphere. This carbon dioxide may be incorporated into the plant body by photosynthesis and then eventually into the bodies of plant-consuming fish and fish-eating animals such as shark, tuna, waterfowl, whale, and man. Some of this carbon is returned to the ocean by respiration of marine organisms. Some carbon is used by clams, oysters, scallops, and corals to build limestone shells and "skeletons." Tremendous quantities of carbon are "locked up" in coral reefs off the coasts of California and Florida, and in the Great Barrier Reef off the Australian coast—a mass of limestone 180 feet thick and 1,260 miles long, composed of countless billions of coral skeletons.

Some microscopic marine protozoans also form calcium carbonate shells. Ralph Buchsbaum vividly describes the process:

It is astounding to contemplate the probable number of individual shells composing the chalk cliffs of Dover, England, or the large chalk beds (1,000 feet thick in places) of Mississippi and Georgia. . . . The deposition of the shells, if we are to judge by the present rate of accumulation at the bottom of the Pacific, was about two feet in a hundred years. Most of the shells now being deposited are those of the foraminifer *Globigerina*, which floats in the surface waters. These animals are constantly dying and their skeletons sinking in a slow but steady rain to the ocean floor, where they form a gray mud called "globigerina ooze." About 30 per cent of the floor of the ocean (40,000,000 square miles) is covered with globigerina ooze. Some deposits form chalk, with as much as 90 per cent calcium carbonate. Nearer the shore the deposits contain sediments which have been washed from the land and the resulting rock is a fossiliferous limestone such as the famous Indiana building stone (1).

Eventually, as a result of weathering processes that operate for millennia, small amounts of the carbon from coral reefs, globigerina ooze, and the shells of clams and oysters are returned to solution in the ocean waters.

For millions of years the carbon cycle was in dynamic equilibrium, the carbon entering the atmosphere compensating for the carbon being removed. However, by his accelerating consumption of fossil fuels to provide heat and power, man has released about 200 billion tons of carbon dioxide into the atmosphere, causing a 10 per cent increase in the atmosphere's carbon content (from 290 ppm to 320 ppm). It is estimated that by 2000 the atmospheric carbon will increase another 25 per cent, to almost 400 ppm. Scientists are not sure what effect this will have on human survival. Some authorities believe, however, that it might cause marked climatic changes, some of which might be deleterious. For example, atmospheric carbon dioxide acts as a "heat trap" for the earth, preventing excessive heat loss by radiation. With greatly increased quantities of heat-trapping carbon dioxide in the atmosphere, the earth's average temperature may rise sufficiently to melt the polar ice caps. The resultant increase in ocean levels would cause the flooding of populous coastal cities such as New York, Boston, Washington, New Orleans, and Los Angeles.

Laws of Thermodynamics. Pertinent to our study of food chains and energy pyramids (in the next few pages) are the *laws of thermodynamics*. The first law states, "Although energy cannot be created or destroyed, it may be converted from one form to another." Thus, the fuel energy of the coal we burn today actually represents the energy of sunbeams that flooded the earth about 300 million years ago. This *solar energy* was "trapped" by plant chlorophyll, converted into *chemical energy*, and "locked" in the organic molecules of the plant. Eventually these plants were converted to coal. When coal is burned in an electric power plant, the coal's chemical energy is converted into *thermal energy*, which in turn is used to generate steam; the steam in turn drives a turbine (*mechanical energy*) that the generator finally converts into *electrical energy*. Eventually, when you turn on a study lamp in your dormitory room (to study ecology), the electrical energy is converted into *radiant energy*. In this example energy was progressively changed from radiant to chemical to thermal to mechanical to electrical and, finally, back to radiant energy.

The second law of thermodynamics states, "Whenever one form of energy is converted to another, a certain amount is lost as heat." Let us give an example. About 25 per cent of the energy in gasoline consumed by your car is converted into the mechanical energy that propels you along the highway. On the other hand,

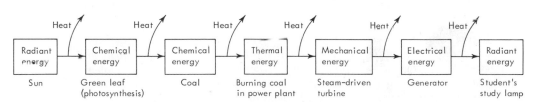

Figure 2-7. *An energy conversion series.*

about 75 per cent of the consumed energy is converted into heat, useless as power, but rather nice to have around during a mid-winter trip. Eventually this heat energy is "lost"; that is, it eventually radiates from the car and is dissipated.

Food Chains. A *food chain* may be defined as the "transfer of energy and nutrients through a succession of organisms via repeated processes of eating and being eaten." Man forms the terminal link of many food chains. Two representative chains would be corn-pheasant-fox and spruce-budworm-warbler. In each case the initial "link" is a green plant, or *producer*, which produces chemical energy in a form (glucose) available to succeeding consumer (animal) links. Over 270 billion tons of sugar are produced by green plants annually, most of it (70 per cent) by marine algae, lesser amounts by terrestrial and freshwater vegetation.

Food Webs. A *food web* may be defined as an "interconnected series of food chains." In actuality a food chain virtually never exists as an isolated entity, except in an ecology textbook. Consider the food chain corn-pig-man, for example. A pig

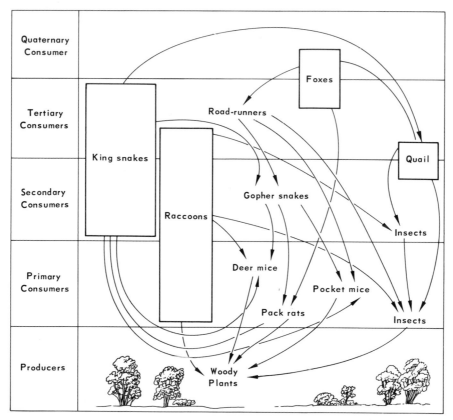

Figure 2-8. *Food web in a California chaparral. All the consumers depend either directly or indirectly on the woody shrub "producers." Foxes, quail, and king snakes occupy two trophic levels. Raccoons occupy three levels. Gopher snakes will occasionally assume the role of scavenger as well as predator.* [*Adapted from Arthur S. Boughey,* Ecology of Populations (*New York: Macmillan Publishing Co., Inc., 1968*).]

eats other foods beside corn—such as rats, mice, insects, grubs, earthworms, baby chicks, grass, weeds, and garbage. Similarly, in addition to pork, a man consumes everything from artichokes to zwieback, from kippered herring to pheasant-under-glass. In nature, therefore, food chains exist primarily as separate strands of an interwoven food web. Note in Figure 2-8 that such dominant carnivores as raccoons, foxes, and king snakes prey on at least three major organisms. As a general rule, the greater the number of *alternative channels* through which energy can flow, the greater the *stability* of the food web and ecosystem.

Just why should a complex food web have stability? Let's see. In the California chaparral foxes obtain their nourishment by preying mainly on roadrunners, quail, and pack rats and to a lesser degree on insects, mice, berries, and fruits. Now suppose that the quail population was sharply reduced, possibly because of an infectious disease outbreak or adverse weather during the nesting period. Under these conditions the fox population would shift the predatory pressure it had exerted on quail to some (or all) of its alternative prey, without suffering from nutritional hardship. Reduced predatory pressure on the resilient quail population, in turn, might permit it to "rebound" quickly if the following breeding season is reasonably productive of young quail.

Many of the ecological problems man has unwittingly brought upon himself, have resulted from his attempt to *simplify* ecosystems and hence promote their *instability*. The Irish potato famine of the 1840's provides a particularly illuminating example, as described by Moran, Morgan, and Wiersma, of the University of Wisconsin at Green Bay:

> Ireland's soil and climate are ill-suited for most crops. From the time of its introduction at the end of the 16th century, the potato was the main source of Ireland's food energy because it grew well and yielded a much higher number of calories per acre than other food crops. As potato production flourished, the population approximately doubled between 1780 and 1845 to a level of 8,500,000. In that year a fungus that caused a plant disease known as potato blight entered Ireland from Europe. The potatoes were susceptible to the fungus and large numbers of potato plants died during the five years that the blight lasted. Because the Irish had no substitute food source, roughly *one million* of them died from starvation or disease between 1845 and 1850 and another million emigrated. In a period of five years the population declined 25 per cent, and the country's economic and social structure was dealt a staggering blow —all largely the result of oversimplifying the food web (12).

Ecological Pyramids

PYRAMID OF NUMBERS. In a *predator* food chain the numbers of individuals are greatest at the producer level, less at the herbivore level, and smallest at the carnivore level. This concept is known as the *pyramid of numbers*, first advanced in 1927 by the eminent British ecologist Charles Elton. Figure 2-9 illustrates the pyramid of numbers actually recorded in an acre of bluegrass. However, both the numerical and size relationships of organisms are inverted in food chains in which parasites form the terminal links. This is apparent in the chain dog-flea-protozoan or in the corn-roundworm-bacteria chain, where both protozoans and bacteria are hyperparasites of the parasitic fleas and roundworms. Because numbers pyramids do not provide an accurate picture of either the biomass or energy relationships between trophic levels, they are of somewhat limited value.

PYRAMID OF BIOMASS. The ecologist refers to the weight of living substance (protoplasm) in an organism, a population, or a community as its "biological mass,"

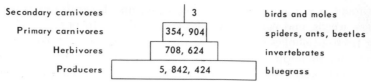

Secondary carnivores	3	birds and moles
Primary carnivores	354, 904	spiders, ants, beetles
Herbivores	708, 624	invertebrates
Producers	5, 842, 424	bluegrass

Figure 2-9. *Pyramid of numbers occurring in a one-acre plot of blue grass. Organisms are arranged according to trophic (food) levels. [Adapted from Eugene P. Odum,* Fundamentals of Ecology *(Philadelphia: W.B. Saunders Company, 1953). Plant data from Francis C. Evans and Stanley A. Cain, "Preliminary Studies on the Vegetation of an Old Field Community in Southeastern Michigan," Contribution of the Laboratory of Vertebrate Biology, University of Michigan, 51 (Ann Arbor: University of Michigan Press, 1952), pp. 1–17. Animal data from G.N. Wolcott, "An Animal Census of Two Pastures and a Meadow in Northern New York," Ecol. Mono., 7 (1937), pp. 1–90.]*

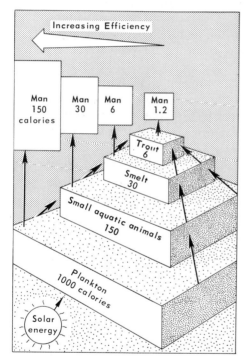

Figure 2-10. *Energy pyramid. If man were the only other link in the plankton-man food chain, more than 100 times the energy would be available to him than as the terminal link of the plankton-aquatic animal-smelt-trout-man food chain. [Adapted from Robert B. Platt and George K. Reid,* Bioscience *(New York: Reinhold Publishing Corp., 1967). After Lamont C. Cole, "The Ecosphere,"* Sci. Amer., *198 (1958).]*

or *biomass*. In a typical food chain ending in a predator, such as sagebrush-antelope-cougar, there is a progressive reduction in total biomass for each successive trophic level.

PYRAMID OF ENERGY. The physicist defines energy as the capacity to do work. All organisms require energy for their life processes. Animals require energy for the ingestion, digestion, and absorption of food; for the conversion of food into protoplasm; for the synthesis of hormones and enzymes; for the circulation of blood; for the maintenance of body temperature; and for respiration, excretion, and locomotion. Plants require energy to carry on photosynthesis, to synthesize growth hormones and leaf pigments, and to produce flowers and seeds. All organisms require energy for growth and reproduction. Unlike elements, *energy cannot be cycled, but is continuously being dissipated from ecosystems* and hence must be continuously replenished by means of the incident solar energy. (Fig. 2-10)

In America's rapidly expanding urban ecosystem, such solar energy converters as elm trees and rose bushes are not considered suitable for human consumption. Therefore photosynthesized energy-rich foods must be continuously imported from agricultural ecosystems many miles distant. This dependence is becoming increasingly acute, especially in California, where 100 acres of prime agricultural land is daily being obliterated with an asphalt-concrete-wood-steel cover in the form of highways, parking lots, shopping centers, and homes.

It has been estimated that "the solar energy striking the surface of the United States every *twenty minutes* is sufficient to meet the country's entire power needs for one year, if it could be harnassed" (15). A very small percentage of this solar energy bathes green plants. Moreover, green plants are only 1 per cent efficient in converting this solar energy to the chemical energy of sugar molecules. A herbivore, such as a cow is only 10 per cent efficient in converting alfalfa or grass into beef, while flesh-eating man similarly is only 10 per cent efficient in converting beef to human flesh. A diagram representing these relationships follows:

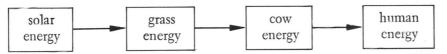

Much of the energy input is lost by *respiration*, a process in which the original food energy is converted to a form that can be used to sustain the organism's life functions (digestion, circulation, respiration, excretion, movement, growth, and so on). Because of this inefficiency in energy transfer along the human food chain man eventually derives only 1 food calorie from an original supply of 1 million solar calories. Consider the grass-cow-man food chain. About 1,000 pounds of grass would be required to produce 100 pounds of beef to produce 10 pounds of man, as depicted in the following energy pyramid:

Man —
10 pounds
Cow — 100 pounds
Grass — 1,000 pounds

It is apparent that the second law of thermodynamics imposes a limit on food chain length. Most terrestrial food chains have only three or four links. In the unusually long food chain clover-grasshopper-frog-snake-hawk, which might operate in a wet meadow, the hawk uses only 0.0001 per cent of the incident solar energy. Some marine food chains leading from algae to tuna might be so long that 100,000 pounds of algae would be required to produce a single pound of tuna.

Knowledge of these energy relationships enable us to understand the striking difference between Asiatic and American diets. The United States consumes 35 per cent of the total energy used in the world, even though it forms only 6 per cent of the global population. In other words, we are consuming six times our "fair" share. (Of course, most of this energy is not consumed as food, but as power-and-heat-generating fuel.) If you lived to be seventy you probably would have consumed 10,000 pounds of meat, 28,000 pounds of milk and cream, and additional thousands of pounds of grain, sugar, and specialty foods. However, a seventy-year-old Asiatic probably would have eaten only *1 per cent as much meat as you.* In the "energy poor" nations, such as China and India, it is no accident that human food chains frequently have only *two* links, in which herbivorous man has replaced the cow, sheep, or pig. Such a chain might be represented:

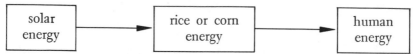

More energy is available to the Asiatic (or the New York slum dweller) by moving "up" the chain—closer to the producer base. Americans still live in a "land of milk and honey" (as well as pork chops and beef steaks). However, the time may well come, as a result of our mushrooming population (expected to reach 300 million by the year 2000), when we will be faced with the ecological ultimatum: "Either shorten your food chains or tighten your belts!" Of course, it is much more delightful to feast on chops and steaks, but the second law of thermodynamics may yet impose the somber transition to algae cakes and bean soup.

Primary production refers to the total amount of sugar produced by photosynthesis; in the world as a whole it amounts to 270 billion tons annually. The ecologist frequently refers to the primary production of a lake, meadow, woodlot, or some other ecosystem. All living organisms carry on *respiration*, a process by means of which glucose (and other organic compounds) is "burned up" or oxidized; the generalized equation is:

$$\underset{\text{(sugar)}}{C_6H_{12}O_6} + \underset{\text{(oxygen)}}{6O_2} \rightarrow \underset{\text{(carbon dioxide)}}{6CO_2} + \underset{\text{(water)}}{6H_2O} + \text{energy} \quad \text{(some is always lost as heat)}$$

Note that this equation is exactly the opposite of the overall equation for photosynthesis:

$$\text{solar energy} + \underset{\substack{\text{(carbon} \\ \text{dioxide)}}}{6CO_2} + \underset{\text{(water)}}{6H_2O} \rightarrow \underset{\text{(sugar)}}{C_6H_{12}O_6} + \underset{\text{(oxygen)}}{6O_2}$$

Thus the *raw materials* of photosynthesis—carbon dioxide and water—are the *products* of respiration (and are eliminated by lungs and kidneys in higher animals), while the *products* of photosynthesis—glucose and oxygen—are the *raw materials* of respiration. Because plants must respire, ecologists distinguish between *gross production*, which is the *total* amount of energy captured by the plant, and *net production*, which is the energy that remains after respiration (7). This net production may be consumed by herbivores. Unlike plants, animals are able to secure energy only by the consumption of energy-bearing food.

Tolerance Ranges. In the physical and biotic environment of any organism are factors that can restrict growth, interfere with reproductive success, and even cause death. They are called *limiting factors.* The concept of limiting factors was first introduced in 1840 when a German biochemist, Justus Liebig, noted that the growth of plants was frequently limited by deficiencies of certain elements occurring naturally in the soil, such as zinc, cobalt, manganese, and copper. These elements have become known as "trace elements" because most living plants and animals require them in extremely minute quantities (13). For example, a variation in the

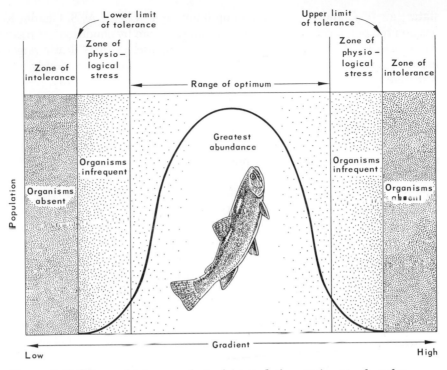

Figure 2-11. *Law of tolerance. A species population attains a peak under optimal environmental conditions. As such environmental factors as oxygen, carbon dioxide, water, temperature, and so on become less favorable, the population gradually decreases. Although organisms might survive temporarily in a marginal habitat (zone of physiological stress), they would eventually lose out in competition with better-adapted species.* [Adapted from Robert L. Smith, Ecology and Field Biology (New York: Harper & Row, Publishers, 1966). Used by permission of the publishers.]

concentration of zinc in the soil amounting to one part in 200 million may mean the difference between a sick or healthy plant.

Victor Shelford, a pioneer in plant ecology, has shown that organisms may be equally limited by *too much* of a certain environmental factor. For example, a cabbage growing in your backyard vegetable patch requires a minimal amount of soil moisture for vigorous growth, because water is basic to the photosynthetic process. Conversely, if that same cabbage were submerged by spring flood waters, the diffusion of carbon dioxide into the leaves would be so greatly reduced that the cabbage would fail to survive. For each organism, therefore, there exists a specific tolerance range for any essential environmental factor below or above which the organism's activity is adversely affected. Note that in Figure 2-11 populations are highest in the optimum range and then gradually taper off (in the familiar bell-shaped curve) to low densities in the zones of physiological stress. Beyond the stress regions are the zones of intolerance in which the values of the factor (water, temperature, soil elements) are so extreme that continued survival is impossible (10, 13, 14). Thus the limits of temperature tolerance for the developing eggs of the brook trout (a denizen of cold, clear, gravel bottom streams in the northeastern states) are 0° C and 12° C, with an optimum of 4° C (9). As S. Charles Kendeigh has pointed out, a species distribution is limited more by conditions of physiological stress than by the actual *limits* of tolerance themselves, for "death verges on the limits of toleration, and the existence of the species would be seriously jeopardized if it were too frequently exposed to these extreme conditions" (10).

Population Growth Curves. The population of any organism will be the result of the interaction of the two antagonistic forces of the environmental resistance (ER) and the biotic potential (BP), with the BP tending to "push" the population upward and the ER tending to push it downward. It is apparent, then, that the increase, decrease, or stability of a given population depends on the values of ER and BP. When the BP is greater than the ER, the population rises. Conversely, when the ER is greater than the BP, the population declines. When both values are the same, the population attains a stability in the form of a dynamic equilibrium (3, 10, 13, 14).

Whenever a species becomes established in a new habitat with good carrying capacity, its population will show a characteristic S-shaped, or sigmoid, growth curve. Such a curve usually has four phases, known in chronological sequence as (1) the establishment phase, (2) the explosive (or logarithmic) phase, (3) the deceleration phase, and (4) the dynamic equilibrium phase. Once the population has reached the equilibrium phase, no further substantial population surges are possible, for at this point in its growth the population has attained the so-called *carrying capacity* of the habitat. In other words, it has reached the maximum population that the

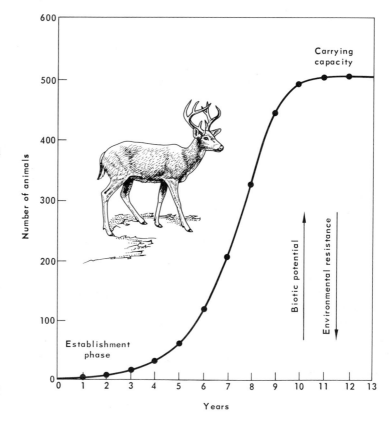

Figure 2-12. *Population growth curve. Note the S-shaped (sigmoid) form. The antagonistic influences of the biotic potential and environmental resistance are indicated by arrows. This curve shows the population increase of deer introduced into a new environment with a 500-animal carrying capacity.* [Adapted from Raymond F. Dasmann, Environmental Conservation (New York: John Wiley & Sons, Inc., 1959).]

habitat will support under prevailing conditions over a long period of time. (Fig. 2-12.)

A number of exotics introduced into the United States from abroad—such as the English sparrow, European starling, and German carp—have followed sigmoid growth curves. Thus, a few pairs of house sparrows were introduced to the United States in 1899 and within *ten* years the sparrow population had increased to many thousands of birds. Although introduced with good intentions (the sparrow was brought over from Europe to control insect pests), many exotics have destroyed wildlife habitat, disseminated disease, or aggressively competed with more valuable wildlife species for food, cover, and breeding sites.

A. S. Einarsen describes the population growth of pheasants on Protection Island, off the west coast of Washington, after an initial 1937 stocking of two cocks and six hens. Careful censuses were taken yearly from 1937 until 1942, when the study was abruptly halted by World War II. Servicemen stationed on the island promptly applied rather intensive "environmental resistance." Up to this time, however, the birds had closely followed the sigmoid growth curve and had increased to 1,898 birds, a 230-fold increase over the original population (5).

A given crop of pine, bluegills, or deer may be periodically harvested to give a yield. One of the most important problems facing scientists in the fields of forestry, wildlife management, agriculture, livestock ranching, and fisheries is how to secure the maximum sustained yield, or *optimum yield*, from a given resource. In these cases man is interested in harvesting net production for his economic gain. If the yield is greater than net production, it may so greatly reduce a given population as to depress its reproductive potential. On the other hand, if the harvest is less than the net production, the resource is not being managed for maximum economic return. Moreover, when population density rises, the density-dependent factors of competition, disease, and predators affect the yield adversely. There is a point in the growth curve of any species where productivity is highest. This is between the accelerating and inhibiting phases of the curve. Research has revealed that in most species this point is attained when the population is roughly 50 per cent of the carrying capacity (10).

Population Regulation by Density-independent Factors. Populations of organisms are controlled by both *density-dependent factors* and *density-independent factors*. The influence of density-independent factors is constant regardless of density and characteristically causes sharp population fluctuations. Heat, cold, drought, floods, blizzards, and hailstorms are obviously all density independent. Hail can decimate a field of young wheat or curtail reproduction in fruit trees. Hurricanes and tornadoes can level vast acreages of valuable spruce and pine. Heavy rains in late spring may sharply limit the hatching success of game birds. A severe spell of cold weather along the Texas coast in January, 1940, inflicted considerable fish mortality; the percentage decline in the catch of flounders, a fish highly vulnerable to cold, was 92.6 per cent at Laguna Madre, 93.6 per cent at Matagorda, and 95.4 per cent at Aransas, despite considerable variation in size of the original flounder population in these three regions (8). Siltation may smother salmon eggs. Pesticide-contaminated food supplies may cause direct mortality among songbirds or impair their reproductive success. Robin populations in certain DDT-sprayed areas in Wisconsin were reduced by 69 to 98 per cent. Drought may so reduce water levels in a marsh as to increase muskrat vulnerability to fox predation. Many human

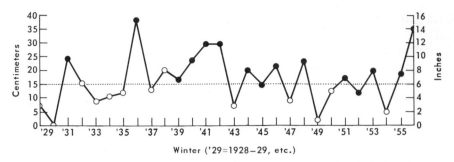

Figure 2-13. *Importance of snow depth as a density-independent factor in the regulation of partridge populations in southwestern Finland. Because the partridge is primarily a ground-dwelling herbivore, a dense snow cover could either cause death directly from starvation or contribute indirectly to increased mortality from disease. Graph shows fluctuations of snow level above and below the critical 6-inch depth. Partridge populations the ensuing autumn are shown as having either increased (open circles) or decreased (solid circles). [Adapted from Lawrie Sivonen, "The Correlation Between the Fluctuations of Partridge and European Hare Populations and the Climatic Conditions of Winters in Southwest Finland During the Last Thirty Years," Papers on Game Research, Helsinki, 17 (1956), pp. 1–30.]*

activities are density independent with respect to their affect on wildlife. Thus, marsh drainage has severely depleted waterfowl populations. The heated effluent from power plants have either killed game fish or caused them to migrate. The passenger pigeon's extinction was caused in part by the removal of its deciduous forest breeding habitat by the farmer and logger. Some human influences, however, have resulted in population increments rather than decrements. For example, house sparrow populations have flourished because of the abundance of suitable nesting sites and food (waste grain and manure), associated with human settlement. The removal of forests in the eastern United States has permitted the eastward extension of such species associated with grassland habitats as the coyote and horned lark.

Population Regulation by Density-dependent Factors. Density-dependent factors operate within the limits imposed by density-independent factors. Biotic factors are frequently density dependent. They tend to keep a population in dynamic equilibrium with the environment (10, 13, 14). Just as a governor on a car engine prevents the car from going too fast, so these factors prevent populations from increasing to a level which might result in massive death from starvation or disease. Conversely, when populations decrease below carrying capacity, the declining influence of the density-dependent factors eventually results in a gradual population build-up.

When the number of oaks on an acre increases, competition for sunlight, soil nutrients, and moisture increases proportionately. Individuals with less extensive root systems may die as a consequence of nutrient and moisture deficiencies. Stunted individuals may die because their sunlight is intercepted by taller trees.

Among animals it is apparent that when food, water, cover, nesting sites, breeding dens, and space are in limited supply, any population increase will intensify competition. Inevitably, this competition will have adverse effects on the physically unfit. Even if they do not incur direct mortality because of fighting, they may be required to disperse to a marginal habitat where death from malnutrition or predation may await them. When the density of pink salmon in impoundments becomes excessive, not only are fewer eggs released, but many are destroyed because of the inordinate stirring of gravel. It has been suggested that lowered fecundity of birds at high densities results from reduced food availability and increased fighting. Sometimes "shock disease," resulting from the stresses associated with crowding and fighting, operates as a density-dependent factor. For example, a herd of four to five Sika deer, introduced in 1916 on 280-acre James Island in Chesapeake Bay, increased to a peak of almost 300, at which point the density was roughly one per acre. Three years later 60 per cent of the herd died, presumably from stress-induced "shock disease."

When population densities are high, predatory mortality tends to increase, not only because individual predators may kill more prey than they require to satisfy their food requirements, but because there may be an influx of predators to the area of high prey density and because inferior prey are crowded out to marginal habitat. An intensive study by Paul L. Errington of horned owl predation on winter populations of bobwhite in Wisconsin and Iowa from 1930 to 1935 showed a definite correlation between prey density and predation intensity as expressed in the percentage of owl pellets containing feathers and bones of quail (6).

The percentage of diseased or parasitized organisms in a population increases with population density, presumably as a result of the increased possibilities of transmission. With his monotypic agriculture and silviculture (large plots planted to a single crop species) man has unwittingly increased the possibilities for the infection of his crops with parasites and disease organisms. The population-limiting effects of wheat rust, corn smut, and Dutch elm disease are widely known. Oak wilt is caused by a fungus that is transmitted from tree to tree either by root grafts or beetles—the greater the concentration of oaks, the easier the transmission. The incidence of infectious diseases in man increases with population density, as is well substantiated by the massive mortality caused by the influenza virus among our soldiers during World War I. Infectious disease is an important controlling factor only during the occurrence of epidemics or epizootics. Because the causative organisms of infectious

Figure 2-14. *Density-dependent mortality in a Wisconsin quail population. As population density increased, there was a corresponding increase in competition for mates, food, water, cover, and territory. Crosses indicate the percentage of the quail population incurring mortality during late summer and fall. Note that the per cent mortality increased with population density, from roughly 12 per cent for a population of 150 to over 60 per cent for a population of 1,400. [Adapted from Eugene P. Odum,* Fundamentals of Ecology *(Philadelphia: W. B. Saunders Company, 1959). Data from Paul L. Errington, "Some Contributions of a Fifteen-Year Local Study of the Northern Bobwhite to a Knowledge of Population Phenomena,"* Ecol. Mono., *15, pp. 1–34.]*

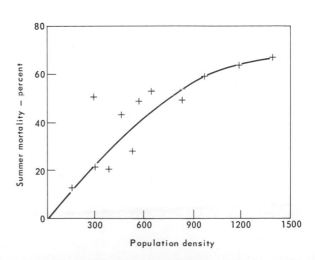

disease (viruses, protozoa, bacteria) may be transmitted by contact, by ingestion of contaminated food, and by animal agents (vectors), it is readily apparent that their influence is directly proportional to host density.

In certain colonial sea birds the nest-building instinct is not activated until population density has increased to a critical minimal level. It has been suggested that this factor may have contributed to the extinction of the heath hen and passenger pigeon.

Although we have segregated population-regulating mechanisms into two groups, density-independent and density-dependent, it is actually exceedingly difficult to distinguish one from the other in the field, because a given organism's density at a given moment is the result of a combination of both density-independent and density-dependent factors acting concurrently.

Biological Succession. Biological succession is the replacement of one community of organisms (plant or animal) by another in an orderly and predictable manner. In a plant succession the plants of each successional stage (grass, shrub, tree) cause changes in incident sunlight, wind velocity, and temperature, as well as in the structure, depth, moisture, and fertility of the soil. These changes result in the replacement of the original stage by another better adapted to the modified environment (10, 13, 14).

EXAMPLE: A PRIMARY SUCCESSION. A succession that develops in an area not previously occupied by a community is known as a *primary succession*. It may become established on a jagged outcrop of granite, on a lava-covered slope, on rubble left in the wake of a landslide, or perhaps on the slag heaps of an open-pit mine.

We shall trace a primary succession that might occur on a rocky substratum in the deciduous forest region of the eastern United States. The initial stage is called the *pioneer community*. Plants of this stage are adapted to withstand great extremes of temperature and moisture. A typical pioneer plant that might become established on a bare, wind-swept rocky outcrop might be the *crustose lichen*, whose wind-dispersed reproductive bodies, called *spores*, might be blown into the area. The crustose lichens form a grayish-green crust on the rocks. Although the substratum itself may be dry, the lichen spores nevertheless will develop if adequate atmospheric moisture is available. Once established, lichens begin to modify their immediate localized environment, or *microhabitat*. Weak carbonic acid (H_2CO_3) begins to corrode the underlying rock. Adjoining plants form a trap in which particles of wind-blown sand, dust, and organic debris begin to accumulate. When an occasional lichen dies, bacteria and small fungi effect its decay. The resultant organic material and the excreta of minute lichen-eating insects that have invaded the microhabitat enrich the relatively sterile soil that has accumulated. This soil now acts as a sponge, rapidly absorbing water that falls as dew or rain. Once sufficient soil has accumulated, mosses and ferns may become established, also by means of wind-distributed spores. Ferns eventually shade out the lichens and replace them in the succession. The soil becomes further enriched with the decay of fern fronds each autumn. Eventually, as the decades pass, wind-blown pine seeds may fall in the area. They may have originated in some hilltop pine forest or may have been brought by seed-eating birds, such as the pine siskin or red crossbill. The young, sun-tolerant pine seedlings in turn compete successfully with the ferns and eventually replace them in the succession.

As the seasons pass, gray squirrels may temporarily enter the area to bury acorns

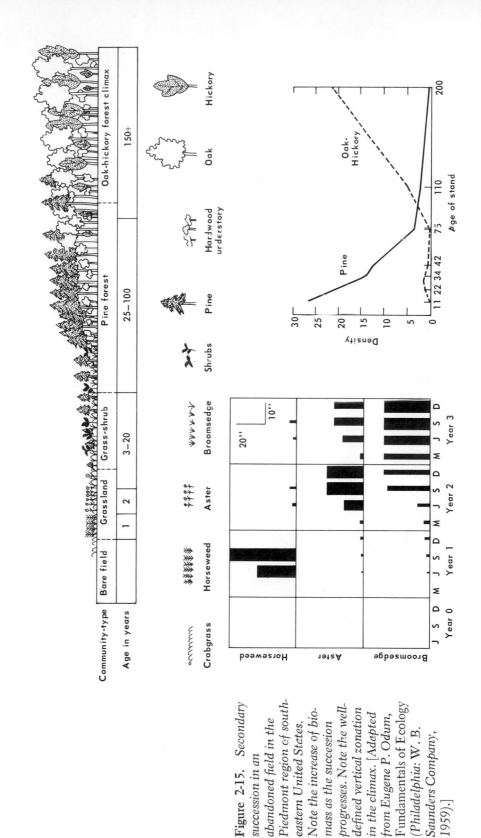

Figure 2-15. *Secondary succession in an abandoned field in the Piedmont region of southeastern United States. Note the increase of biomass as the succession progresses. Note the well-defined vertical zonation in the climax. [Adapted from Eugene P. Odum, Fundamentals of Ecology (Philadelphia: W. B. Saunders Company, 1959).]*

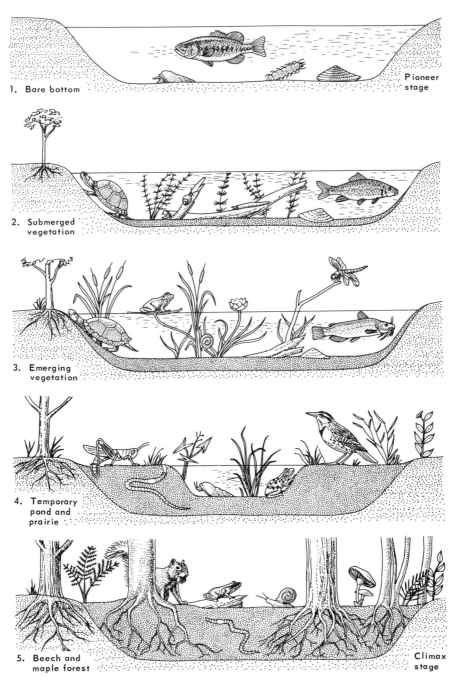

1. Bare bottom   Pioneer stage

2. Submerged vegetation

3. Emerging vegetation

4. Temporary pond and prairie

5. Beech and maple forest   Climax stage

Figure 2-16. *Aquatic succession beginning with bare bottom pond (pioneer community) and terminating in beech-maple forest (climax). This type of succession is thought to be typical of many ponds in the Midwest. Note the gradual accumulation of humus (shown in solid black).* [*Adapted from R. and M. Buchsbaum,* Basic Ecology *(Pittsburgh, Penn.: Boxwood Press, 1957).*]

brought in from a neighboring oak stand, or acorns may be accidentally dropped by a wandering raccoon or by a bluejay during a flight over the young pines. The acorns germinate readily in the relatively fertile soil, which has been developing for centuries, since the beginning of the succession. Young oak seedlings, which are vulnerable to direct sunlight, develop successfully in the reduced light under the pine canopy. As an occasional pine dies, its position in the community will be usurped by an oak. Ultimately an oak forest, with its characteristic complement of plants and animals, will become established as the stable terminal climax of the succession. Thus, the bare, wind-swept rock outcrop is eventually replaced after several centuries by the moist, shadowed interior of a deciduous forest.

Although we have emphasized the succession of *plant communities* because vegetational changes are more basic and conspicuous, it should be emphasized that a succession of *animal* communities occurs also. The occurrence of a given animal species within a community is dependent upon such factors as flood, water, cover, breeding sites, humidity, and temperature, all of which change with the plant succession. Thus, Johnston and Odum, in a study of the breeding bird populations of a *secondary succession* developing from abandoned fields in the Georgia Piedmont region, found marked differences in the various stages (9). Some of their data is summarized in Figure 2-15. In this succession the field sparrow, towhee, and cardinal play important roles in seed dispersal. The seeds of some plants actually germinate better after having passed through a bird's digestive tract, apparently because its digestive juices dissolve the seed coat.

Mammalian communities show a similar change in species composition and density with the progress of the succession. Thus, in the Johnston and Odum study meadow mice representative of the grass stage were replaced by cotton mice and golden mice in later forested stages. Similarly, cottontails and grass snakes of the grass stage were succeeded by oak-hickory representatives, such as the opossum, racoon, and squirrel. An aquatic succession is illustrated in Figure 2-16.

The Biomes. Anyone who has driven from New England to California is acutely aware of the marked landscape changes—from evergreen stands in Maine to beech-maple forests in Ohio, from the wind-swept Kansas prairie to the Arizona desert. Each of these distinctive areas represents a different *biome*. A biome may be defined as the largest terrestrial community that can be easily recognized by a biologist; it is the biological expression of the interaction of climate, soil, water, and organisms (13). Although the name of the biome is usually based on its climax vegetation, it should be emphasized that it is composed of both plant and animal components and that it embraces *developmental communities* leading to the climax community, as well as the climax itself. Thus, in northern Minnesota early successional stages of birch-aspen, as well as climax spruce-fir would be included in the *northern coniferous forest* biome, or *taiga*. We shall examine the distribution, physical features, and biota of certain North American biomes discussed in a conservation context later in this book.

TUNDRA. The *tundra*, which embraces about 20 million square miles, extends around the globe in the northern latitudes between the belt of perpetual ice and snow to the north and the timberline to the south. The ecology of the tundra, because of its relative simplicity, is better understood than that of other biomes. During June and July the far northern tundra near the Arctic Circle is the celebrated land of the midnight sun. Conversely, in January the sun remains below the horizon

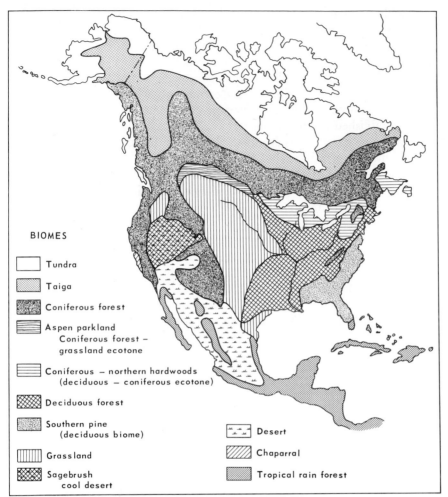

BIOMES

☐ Tundra

▨ Taiga

▦ Coniferous forest

☰ Aspen parkland
Coniferous forest –
grassland ecotone

☰ Coniferous – northern hardwoods
(deciduous – coniferous ecotone)

▨ Deciduous forest

░ Southern pine
(deciduous biome)

▥ Grassland

▨ Sagebrush
cool desert

▨ Desert

▨ Chaparral

▨ Tropical rain forest

Figure 2-17. *Biome distribution in North America. Note the southward extension of the coniferous forest biome in the mountains. Within the United States, tropical rain forest occurs only in Florida. See text for comments on other biomes.* [*Adapted from Robert L. Smith, Ecology and Field Biology (New York: Harper & Row, 1966). Used by permission of the publishers.*]

Figure 2-18. *Tundra biome. Cold Bay, Alaska. The soil freezes to a depth of four to five feet, but thaws out during the summer. The surface of this region is characterized by mounds about five feet in diameter and up to two feet high. The vegetation includes crowberry, dwarf willow, sedges, and various grasses and mosses.* [*U.S. Department of Agriculture*]

42

throughout the diurnal cycle. Annual precipitation is less than 10 inches, most of which occurs as summer or autumn rain. Snowfall is scant. Mean monthly temperatures range from —30° F in winter to 55° F in summer. The upper level of the permanently frozen soil (or *permafrost*) occurs at a depth of 6 to 18 inches. In spring and summer the thawed-out ground is characteristically soggy. Because of poor drainage and low evaporation rate and despite light precipitation, the accumulating melt waters of late spring form thousands of tiny lakes. Characteristic producers are mosses, sedges, grasses, reindeer lichen, and dwarf willows up to 100 years old. Representative animals of the tundra include the caribou, musk ox, collared lemming, willow ptarmigan, snowy owl, and golden plover (10, 13, 14).

BOREAL FOREST. The boreal forest, or *taiga*, is that part of the coniferous forest biome that forms an extensive east-west belt immediately south of the Arctic tundra and ranges southward into the northern United States from Washington to Maine. Characteristic *physical features* include annual rainfall of from 15 to 40 inches, average annual temperatures of from 20° F in the winter to more than 70° F in the summer, and a 150-day growing season. Dominant climax vegetation includes black spruce, white spruce, balsam fir, and tamarack. White birch and quaking aspen are representative of the earlier successional stages. Moose, snowshoe hare, and lynx are representative animals (10, 13, 14).

DECIDUOUS FOREST. The deciduous forest biome attains its greatest development east of the Mississippi immediately south of the coniferous forest. Fingers of deciduous forest extend westward into the prairie country along major watercourses, in response to localized increases in soil moisture. Annual precipitation ranges from 30 to 60 inches. Average January temperatures vary from 10° F in the north to 60° F in the south; average July temperatures range from 70° F in the north to 80° F in the south. The growing season (frost-free period) ranges from 5 months in the north to 10 months in the south. The deciduous forest is divisible into several major associations, among which are maple-basswood, beech-maple, oak-chestnut, and oak-hickory. Representative consumers include the red-eyed vireo, ovenbird, deer mouse, gray squirrel, opossum, and white-tailed deer.

GRASSLAND, OR PRAIRIE. The major grasslands of the United States occur in two regions: the Great Plains, a vast area extending from the eastern slopes of the Rockies to the Mississippi River, and the more moist portions of the Great Basin lying between the Sierras on the west and the Rockies on the east. In north temperate latitudes, grasslands apparently represent the vegetational expression of an average annual precipitation that is excessive (over 10 inches) for development of desert vegetation and inadequate (under 30 inches) for development of forest. Winter blizzards and summer drought may be severe. There is evidence that devastating fires periodically have burned the prairie. Dominant vegetation includes the big bluestem, little bluestem, buffalo grass, and grama grass. The horned lark and burrowing owl are characteristic birds. Dominant mammals include the pronghorned antelope, badger, white-tailed jackrabbit, coyote, and pocket gopher.

DESERT. American deserts are located in the hotter, drier portions of the Great Basin and in parts of California, New Mexico, Arizona, Texas, Nevada, Idaho, Utah, and Oregon. Deserts occur primarily to the leeward of prominent mountain ranges, such as the Sierra Nevada and the Rocky Mountains. The prevailing warm, humid air masses from the Pacific Ocean gradually cool as they move up windward slopes and release their moisture as rain or snow. The region to leeward of the mountains lies in the "rain shadow," where precipitation is minimal. A desert type of com-

Figure 2-19.   *Resident of the grassland biome. The black-tailed prairie dog at the edge of its crater-like burrow entrance. The levee not only serves as a lookout post but prevents flash-flooding of burrow. Washington, D. C., Zoo. [Soil Conservation Service, U.S. Department of Agriculture]*

munity generally results in those areas getting less than 10 inches of annual precipitation. Rainfall, moreover, may not be uniformly distributed, but may fall periodically in the form of cloudbursts that cause flash floods and soil-eroding run-off. An extremely high evaporation rate aggravates the severe moisture problem. For example, the water that theoretically could evaporate from a given land acre in one year may be *thirty* times the actual amount received as precipitation. Summer temperatures range from about 50° F at night to about 120° F during the day. Desert floor temperature reaches 145° F in summer.

Only organisms that have evolved specialized structural, physiological, and behavioral adaptations to extreme heat and aridity can survive in the desert. Characteristic producers are prickly pear cactus, suaharo cactus, greasewood, creosote bush, and mesquite. Plant adaptations for desert survival include either extremely shallow or extremely deep root systems; uniformly and widely dispersed plant distribution

Figure 2-20. *Desert biome, Arizona. Note the gravel pavement and widely spaced plants. The tall plant in the right background is the saguaro cactus, many of which live to be 100 years old.* [U.S. Department of Agriculture]

patterns (to ensure an adequate supply of moisture for the individual plant); succulent water-storage tissues; abbreviated life spans, which permit plants to take advantage of short wet periods (some plants complete their entire life cycle in eight weeks); and waxy leaf coverings and recessed stomata, to minimize water loss from evapotranspiration.

Conspicuous among desert animals are the western diamondback rattlesnake, Gila monster, greater roadrunner, Gila woodpecker, white-winged dove, Gambel's quail, black-tailed jackrabbit, antelope jackrabbit, kangaroo rat, pocket mouse, kit fox, collared peccary, and ringtail. Desert adaptations among animals include waxy (insects), scaled (reptiles), and armorlike (armadillo) body coverings that are impervious to water; the excretion of solid nitrogenous wastes (uric acid crystals); the ability to utilize metabolic water to the exclusion of ingested water (pocket mouse, kangaroo rat); the ability to obtain water from the blood and tissue fluids of prey; and the development of burrowing (kangaroo rat) and nocturnal behavior (ringtail, armadillo, and diamondback) (10, 13, 14).

BIBLIOGRAPHY

1. Buchsbaum, Ralph. *Animals Without Backbones.* Chicago: U. of Chicago, 1948.
2. Clapham, W. B., Jr. *Natural Ecosystems.* New York: Macmillan, 1973.
3. Dasmann, Raymond F. *Environmental Conservation.* New York: Wiley, 1959.
4. Ehrlich, Paul R., and Anne H. Ehrlich. *Population, Resources, Environment.* San Francisco: Freeman, 1970.
5. Einarsen, A. S. "Some Factors Affecting Ring-necked Pheasant Population Density," *Murrelet,* 26 (1945), 39–44.
6. Errington, Paul L. "What Is the Meaning of Predation?" *Smiths: Report for 1936* (1937), 243–252.
7. Golley, F. B. "Energy Dynamics of a Food Chain of an Old Field Community," *Ecol. Mono.,* 30 (1960), 187–206.
8. Gunter, Gordon. "Death of Fishes Due to Cold on the Texas Coast," *Ecol.,* 22 (January 1940), 203–208.
9. Johnston, David W., and Eugene P. Odum. "Breeding Bird Populations in Relation to Plant Succession on the Piedmont of Georgia," *Ecol.,* 37 (1956), 50–62.
10. Kendeigh, S. Charles. *Animal Ecology.* Englewood Cliffs, N.J.: Prentice-Hall, 1961.
11. Lindemann, Raymond L. "The Trophic-Dynamic Aspect of Ecology," *Ecol.,* 23 (1942), 399–418.
12. Moran, Joseph M., Michael D. Morgan, and James H. Wiersma. *An Introduction to Environmental Sciences.* Boston: Little, Brown, 1973.
13. Odum, Eugene P. *Fundamentals of Ecology,* 3rd ed. Philadelphia: Saunders, 1971.
14. Smith, Robert L. *Ecology and Field Biology.* New York: Harper, 1966.
15. Southwick, Charles H. *Ecology and the Quality of Our Environment.* New York: Van Nostrand, 1972.
16. Turk, Amos, Jonathan Turk, and Janet T. Wittes. *Ecology, Pollution, Environment.* Philadelphia: Saunders, 1972.

3.

Nature of Soils

Coal, gas and oil are the legacy to us of past sunshine, stored below the surface of the earth. Soil, the dark carpet upon the earth, is a similar legacy and a more precious one because it is more important that we eat than delegate our work to machines. The generations of plants and animals that form the soil and are sustained by it during their brief existence pass on. What remains, as evidence of their activity in catching and transforming the sun's energy, is the organized soil. It is vulnerable to our blundering, immensely rewarding to good husbandry.

Paul B. Sears,
Where There Is Life,
New York: Dell Publishing Co., Inc., 1962

"In the sweat of thy face shalt thou eat bread, till thou return unto the ground, for out of it wast thou taken: for dust thou art, and unto dust shalt thou return." This passage from the Biblical story of creation

(Genesis 3:19), written by Moses over 3,000 years ago, can be well appreciated by the soil scientist and ecologist of today. As we have learned in our discussion of food chains and pyramids, it is in the soil that all higher terrestrial plants have their roots and from which they absorb life-sustaining moisture and nutrients. Man, in turn, feeds directly upon these plants, upon plant-eating animals, or upon carnivores that prey on herbivores. Thus, virtually all terrestrial life ultimately derives from the dust of the earth. And when man eventually dies, the soil-derived elements in his body will be restored to the earth by the process of bacterial decay.

The average city dweller equates soil with "dirt," but to the farmer soil is the essence of survival. His economic well-being is inextricably linked with the quality of his land. It may mean the difference between a squalid four-room shack and a comfortable ranch house, between an old "klunker" and a new car, or between an eighth-grade and a university education for his children. A few years ago there were *3.7 million individual farms in America embracing somewhat over 1 billion acres of land*. The total value of both farm land and buildings was estimated at $130 billion (17).

Empires and nations, like individuals, are dependent upon the soil. As a nation's soil resources are fertile and abundant, in like measure will that state have vigor and stability. When this resource is exhausted because of mounting demands of a swelling population or long mismanagement, the nation's survival is in jeopardy. Some authorities believe that the decline and fall of the mighty Roman Empire may be attributed as much to the deterioration of soils in the Roman "granary" of north Africa as to political corruption and the invader's prowess. Throughout the annals of recorded human history, soil has been valued highly and has been as attractive a war prize as armaments, buildings, industries, or slaves. During the long search for fertile soil, hitherto peaceable, responsible empires have turnd into militant aggressors.

Soil Formation

The development of a mature soil is a complex phenomenon involving the interaction of physical, chemical, and biological processes. The time required depends not only on the intensity of these processes but on the nature of the parent material. Authorities estimate that the development of 1 inch of topsoil derived from hard rocklike basalt or granite may require from 200 to 1,200 years, depending on the climate. However, soft rocks, such as volcanic ash and shale and such parent material as sand dunes and river sediments, may develop into mature vegetation-supporting soil within a few decades. Many soils do not develop from underlying bed rock but are derived from materials transported by glaciers, wind, or water. The major processes in soil formation are *physical, chemical,* and *biological.*

Physical Processes. Rapid heating and cooling may induce differential contraction and expansion, which eventually causes rocks to scale, split, and shatter. This process assumes a particularly prominent role in the arid climates of the desert biome, where the diurnal cycle, especially during summer, may be marked by violent shifts in temperature. Thus, at noon the hot floor of Arizona desert may register 145° F and by midnight may have dropped to 65° F.

Thawing and freezing is characteristic of temperate latitudes where there is relatively abundant rainfall. During a winter thaw, rivulets of water from melted snow and ice gradually infiltrate the pores and cracks of surface rock. During a subsequent freeze, the water expands with considerable force, causing rock to flake and fragment.

Chemical Processes. Chemical processes of soil formation frequently occur simultaneously with the physical processes. Chemical activity usually causes minerals to lose their sheen and become porous and soft. Among the principal chemical processes involved in soil formation are *hydrolysis, oxidation,* and *solution.*

HYDROLYSIS. Derived from the Greek, *hydrolysis* literally means "the process of breaking down or disintegrating with water." Hydrolysis is a type of chemical reaction with water that results in mineral decomposition.

OXIDATION. Because oxidation involves the combination of oxygen with a mineral, it occurs most intensively at the upper surface of rock. It is a characteristic weathering process in iron-bearing deposits. Ferrous oxide (FeO), for example, may be oxidized to form ferric oxide or hematite (Fe_2O_3). As a result of oxidation, the iron-containing rock is more easily disintegrated.

SOLUTION. The solution of minerals occurs prominently in limestone rock. Here the percolating water, bearing dissolved carbon dioxide, gradually eats away the substratum to form minute pores, channels, and crevices. The dissolved materials may be transported a considerable distance before precipitating out and eventually contributing to the formation of soil. Under certain conditions huge subterranean chambers are formed, such as Kentucky's Mammoth Cave or New Mexico's Carlsbad Caverns. These caverns are the products of limestone solution occurring over many centuries and their multicolored stalagmites and stalactites form labyrinths of awesome beauty.

Biological Processes. The development of a mature soil is also dependent upon the activity of a great number and diversity of organisms. The all-important bacteria influence soil structure, aeration, moisture content, and fertility in many ways that will be discussed later in this chapter. Lichens and mosses that have become established on a rocky substratum may trap wind-blown organic debris—such as plant fibers, seeds, dead insects, excrement, and so on—to a depth sufficient to form a film over the rock's surface. They may also secrete a very dilute carbonic acid (H_2CO_3), which slowly dissolves the rock, thus accelerating its ultimate incorporation into a mature soil. Finally, upon their death, the lichens and mosses will decompose and eventually enrich the soil with their constituent elements. Rock may be splintered by the actively growing roots of trees. Rooted vegetation absorbs nutrient salts from lower levels and deposits them at the soil surface when it dies. Through the centuries, the hoofs of antelope, buffalo, mountain sheep, deer, and livestock have gradually fragmented and pulverized underlying rock. The burrowing activities of earthworms, millipedes, digger wasps, beetle larvae, bull snakes, burrowing owls, pocket gophers, and ground squirrels promote soil aeration and facilitate water passage. Soil fertility is enhanced by animal excrement, especially that of earthworms, arthropods, birds, and mammals.

Sources of Parent Materials. The parent material from which soils develop may be the underlying weathered bedrock. On the other hand, most parent materials are carried for considerable distances by the action of glaciers, water, and wind.

Figure 3-1. *Geological erosion. Note the glacial striations on this rock formation in Wyoming. The boulder in the foreground has been smoothed and rounded by moving glaciers, one of the physical processes involved in soil formation.* [U. S. Forest Service]

Figure 3-2. *Infrared aerial view of the Missisquoi River watershed, Vermont. The delta of the river, formed by water transport of thousands of tons of silt, is visible in the foreground.* [Soil Conservation Service, U. S. Department of Agriculture]

GLACIAL ACTIVITY. During the Pleistocene period (1,000,000 to 10,000 B.C.), four massive glacial advances moved southwestward from Canada into the northeastern states as far as Ohio, Indiana, Illinois, and Iowa. During these movements so much ocean water was "locked up" in glacial ice that the ocean level dropped about 250 feet. The massive, dome-shaped glaciers acted like gigantic files, shearing off hilltops and mountain peaks, gouging out depressions, and pulverizing large boulders. Rocks, gravel, sand, silt, and clay accumulated underneath the moving glacier. Consequently, when the ice finally melted, a mantle of *glacial drift* remained, which served as fresh parent material for the development of future soils. Glaciation has generally enhanced the value of soils for agriculture by increasing soil fertility and by leveling the terrain in a way that renders it susceptible to modern cultivation techniques.

OCEAN WAVES AND RIVER CURRENTS. Ocean waves are powerful rock-grinders. Boulders are dashed about in the raging surf like so many marbles, many of them being chipped and broken in the process. Rivers also play an important role in soil building. Pebbles of a stream bed may be worn smooth by the scouring action of the current. Each stream carries in suspension a load of sand, silt, and clay. Much of this material may ultimately be transported to the ocean at the river's mouth to form a delta. The Mississippi River alone discharges roughly 700 million tons of sediment into the Gulf of Mexico each year. When the major rivers of the world—such as the Mississippi, Nile, and Amazon—periodically overflow their banks, a nutrient-rich load of sediment is deposited along the river bottoms. This special type of soil, called *alluvial soil*, is said to support almost one third of the world's agriculture.

WIND ACTION. The blasting effect of billions of minute, wind-blown sand grains inexorably wears smooth even the roughest boulders. Many of the smoothly rounded outcrops in our arid Southwest have been fashioned by wind erosion. The tiny rock particles may be transported for many miles before settling and becoming part of the soil.

Soil Properties

The major properties of soils are *texture, structure, acidity, gaseous content, moisture content,* and *biotic composition.* An understanding of the nature of these characteristics is an essential prerequisite to the study of soil profiles, soil types, soil productivity, and soil management.

Texture. By *texture* is meant the size of the individual mineral particles as well as the proportion in which they occur. For convenience and efficiency in the study of mineral particles, the USDA has classified soil particles as *gravel, sand, silt,* and *clay,* depending upon size. It should be emphasized that these textural classes are relatively stable. Despite the dynamic nature of soil, despite the continuous physical, chemical, and biological activities that are continuously transforming it, and regardless of the soil management activities of the farmer, gravel will not change to sand, or silt to clay, within the average human lifespan.

GRAVEL. Soil particles that are over 1 millimeter in diameter are classified as gravel.

SAND. Particles of sand range from 0.05 to 1 millimeter in diameter. This textural class shows very little plasticity or cohesiveness, as is well known to anyone who has

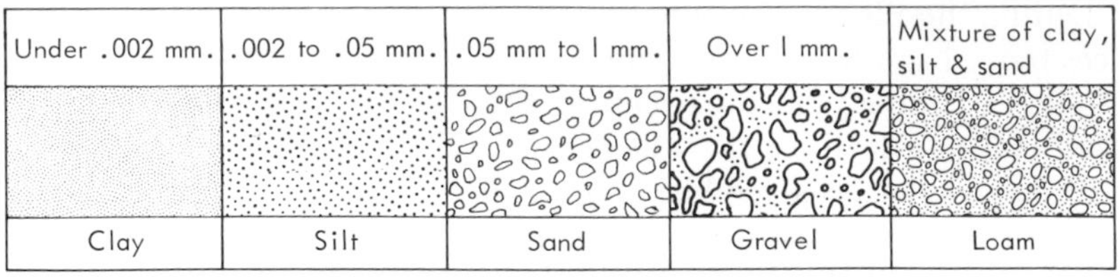

Under .002 mm.	.002 to .05 mm.	.05 mm to 1 mm.	Over 1 mm.	Mixture of clay, silt & sand
Clay	Silt	Sand	Gravel	Loam

Figure 3-3. *Soil textural classes.*

tried to build a sand castle. Because the spaces (*macropores*) between the individual sand particles are quite large, sand is usually well aerated and has good drainage. Because it is composed of quartz (SiO_2), however, which is chemically inactive, it will yield very few nutrients for crop growth.

SILT. The individual particles of silt are microscopic in size (0.002 to 0.050 millimeters). Silt shows a slight tendency to become plastic and sticky when wet. Because silt, like sand, is composed primarily of quartz (SiO_2), its nutrient-supplying ability is poor. When unmixed with other soil texture classes, it is agriculturally unproductive.

CLAY. The individual clay particles are so minute (less than 0.002 millimeters) that they are not even visible with an ordinary microscope. The plasticity and cohesiveness of moistened clay permit it to be fashioned into pots, bowls, and vases. Because of this stickiness when wet, clay soils are worked only with difficulty and are therefore called heavy soils, in contrast to the easily worked light soils that are composed primarily of sand. The more plastic clay becomes, the more likely it is to "puddle," that is, to undergo reduction in pore space and incur reduced permeability to air and water. When clay soils dry out, the individual particles contract so as to form hard clods. As John Vosburgh observes: "Baked by the sun, clay soil will keep out water almost as effectively as tile, which is but clay baked by man" (18).

The total amount of air space in clay is somewhat greater than in sand. Because much of this air space is represented by extremely minute pores (*micropores*), however, the actual rate of water percolation and air movement through clay is much slower than it is through sand. Water in the micropores is held so tenaciously that it is unavailable for most plant root systems. Moreover, because young plant rootlets do not readily penetrate poorly oxygenated clay, soil composed exclusively of clay is quite unproductive.

Because of its electrical properties clay serves as an important reservoir of plant food. Because the surfaces of the microscopic clay particles are negatively charged, they are able to adsorb many positively charged soil elements, such as calcium, magnesium, potassium, phosphorus, zinc, and copper. Clay frequently retains these nutrients despite the leaching tendencies of percolating water.

On the other hand, clay particles have relatively poor ability to retain negatively charged nitrate particles. As a result nitrates are leached from the soil by rainfall, or washed away with run-off waters. These nitrates then fertilize lake and pond waters and eventually convert open-water, game-fish lakes to weed-grown, rough-fish lakes —a process called *eutrophication*, which will be discussed later. To prevent such excessive nitrate loss from farm lands, James Bonner, of the California Institute of Technology, has suggested adding a resin to the soil that has the ability to "hold" the negatively charged nitrate particles. Such a proposal, of course, would have to

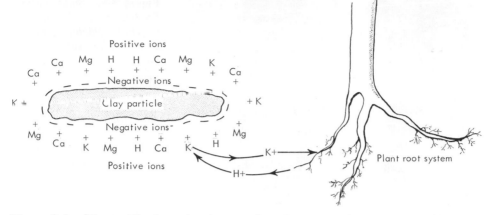

Figure 3-4. *The positive ions of various nutrient elements such as potassium (K), calcium (Ca), and magnesium (Mg) are attracted to the negatively charged surface of the clay particle. Note that these nutrient ions are replaced by hydrogen ions from the root systems of plants and then absorbed by the plants. It is this role of the clay particle that makes it an invaluable component of agricultural soil.*

be studied very carefully, lest this new technological "advance" create a more serious problem than the one it was supposed to cure (8).

LOAM.   Very few agricultural soils are composed exclusively of one textural class; usually they represent a mixture in which all four of the major classes (gravel, sand, silt, and clay) are represented in varying proportions. The most desirable soil from an agricultural standpoint is *loam*, which represents a mixture of heavy and light soil materials in the following proportions: sand, 30 to 50 per cent; silt, 30 to 50 per cent; and clay, 0 to 20 per cent. In the best loams the most desirable qualities of sand and clay are combined and their adverse characteristics are precluded.

Structure.   We may define soil *structure* as the arrangement or grouping of its primary particles (gravel, sand, silt, and clay) into granules.

The aeration, moisture content, fertility, and erosion resistance of a soil are all to some degree dependent upon its structure. Plowing, cultivation, liming, and manuring may improve the soil's productivity primarily by changing its structure. Other factors affecting soil structure include alternate freezing and thawing, drying and wetting, penetration by plant roots, burrowing activity of animals, addition of slimy secretions from soil animals, and decomposition of plant and animal residues in the soil.

GOOD STRUCTURE.   A good soil structure (that is, one that promotes crop or timber production) has a spongy or crumbly quality. It has an abundance of pores through which life-sustaining oxygen diffuses and through which water can move to the root systems of crop plants. Soil with good structure feels resilient and springy under foot. Such soil is more resistant than poorly structured soil to the erosive effects of wind, rain, and run-off water. Farmers can effectively promote good soil structure by the addition of organic matter, either by manuring or by plowing under cover crops and crop residues (stubble).

Soil structure can also be improved with compost—partially decomposed garbage.

Figure 3-5. *Soil structure. Profiles of soil taken near Newkirk, Oklahoma. Soil sample at left was under poor land treatment, soil at right under excellent cropping system. Poor treatment is reflected in poor structure and low organic matter; good treatment has resulted in good structure and high organic content.* [*Soil Conservation Service, U. S. Department of Agriculture*]

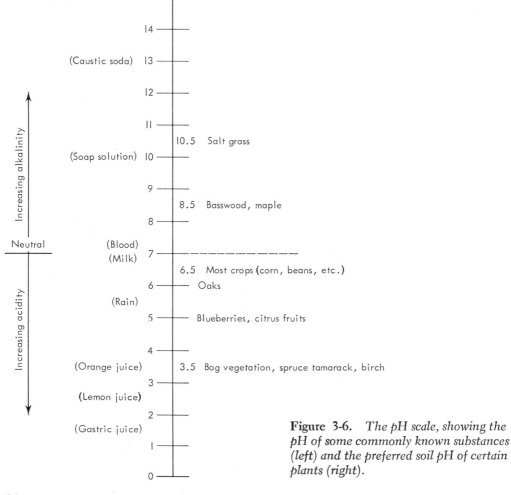

Figure 3-6. *The pH scale, showing the pH of some commonly known substances (left) and the preferred soil pH of certain plants (right).*

Although not extensively used as yet in the United States, composters in Holland use 11 per cent of the Dutch refuse load. One company alone produces 200,000 tons of compost annually from the municipal wastes of eight cities with an aggregate population of 1 million. The famed Riesling wines are made from grapes coming from vineyards growing on steep slopes overlooking the Rhine. Without liberal applications of compost, which improved the soil's resistance to erosion, these vineyard soils would long since have been washed into the Rhine far below (13).

POOR STRUCTURE. A soil with poor structure has a minimum of pore spaces, or "chambers," for air and water, because of the closely packed soil particles. Moreover, the individual soil particles tend to break up or fall apart. The soil has little resiliency. Because water infiltration is greatly reduced, in arid regions irrigation water may not penetrate to satisfactory depths for crop production. In humid areas, however, poorly structured soils produce drainage problems in low-lying sites, whereas on uplands they may result in severe water run-off and erosion. Although most virgin soils in the grassland and deciduous forest biomes of America originally had good structure, many decades of intensive farming gradually brought about their deterioration.

Soil Acidity (pH). Soil scientists employ the symbol pH as a quantitative measure of hydrogen *ion* concentration. (The hydrogen ion is a positively charged part of the hydrogen atom.) Soils may vary from a pH of 4.5 (strongly acid) to 9 (strongly alkaline). Soils having a pH of 7 are considered *neutral*. Most vegetables, grains, trees, and grass grow best in soil that is very mildly acid (about 6.8). (When many of the minerals, such as calcium, potassium, and phosphorus, are displaced by hydrogen ions on the clay-humus particles, the pH goes *down*, that is, the soil becomes *more acid*. When most of the minerals are retained on the clay-humus particles the pH goes *up*, that is, the soil becomes *less acid*.) A few species of plants such as the valuable long-leaf pine of the South, prefer a more acidic soil. Hardwood forest (oak, maple, beech) soils are usually more alkaline than coniferous forest (pine, spruce) soils. With the help of a soil scientist from the local Soil Conservation Service district, the farmer or city dweller can determine the pH of his land. If too acid, the use of limestone may be advised. For example, to raise the pH of acid soil from 5.5 to 6.5 a 7-inch layer over a 1,000-square-foot area would require 30 pounds of finely ground limestone (18).

Gaseous Content. Only about 50 per cent of soil volume is actually represented by solid materials such as minerals, plant and animal bodies, and organic residues. The remaining 50 per cent is represented by pore spaces (macropores and micropores), which occur between the individual soil particles and/or aggregates. When soil is extremely dry because of a protracted drought, these spaces are filled with air. When soil is waterlogged after a violent thunderstorm, they may be filled with water.

In a sense, one can consider soil as continuously inhaling and exhaling. Oxygen, which is present in greater concentration in the atmosphere than in the soil, diffuses into the soil pores, whereas *carbon dioxide*, which may approach a concentration of 10 per cent in soil spaces, continuously moves from soil into the atmosphere, where the concentration is about 0.03 per cent. The importance of soil oxygen for plant growth is well demonstrated in apple trees, which require a concentration of 3 per cent merely to survive, or 5 to 10 per cent for elongation of existing roots, and of 12 per cent before new roots will develop. When soil is poorly aerated, the nitrogen-fixing activity of *Rhizobium* (root-nodule bacteria) and *Azotobacter* (free-living form) are adversely affected, thus impairing soil fertility. Moreover, an oxygen-deficient soil curtails the development of crop roots, may cause root deformities, and may severely restrict their role in water and nutrient absorption.

Moisture Content.   Water serves several important plant functions. It is essential for photosynthesis and the conversion of starch to sugar. It enables plants to maintain an effective shape or position for reception of incident sunlight by maintaining their turgidity. Water is the solvent medium by which minerals are transported upward to the leaves and sugar is transported downward to the roots. Finally, it is an essential protoplasmic constituent, contributing 85 to 90 per cent of the weight of actively growing organs such as buds, rootlets, and flowers. And of course, many animals, living in desert regions as we have mentioned earlier, secure life-sustaining water by consuming succulent water-bearing plant tissues—despite the virtual complete absence of drinking water.

Soil is said to be *saturated* when the air in all the micropores and macropores has become replaced with water. This may occur after low-lying fields have been flooded following a severe thunderstorm or excessive irrigation.

Field capacity refers to the amount of water that remains after the excess has drained away from soil that has become water saturated. Most upland crops such as corn and cotton cannot survive in soils that are water saturated or at field capacity because of the greatly reduced oxygen content. Rice, however, grows well under these conditions.

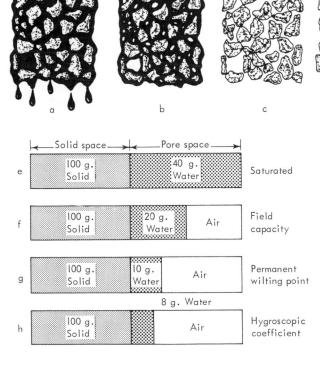

Figure 3-7.   *Water content of the soil, shown at saturation (a,e); at field capacity (b,f); at its permanent wilting point (c.g); and in a state of extreme desiccation, the hygroscopic coefficient (d.h).* [Adapted from H.O. Buckman and N.C. Brady, The Nature and Properties of Soils, 7th ed. (New York: Macmillan Publishing Co., Inc., 1969); and W.B. Clapham, Jr., Natural Ecosystems (New York: Macmillan Publishing Co., Inc., 1973).]

Vigorously growing crops continuously remove soil moisture. As soil moisture is reduced, a critical point is reached when the "pull" of the plant roots for water is not sufficient to prevent permanent wilting. This point is known as the permanent wilting point—a phenomenon experienced by many a farmer or suburban gardener who has seen his plot of beans and lettuce wilt and shrivel during a late summer drought.

Biotic Composition. Soil is composed of more than just inanimate rock and air and water; it is very much alive and represents the world's largest zoo and botanical garden rolled into one. Were we to take a single grain of fertile topsoil and examine it under a microscope, we would find it swarming with minute organisms. These creatures play a basic role in determining the soil's chemistry, air and water relationship, and fertility.

We shall describe the activities of the major groups of soil plants (bacteria, fungi, and algae) and soil animals (protozoa, nematodes, insects, and earthworms) in building and transforming the soil.

BACTERIA. The top foot of an acre of fertile soil may contain 1,000 pounds of bacterial biomass (6). In a very real sense, bacteria burn up the organic content of the soil. (Unfortunately, however, they are not able to break down some complex organic materials synthesized by modern man such as plastics and chlorinated hydrocarbon pesticides (DDT). On a hot day in July, the bacteria of 1 acre burn carbon at a rate equivalent to burning 1.6 pounds of soft coal hourly and generating up to 1 horsepower of energy (1). The energy thus liberated from the organic material is then used by the bacteria in converting soil nutrients into a form available to crops.

Soil bacteria normally do not occur as isolated cells but are found in clumplike, matlike, or filamentous colonies around individual soil particles (6). Bacterial populations, which may form up to 0.03 per cent of the weight of top soil (2), are concentrated in the upper layers of soil, where oxygen and bacterial food in the form of plant debris are abundant. The roots and root hairs of plants are frequently completely enclosed in a bacterial film. The soil in the immediate vicinity of root systems may be from ten to fifty times more dense with bacteria than other soil (6).

FUNGI AND MOLDS. The fungi and molds, like the bacteria, lack chlorophyll and hence cannot carry on photosynthesis. They secure their energy and carbon from organic residues.

All of us are familiar with the cottony bread mold or the various gray, black, white, and green molds that flourish on decaying fruit and fruit preserves. The larger forest fungi, such as the toadstools, puffballs, and mushrooms, are also well known. Very few of us are aware, however, of the mold and fungi of soils, many of the 200 species of which are of microscopic size. There may be 1 million fungi in 1 gram of dry soil, and their per acre biomass may reach 1,200 pounds.

Molds occur prominently in the acid soils of deciduous and coniferous forests. Because most soil bacteria are intolerant of acid conditions, the decay and rot of leaf litter is primarily effected by fungi and molds, with some assistance from millipedes, mites, and springtails. Fungi are most effective decomposers and break down even such complex leaf litter compounds as cellulose and lignin with their digestive enzymes. Up to 50 per cent of the decomposed plant debris may then be channeled into the living substance of the soil molds. Molds are unable to thrive in boggy soils because of the limited oxygen available; the resultant accumulation of

Figure 3-8. *Fungi and bacteria, with the aid of soil animals, will eventually bring about the decay of these fallen trees and thus contribute to the fertility of the forest soil. Allegheny National Forest, Pennsylvania.* [U.S. Forest Service]

brownish, partly decomposed plant fibers is known as peat. In many northern European countries, such as Norway, where high grade coal is scarce, peat is collected, dried, and used as low grade fuel.

ALGAE. Soil algae are simple plants and are usually unicellular and microscopic. In addition to bearing chlorophyll, some may possess blue, golden, brown, or red pigments. The major groups are the blue, the blue-green, the yellow-green, and the diatoms. Occasionally, after heavy rainstorms the red algae populations will increase greatly, causing light-colored soil to turn a faint crimson color (6). Because algae are chlorophyll-bearing organisms, they must live near the soil's surface, where there is sufficient sunshine for photosynthesis. After the application of commercial fertilizers the soil may turn green, because of the increased amount of green algae. Algae densities up to 800,000 organisms per gram of dry soil have been estimated in samples from Utah. By the release of oxygen, soil algae may aid in soil aeration. Algae may serve as food for other soil organisms. In some areas, such as in grasslands, where blue-green algae are populous, they may serve an important nitrogen-fixing function. The sustained fertility of the Asiatic rice paddies, even after centuries of use, has been partially attributed to this role of the blue-green algae.

In addition to these teeming populations of microflora, the soil community also includes a zoological garden of almost infinite variety, ranging in size from the microscopic, unicellular *protozoa* to relatively large burrowing mammals, such as the pocket gopher and mole.

PROTOZOA. There are over 250 species of soil-dwelling protozoa. Several million protozoa may occur in a teaspoonful of fertile soil (6). Their total biomass may approach 200 pounds per acre. Protozoans are primarily restricted to the upper soil layers where suitable food and soil oxygen are abundant.

NEMATODES. Nematodes are nonsegmented worms that range from the microscopic to over a foot long. Because of their slender shape they have been called eel worms or horse hair worms. Up to 45 billion of these threadlike worms may occur in an acre; fifty may occur in a grain of dry soil. In the South the parasitic forms have severely damaged vegetable crops. On Long Island, New York, the golden nematode is highly injurious to potato crops.

INSECTS. Insects form a most interesting component of the soil community. Included among the thousands of species are the larvae of the seventeen-year locust, mound-building ants, beetle larvae, burrow-digging wasps, and the diminutive springtails. Many insects swarm in the leaf litter of the forest, ingesting and partially digesting the leaf fragments, converting them into a form more readily decomposed by the activity of soil fungi and bacteria. All soil-dwelling insects contribute to the porosity, drainage, and aeration of the soil by their burrowing activities. According to Francis F. Clark, up to eighty-four cicada emergence holes (by means of which the larvae leave their subterranean haunts to assume an arboreal life as a winged adult) have been counted in a single square foot of ground (5).

EARTHWORMS. In the topsoil of well-manured agricultural land, the population density of the earthworm may reach 1 million per acre. (The fisherman searching for "nightcrawlers" might not agree!) The per-acre biomass, up to 1,100 pounds, may exceed the total biomass of all other soil animals combined! Earthworms prefer soil that is well drained, rich in decomposing organic matter, well supplied with calcium, and with a pH above 4.5. Good drainage prevents flooding of their burrows; decomposing organic debris serves as food.

Earthworms literally eat their way through the soil, sucking in dirt, manure, plant fragments, seeds, insect eggs and larvae, and numerous minute animals, dead and alive, through their mouth with their muscular, suctionlike pharynx. This activity is most prominent in the upper 6 inches of topsoil. After thoroughly grinding this material in the gizzard and digesting it, residues are ejected through the anus in the form of *casts*. There can be as much as 8 tons per acre of these spherical casts in a cultivated field. A study of arable land in Connecticut showed that earthworm casts contained 366 per cent more nitrogen, 644 per cent more phosphorus, and 1,109 per cent more potassium than surrounding soil. By their burrowing activity, earthworms promote soil aeration and drainage and facilitate downward growth of plant roots. By voiding nutrient-rich casts and nitrogen-containing excretions, they increase soil fertility. Earthworms may bring up to 18 tons of soil to the surface per acre per year. Soil that has been worked over by earthworms usually has a characteristic granular structure.

Soil Profile

When one looks at the exposed face of a road cut or the wall of a rock quarry, it is apparent that some soil is organized into horizontally arranged layers, or *horizons*. Each of these horizons is distinct with regard to thickness, color, texture, and chemical composition. This cross-sectional view of the various horizons is known as the *soil profile*. Each profile is the expression of a specific combination of soil formation factors, including parent rock, soil age, topography, climate, and organisms.

The major layers from the ground surface downward to bedrock are designated as horizons A (topsoil), B (subsoil), C (parent material), and D (bedrock) (10).

These horizons will not all be equally distinct in the different soil types. In fact, in immature soils, where weathering has not fully progressed, some horizons may be missing, whereas in certain soils laid down by water-borne sediment, known as *alluvial soils,* or in soils that have been thoroughly mixed by the burrowing activity of mammals, the stratified pattern may be lacking completely.

The profile of a typical soil is the product of the interaction of vegetation, temperature, rainfall, and soil organisms on parent rock materials operating for many thousands of years. The soil profile, therefore, tells us a great deal about soil history. It represents a kind of soil autobiography by which we can learn much about its origin and development. From the practical standpoint the soil profile is of great economic importance, for it can tell the agronomist immediately whether the soil is best suited for agricultural crops, for rangeland, for timber, or for wildlife habitat and recreation. (Fig. 3-10) The profile also reveals the suitability of the soil for various urban uses such as site determination for homes, highways, sewage disposal plants, sanitary landfills, septic tanks, and the laying of power cables.

Let us examine the basic characteristics of a hypothetical composite soil profile, beginning with the uppermost horizon and moving downward to bedrock. (See Fig. 3-12.)

A HORIZON. Mankind is dependent upon the thin envelope of topsoil that covers much of the earth. In America its thickness ranges from 1 inch on the slopes of the Rockies to almost 2 feet in Iowa corn country. It is from the topsoil, or A horizon, that crop roots absorb vital water. It is within this stratum also that soil organisms abound. The upper portion is composed of loosely arrayed organic debris. It perhaps is most conspicuous in the temperate deciduous forest, where it is represented by leaf litter, fallen twigs, fruits, nuts, and animal excrement. By the end of autumn this material may form an aggregate weight of up to 1 ton per acre. As this organic debris decomposes it is known as *humus.*

Toward the bottom of the A horizon is a light-colored mineral layer. In a sense, it represents a layer of "impoverishment" because of the excessive leaching of soluble soil nutrients by water and organic acids percolating downward from above.

B HORIZON. The B horizon, commonly called the *subsoil,* is a "zone of accumulation" into which silicates, clays, iron and aluminum compounds, and organic matter are carried by percolating waters from the A horizon. It is in this horizon that the dense, impermeable *hardpan* develops.

C HORIZON. The C horizon is composed of the unconsolidated, weathered parent material from which the mineral component of the A and B horizons will ultimately be derived. About 97 per cent of the parent materials in the United States were transported to their present sites by ice, water, wind, and gravity. This parent material will in part determine soil texture and the rate of water absorption and release. It will also determine much of the future soil's nutrient content such as nitrogen, phosphorus, calcium, potassium. Moreover, it will influence the soil's acidity or alkalinity. Thus, if parent material is granitic, soil will mature slowly and tend to be acid; conversely, where limestone represents the parent material, the soil will develop rapidly and tend to remain alkaline even in humid climates that would otherwise promote an acid soil. Granitic soils are usually less productive than limestone soils.

D HORIZON. The D horizon consists of the unweathered bedrock formed by geological processes such as sedimentation and volcanic activity.

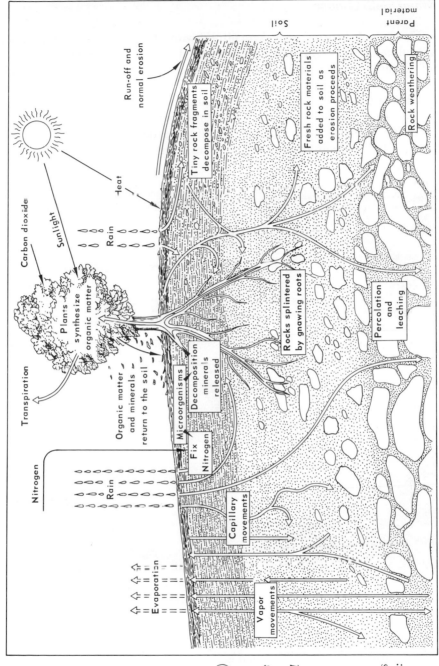

Figure 3-9. *Development of the soil profile by the interaction of climatic and biotic factors with parental rock and physiographic features. Rainfall is an essential source of water for photosynthesis and for life maintenance in all organisms (bacteria, fungi, earthworms, grass, trees, and so on) involved in soil development. In combination with land topography, precipitation determines the rate and extent of normal (accelerated) erosion. Although some topsoil is continuously subjected to natural (slow) erosion, this is partially offset by the addition of fresh rock-derived materials to the soil body. [Adapted from George L. Clarke, Elements of Ecology (New York: John Wiley & Sons, Inc., 1954). After Charles E. Kellogg, The Soils That Support Us (New York: Macmillan Publishing Co., Inc., 1941).]*

Soil

Parent material

Run-off and normal erosion

Tiny rock fragments decompose in soil

Fresh rock materials added to soil as erosion proceeds

Rock weathering

Rocks splintered by gnawing roots

Percolation and leaching

Carbon dioxide

Sunlight

Rain

Heat

Plants synthesize organic matter

Transpiration

Organic matter and minerals return to the soil

Microorganisms

Decomposition minerals released

Fix Nitrogen

Nitrogen

Rain

Capillary movements

Evaporation

Vapor movements

61

Major Soil Groups

The U.S. Department of Agriculture, with the assistance of the various state agricultural experiment stations, has mapped more than 70,000 *soil types* over 500 million acres. Soil types are designated by locality (city, river, county, and so on) and texture—for example, Miami silt loam, Fargo clay, or Plainfield sand. In a 1,100-square-mile region near Merced, California, at least 290 soil types have been distinguished. Soil types are assembled into about twenty *soil groups*. For our purposes it will be necessary only to identify and describe a few representative soil groups—true podzols, chernozems, and the desert soils. (Fig. 3-11)

Figure 3-10. *Soil maps. The U.S. Soil Conservation Service has probed, examined, and mapped the 70,000 different soil types in the United States. Soil surveys hold the key to proper land management and are used primarily by the private land owners—farmers and ranchers—to determine the proper cultivation and conservation measures for their land. But the soil surveys are also important to foresters, county agents, land developers, real estate offices, highway engineers, libraries, and sanitation boards.* [U. S. Department of Agriculture]

Figure 3-11. *Major soil groups of North America.* [*Adapted from Raymond F. Dasmann,* Environmental Conservation (*New York: John Wiley & Sons, Inc., 1968*). *After Vernon C. Finch and G. T. Trewartha,* Elements of Geography, Physical and Cultural (*New York: McGraw-Hill Book Co., 1942*); *and C. E. Kelley,* Soils and Man (*Washington, D. C.: U. S. Department of Agriculture, 1938*).]

Podzol Soils. *Podzolization* occurs in a cool, humid climate under forest vegetation. The litter of forest leaves, fruits, and branches decomposes, largely because of fungal activity, to produce a dark brown, extremely acid humus. Percolating water and organic acids carry soluble carbonate and sulphate salts, as well as aluminum and iron compounds, downward from the A to the B horizon. This leaching causes the lower part of the A horizon to assume a gray, ashlike appearance. (The term *podzol* is derived from two Russian words, *pod*, which means *under*, and *zola*, which means *ash*.) The lower portion of the B horizon, on the other hand, because of the addition of iron compounds and organic materials, assumes a distinctive coffee-brown color. (Fig. 3-12)

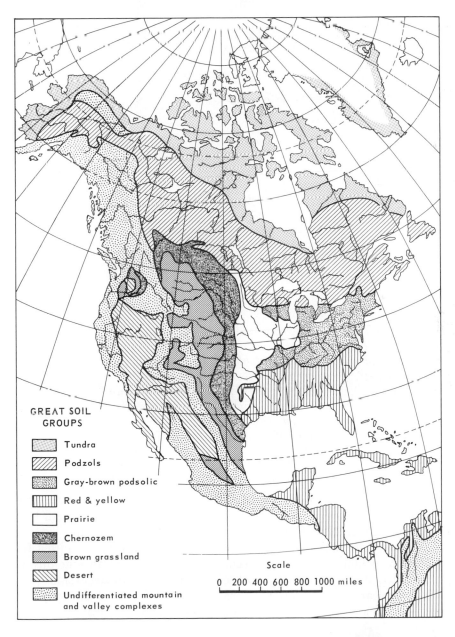

GREAT SOIL
GROUPS

- Tundra
- Podzols
- Gray-brown podsolic
- Red & yellow
- Prairie
- Chernozem
- Brown grassland
- Desert
- Undifferentiated mountain and valley complexes

Scale

0   200 400 600 800 1000 miles

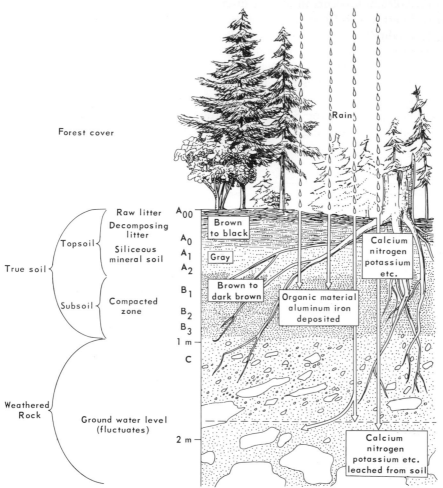

Forest cover

Raw litter	A_{00}
Decomposing litter	A_0
Siliceous mineral soil	A_1 A_2

True soil

Topsoil

Subsoil

Compacted zone

B_1

B_2
B_3

1 m

C

Weathered Rock

Ground water level (fluctuates)

2 m

Rain

Brown to black

Gray

Brown to dark brown

Calcium nitrogen potassium etc.

Organic material aluminum iron deposited

Calcium nitrogen potassium etc. leached from soil

Figure 3-12. *Profile of podzol soil. Note the accumulation of a dense mat of spruce and pine needle litter. The gray color of the thin layer of topsoil contrasts sharply with the dark-brown B horizon. Soluble calcium, potassium, and nitrate salts are leached by the abundant rainfall (over 30 inches annually) beyond the zone of plant root availability down to the C horizon. Although this figure is representative of podzols, considerable variation is possible because of regional differences in climate and parental materials.* [Adapted from George L. Clarke, Elements of Ecology (New York: John Wiley & Sons, Inc., 1954).]

THE TRUE PODZOLS. The classic example of podzolization occurs in the *true podzol* soils. These soils develop under the coniferous forests of the northern lake states, in the uplands of New England, and at high elevations in the western mountains. Because these soils are inherently infertile, they can best be utilized for timber production, wildlife habitat, and scenic wilderness. Many an enterprising farming venture based on tilling the podzol soils of northern Michigan and Wisconsin in the early part of this century ultimately failed because of the relatively short growing season and the extremely acid and infertile soil. Unless true podzol soil is heavily limed and fertilized, it depreciates rapidly. This is corroborated by many an abandoned farm home now being swallowed up by encroaching second-growth forest. An outstanding exception to the general failure of true podzols as agriculturally productive soils is the famous potato-growing area in Aroostook County, Maine, where intensive fertilization is practiced.

THE GRAY-BROWN PODZOLS. The *gray-brown podzols*, which derive their name from the color of the lower part of the A horizon, occur just south of the true podzols in Minnesota, Wisconsin, Illinois, Michigan, Indiana, Ohio, New York, Pennsylvania, and all the New England states. Less intensively podzolized than the true podzols, the gray-brown have developed under a deciduous forest cover. The extensive leaf littter derived from herbs, shrubs, and trees, sometimes amounting to a ton per acre annually, decomposes much more readily and releases more calcium than the hard mat of needles that forms under coniferous forests. As a result, the gray-brown podzols are less acid and more fertile than the true podzols. These are the soils on which America's pioneer farmers heavily depended. Although the original fertility of such soils is quickly depleted, rainfall and climate are normally benign. Therefore, when proper soil conservation practices are maintained, a great spectrum of agricultural activity can be supported, from the raising of grains, tobacco, potatoes, and fruit to the development of lush pastures for beef and dairy cattle.

Chernozem Soils. *Chernozem* is the Russian word for *black earth*. It refers to the extremely fertile, blackish-brown topsoil that may accumulate to a depth of 3 to 4 feet. Developing primarily under mixed-grass prairie, the chernozems extend in a north-south belt 150 miles wide in the Great Plains from the western edge of the tall grass prairie to the eastern margin of the short grass prairie. *Calcification* of the subsoil resulting from leaching of soluble calcium carbonate from above is a dominant characteristic. However, because of an annual rainfall of only 15 to 25 inches, which is usually in the form of brief summer thunder showers, leaching does not carry the calcium through to the C horizon. It is instead deposited in the lower subsoil, where it precipitates out and forms a grayish or yellowish band. The topsoil of the chernozem, characterized by rich organic and nutrient mineral content as well as a highly desirable granular structure, is intrinsically more fertile than any other soil type in the United States. The relatively undependable and low annual rainfall limits its productivity, however. During wet years bumper crops are commonplace, but during years of excessive heat and drought, crop failures may be extensive. Major northern crops produced in these soils are high-quality corn, wheat, barley, oats, and rye. Sorghum is a prominent southern crop.

Desert Soils. The desert soils occur in the desert biome, where the annual rainfall averages from about 3 to 12 inches. Desert soils occur extensively in southern and eastern California, southeastern Oregon, Nevada, southern Idaho, southwestern Arizona, western Utah, western Wyoming, southern New Mexico, and western Texas. Vegetation consists to a large degree of specialized drought-adapted plants, called *xerophytes*, such as sagebrush, creosote bush, ocatillo, mesquite, shadscale, and cactus. Because these desert plants are widely spaced, with extensive areas of bare soil between them, water and wind erosion may be severe and may leave a layer of stones called the *desert pavement*. There is a relatively small component of

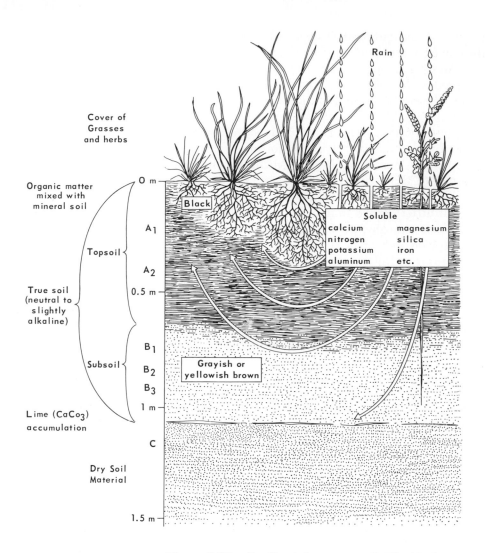

Cover of
Grasses
and herbs

Rain

Organic matter
mixed with
mineral soil

0 m

A₁

Topsoil

A₂

0.5 m

True soil
(neutral to
slightly
alkaline)

Black

Soluble
calcium   magnesium
nitrogen   silica
potassium   iron
aluminum   etc.

B₁

Subsoil

B₂

B₃

Grayish or
yellowish brown

1 m

Lime (CaCo₃)
accumulation

C

Dry Soil
Material

1.5 m

Figure 3-13. *Profile of chernozem soil. The black
color of the 2-foot thick A horizon contrasts with the
light color of the 1-foot thick B horizon. Note that
because of the light rainfall (10 to 30 inches
annually) the soluble mineral salts (except for lime,
which accumulates at the base of the B horizon) are
not leached extensively from the A horizon but are
available to plants. Observe the extensive mesh of
root systems in the A horizon. Upon plant death, the
in situ decomposition of the root systems releases
nutrients that become immediately available for
future plant generations. Loss of these nutrients by
erosion is obviously minimal. The actual dimensions
of the chernozem horizons illustrated are typical but
may vary considerably depending on regional differences in parental material and climate.* [Adapted
from George L. Clarke, Elements of Ecology (New
York: John Wiley & Sons, Inc., 1954).]

Figure 3-14. *Profile of chernozem soil formed from glacial till in South Dakota. Note thick, dark A horizon and the whitish flecks (calcium deposits) in the B horizon. Scale is calibrated in feet. [Soil Conservation Service, U. S. Department of Agriculture]*

organic matter in the thin band of topsoil. However, because leaching is minimal, the nutrient content of the soil is relatively high. With proper soil management and effective irrigation, certain desert areas, such as the Imperial Valley of California, can produce a variety of valuable crops. Generally, however, desert soils can best serve as rangelands. The rangeland value can be greatly enhanced by such management practices as artificial reseeding, deferred grazing, eradication of water-absorbing weeds, and selective breeding of heat-and-drought-resistant livestock.

BIBLIOGRAPHY

1. Allen, Shirley W., and Justin W. Leonard. *Conserving Natural Resources.* New York: McGraw-Hill, 1966.
2. Bear, Firman E. *Chemistry of the Soil.* New York: Van Nostrand, 1964.
3. Bennett, Hugh Hammond. *Soil Conservation.* New York: McGraw-Hill, 1939.
4. ————. *Elements of Soil Conservation.* New York: McGraw-Hill, 1955.
5. Clark, Francis E. "Living Organisms in the Soil," *Soils: The 1957 Yearbook of Agriculture.* Washington, D.C.: U.S. Department of Agriculture, 1957, 157–165.

6. Dale, Tom, and V. G. Carter. *Topsoil and Civilization*. Norman: University of Oklahoma, 1955.
7. Dasmann, Raymond F. *Environmental Conservation*. New York: Wiley, 1959.
8. Ehrlich, Paul R., and Anne H. Ehrlich. *Population, Resources, Environment*. San Francisco: Freeman, 1970.
9. Fuller, Harry J., and Oswald Tippo. *College Botany*. New York: Holt, 1954.
10. Jenny, Hans. "Soil as a Natural Resource," in Martin R. Huberty and Warren L. Flock, eds., *Natural Resources*. New York: McGraw-Hill, 1959.
11. Kellog, Charles E. *The Soils That Support Us*. New York: Macmillan, 1941.
12. Lyon, T. Lyttleton, and Harry O. Buckman. *The Nature and Property of Soils*. New York: Macmillan, 1941.
13. Marx, Wesley. *Man and His Environment: Waste*. New York: Harper, 1971.
14. Smith, Guy-Harold, ed. *Conservation of Natural Resources*. New York: Wiley, 1958.
15. Taylor, Sterling A. "Use of Moisture by Plants," *Soils: The Yearbook of Agriculture*. Washington, D.C.: U.S. Department of Agriculture, 1957.
16. U.S. Department of Agriculture. *Land: The Yearbook of Agriculture*. Washington, D.C.: 1958.
17. ———. *Agricultural Statistics*. Washington, D.C.: 1965.
18. Vosburgh, John. *Living with Your Land*. New York: Scribners, 1968.
19. Waksman, Selman A. *Soil Microbiology*. New York: Wiley, 1952.
20. Wheeler, Margaret F., and Wesley A. Volk. *Basic Microbiology*. New York: Wiley, 1964.

4.

Depletion, Restoration, and Maintenance of Soils

The wind grew stronger, whisked under stones, carried up straws and old leaves, and even little clods, marking its course as it sailed across the fields. The air and the sky darkened and through them the sun shone redly, and there was a raw sting in the air . . . as that day advanced the dusk slipped back toward darkness, and the wind cried and whimpered over the fallen corn . . . When the night came again it was black night, for the stars could not pierce the dust to get down, and the window lights could not even spread beyond their own yards . . . Houses were shut tight, and cloth wedged around doors and windows, but the dust came in so thinly that it could not be seen in the air, and it settled like pollen on the chairs and tables, on the dishes . . . In the middle of the night the wind passed on and left the land quiet. The dust-filled air muffled sound more completely than fog does. The people, lying in their beds, heard the wind stop . . . In the morning the dust hung like fog, and the sun was as red as ripe

*new blood. All day the dust sifted down from the sky, and the next day it sifted down
. . . It settled on the corn, piled up on the tops of the fence posts, piled up on the
wires; it settled on roofs, blanketed the weeds and trees. And the women came out of the
houses to stand beside their men—to feel whether this time the men would break.*

John Steinbeck, *The Grapes of Wrath*,
New York: The Viking Press, Inc., 1939, 1967

America is usurping prime agricultural land for *nonfood* purposes (sites for airports, highways, shopping centers, parking lots, suburban sprawl, and so on) at an alarming rate. It is estimated, for example, that California is losing 100 acres per day for such purposes. Moreover, we have adversely affected the nitrification process by our extensive use of chlorinated hydrocarbons. In addition we are losing 2 billion tons of soil each year as the aftermath of such vegetation-denuding practices as home and road construction, stream channelization, and strip mining. And yet, paradoxically, never before in history has man been so *dependent* upon this very soil he so seemingly disdains. Two of every three people in the world are either malnourished or go to bed hungry. At this very moment, in China, India, Africa, and South America, there are millions of desperate mothers clutching starving infants to their breasts. And the situation will probably worsen— dramatically—for by 2000 the number of human stomachs the world over will increase from the current 3.8 billion to about 7 billion! Certainly never in history has man had the need to develop a greater responsibility toward his soil heritage.

History of Land Abuse Abroad

When we study the history of land use among the ancient civilizations of Asia, Africa, and Mediterranean Europe, we find an appalling misuse of what was originally a valuable, life-giving resource. At one time the soil in these areas supported a flourishing agricultural economy. Villages grew into great, prosperous cities. Empires flourished and became powerful. But gradually, as the land was mistreated and erosion took its toll these proud empires withered and fell. Populations starved or dispersed. Where once there were magnificient cities, there now remains nothing but desolation, eloquent testimony to the massive soil abuse wrought by man.

Mesopotamia. The word *Mesopotamia* ("between the rivers") refers to the location of this semiarid land between two rivers, the Tigris and the Euphrates. The source of these rivers is in a region of more abundant rainfall in the mountains to the north. Mesopotamia is the Biblical "land of milk and honey" and presumably was the site of the Garden of Eden described in Genesis. This is the land of Noah, Abraham and Isaac, the Ark, and the Tower of Babel. It plays a fundamental part in the Jewish, Christian, and Moslem faiths.

Mesopotamia may have contributed more to the advancement of civilization and culture than any other region of similar size. Here, in the alluvial flood plains between the two rivers, agriculture was born about 7,000 years ago (25). The oldest known writings of man (dating from 3,000 years before Christ), concerning a plague of crop-devouring locusts, originated from the lower delta of the Tigris and Euphrates (32). This land, properly called the cradle of European agriculture, has always been arid. The thriving agricultural economy, on which a succession of eleven empires was based, depended on irrigation waters channeled from the Tigris and Euphrates by an intricate system of canals built at least 4,500 years before Christ (10, 25). According to some authorities it was possible for these people to irrigate 21,000 of the 35,000 square miles of flood plain. Flooding was a hazard; to protect their fields from floods the Chaldeans restrained the rivers with massive dikes, some of which were over 100 feet thick (32). Food surpluses raised on the fertile land freed millions of people from the necessity of farming, so that they could work in industry, science, and trade. Out of this system emerged a civilization with paved streets, a code of laws, mathematics, astronomy, cuneiform writing, and the calendar.

Because of heavy grazing pressure (exerted by large flocks of sheep and goats), deforestation, and intensive cropping of steep slopes, the Armenian uplands in which the Tigris and Euphrates had their source were massively eroded by water run-off (11). The rivers became discolored with soil washed from the hills. The accumulated sediment removed from the clogged canals over the centuries now forms huge mounds 50 feet high. The silt load carried by these rivers has filled the Persian Gulf to a point 180 miles from where they originally emptied into it! The vital irrigation canals, continuously plagued with loads of sediment, were kept open only by constant vigilance and backbreaking labor, supplied either by slaves numbering up to 10,000 or by prisoners of war. As early as 3,000 B.C., the Code of Hammurabi provided punishment for anyone who neglected his responsibility in keeping the canals free of sediment (32). As long as they were open, agriculture prospered and the orchards and fields produced bounteous crops. Periodically, however, because of either revolution or invasion by barbaric tribes, the irrigation canals were left unattended and gradually deteriorated beyond repair. The *coup de grâce* was delivered to the irrigation system by conquering hordes of Mongols and Tartars about A.D. 1200–1300.

It should be emphasized that the problem that this land experienced in centuries past and that it continues to have even today is not due to lack of fertile soil (25); it is due to the enormity of an engineering task made compulsory by land abuse at the highland headwaters of the Tigris and Euphrates. When the Mesopotamian agricultural economy was flourishing, it may have supported a population of close to 25 million people (25). Today, in sharp contrast, the population of all Iraq (the modern state that includes the lands of ancient Mesopotamia) is a mere 4 million. The once proud capital of Babylon, at one time the most powerful city on earth, now lies buried under wind-blown desert sands.

North Africa—City of Timgad. When the Roman Empire was at its zenith, most of the land bordering the Mediterranean, including north Africa, was in its domain. The grain grown in north Africa was shipped to Rome to feed its citizens and armies. Timgad was a showpiece community established by the Romans in north Africa in the first century A.D. (25). It was a magnificent town laid out in a symmetrical pattern. Its architectural, engineering, and artistic developments were the marvel of the age. It had a large municipal aqueduct, which brought water to the people from a great spring three miles away; a public library; a sculpture-adorned forum and seventeen great Roman baths complete with mosaic tile. There were also olive presses and a huge theater with a capacity of over 2,500 people (25). The virgin vegetation on the undulating hills around the town had apparently been

Figure 4-1. *Ancient Roman city of Timgad, northern Africa. Man is standing beside a base stone of an olive oil press, evidence of olive tree culture in the region (January 1939). [Soil Conservation Service, U. S. Department of Agriculture]*

a grassland with a scattering of trees. Through the ages, tangled roots of grasses had "sewn" the top layer of soil in place, secure from erosive effects of wind and rain. The agriculturists of Timgad converted these lands into farms and olive orchards. The agricultural economy, apparently based on sound soil management techniques, flourished for many centuries. Then, in the seventh century A.D., disaster came to Timgad in the form of hordes of nomadic invaders (25). The people of Timgad presumably were either dispersed, enslaved, or butchered. The invaders substituted a crude, soil-abusing pastoral culture for Timgad's prosperous crop and orchard culture. The surrounding hills were subjected to intensive over-grazing by great numbers of sheep and goats. Huge dust storms clouded the horizon and descended upon the town. As centuries passed, load after load of wind-blown soil gradually buried Timgad. Only a portion of an arch and three slender columns projected above the shifting dunes. Finally, in 1912, Timgad, lost to mankind for 1,200 years, was rediscovered by a team of French archeologists. Three decades of excavation work revealed the past magnificence of this once proud African outpost of Roman culture (25).

History of Land Abuse in America

Now let us find out what America's record is with regard to the use and abuse of the land. When the first white settler set foot on our shores, he found spread before him a land of almost incredible natural wealth. Dense forests cloaked the rolling hills in one vast mantle of green. Except for an occasional fire triggered by a lightning storm, forest destruction was virtually nonexistent. For untold centuries, autumn after autumn, the leaf fall blanketed the forest floor, decomposed, and eventually became incorporated into the soil. The excretions and bodies of many generations of woodland animals also contributed to the ultimate fertility of the primeval soil.

It is true that 10 million North American Indians had occupied the continent for many generations before the white man, perhaps for 10,000 years. But the impact of the Indian culture on the resource wealth was negligible. The Indians had no cattle or horses that could overgraze and expose the rich soil; they had no plow for upturning the soil, no axe for cutting huge swaths into the forest. Although they did practice a light, shifting type of agriculture, for the most part they survived by hunting and fishing; by collecting berries, fruits, nuts, eggs, and tubers; and by relocating their villages periodically to ensure access to prime hunting grounds (25).

As Angus McDonald states in "Early American Soil Conservationists," "the felling of the first tree by colonists in the New World, though never mentioned by historians, was an act of great significance. It marked the beginning of the most rapid rate of wasteful land use in the history of the world" (27).

Clearings were made in the forest in which the settler could sow amid the half-charred stumps. He planted corn in hills in the fashion of the Indian, many of whose agricultural and hunting practices he learned to adopt. The colonist cultivated the corn hills with crude hoes. Plows were almost nonexistent. (Plymouth, Massachusetts, for example, had no plow for its first twelve years of establishment.) The first American farmer used ancient methods of planting and harvesting grain that were reminiscent of those used in Palestine 3,000 years before. If he was fortunate, he perhaps had a few cattle, horses, or pigs, which he grazed at the edge of the clearing. He planted and raised the same crops year after year on the same patch of ground.

Although the first settlers did not come to the Chesapeake Bay region until 1607, and the Puritans did not land at Plymouth Rock until 1620, already by 1685 some of the settlers along the eastern seaboard noticed that corn did not grow as high as it once did and that the ears were getting much smaller. Eventually the topsoil, once primed with fertility accumulated through the ages, either deteriorated because of the intense one-crop farming or was washed away. Settler after settler, weary with the losing battle for agricultural survival, well aware of the seemingly unlimited bounty of fertile land "out West," pulled up stakes, chopped down a little more of the forest, grubbed out a few more stumps, uprooted a few more shrubs, built another cabin, and gradually carved out a new farm at the forest margin.

In the South, soil exhaustion first occurred in the tidewater region, because of intensive tobacco cropping; then, as a result of one-crop cotton farming, soil exhaustion occurred in the Piedmont region and westward into eastern Texas. Cotton and tobacco are both clean-tilled row crops, which provided little vegetative protection to the erosion-vulnerable southern soils. Today erosion has taken a greater toll in our southeastern states than anywhere else in America.

Guided by the philosophy of Thomas Jefferson, the federal government's official policy in disposing of the public domain west of the Mississippi was to use it as a catalyst in the settlement and development of this sparsely populated region. With the passage of the Homestead Act in 1862, the federal government gave the farmer or rancher title to 160 acres of land, provided the land was received in good faith and was occupied for at least five years. This act put the farmer or rancher in the curious position of finding it cheaper to acquire new land than to struggle to build up the fertility of his worn-out, sterile land. In order to secure title to the land under this act, the homesteaders were virtually compelled to break up the virgin prairie sod, whether or not they actually wished to do so.

Large tracts of public land were rapidly converted into privately owned holdings. In only a few weeks after the Oklahoma Territory was opened up for homesteading, the population zoomed from almost nil to 60,000. By 1900 there were over 390,000 farmers and ranchers in the territory, attracted by the liberal features of the Homestead Act (45). During the period from 1860 to 1910 (in which the number of ranches and farms increased from 2 million to over 6 million), about 234 million acres of land passed from public to private ownership.

Twenty inches of precipitation annually is considered marginal for crop production. The arid and semiarid Great Plains frequently have less. During periods of severe drought, precipitation may be considerably less than 5 inches annually. Meteorologists inform us that throughout history, even before the white man's coming, the Great Plains experienced alternating cycles of drought and adequate

Figure 4-2. *Dust storm approaching Springfield, Colorado, on May 21, 1937. This storm reached the city limits at exactly 4:47 P.M. Total darkness lasted about one-half hour. [Soil Conservation Service, U.S. Department of Agriculture]*

rainfall. However, although major drought appears to have recurred at roughly thirty-five year intervals, the precise time of its occurrence has not been predictable.

Drought visited the Great Plains in 1890 and again in 1910. During each dry spell, crops withered and died. Farms and ranches were abandoned only to be re-occupied during the ensuing years of adequate rainfall.

Then came the Big Drought. For five years, from 1926 to 1931, there was hardly enough rain to settle the dust. On the ranches the buffalo grass and the other prairie grasses lost their vigor and withered. Overstocked pastures were clipped to ground level by scrawny cattle. Much livestock was mercifully slaughtered. Droughts had visited the plains before. So had wind storms. But never before in the history of the North American prairie was the land more vulnerable to their combined assault. Gone were the profusely branching root systems of the buffalo grass, the grama grass, the big bluestem, and the little bluestem, which had originally kept the rich brown soil firmly in place. Gone was the decomposing organic material which had aided in building up stable soil aggregates and the soil cover of grass mat and sagebrush. On the ranches soil structure deteriorated under the concerted pounding given it by millions of cattle. On the wheat and cotton farms, soil structure broke down under the abuse inflicted by the huge machinery used in plowing, cultivating, and harvesting. The stage was set for the "black blizzards." In the spring of 1934 and again in 1935, winds of gale velocities swept over the Great Plains. In western Kansas and Oklahoma, as well as in the neighboring parts of Texas, Colorado, and Nebraska, the wind whirled minute particles of clay and silt far upward into the prairie sky. Brown dust clouds up to 7,000-feet thick filled the air with an upper edge almost 2 miles high (30). One storm of May 11, 1934, lifted 300 million tons of fertile soil into the air. (This roughly equals the total soil tonnage scooped from Central America to form the Panama Canal.) In many areas, the wilted wheat was uprooted and blown into the air. In the Amarillo, Texas, area during March and April of 1935, 15 wind storms raged for 24 hours; 4 lasted over 55 hours (24).

Dust from Oklahoma prairies came to rest on the deck of a steamer 200 miles out in the Atlantic. Dust sifted into the plush offices of Wall Street and smudged the luxury apartments of Park Avenue. When it rained in the blow area, the drops would sometimes come down as dilute mud. In Washington, D.C., mud splattered buildings of the Department of Agriculture, a rude reminder of the problem facing it and the nation. A thousand miles westward, harried housewives stuffed water-soaked newspapers into window cracks to no avail. The dust sifted into kitchens, forming a thin film on pots and pans and fresh-baked bread. Blinded by swirling dust clouds, ranchers got lost in their own backyards. Motorists pulled off to the side of the highways. Hundreds of airplanes were grounded. Trains were stalled by huge drifts. Hospital nurses placed wet cloth on patients' faces to ease their breathing. In Colorado's Baca County (March, 1935), forty-eight relief workers contracted "dust pneumonia," four of whom died. Five youngsters belonging to a New Mexico mother smothered to death in their cribs (14).

When the winds finally subsided, ranchers and farmers wearily emerged to survey the desolation. Two to 12 inches of fertile clay and silt soils had been carried to the Atlantic seaboard. The coarser sand, too heavy to be air-borne, bounced across the land, sheared off young wheat, and finally accumulated as dunes to the leeward of homes and barns. Heavily mortgaged power machinery became shrouded in sand.

The dust storms of the 1930's inflicted both social and economic suffering. Yet a few ranchers and farmers were philosophical about their misfortunes and could

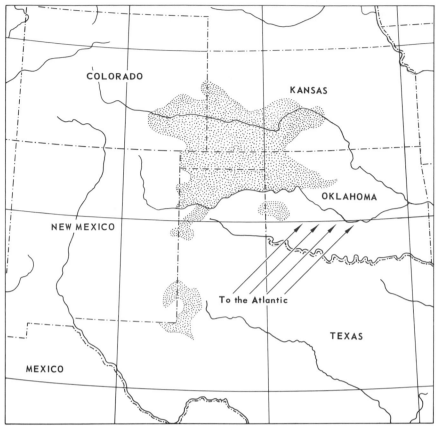

Figure 4-3. *The Dust Bowl region. Black areas on this map incurred severe wind erosion during the 1930s. Topsoil was blown as far as the Atlantic Ocean. Over 1 million farm-acres lost 2 to 12 inches of topsoil. [Adapted from Raymond F. Dasmann,* Environmental Conservation *(New York: John Wiley & Sons., Inc., 1968) After Soil Conservation Service map.]*

Figure 4-4. *Dust storm in Prowers County, Colorado, approaching at velocity of 30 miles per hour. It lasted from 4:15 P.M. to 7:00 P.M. [Soil Conservation Service, U.S. Department of Agriculture]*

even crack jokes about the birds flying backward "to keep the sand out of their eyes" and about the prairie dogs "digging burrows 100 feet in the air!" However, for most dust-bowl victims, the dusters were not very funny. Many victims were virtually penniless. The 300 million tons of topsoil removed in a single storm on May 11, 1934, represents the equivalent of taking 3,000 farms of 100 acres each out of crop production. Dust-bowl relief up until 1940 alone cost American taxpayers over $1 billion; $7 million (more than was paid for all Alaska) was pumped into a single Colorado county alone (14). The only recourse for many of these ill-fated farmers was to find a new way of life. They piled their belongings into rickety cars and trucks and moved out—some to the Pacific coast, some to the big industrial cities of the Midwest and East. However, our nation was still in the throes of a depression, and many an emigrating family found nothing but frustration, bitterness, and suffering at the end of the road.

The first data on erosion losses were obtained at the Agricultural Experimental Station at Spur, Texas, beginning in 1926. Gradually, with congressional authorization and appropriation, this program was greatly expanded to a national scale. With encouragement from the National Resources Board and then Secretary of the Interior Harold L. Ickes, the newly formed Soil Erosion Service, under the leadership of H. H. Bennett, long a crusader for a national program of soil erosion control, conducted a Reconnaissance Erosion Survey in 1934 (18). Completed in only two months by a team of 115 erosion specialists, it was unique, not only because it was the first national survey, but because kinds of erosion as well as degree of severity were classified. The survey revealed that formerly productive agricultural land had to be abandoned in the Southeast, South, and Southwestern regions of the United States because of severe sheet erosion. Of the 322 million acres that were affected by serious wind erosion, most were located in the Great Plains from southwest Texas northward to the Dakotas. Within this zone, 9 million acres were destroyed and 80 million acres were seriously damaged. *Twenty-five to 75 per cent of the*

Figure 4-5. *Abandoned Oklahoma farmstead, showing the disastrous results of wind erosion.* [*Soil Conservation Service, U.S. Department of Agriculture, Photo by B.C. McLean*]

Figure 4-6A. *Geological erosion. The Grand Canyon of the Colorado River, Arizona, as seen from the north rim, a colossal example of the effects of geological erosion operating for millennia.* [Soil Conservation Service, U.S. Department of Agriculture]

topsoil was depleted from a total area of 663 million acres. There was extensive gullying, and in 90 per cent of the cases it was associated with sheet erosion. Severe gullying occurred on 337 million acres. As late as 1942, total annual erosion damage inflicted on the American people amounted to $3.8 billion, or an annual loss of $20 for every man, woman, and child in the United States.

Nature of Soil Erosion

We have observed the manner in which Americans have abused their soil, almost from the day the Pilgrims set foot on it at Plymouth Rock. During the three-century history of soil abuse in the United States, erosion has played a predominant role. Let us now focus our attention on this insidious process and find out what today's soil conservationists are doing not only to arrest erosion, but to rehabilitate the soil.

Definition. The word *erosion* is derived from the Latin word *erodere*, meaning "to gnaw out." Erosion may be defined as the process by which rock fragments and soil are detached from their original site, transported, and then eventually deposited

Figure 4-6B. *Accelerated erosion. Water erosion caused the severe gullies on this North Carolina farm.* [*U.S. Department of Agriculture*]

at some new locality. The agent of erosion may be wind, water, waves, glaciers, soil slip, or other rock particles.

Geological Erosion or Natural Erosion. *Geological erosion* is a process that has occurred at an extremely slow rate ever since the earth was formed 4 to 5 billion years ago. In fact, the mountains, valleys, plains, canyons, and deltas on the earth's surface were sculptured by water and wind erosion working through vast periods of time. The Appalachian Mountains were at one time as tall and rugged as the Rocky Mountains; but since their formation 200 million years ago, at the beginning of the Mesozoic period, they have been gradually worn down by erosive forces. Were it not for geological erosion, New Orleans would be resting on the bottom of the Gulf of Mexico, for the delta on which it is built was formed by deposition of soil transported by the Mississippi River from sites as much as 1,000 miles away. The Grand Canyon originated as a shallow channel 100 million years ago. It was ultimately scoured to its awesome 1-mile depth by the churning waters of the Colorado.

Accelerated Erosion. Geological erosion, then, has continued to operate at a slow, deliberate pace for millions of years. However, with man's appearance on the world

Figure 4-7. *Aerial photo of Peabody strip coal mining operation near Nucla, Colorado, May 1972. Without proper revegetation of these barren spoil heaps, soil erosion and acid mine drainage will probably be severe.* [E. P. A.—Documerica—Bill Gillette]

scene, a species intruded that could "reshape" the natural environment. Because of his activities an artificial type of erosion began, which has operated at a much faster rate than natural erosion. It is with this *accelerated erosion* that the conservationist is primarily concerned.

In recent years severe soil erosion losses have been generated by the stream channelization activity of the U.S. Army Corps of Engineers. Their flood control objective is certainly praiseworthy. But in the course of converting a relatively shallow meandering stream into a rather straight deep channel, as has been done in several southern states, much soil along stream margins (as well as the spoil) became vulnerable to erosion. Well over 2 million acres have been scarred in Kentucky, Pennsylvania, Ohio, West Virginia, and other states by strip-mining operations. By 1980 the U.S. Bureau of Mines predicts that roughly 5 million acres will be disturbed—an area the size of New Jersey. During these operations the upper layers of soil are scooped away to expose the coal veins underneath. One of the giant type of power shovels now employed can chew up 140 cubic yards at one gulp (29). While the mining companies did gain many tons of coal, the nation as a whole has lost at least 120 million tons of soil, as a result of the erosion aftermath.

Factors Determining Rate of Water Erosion. The intensity of erosion depends upon the interaction of a number of factors, including (1) *volume and intensity of precipitation*, (2) *topography of terrain*, (3) *kind of vegetational cover*, and (4) *soil condition* (28).

VOLUME AND INTENSITY OF PRECIPITATION. *Annual* precipitation in the United States ranges from virtually nothing in some parts of Death Valley, California, to 140 inches in parts of Washington state. Such pronounced differences in rainfall will be expressed in part by differential erosion rates. However, even more important is the *seasonal* rainfall pattern.

A town in Florida once experienced a deluge of 24 inches of rain in only 24 hours. The ensuing soil loss, resulting from run-off waters, must have been severe. On the other hand, were this 24-inch rainfall the result of daily 1-inch drizzles occurring over a period of 24 consecutive days, the erosion threat would have been negligible, simply because the soil would have had sufficient time in which to absorb the water. Surprisingly, even in the arid deserts of Nevada and Arizona, where annual rainfall averages 5 inches, excessive erosion occurs because the entire annual precipitation materializes in the form of a few torrential cloudbursts. As a result, the desert floor is dissected with canyons gouged out by run-off waters.

TOPOGRAPHY OF TERRAIN. It would be expected that intensity of water run-off and soil erosion would be partially dependent upon the relative slope of the terrain. Steepness of slope is indicated in terms of percentages. Thus, a 10 per cent slope would be one that drops 10 feet over a horizontal distance of 100 feet. Research conducted by soil scientists has shown the effect of slopes on soil and water losses on farms planted to row crops, crops in which the land is exposed between the rows. In each of two studies cited by Bennett on similar soils, a roughly 100 per cent increase in slope resulted in an approximately 300 per cent increase in soil loss caused by erosion. In a third study, a 116 per cent increase in slope (from 3.7 to 8) resulted in a 348 per cent increase (from 19.7 tons to 68.8 tons) in soil loss (5).

KIND OF VEGETATIONAL COVER. In the foothills of the southern Appalachians, Cecil sandy clay loam is a representative erodible soil. Pronounced differences in soil

Figure 4-8. *Effect of different vegetal covers on water erosion rates. Erosion rate from land covered by row crops equals 100 per cent. Soil erosion losses under forest duff is only 3 per cent the loss under row crops. Range in good condition is almost twice as effective as poor range in retarding erosion. Observe the erosion vulnerability of clean-tilled orchards. Flash floods sweeping through California orchards have repeatedly wreaked a heavy loss in topsoil. [Adapted from Ruben L. Parson,* Conserving American Resources *(Englewood Cliffs, N. J.: Prentice-Hall, Inc., 1956). After* Journal of the American Water Works Association, *41, 10 (October 1949).]*

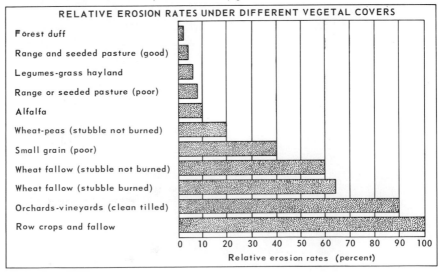

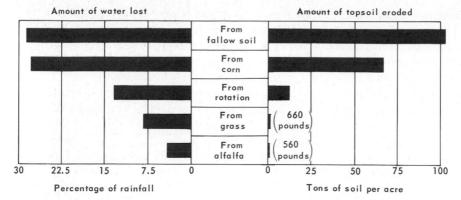

Amount of water lost | Amount of topsoil eroded

| From fallow soil |
| From corn |
| From rotation |
| From grass (660 pounds) |
| From alfalfa (560 pounds) |

30   22.5   15   7.5   0   0   25   50   75   100

Percentage of rainfall   Tons of soil per acre

Figure 4-9. *Influence of vegetational cover on soil erosion and water run-off. Data from research conducted by the Soil Conservation Service at Bethany, Missouri, on Shelby loam on land with an 8 per cent slope. Average annual rainfall in the area is 40 inches.* [From Conserving Natural Resources by Allen and Leonard. Copyright © 1966 by McGraw-Hill, Inc. Used by permission of McGraw-Hill Book Company.]

Figure 4-10. *Only one inch of rain caused this erosion on a burned-over slope in California's Los Padres National Forest.* [U.S. Department of Agriculture, Photo by Wynne Maule]

loss occur under varying types of vegetational cover. Bare soil erodes 2.5 times more rapidly than land planted to cotton, more than 4,000 times as rapidly as grass-covered land, and almost 32,000 times more quickly than land covered with virgin forests (5). In urban environments, any construction such as highway, airport, or apartment involves stripping away protective vegetative cover and exposing the naked soil to the erosive effects of wind and water. In 1 square mile of such "developed" land near Washington, D.C., 690 tons of sediment was lost compared to only 146 tons in a square mile area where development had not yet begun (45).

SOIL CONDITION. The structure of a soil can be improved by plowing under a crop of clover or alfalfa (green manuring) or simply by adding decaying organic material, such as leaves or barnyard manure. Studies in Iowa have shown the effect of manuring corn croplands. Lands manured with 16, 8 and 0 tons per acre incurred soil losses of roughly 4, 9, and 22 tons per acre, respectively (5). Soil loss from nonmanured land was over five times that from heavily manured soil. The addition of organic material apparently improved the soil's water-absorbing ability. This trait, in turn, would be expressed in a more dense, vigorous growth of corn. The vegetative mantle thus established would further protect the soil. The developing corn root systems would also penetrate more vigorously between the individual soil particles and tend to bind them in place.

Soil Erosion Control in the Rural Environment

We shall discuss some of the major land management practices by means of which excessive soil erosion may be controlled. These practices include *contour farming, strip cropping, terracing, gully reclamation,* and establishment of *shelter belts.*

Contour Farming. *Contour farming* may be defined as plowing, seeding, cultivating, and harvesting across the slope, rather than with it. It was practiced by Thomas Jefferson, who wrote in 1813, "We now plow horizontally, following the curvature of the hills . . . scarcely an ounce of soil is now carried off." Jefferson, however, was an exception. In the early days of American agriculture, the farmer who could plow the straightest furrows (usually up and down slopes) was considered a master plowsman and was praised by his neighbors.

An experiment conducted on a Texas cotton field with a 3 to 5 per cent slope revealed that average annual water run-off from a noncontoured plot was 4.6 inches, whereas that for a contoured plot was 65.3 per cent less, or 1.6 inches.

Strip Cropping. On land with a decided slope, planting crops on contour strips will be an effective erosion deterrent. For effective control the width of the contour strip should vary inversely with the length of the slope. When viewed from a distance, the farmland appears as a series of slender, curving belts of color. A wide-row cultivated crop—such as corn, cotton, tobacco, or potatoes—and a cover crop of hay or legumes are alternated along the contours. Strip cropping is combined frequently with crop rotation, so that a strip planted to a soil-depleting, erosion-facilitating corn crop one year will be sown to a soil-enriching and protecting strip of legumes the next.

Figure 4-11. *Bell County, Texas. The pattern of farm conservation is reflected in the fields of this Texas farmer, who uses contour farming to reduce rainwater run-off and its erosive effects on soil. The different shades are caused by different crops (strip cropping) and the pattern conforms to the contours of his fields, with the highest elevation where the smaller rings are. Besides slowing water so that it can soak into the soil better, such measures reduce siltation, the most common cause of water pollution in the United States, according to the U.S. Department of Agriculture. [Soil Conservation Service, U.S. Department of Agriculture]*

Figure 4-12. *Contour strip cropping on a Washara County, Wisconsin, farm characterized by silt loam with a 4 per cent slope. [Soil Conservation Service, U.S. Department of Agriculture]*

Figure 4-13. *Terracing. A system of parallel level terraces has controlled sheet erosion on this farm near Templeton, Iowa. Slope is 5 to 11 per cent.* [*Soil Conservation Service, U.S. Department of Agriculture*]

Terracing. *Terracing* has been practiced by man for centuries. It was used by the Incas of Peru and by the ancient Chinese. These civilizations, plagued with relatively dense populations and a modicum of arable land, were forced to till extremely steep slopes, even mountainsides, in order to prevent extensive hunger. The flat, steplike bench terraces that these ancient agriculturists constructed, however, are not amenable to today's farming methods. The modern terrace may be defined as an embankment of earth constructed across a slope in such a way as to control water run-off and minimize erosion. To be effective, terraces must check water flow before it attains sufficient velocity (3 feet per second) to loosen and transport soil.

Gully Reclamation. Gullies are danger signals that indicate land is eroding rapidly and may become a wasteland unless erosion is promptly controlled. Some gullies work their way up a slope at the rate of 15 feet a year. In North Carolina a 150-foot-deep gully was gouged out in only 60 years—"swallowing" up fence posts, farm implements, and buildings in the process. If relatively small, a gully may be plowed in and then seeded to a quick-growing "nurse" crop of barley, oats, or wheat. In this

Figure 4-14A. *(Before) Gully erosion on a Minnesota farm. It was scalped and then planted with productive vegetation, primarily locust trees. [U.S. Department of Agriculture]*

Figure 4-14B. *(After) Five growing seasons later, the locusts averaged 15 feet in height, and not only served to control erosion but provided wildlife cover and beautified the landscape. [Soil Conservation Service, U.S. Department of Agriculture]*

way, erosion will be checked until sod can become established. In cases of severe gullying, small check dams of manure and straw constructed at 20-foot intervals may be effective, because silt will collect behind the dams and gradually fill in the channel. Dams may be constructed of brush or stakes held secure with a woven wire netting. Earthen, stone, and even concrete dams may be built at intervals along the gully. Once dams have been constructed and water run-off has been restrained, soil may be stabilized by planting rapidly growing shrubs, vines, and trees. Willows are effective. Not only does such pioneer vegetation forestall future erosion, but it obliterates the ugliness of gaping gullies and provides food, cover, and breeding sites for wildlife.

Shelter Belts. In 1935 the federal government, in a strenuous attempt to prevent future dust bowls, launched a massive shelter belt system. Belts of trees were planted across the Great Plains from North Dakota south to Texas. The impetus provided by this project has resulted in thousands of miles of tree belts whose green checkerboard patterns have added color and variety to an otherwise monotonous prairie

Figure 4-15. *This North Dakota farm is well protected from wind and snow by a 17-year-old windbreak of conifers, fruit trees, and shrubs.* [*Soil Conservation Service, U.S. Department of Agriculture*]

Figure 4-16. *Ten-row shelter belt and farmstead windbreak in Osborne County, Kansas. It consists of Russian olive, red cedar, ponderosa pine, bun oak, hackberry, green ash, honey locust, Chinese elm, and osage orange planted at 8-foot intervals. The belt is 160 rods long, part of it on contour.* [Soil Conservation Service, U.S. Department of Agriculture, Photo by B.C. McLean]

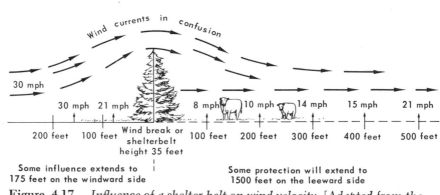

Figure 4-17. *Influence of a shelter belt on wind velocity.* [*Adapted from the Kansas State Board of Agriculture*]

landscape. In the cooler north and central plains, a typical shelter belt would consist of one to five rows of trees planted on the western margin of the farm in a north-south line, to intercept winter's prevailing westerly winds. Conifers such as red cedar, spruce, and pine provide the best year-round protection. For the southern plains, drought-resistant trees such as Scotch pine, Austrian pine, Chinese elm, and thornless honey locust are desirable (16). Soil blowing can be retarded even further by planting a few rows of corn or a belt of grain between the rows of trees. As indicated in Figure 4-19, a properly designed shelter belt of adequate height and thickness may reduce a wind velocity of 30 miles per hour to only 8 miles per hour to leeward. The beneficial influence may extend 175 feet to windward and 1,500 feet to leeward of the trees (1). Although windbreaks occupy valuable land that otherwise could be used for crop production, are relatively slow to grow, and must be fenced from livestock until well established, the accrued benefits far outweigh these minor disadvantages (18). To determine the value of windbreaks, 331 South Dakota farmers were asked in 1955 to provide information concerning their crop yields after shelter belts were established on their lands. Over 88 per cent indicated that yields had increased measurably (16). (Fig. 4-19)

Soil Conservation Service and Its Program

The "black blizzards" of the 1930's may have had one redeeming feature: They alerted a hitherto apathetic nation more forcefully to the plight of her soil resources than a thousand urgent speeches could have done.

The federal government finally faced up to the soil erosion problem. In 1934 the recently formed Soil Erosion Service (SES) set up forty-one soil and water conservation demonstration projects. The labor force for these projects was supplied by Civilian Conservation Corps workers drawn from about fifty camps (18). The projects impressed Congress so forcefully that it established the Soil Conservation Service (SCS) in 1935. The major function of the SCS has been to provide technical assistance to farmers and ranchers so that they utilize each acre of land according to its capability, with methods that are consistent with the needs of the soil as those of the landowner. A cardinal feature of the SCS program has been to focus the professional assistance of agronomists, agricultural engineers, botanists, zoologists, ecologists, hydrologists, foresters, and soil scientists on the problem of appropriate land use. The knowledge our scientists and technologists have accumulated to date, relative to the nature, productivity, development, replenishment, erodability, and abuse of soils, has enabled the SCS to set up, with the cooperation of state and county agencies, a national land capability inventory of a general nature, as well as a detailed land capability inventory for farmers and members participating in SCS programs.

The administrative and operative unit of the Soil Conservation Service program is the SCS district, which is organized and run by farmers and ranchers. Each district is staffed with a professional conservationist and several aides who work directly with the farmer on his land. These technicians have had training in many related areas and represent, ideally, a soil scientist, hydrologist, land appraiser, botanist, zoologist, agronomist, chemist, forester, game manager, and agricultural engineer all wrapped up in one superindividual. Any farmer located within the Soil Conservation Service district may request assistance in setting up and maintaining sound conservation practices in the management of his farm. Participation in the SCS program is purely voluntary. By 1974, over 3,000 SCS districts had been organized (19), embracing roughly 5 million farms and 96 per cent of the nation's farm and ranch land.

In the event that a farmer requests technical assistance from his SCS district, four principal steps are followed in executing the conservation program for his farm.

First, the technician and the farmer make an *intensive acre-by-acre survey* of the farm. On the basis of such criteria, including slope, fertility, stoniness, drainage, topsoil thickness, and susceptibility to erosion, the technician maps out each parcel of land on the basis of its capability. Each plot is ascribed a capability symbol in the form of a Roman numeral or color. This capability map is then superimposed on an aerial photograph.

Second, the farmer *draws up a farm plan* with assistance from the technician. This plan involves decisions on how each acre will be used and how it will be improved and protected. In other words, shall a given acre be used for crops, pasture, forests, or wilderness area? Usually alternative uses and treatments are considered. Some

Figure 4-18. *Kit Carson County, Colorado. Conservation farming has brought about many new cultural methods. Stubble mulch tillage, shown here, a method of cultivation that leaves the soil surface protected, was encouraged by the Soil Conservation Service in the Great Plains and has spread to many other areas through the nation.* [Soil Conservation Service, U.S. Department of Agriculture]

Figure 4-19. *A conservationist and a soil scientist examine an alfalfa stand at Maple Lake, Minnesota, for insect damage and phosphate-potash deficiency. The land is class III with 7 per cent slope. The corn will make 80 to 85 bushels per acre.* [Soil Conservation Service, U.S. Department of Agriculture]

changes, of course, will not be made simply because they are impractical. The farmer would not move his barn, for example, just because the soil underneath is good for growing corn! In addition to the type of soil, such factors as farm size, amount of rainfall, potential market for crops, and the farmer's age and skills all enter into his ultimate choice concerning the use of his land.

Third, the treatment and uses called for in the plan are *actually applied* to the farm by the farmer, with assistance from one or more technicians. Although much of this application can be completed by the farmer himself, he may find it helpful to enlist the aid of the conservation technicians in connection with such techniques as terracing, contour plowing, strip cropping, establishment of farm ponds, gully control, shelter belting, proper use of cover crops in erosion control, use of legumes in fertility improvement, development of hedgerows as wildlife habitat, and selective cutting involved in the periodic harvest of his wood lot.

The final and most important phase of the program is its *maintenance* from year to year, with the assistance of conservation technicians. As time passes, agricultural geneticists might develop a new strain of rust-resistant wheat or a tick-resistant breed

of cattle; a plant may be introduced from the Orient or from South America that is more effective in fixing nitrogen than are native legumes; a new subspecies of bluegill may be discovered that thrives in farm ponds, or perhaps a new method of tilling wetlands will be available. These new developments then can gradually be incorporated into the overall conservation program.

The SCS program has shown considerable stability despite minor variations from year to year. Each year roughly 3 per cent of our nation's farms are involved in about 100,000 basic conservation plans formulated by the SCS. Typically, contour farming practices under SCS technical aid are newly applied to about 3 to 5 million acres annually; the same amount of range and pasture acreage is seeded. Roughly 4 million acres of land are newly cover cropped. Each year, 50,000 to 75,000 new farm ponds are constructed, and 40,000 to 50,000 new terraces are built. Moreover, under the SCS farm program, smaller acreages of land are improved for irrigation, drained, or planted to trees. Roughly 5 per cent of the cropland is annually covered by newly applied SCS-directed practices.

Nature of Soil Nutrients

Of the roughly 100 elements naturally occurring in nature, about 17 are required by plants and about 19 are required by animals (including man), for health, growth, and reproduction. Four of these essential elements—carbon, hydrogen, oxygen, and nitrogen—derived from air and water, form roughly 96 per cent (by weight) of the fresh plant body. When a plant or animal is burned, these elements are driven off in gaseous form; the solid ash left behind includes the soil-derived mineral elements. The ash forms roughly 5 per cent of the dry weight of a plant and 10 to 15 per cent of the dry weight of man. Boron, which is essential to some plants, is not required by animals. Conversely, iodine and fluorine, valuable to animals, are not essential to plants. Mineral nutrients that are utilized by organisms in large quantities are usually classified as *macronutrients*; those required in only minute amounts are called *micronutrients*. Plant growth may be retarded not only when an element is not present in proper amounts in the soil, but also when it is in a form not readily usable by the plant or when it is not in proper balance with other soil nutrients.

Macronutrients. The *macronutrients* essential for plants include carbon, hydrogen, oxygen, nitrogen, phosphorous, sulfur, potassium, and calcium. Nitrogen is required by plants for the synthesis of protein, nucleoprotein, amino acids, and enzymes. It is essential for the processes of growth, seed production, respiration, and photosynthesis. Over every acre of land there are 34,500 tons of gaseous nitrogen (unavailable to plants) (2). According to the former Bureau of Chemistry and Soils, the highest nitrogen content occurs in a podzol soil in Massachusetts and the lowest in a red and yellow soil in South Carolina. Because carbon, hydrogen, and oxygen are usually abundantly present in air or water, they do not ordinarily represent limiting factors for plant development, except in case of drought, unusually cold weather, or plant disease. As R. L. Cook has pointed out, it should be remembered that many of the symptoms employed as indicators of nutrient-inadequate soil (unusual leaf color, stuntedness, abnormal shape of leaf and stem, leaf and root deterioration) may also be symptoms of parasitic diseases caused by bacteria, fungi, nematodes, or insects (9).

Micronutrients. *Micronutrients* essential to plants include iron, boron, copper, manganese, zinc, molybdenum, and chlorine (9). The amounts required by crops are exceedingly small. A clover field requires only *1 ounce of molybdenum per acre* (39). Boron requirements are met with one part boron in 1 million parts water, whereas molybdenum requirements are met with 1 part molybdenum in 1 billion parts water (9). Seven tons of Maine potatoes possessed only 0.2 pound of boron as compared with 143 pounds of nitrogen. Zinc may form only 0.0004 per cent of some plant leaves (37) and is a limiting factor for potatoes in northwestern Minnesota and for sweet corn, peas, and sugar beets in southeastern Wisconsin.

Plants absorb aluminum and titanium, which are of no presently known use to either plants or animals. Iodine, fluorine, sodium, and cobalt, which have no apparent plant function but are indispensable to animals, are also taken from the soil (3).

Several years ago a mysterious malady caused severe anemia and death among cattle of several midwestern states including Michigan and Wisconsin. In the ensuing investigation it was found that the soil on the farms where the disease was most serious was deficient in *cobalt*. Hence the forage grasses absorbed inadequate amounts from the soil, eventually resulting in cobalt deficiencies among livestock. Cobalt apparently is indispensable to the proper synthesis of vitamin B_{12}, which in turn is essential for normal red blood cell production by the cow's red bone marrow. A mere 2 *ounces* of cobalt chloride per acre per year applied to the soil will correct the deficiency.

Iodine is another interesting micronutrient. Although not required by plants it is indispensable to the health of both livestock and man. It is an essential component of the hormone *thyroxine* produced by the thyroid gland. When babies suffer from iodine deficiency, their physical, sexual, and mental development is arrested and they become *cretins*—sterile, pot-bellied dwarfs with extremely low IQs. When an adult becomes iodine deficient he may develop an overgrowth of the thyroid called a *goiter*. (In the days of ancient Rome, men considered large goiters in females as being sexually attractive.) Investigations have shown a high correlation between the incidence of goiter and iodine-deficient soils. A typical "goiter belt" in the United States was located in the Great Lakes region. Today goiters are relatively uncommon because their development can be forestalled by the simple expedient of using *iodized salt* (ordinary table salt, sodium chloride, with the addition of a small percentage of potassium iodide) at the dinner table.

Depletion of Soil Nutrients

Depletion by Cropping. Before the white man came to North America, this vast continent was populated by 10 million native Indians, considerably fewer people than inhabit the Chicago area today. Although these Indians raised a few crops (corn, pumpkins, beans, squash, and potatoes), for the most part they depended on hunting, fishing, and the gathering of berries, fruits, and nuts. The extensive biomes of prairies, deciduous forest, and coniferous forest were modified very little by human activity. Generation after generation of big bluestem grass, oak, hickory, beach, maple, spruce, fir, and pine lived and died. During their life span these plants absorbed large quantities of life-sustaining nutrients from the soil, channeling them into billions of tons of wood, bark, leaves, flowers, roots, and seeds. Eventually, however, when these organisms died, their body nutrients were restored to the soil from which they originated. Soil fertility was also replenished by excreta and decaying carcasses of millions of birds and mammals.

Then came the white man's agriculture, which replaced forest and prairie vegetation with corn, wheat, cabbage, beans, and potatoes. As a result, the normal cycling of soil elements was greatly retarded. For example, a 100-bushel corn crop extracts 78 pounds of soil nitrogen, 36 pounds of phosphoric oxide, 26 pounds of potassium oxide, 25 pounds of calcium, and 18 pounds of magnesium. A 15-ton cabbage harvest absorbs 40 pounds of sulfur (22). One hundred forty-three pounds of nitrogen are removed by a 7-ton potato crop. The uptake of soil nutrients accounts for 10 per cent of a crop's total dry weight (11). Where once they were cycled, many soil nutrients now move down a one-way street—first being channeled into plant or animal crops, then into human digestive tracts and biomass, and then finally as human excrement, being flushed by sewage systems into rivers, lakes, and oceans. (This may also cause enrichment—*eutrophication*—of lake waters and contribute to undesirable "blooms" of algae.) Livestock manure may have returned soil nutrients in some regions, especially before the farm tractor, but it was not sufficient to halt the trend toward soil impoverishment. As Firman Bear so eloquently states, "in many areas of the United States, the land has been turned into a nearly lifeless organic medium that must be nursed along like an invalid at the threshold of death" (3).

Depletion by Erosion.   Along with land cropping, the processes of accelerated erosion (which shortsightedness, ignorance, and greed precipitated) have also extracted a heavy toll on soil fertility. Bennett describes the fertility-depleting effects of a 1937 dust storm that originated in the Texas-Oklahoma panhandle and moved northeastward into Canada. Soils laid down on snow-covered land in Iowa were compared with samples from a dune near Dalhart, Texas. Analyses revealed that soil blown into Iowa contained 10 times as much organic matter, 9 times as much nitrogen, and 19 times as much phosphoric acid as the dune material that accumulated near the storm's origin (5). Theoretically, it might be conceivable that Iowa farmers would benefit from this nutrient "windfall" by growing bumper corn crops on transplanted Texas soil. Unfortunately, however, much wind-blown topsoil accumulates in residential or industrial areas, and some nutrient-rich soil may be blown out to sea and be lost forever.

Water erosion has also taken its toll of productive soil. Thus, the Mississippi River alone annually discharges 730 million tons of soil into the Gulf of Mexico (1). Each year the combined agents of wind and water deprive America's future generations of crops, livestock, wildlife, and men of nearly 3 billion tons of potentially valuable soil.

Depletion by the Use of Pesticides.   Ironically, the very "wonder chemicals"— pesticides—that the farmer sprays on his crops to protect them may, in the final analysis, play an important role in reducing his ability to raise crops some years later. Studies have shown that roughly *40 per cent* of such "persistent" pesticides as aldrin, chlordane, DDT, endrin, and toxaphene will persist in sandy loam soil intact at least *fourteen* years after they were applied (15). The use of such chlorinated hydrocarbon pesticides would seriously impair soil fertility were the nitrogen-fixing and nitrification bacteria adversely affected. Turk, Turk, and Wittes express appropriate concern:

The effect on these organisms [bacteria] of an increasing concentration of poison in the soil is largely unknown. In many heavily sprayed areas of the world man is harvesting more food per acre than ever before. Yet some facts are coming to light which may presage future disaster. Studies in Florida have shown that *some chlorinated pesticides seriously inhibit nitrification by soil bacteria.* (Italics added.) As is the case for many types of ecological disruptions, the long-term results are not known. Perhaps bacteria are immune, or will become immune, to pesticide spraying. But the stakes in the gamble are large, for if the micro organisms in the soil die, large plants . . . cannot live . . . (40).

Restoration of Soil Fertility

We shall describe the following methods of restoring soil fertility: application of organic fertilizers (animal manure, green manure, legumes), inorganic fertilizers, and crop rotation.

Use of Organic Fertilizers

USE OF ANIMAL MANURE. By animal manure is meant the dung and urine of all farm animals such as horses, cattle, swine, sheep, and goats, as well as poultry. Animal manure benefits the soil by increasing the nutrient and organic matter content, stimulating growth and reproduction of crops, as well as soil bacteria and fungi, and thereby eventually improving soil structure.

In 1748 colonial farmers were already advised by Jared Eliot that liberal applications of animal manure would increase soil fertility. The manure tonnage annually produced per thousand pounds live weight of farm animal amounts to 15, 13, and 9 tons for the pig, cow, and horse, respectively. Seventy-five per cent of a ton of cow manure is water; the remaining 500 pounds of organic material contains 10 pounds of nitrogen, 5 pounds of phosphoric acid (P_2O_5), and 10 pounds of potash (K_2O). A cornfed dairy cow returns to the soil (in excrement) 75 per cent of the nitrogen, 80 per cent of the phosphoric acid, and 90 per cent of the potash obtained from her feed. Precautions must be exercised. Manure that is lying exposed to weather before being spread on the land may lose half of its nutrients through the leaching action of rain. Because legumes and grasses respond well to mineral fertilizers, farm manures should be saved for such rotation crops as corn, cotton, tobacco, cabbage, and potatoes (26). The application of 5 tons of manure per acre in Michigan yielded 46 bushels of corn per acre in contrast to the 35-bushel per yield of non-manured land, a 31.4 per cent increase. Irrigated alfalfa in Washington responded to a 6-ton per acre manure application with a 1,000-pound per acre yield increase.

Animal manure improves soil structure. It causes the particles in loose sandy soils to bind together so that water retention is increased. The organic matter makes sticky clay soils more granular and porous, thus promoting both ease of tillage and aeration.

USE OF GREEN MANURE. The process of turning under green crops to improve soil productivity is known as *green manuring*. Its effects on soil are similar to those of animal manure. With the latter becoming more scarce as farms become more mechanized, green manure has assumed an especially significant role.

USE OF LEGUMES. On the average, an acre of agricultural land probably loses 60 to 70 pounds of nitrogen yearly in the form of crops that have been harvested, as well as 20 to 25 pounds because of soil erosion. Thus, roughly 80 to 95 pounds of

Figure 4-20. *Green manuring. Hairy vetch (a legume) being plowed under at a farm near Storey, Oklahoma, prior to planting a cotton crop. [Soil Conservation Service, U.S. Department of Agriculture, Photo by Fred Fortney]*

nitrogen per acre will be required annually to prevent a deficit. This can be done with legumes.

Several species can be utilized, including alfalfa, red clover, sweet clover, cowpeas, soybeans, lespedeza, vetch, and crotalaria. The nitrogen fixed by the nodule bacteria is added to the soil and becomes available to the next crop in the rotation. The actual amount of nitrogen fixed varies with the species of host plant, as well as with the number of virulent bacteria of the proper species available in the soil. In a ten-year experiment at Ithaca, New York, the relative fixation ability was determined as follows (26), taking alfalfa as 100:

Alfalfa	100
Sweet clover	67
Red clover	56
Soybeans	42
Field beans	23
Field peas	19

Although all nodule bacteria belong to the genus *Rhizobium*, a given species is compatible for only certain legumes. Thus, *Rhizobium melilote* effectively inoculates alfalfa and sweet clovers, whereas *Rhizobium trifolii* is compatible for white Ladino, red, alsike, and crimson clovers. If the legume to be used is native to the area, the correct bacteria usually have already been established. However, inoculation of the legume seed with the compatible bacteria at planting time may be necessary when an exotic legume is employed or when the appropriate bacterial population does not survive during the interval between crops. Seed stores generally have packaged inoculants containing nitrogen-fixing bacteria available for purchase by the farmer. Use of the inoculant ensures that the legume will acquire the proper nodule bacteria early in its development.

OTHER SOURCES. A variety of organic fertilizers may be derived from plant and animal residues. Sources include dried blood, animal wastes obtained from slaughterhouses, steam-treated garbage, dried and ground human sewage, sludge, dried fish scraps from cannery waste, and ground cottonseed meal. Even though most countries utilize human waste to increase soil fertility, this practice has been largely disdained in the United States. In recent years a few sewage disposal plants have prepared commercial fertilizer from sewage sludge. For many years the city of Milwaukee has marketed a sludge product called "Milorganite," which has been used as a fertilizer and soil conditioner. Chicago is planning to use its sewage sludge to fertilize sandy farm lands in the vicinity. It is expected that by 2015 the nitrogen-and-phosphorus-rich sludge would be piped or sprayed on 21,500 acres and that bumper crops of field corn and pasture grasses will be raised on the previously non-productive soil (28). With the rapidly increasing number of cattle feedlots in the United States steer manure has become available in large quantities. (In feedlots cattle are crowded together and provided with feed.)

An interesting source of organic fertilizer is represented by the excrement of wild birds and bats. Fish-eating cormorants have maintained dense breeding colonies on the rockbound Chincha Islands off the coast of Peru. Over the centuries, the guano of these birds has hardened and accumulated to a depth of over 100 feet. For many years these deposits, rich in both nitrogen and phosphorus, were "mined" and shipped all over the world, including the United States, as a form of fertilizer.

Use of Inorganic Fertilizers

NITROGEN FERTILIZERS. Nitrogen forms up to 0.3 per cent by weight of dark brown prairie topsoil—a total of 4,000 pounds per acre (1). A study by Dickson and Crocker showed that the amount of nitrogen in virgin pine forest soils of known age on the slopes of Mount Shasta, California, gradually increased with soil maturity. A steady state, however, was attained after 500 years when nitrogen content leveled off at 4,148 pounds per acre. However, once such virgin soil is subjected to intensive cropping or severe erosion, this initially abundant nitrogen content may be rapidly depleted.

The greatest single inorganic source of nitrogen currently used in American agriculture is a synthetic ammonia process in which nitrogen and hydrogen is combined under pressure in the presence of a catalyst. The nitrogen may be in the form of ammonia and ammonium salts or in the form of urea and nitrates derived from the ammonia. The direct application of anhydrous ammonia to soil was proved feasible in 1947 at the Mississippi Agricultural Experiment Station. Its use has increased more rapidly than that of any other fertilizer.

Surprisingly enough, the modern motor car, with its high compression internal combustion engine, has become a source of soil enriching nitrates. Apparently as a result of the high temperatures generated when gasoline is combusted, the nitrogen (which forms 70 per cent of the air) in the gas-air mixture is converted into nitrate form and then spewed out in the exhaust. Eventually this material settles on the ground, thereby improving its fertility. In agricultural areas bordering heavily trafficked freeways, somewhat less commercial fertilizer is required as a result.

COMPLETE FERTILIZERS. A complete fertilizer is a mixture (in varying ratios) of nitrogen, phosphorus, and potassium fertilizers. It must carry on the container a printed guarantee as to its component nutrients. Such a guarantee is usually stated in percentages. Thus, one 5-10-5 mixture contains 5 per cent total nitrogen, 10 per cent available phosphoric acid, and 5 per cent water-soluble potash. In utilizing inorganic fertilizers, the farmer not only must provide a crop with the total nutrients required for proper growth, but must provide them at the proper time. The same crop may require more of a given element at one time than another. Thus, corn requires the largest amount of potassium from June 20 to July 20, whereas its greatest nitrogen and phosphorus demands occur from July 20 to August 19.

DISADVANTAGES. The inorganic fertilizers, however, are not an unmixed blessing, for their continued use may result in subtle adverse changes of soil structure and contribute to water pollution problems. These disadvantages have been described by Barry Commoner, noted ecologist:

> Another example of new problems created by what seem to be technological achieve-ments is provided by modern agricultural technology, which is largely based on re-placing the dwindling natural supply of plant nutrients in the soil by the massive use of inorganic fertilizers, especially nitrogen. These fertilizers greatly increase immediate crop yields; but at the same time, the impoverishment of soil organic matter, by altering the physical character of the soil (especially its porosity to oxygen), sharply reduces the efficiency with which the added fertilizer is taken up by the crop. As a result, unused nitrogen fertilizer drains out of the soil into rivers and lakes, where it joins with the nitrate imposed on the water by the effluent of sewage treatment plants, causing overgrowths of green plants and the resultant organic pollution. The drainage of nitrogen from fertilizer has already destroyed the self-purifying capability of nearly every river in Illinois. . . (8).

The gravity of these problems can be better appreciated when one realizes that the use of commercial fertilizers in the United States has increased *twelve-fold* in the last twenty-five years.

The exorbitant use of nitrate fertilizers in the United States has also been indi-rectly responsible for an increased rate of *methemoglobinemia*, a serious blood disease of infants that may be lethal. Apparently the excessive nitrate not absorbed by crop root systems may be leached downward to the water table by rainwater and eventually contaminate private or municipal wells. The nitrate in itself is not highly deleterious. However, when it enters the child's intestines, the nitrate is converted into *nitrite*. The nitrite then combines with the hemoglobin (red blood pigment) to form methemoglobin. Unfortunately, the capacity of methemoglobin to carry oxygen is much less than that of hemoglobin. As a result, the infant attempts to compensate by breathing more rapidly and strenuously. In severe cases mental impairment results because of the oxygen deprivation incurred by the brain. Occa-sionally this disorder causes suffocation of the infant. The streams of California's Central Valley have perhaps the highest nitrate level in the nation. Public health authorities in this area have suggested that babies be given only bottled water (15). Illinois, Missouri, Minnesota, and Wisconsin have all had a disturbing number of methemoglobinemia cases.

Crop Rotation. Effective crop rotation techniques may simultaneously promote soil fertility and minimize erosion. A typical three-year rotation pattern might in-volve a wide-row, cultivated soil-depleting crop (corn, tobacco, cotton) the first year; a narrow-row, noncultivated soil-depleting crop of wheat, barley, or oats the second year; and a dense, noncultivated cover crop (grasses, legumes) the third year. The grass-legume crop of the terminal rotation year would cover the soil with an almost continuous shield of leaves and stems, which would receive the full impact of rainfall and minimize erosion. Moreover, the nitrogen-fixing bacteria of the legume nodules would "fix" about 200 pounds of nitrogen per acre. When properly practiced, crop rotation would do much either to build up impoverished soils or to maintain fertility of good soils.

Soil Nutrients and Human Health

Some authorities have been concerned that both agronomists and farmers are so preoccupied with crop yield that the crop's nutritional value is inadvertently being ignored. *Quantity* is being confused with *quality*. And to increase crop quantity, American farmers add inorganic nitrate fertilizers. As Commoner has so pungently stated, "farmers are hooked on nitrates like a junkie is hooked on heroin" (15). As A. G. Norman, of the University of Michigan, writes, "High yields are not . . . synonymous with a high content of nutrient elements. . . . Crops from well fertilized plots may have a *lower* content of some [health] essential elements than those from poorly yielding plots, the *addition* of a fertilizer may cause a *reduction* in content of some of the other nutrient elements . . ." (17).

Despite remarkable accomplishments in nutritional research within the last few decades, we frankly are not able to pinpoint all the nutrients in vegetables and grains that are essential to human health. As Lewis Herber states, "We do not even know how many vitamins there are or which ones are essential" (17). An ear of corn, an orange, or cabbage may appear attractive and wholesome, and may even be delicious. However, if certain health-essential constituents are lacking man may well incur serious nutritional inadequacies if he subsists extensively on food grown in soil "doctored up" with a few inorganic commercial fertilizers in the interests of crop *volume* rather than human health.

Projected Cropland Requirements

From the preceding discussion it is apparent that science and technology have improved attitudes toward the importance and vulnerability of our land resource (especially during the immediate aftermath of the Dust Bowl calamities) and have been instrumental in soil rehabilitation. With the Soil Conservation Service leading the way, wind and water erosion has been retarded and soil structure and fertility have been restored on millions of acres. As a direct result America has been more than able to fill domestic food and fiber requirements. We even have food surpluses that can be shipped to hungry millions abroad. But what of the future, when there will be many more stomachs to fill? For example, the number of people is increasing at the rate of 1 every 11 seconds, 5 every minute, 325 every hour, 8,000 every day, 56,000 every week, and 3 million every year. America's projected crop and land requirements for 2000 would seem to give cause for concern. For example, our cropland needs for cotton will increase from 15 million (1960) to 20 million acres (2000), soybean cropland requirements will increase from 23 million acres (1960) to 44 million acres (2000), and land requirements for hay will zoom from 67 million acres (1960) to 118 million acres by the year 2000. For our ten most important crops (including grains, wheat, cotton, soybeans, and hay) overall requirements will rise from the 319 million acres of 1960 to 378 million acres by 2000, a 12.2 per cent increase, leaving America with a 60 *million-acre cropland deficit.*

As a result of our rapid population increase, and shifting dietary standards, demand for cattle and calves (live weight) will increase from the 1960 figure of 28.6 billion pounds to 69.8 billion pounds (2000); demand for hogs will rise from 20 billion pounds (1960) to 44.3 billion pounds by 2000; egg consumption will jump from 62 billion (1960) to 119 billion by 2000. These human consumer demands obviously rest upon a producer food chain base of livestock feed plants, which in turn will require an increased cropland acreage.

How can the impending dilemma posed by the cropland deficit be handled? Probably not by actual acreage increases. After all, virtually all suitable acreage is already being utilized. According to Landsberg, Fischman, and Fisher, in their *Resources in America's Future,* and other leading economists, this deficit can be made up principally by increased yields from the existing acreage (23). First, more intensive use could be made of *organic fertilizers,* such as the feces of cows, pigs, and sheep, as well as "green" manure. Even domestic sewage effluent has considerable potential. It might be piped to rural areas and sprayed over farm lands. This has been done experimentally at Pennsylvania State University with substantial increases in crop production. More extensive use could be made of compost (partially decomposed garbage) and dried sewage sludge as soil conditioners—agents that would improve soil structure, enhance water absorption qualities, and reduce its erodability.

Second, yields can be increased by the use of *drought-, disease-, insect-, and wind-resistant crop varieties* that are currently being developed by plant geneticists. For example, the use of hybrid corn has virtually doubled corn production in Wisconsin and Iowa in recent years.

Third, *crop production patterns can be modified* to increase yields. A good case in point is the recent translocation of considerable cotton production from the Gulf states to California, where average per acre yield in 1960 was 981 pounds, 101 per cent higher than the 486 per acre yield in Mississippi and 158 per cent above the Texas yield of 379 per acre.

Fourth, increased per acre yields might result from more efficient farm operations made possible by *consolidations.* Within the past half century American agriculture has experienced dramatic changes in ownership and farm size. For example, in 1920 there were 6,488,000 farms averaging 148 acres in size. By 1966, however, consolidations had absorbed 3 million of these farms, resulting in a 119 per cent increase in average farm size to 325 acres. Moreover, it is predicted that average farm size will rise to 1,100 acres by 2000. Partly because larger farms permit more effective use of modern agricultural machinery, productivity per acre has jumped 7.7 per cent per year since the 1950's. If average farm size increases to the 1,100 acres predicted for the year 2000, land use shifts could be made that would be more consistent with land capabilities; that is, more Class I land could be utilized for crop production, with a resultant release of Class IV land (hilly, stony) for forest and pasture.

Fifth, a revolutionary technology theoretically could result in the *mass production of yeast and algae* that might be utilized as both human and livestock food; crop residues, such as corn cobs and stubble, might eventually be used as a source of livestock feeds, thus releasing a considerable acreage for production of crops directly usable by man.

Sixth, crop production can eventually be increased by expanding *irrigation* farming. Many semiarid lands are inherently fertile, requiring only an adequate water supply to make them productive. By the year 2000 America should be irrigating 55 million of the nation's 75 million irrigable acres (73.3 per cent), 22 million more acres than were irrigated back in 1965.

Seventh, crop production can be increased by *controlling insect and fungus pests* with a judicious combination of chemical (pesticide) and biological control. Pesticide use should be held to a minimum. In some cases it can be replaced entirely with biological methods, such as the use of ladybugs in California to control aphids.

Soil Problems in the Urban-Suburban Environment

Each year more than 1 million acres of agricultural land, lying primarily on "the edge of town" is converted to urban use. Concrete has invaded the cornfield. "Jaguars" and "Mustangs" roar where cattle once roamed. As a result the Soil Conservation Service has found a new challenge. As one SCS spokesman has expressed it, "The country's 3000 soil and water conservation districts have inherited the problems and opportunities of exploding suburbia. A common experience has been the replacement of two or three problems of individual farmers by the soil and water ailments of thousands of new homeowners." And the SCS has prepared soil survey maps to meet not only the needs of prospective homeowners, but also those of highway engineers and layers of underground electric cables. Soils data are very useful to urban planners in helping them "to select and develop desirable spatial distribution patterns for industrial, commercial, residential . . . and recreational development" (43).

Soil Erosions at Construction Sites. Unfortunately, many of the development projects that have been launched are associated with extensive soil erosion largely because of either lack of planning, carelessness, or ignorance concerning the characteristics of the soils involved. For example, according to the Soil Conservation Service, "Studies show that erosion on land going into use for highways, houses or shopping centers is about *ten* times greater than on land in pasture, and *two thousand* times greater than on land in timber . . ." (42). It has further been estimated that soil erosion on a given square mile of farm land may be as low as 50 tons per year. However, if that same square mile is converted into suburban use, annual soil erosion losses may increase sharply to more than 25,000 tons—*a 500-fold increment*. In some Maryland storm drains sediment has collected to a depth of over 2 feet in less than a year. The soil is eventually washed into lakes and streams. Shallow lakes, once valued as swimming and boating sites, are virtually destroyed as sources of recreation and scenic beauty. Many thousands of game fish have been asphyxiated annually because of sediment-clogged gills. Our nation's reservoirs, many of them sources of municipal water supply, are accumulating 1 billion cubic yards of sediment annually. Dredging operations in our rivers and harbors yield another 0.5 billion cubic yards each year! These dredging activities may cost the American taxpayers up to $1 billion yearly, even though many of them live thousands of miles from the construction sites where the erosion problems originated.

Figure 4-21. *Erosion in an urban area, Des Moines, Iowa. A gully is rapidly developing. [Soil Conservation Service, U.S. Department of Agriculture, Photo by Keith Glandon]*

Figure 4-22. *Lake Barcroft, Virginia. More than $200,000 has been spent to dredge urban-induced silt from this lake in Virginia, shown in December 1963. Each year, 450 million cubic yards of soil and other materials are dredged from our rivers and harbors at a cost of about $1 a yard. [Soil Conservation Service, U.S. Department of Agriculture, Photo by Glenn B. Anderson]*

Rampaging run-off waters have virtually destroyed newly built roads before they could be paved. Because of mud slippages, some residents have seen their backyards vanish almost overnight.

What can be done about these problems? Here, again, just as on the rural scene, the Soil Conservation Service is available for technical advice, not only to the developer, but to builders, engineers, planners, architects, public officials, and any other people in the community responsible for erosion control. Erosion control measures should be *incorporated* into any developmental plan or construction project. A few erosion control measures that might be effectively employed at construction sites follow:

1. No more vegetational cover should be bulldozed off the site than is absolutely necessary for immediate construction purposes.
2. If a site has been bulldozed bare of vegetation and the project is delayed, adequate temporary cover can be established by seeding quickly growing plants such as rye, oats, millet, and sudan grass.
3. Boards can be arranged in rows across the steep slopes to form temporary terraces, thus establishing soil and permitting seeding.
4. Denuded areas should be reseeded or sodded as soon as possible. Plants well adapted for stabilizing soil on steep slopes include honeysuckle, Kentucky 31 fescue, crown vetch, and sericea lespideza. Day lilies would provide a flash of color as well.
5. Steep road cuts can be reseeded with a *hydroseeder*, a machine that blows a slurry of seeds, fertilizer, straw mulch, and water onto the slope. The mulch serves to hold the seeds in place and prevent excessive moisture loss caused by evaporation.

Figure 4-23. *A sediment control basin, shown here on March 15, 1966, at Tyson's Corner, Virginia, is one method used to stop mud from silting up nearby streams during construction. This was one of two basins on a large industrial development where the land had been cleared but not built upon. Up to 50,000 tons of sediment a year can run off a square mile of land in this condition. Instead of going into neighboring streams, the sediment will be spread back on the land again. [Soil Conservation Service, U.S. Department of Agriculture, Photo by Glenn B. Anderson]*

6. Newly applied seeds and mulching can be retained on steep inclines with the aid of jute matting. The jute eventually decomposes and improves soil structure.
7. Temporary catch basins may be constructed of stone, earth, or concrete to intercept run-off water and trap its sediment load. After the construction project has been completed and the site revegetated, the basins may be removed and the area graded and blended into the surrounding landscape.

Soil Problems at Landfill Sites. Increasing numbers of American communities are disposing of their municipal solid wastes (garbage and debris) by underground burial in sanitary landfills. However, unless the city officials involved have consulted soil scientists to determine soil suitability before site purchase, serious drainage problems might develop. For example, if the soil is too sandy or gravelly, rainwater and snow melt will seep to lower levels of the soil, eventually carrying potentially toxic chemicals and pathogenic micro-organisms downward to the water table. Eventually these contaminants may move horizontally through an aquifer and pollute the town's water supply. Many communities have been forced to close down such improperly sited landfills and purchase new sites—at considerable expense to the local taxpayers.

Figure 4-24. *Effect of soil slide at Delmar, New York. The large crack in this earth resulted from a slide of unstable soil on May 16, 1963. [Soil Conservation Service, U.S. Department of Agriculture, Photo by Lester Fox]*

Soil Problems of the Home Owner. Let us examine some typical soil-associated problems plaguing the suburban resident:

SOIL SLIPPAGE. When a surface soil layer on a steep slope is underlain by an impervious stratum of rock, slippage may occur when the surface becomes water saturated. For example, an attractive $30,000 home was reduced to rubble when melt water from a heavy snowfall caused mud slippage on the slope above. Nine other homes were seriously damaged. Soil slippage has been highly destructive to homes of wealthy Californians such as movie actors on the precipitous slopes of Beverly Hills, many a $100,000 home being converted to a muddy shambles after a period of heavy rainfall.

SEPTIC TANK PROBLEMS. Many suburbanites do not have access to municipal sewage lines. In order to dispose of domestic waste, whether flushed down the toilet or washed down the sink, they frequently rely on septic tanks. Wastes accumulate in the tanks, undergo gradual bacterial decomposition, pass from the tanks, gradually filter downward through the soil, and eventually are completely broken down into inorganic nutrients—if the soil around the tank is sufficiently permeable. Some prospective home builders are very careful about checking police and fire protection, taxes, insurance, quality of schools, and so on, before they purchase a lot. Regrettably, however, these same people completely neglect checking the soil permeability with the assistance of their SCS district office. Such an oversight might be disastrous —as it was to the owners of twenty $25,000 homes in an attractive Chicago subdivision (45), a few years ago. Bright green patches appeared on lawns around the spectic tanks. Vile odors permeated the air and frustrated attempts at outdoor barbecues. A soil percolation check [1] by health authorities revealed that soil permeability was nil. The construction of fifty-two additional homes was halted by county authorities pending a sewer trunk line installation.

TOP SOIL REMOVAL. John Vosburgh, in his fine book *Living with Your Land*, describes a frustrating and costly experience that befell a home builder simply because his soil knowledge was nil. A New York artist purchased an attractive suburban lot from an unscrupulous developer. He was not aware that the developer had scooped off the valuable top soil and sold it at a tidy profit to a landscaper. Even though the site with topsoil intact was sufficiently productive to raise truck crops, once the topsoil was stripped away, there wasn't enough fertile soil left to grow a dandelion. The artist was forced to purchase fertile top soil ("black dirt") at a cost of $20 per truck load. Not only this:

> the garage started sinking. Water had weakened the ground underneath it and the cave-in was threatening to pull the house in with it. It cost $750 to have the garage straightened and the ground underneath it shored up. Some of his neighbors had similar experiences. One reported his patio was sinking. Several saw their game rooms turn into wading pools. . . . The owners were baffled because their houses were approved by building inspectors. . . . (45)

[1] It is a simple matter to make a "perc" test of your soil. All you have to do is dig several holes to a depth of three feet and fill with water. If the water drains away within one hour your soils have good permeability; if water still remains in these holes, the permeability is poor. Some communities will not issue a building permit unless the soil on the lot passes a "perc" test conducted by a local health department.

BIBLIOGRAPHY

1. Allen, Shirley W., and Justin W. Leonard. *Conserving Natural Resources*. New York: McGraw-Hill, 1966.
2. Allison, Franklin E. "Nitrogen and Soil Fertility," *Soil: The Yearbook of Agriculture*. Washington, D.C.: U.S. Department of Agriculture, 1957.
3. Bear, Firman E. *Earth: The Stuff of Life*. Norman: University of Oklahoma, 1962.
4. ———. *Chemistry of the Soil*. New York: Van Nostrand, 1964.
5. Bennett, Hugh Hammond. *Elements of Soil Conservation*. New York: McGraw-Hill, 1955.
6. Blakely, J., J. Coyle, and J. G. Steele. "Erosion on Cultivated Land," *Soil: The Yearbook of Agriculture*. Washington, D.C.: U.S. Department of Agriculture, 1957.
7. Clark, William R. *Farms and Farmers*. Boston: Page, 1945.
8. Commoner, Barry. "Salvation: It's Possible," *The Progressive* (April 1970), 12–18.
9. Cook, R. L. *Soil Management for Conservation and Production*. New York: Wiley, 1962.
10. Dale, Tom, and Vernon G. Carter. *Topsoil and Civilization*. Norman: University of Oklahoma, 1955.
11. Dasmann, Raymond F. *Environmental Conservation*. New York: Wiley, 1959.
12. Dean, L. A. "Plant Nutrition and Soil Fertility," *Soils: The Yearbook of Agriculture*. Washington, D.C.: U.S. Department of Agriculture, 1957.
13. Donahue, Roy L. *Soils: An Introduction to Soils and Plant Growth*. Englewood Cliffs, N.J.: Prentice-Hall, 1965.
14. Eddy, Don. "Up from the Dust," *Reader's Dig.*, 37 (1940), 20–22.
15. Ehrlich, Paul R., and Anne H. Ehrlich. *Population, Resources, Environment*. San Francisco: Freeman, 1970.
16. George, Ernest J., Ralph A. Read, E. W. Johnson, and A. E. Ferber. "Shelterbelts and Windbreaks," *Soils: The Yearbook of Agriculture*. Washington, D.C.: U.S. Department of Agriculture, 1957.
17. Herber, Lewis. *Our Synthetic Environment*. New York: Knopf, 1962.
18. Highsmith, Richard M., Jr., J. Granville Jensen, and Robert D. Rudd. *Conservation in the United States*. Chicago: Rand McNally, 1962.
19. Hill, W. L. "The Need for Fertilizers," *Farmer's World: The Yearbook of Agriculture*. Washington, D.C.: U.S. Department of Agriculture, 1964.
20. Holmes, R. S., and J. C. Brown. "Iron and Soil Fertility," *Soils: The Yearbook of Agriculture*. Washington, D.C.: U.S. Department of Agriculture, 1957.
21. Jacks, G. V., and R. O. Whyte. *Vanishing Lands: A World Survey of Soil Erosion*. New York: Doubleday, 1939.
22. Jordan, Howard V., and H. M. Reisenauer. "Sulfur and Soil Fertility," *Soils: The Yearbook of Agriculture*. Washington, D.C.: U.S. Department of Agriculture, 1957.
23. Landsberg, Hans H., Leonard L. Fischman, and Joseph L. Fisher. *Resources in America's Future*. Baltimore: Johns Hopkins, 1962.
24. Leighton, M. M. "Geology of Soil Drifting on the Great Plains," *Scient. Month.*, 47, 22–23.
25. Lowdermilk, W. C. "Conquest of the Land Through 7,000 Years," *Agri. Info. Bull.*, No. 99. Washington, D.C.: Soil Conservation Service. U.S. Department of Agriculture, 1953.
26. Lyon, T. Lyttleton, and Harry O. Buckman. *The Nature and Property of Soils*. New York: Macmillan, 1937.
27. McDonald, Angus. "Early American Soil Conservationists," *Miscellaneous Pub. No. 1449*. Washington, D.C.: U.S. Department of Agriculture, 1941.
28. Marx, Wesley. *Man and His Environment: Waste*. New York: Harper, 1971.

29. Moran, Joseph M., Michael D. Morgan, and James H. Wiersma. *An Introduction to Environmental Sciences*. Boston: Little, Brown, 1973.
30. *Newsweek*, 5, No. 13 (March 30, 1935), 5–6.
31. Olsen, Sterling R., and Maurice Fried. "Soil Phosphorus and Fertility," *Soils: The Yearbook of Agriculture*. Washington, D.C.: U.S. Department of Agriculture, 1957.
32. Olson, L. "Erosion: A Heritage from the Past," *Agri. Hist.*, 13 (1939), 161–170.
33. Pfeiffer, Ehrenfried. *The Earth's Face and Human Destiny*. Emmaus, Pa.: Rodale Press, 1947.
34. Reitemeier, R. F. "Soil Potassium and Fertility," *Soils: The Yearbook of Agriculture*. Washington, D.C.: U.S. Department of Agriculture, 1957.
35. Rockie, William A. "Soil Conservation," in Guy-Harold Smith, ed., *Conservation of Natural Resources*. New York: Wiley, 1965.
36. Sears, Paul E. "Floods and Dust Storms," *Science*, 83, 9.
37. Seatz, Lloyd, and J. J. Jurinak "Zinc and Soil Fertility," *Soils: The Yearbook of Agriculture*. Washington, D.C.: U.S. Department of Agriculture, 1957.
38. Smith, Guy-Harold, ed., *Conservation of Natural Resources*. New York: Wiley, 1965.
39. Stout, P. R., and C. M. Johnson. "Trace Elements," *Soils: The Yearbook of Agriculture*. Washington, D.C.: U.S. Department of Agriculture, 1957.
40. Turk, Amos, Jonathan Turk, and Janet T. Wittes. *Ecology, Pollution, Environment*. Philadelphia: Saunders, 1972.
41. U.S. Department of Agriculture. "Agricultural Land Resources," *Agri. Info. Bull.* No. 263. Washington, D.C., 1962.
42. U.S. Department of Agriculture. "Controlling Erosion on Construction Sites." Soil Conservation Service. *Agri. Info. Bull.* No. 347. Washington, D.C., 1970.
43. University of Wisconsin Extension Service. "The Soil Survey: A Guide to Rural and Urban Development," *Special Circular No. 91*. Madison, Wis., 1964.
44. Van Slyke, L. L. *Fertilizers and Crop Production*. New York: Orange Judd, 1932.
45. Vosburgh, John. *Living with Your Land*. New York: Scribners, 1968.

5.

Man
And Water

If the question is asked whether life could exist on a certain planet, the first question a biologist asks is: Is water in liquid form available there? If it is not, life as we know it could not exist. All the reactions of life are carried out in aqueous solution. If any single compound should be selected as characteristic of life, it is water.

Hubert Frings and Mable Frings,
Concepts of Zoology,
New York, Macmillan Publishing Co., Inc., 1970.

The noted Greek philosopher Plato (427–347 B.C.) recognized that the earth's rivers were fed by rain and that water moved in a continuous ocean-land-ocean cycle. This knowledge, however, gradually was lost and during the Dark Ages, hundreds of years after Plato, the bizarre notion was advanced that water flowed magically in a never-ending stream from the center of the earth

(12). Today we know that water moves from ocean to air to land to ocean in a pattern known as the *hydrologic cycle*.

The Hydrologic Cycle

Because of the cyclical nature of water movement, a given water molecule may be used over and over again through the centuries. For example, "Cleopatra's bath water has run to the sea and mixed throughout the oceans. About five per cent has already been evaporated and returned to the continents as rain" (7). A few molecules from *her* bath may be present in *your* bath next Saturday.

Although fluctuations in rate of water movement may occur in certain segments of the cycle, the total water volume involved has remained constant for millions of years. The cycle is powered by solar energy and gravity, the daily energy input being *greater than all the energy utilized by man since the dawn of civilization*. In actuality, water is not continuously moving. It may be temporarily stored (for centuries) either within the earth's crust, on the earth's surface, or in the atmosphere. At any instant, only 0.005 per cent of the total water supply is moving through the cycle (17). Familiarity with the hydrologic cycle is basic to an appreciation of the nature and complexity of the serious water conservation problems confronting America today. (Fig. 5-1)

Oceans. We shall trace the major pathways of the hydrologic cycle, beginning with the oceans, which cover 70 per cent of the earth's surface with salt water up to 7 miles deep. The oceans contain 97.2 per cent of the world's total water supply, over 317 million cubic miles. If the earth were a perfectly smooth sphere, the ocean

Figure 5-1. *The hydrologic cycle. [Adapted from Raymond F. Dasmann, Environmental Conservation (New York: John Wiley & Sons, Inc., 1968).]*

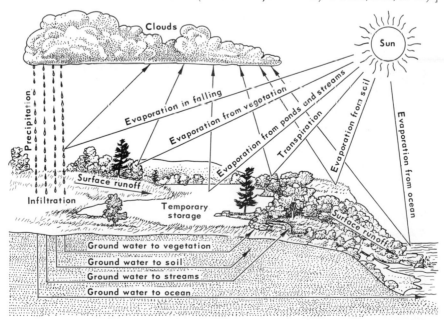

water would be sufficient to submerge the entire globe to a depth of 800 feet. As water molecules at the ocean's surface warm up as a result of incident solar radiation, they gradually rise into the atmosphere as a gas in a process called *evaporation*. Were the oceans not constantly refilled, the oceans would drop by 39 inches yearly (11).

Precipitation. As the water vapor rises, it gradually cools, condenses, and forms clouds. Water that has evaporated from a Kansas wheat field may eventually fall as rain on a college campus in Ohio. Of the 83,700 cubic miles evaporated from the ocean, 71,000 cubic miles return to the ocean as precipitation; only 9,000 fall on land (13). The atmosphere holds a constant volume of less than one-hundred-thousandth (3,100 cubic miles) of the total water supply (11). This atmospheric moisture represents latent energy originally derived from the sun, which is released through storms. An ordinary thunderstorm, of which more than 10,000 occur annually, releases more energy than a 120-kiloton nuclear bomb (13). Moisture-

Figure 5-2. *N. Tongass National Forest, Alaska. Glaciers represent a phase of the hydrologic cycle and are powerful agents of geological erosion as well. This is a view of Mendenhall Glacier. Many of the lakes in the Northeastern states were originally formed from glacial melt water. [U. S. Forest Service]*

laden clouds may be carried inland over coastal areas, such as the Gulf or Pacific coasts, and finally, when cooling off sufficiently (as when they pass upward over the slope of a mountain or when they meet a cold air mass), may release water as rain, snow, hail, or sleet. Our nation's average annual rainfall would be sufficient to cover the entire country (if it were perfectly level) to a depth of 30 inches. In the United States, unfortunately, rainfall is very unevenly distributed, both in time and space. Death Valley receives only 1.7 inches annually, whereas the western slope of the Cascades, not too far distant, receives 140 to 150 inches (11). A certain town in Florida has been deluged with 24 inches of rain in a single day, yet Bagdad, California, once received only 4 inches in 5 years. Where rain falls through atmosphere that is polluted with oxides of sulfur and nitrogen, as is the case in many industrial areas, it is converted into dilute sulfuric and nitric acid. The pH of this rain may be as low as 3, sufficient to corrode water pipes and accelerate the leaching of soil nutrients (15).

Bodies of Organisms. Plants absorb soil water through their root systems. Animals get their water by direct absorption through their body surface (amphibians), by drinking (many birds and mammals), or through the plant tissues (herbivores) and animal tissues (insectivores, carnivores) that they consume. In aggregate only 0.003 per cent of our freshwater supply is present in living protoplasm (1).

Man could live two months without food but would die in less than a week without water. The body of the average human adult contains 50 quarts (100 pounds). Although the body is 65 *per cent water (by weight)*, the percentage for specific organs varies. It is 2 per cent for tooth enamel, 22 per cent for bone, 75 *per cent for brain and muscle*, and 83 *per cent for kidneys*. Water has many functions in the human body. It serves as a solvent that promotes chemical activity. It serves as a transportation medium for nutrients, hormones, enzymes, minerals, nitrogenous wastes, and respiratory gases. It has a thermoregulatory function. The average adult loses 2.5 quarts daily—1.5 quarts by the excretion of urine, 1 pint by perspiration, and 1 pint by expiration. One and one-half quarts are replaced by drinking and the other quart by food ingestion. Death would result were man to lose more than 12 per cent of his body's water content. Most organisms, regardless of body size, food habits, or habitat, from the ameba to the blue whale, have a high water content. Even the desert-dwelling kangaroo rat is 65 per cent water. The subterranean earthworm is 80 per cent water, the *marine jellyfish 95 per cent*. Plants are no exception; the water content for corn, grains, and tomatoes is 70 per cent, 87 per cent, and 95 per cent, respectively (17).

Evaporation and Transpiration. Of the 30 inches of annual rainfall, about 21 inches passes back into the atmosphere by evaporation and transpiration. More evaporation and transpiration occur in forested areas than elsewhere (19). *Evaporation* may take place directly from the surface of wet vegetation, moist soil, lakes, and streams, or from the bodies of animals and their excreta. It is intriguing to contemplate that some of the very water molecules evaporating from your body after a hard game of tennis may some day fall as rain on your own backyard. *Transpiration* is the evaporation that occurs through the stomata of plant leaves. One mature oak tree may transpire *100 gallons per day*, almost 40,000 gallons in a year (11). Many plants transpire more than *2,000 grams* of water for each *gram* of dry matter synthesized (5). The water that passes back into the atmosphere by evapotranspiration cannot be manipulated or controlled by man. Nevertheless, this water has served man well in sustaining forest, rangeland, residential lawn, and multimillion-dollar crop harvests.

Surface Water.   About 9 inches of the 30 inches of annual rainfall in the United States either contributes to the formation of numerous ponds, lakes, and streams from which it inexorably flows toward the ocean, or else percolates as *ground water* downward into the pores and channels of the earth's crust. It is this component of the annual precipitation that is of direct concern to the conservationist, for it is only this supply that yields to human control and manipulation and may be used for domestic, industrial, and agricultural purposes. A gallon of Ohio River water may be reused at least *six* times for municipal and industrial purposes before it finally flows into the ocean.

Even though river channels hold only 0.0001 per cent of the world's water supply, stream flow is the most obvious method by which water returns to the ocean. Even during ancient times people had a fairly good understanding of river-ocean relationships. Thus, we read in Ecclesiastes 1:7, "All the rivers run into the sea: yet, the sea is not full; unto the place from whence the rivers come, thither they return again." Water flow in the 3.25 million miles of river channels in the United States (11) amounts to an average 1,200 billion gallons a day. It may be represented by a tiny mountain stream or a great river such as the Mississippi, which drains over a million squares miles and flows 1,200 miles across mid-America to the Gulf. Measurement of stream flow volume is done by more than 6,000 gauging stations operated by the U.S. Geological Survey (6). Surface water, in the form of streams, ponds, and lakes, satisfies about 80 per cent of man's water requirements. This run-off can be either destructive (floods, erosion) or beneficial. Water soluble nutrients (calcium, potassium, nitrates) may be transported from upstream areas and deposited downstream. The extremely high productivity of low-lying marshes and estuaries derives from this fact (4).

Ground Water.   Instead of forming surface ponds and streams, some of the rainfall and snow melt is absorbed by the soil. In the topsoil and subsoil horizons it is withdrawn by a myriad of plant root systems, transported upward through stems and trunks, most of it to be transpired; a small portion is to be used by countless trillions of chloroplasts, which use it as raw material for photosynthesis. Vast amounts of water move downward into huge porous layers of sandstone, limestone, and gravel. Ninety-seven per cent of the world's supply of fresh water (2 million cubic miles) is retained in such water-bearing formations known as *aquifers* (11). Man is making intensive use of this water. For example, "the sandstones that are yielding, from deep bore holes, great quantities of high quality water for the city of Chicago got that water from rain that fell on the Great Plains far to the west a million years ago, then trickled slowly through the rocks at rates of a few feet or a few inches a year" (22). When in danger of being depleted, they may be recharged artificially by means of injection wells, by spreading water over the land's surface, or by the use of water pits (6). *Our nation's total ground water supply is equivalent to ten years of precipitation.* Moreover, the ground water of the United States in the upper one-half mile is equivalent to all the water that will run off into the oceans over the next century. This subterranean water may flow at varying rates of a few feet to several miles per year. Some industries, and even federal agencies, have "disposed" of their toxic wastes by injecting them deeply into the earth by means of injection wells. Eventually, such wastes may move through permeable layers and contaminate an aquifer. The U.S. Geological Survey estimates that these toxic materials might remain in the aquifer 200 to 10,000 years, thus virtually destroying the aquifer for human use (15). Eventually it discharges into the ocean to complete one turn of the hydrologic cycle.

The upper level of water-saturated ground, which is known as the *water table*, may coincide with the ground surface, forming marshes or springs, or may be situated at a depth of one mile or more. After heavy precipitation the water table rises; during drought or intensive use by man it may subside. In some regions along the Gulf coastal plain, the water table lies so close to the surface that conventional 6-foot grave excavations tend to fill with water and above-ground burial is necessary.

Water Use

How many times and in how many ways have you made use of water today? From moment to moment, from hour to hour, this remarkable combination of hydrogen and oxygen is serving as an indispensable component of our ecosystem. We use it to wash everything from *a 10-ton truck to a baby's ear*. We use it to extinguish fires and clean city streets, to flush sewage and to power industry. It is the basic raw material for numberless products emerging from our factories. It takes 14 gallons of water to make a pound of sugar, 1,000 gallons for a pound of milk, 5,000 gallons to produce a pound of meat. It requires 770 gallons to refine a barrel of petroleum, 65,000 gallons to manufacture an automobile, and 500,000 gallons to launch an ICBM rocket (14). One cup of water was needed to make the page you are reading. We employ our rivers and lakes to transport over 100 billion ton-miles of commercial freight each year. Water is the indispensable medium for sporting thrills enjoyed by millions of duck hunters, canoeists, and anglers. We take water into our bodies in a thousand disguises, from buttermilk to beef stew. We use it to irrigate everything from a backyard garden to a desert wilderness.

The development and utilization of water resources have challenged man's resourcefulness and ingenuity for millennia. More than 4,000 years ago, Hammurabi, King of Babylon, boasted that he made the desert bloom after bringing water to it. Long before Christ's birth the people of Egypt, Greece, and Rome had developed well-designed water supply systems. Jacob's Well, so frequently mentioned in Biblical accounts, was hewn through a slab of solid rock to a depth of over 100 feet and is apparently still in use today. The Romans obtained 300 million gallons per day from fourteen huge aqueducts, which laid end to end would have formed a pipeline over 1,300 miles long. Ruins of these aqueducts may be seen today. According to some authorities, the ultimate collapse of the Roman Empire was caused as much by the eventual deterioration of the water distribution system as by internal corruption or the might of the barbarian invaders. The importance of water to a nation's well-being has been emphasized recently by the chronic Arab-Israeli dispute over water rights to the Jordan River. The recurring water shortage problems arising in the United States and other nations are *not* the result of an *absolute shortage* of total supply; rather, they are problems of *distribution* and *quality* caused by intensive concentrations of water-using industries and people. However, as Charles Southwick states, "To the city dweller in New York or Hong

Kong whose water tap runs dry, or to the refugee of the Middle East who is dying of thirst, it will be little comfort to realize that 29 million cubic kilometers of fresh water are locked in glacial and polar ice caps" (20).

Water Problems

Drought. The *Encyclopedia Americana* defines *drought* as a "period of severe atmospheric dryness and lack of rainfall of sufficient duration to cause widespread damage to crops, extinction of livestock and other economic hardships." Thus defined, a drought always involves financial setbacks, both to the individual and to the nation. According to the U.S. Weather Bureau, a drought exists whenever rainfall for a period of twenty-one days or longer is only 30 per cent of the average for the time and place. The more severe droughts in the United States have been characterized by diminution of stream flow and reduction in ground water levels; heavy mortality of aquatic wildlife, such as fish and waterfowl; extensive destruction of range, pasture, and farm crops; desiccated topsoil, highly vunerable to erosion; malnourished, disease-susceptible livestock; high incidence of forest fires; extreme discomfiture for man; and soaring food prices.

The most probable season for drought is summer, when water requirements of both wild and cultivated vegetation are greatest because of the high rates of photosynthesis and transpiration. Although twentieth-century man has contributed to many of his environmental ills by shortsightedness, greed, ignorance, apathy, or gross mismanagement of his ecosystem, we may exonerate him of virtually all responsibility for droughts. They have occurred with surprising frequency in the United States for over 1,000 years. Long before the U.S. Weather Bureau began keeping records, drought data were recorded by living tree trunks. Because a trunk lays down relatively wide annual xylem rings during periods of normal moisture and narrow rings during drought, by careful study of ring patterns in ancient trees it is possible to reconstruct the moisture conditions of past ages. In this way we have learned that protracted droughts occurred in the American Southwest roughly during the periods A.D. 700–720, 1070–1100, 1275–1300, and 1570–1600. Droughts are not rhythmic in the sense that we can predict that Syracuse, New York, or Atlanta, Georgia, will have a severe drought in 1985 or 2000. Rather, U.S. Weather Bureau records over the past century reveal that dry years alternate with wet years in an irregular pattern. The Great Plains from Texas to Montana, which include the arid part of the grassland biome, average about 35 consecutive drought days each year, and 75 to 100 successive days of drought once in 10 years. Up to 120 consecutive rainless days have been recorded for the southern Great Plains, or Dust Bowl, region.

DELAWARE RIVER BASIN DROUGHT OF 1961–1965. Twenty-two million people, 13 percent of the nation's population (23), in New York, New Jersey, and Delaware depend on water drained by the Delaware River and its tributaries from a 12,000-square-mile watershed. The 400-mile-long Delaware was explored by Henry Hudson in 1609. It has its source in the Catskills, 1,800 feet above sea level. Coursing in a tortuous pattern past wooded slope and farm valley, it flows past Trenton and finally empties into the Atlantic at Delaware Bay. Its waters facilitate the prosperity of many adjacent communities, including Wilmington, Camden, Trenton, and

Figure 5-3. *Extensive drought caused the lowering of the Nisqually River to such a degree that the Alder Reservoir is at a record low, as seen in this picture taken in February 1973. Because production of hydropower was severely curtailed, drought indirectly contributed to the energy crisis. [Photo by Rollin R. Geppert]*

Philadelphia. Both Philadelphia and New York City utilize the water resources of the Delaware River basin, either for drinking, industry, or the numerous water-using tasks of day-to-day living. Water shortages have frequently occurred in this region. In 1664 the Dutch governor of New Amsterdam (New York City) was forced to capitulate to the British because his men had run out of drinking water. In 1881 water was so scarce in New York City that firemen dynamited fires instead of extinguishing them with water. From 1961 to 1965 this region experienced the most devastating drought in the entire history of the Northeast, with the water deficit affecting 300,000 square miles.

What was the cause of this most recent drought? According to some weather people, the 1961–1965 drought can be blamed on a shift in the pattern of certain cold Canadian air masses. They did not move far enough south into the New England region to cause the warm humid air moving northward from the Gulf coast to release its moisture. Instead, the two air masses converged over the north Atlantic, where precipitation finally occurred.

As a result of the Canadian air mass shift, the mountain streams of upstate New York were reduced to a trickle. Famous trout streams, almost legendary among fishermen, were waterless. Resorts closed in midsummer. In 1963, because of the threat of forest fires, Governor Scranton of Pennsylvania caused consternation among thousands of would-be deer hunters by closing his state's forests for the hunting season. Wild game of many species suffered heavy mortality as a result of vanishing food supplies and protective cover. The hunting and fishing vacation lands of 30 million people were so adversely affected that the resort industry alone suffered an annual loss of many millions of dollars.

As of 1965, New York State's reservoir system, based upon detailed studies of 90 years of weather history, had a total capacity of 572 billion gallons, equivalent to a 15-month water reserve. From the study, it had been determined that the largest drought to be expected would last 2 years. However, the Delaware River basin drought lasted 4 years. By August, 1965, reservoir water had dropped to 212 billion gallons. If the drought had continued, the reservoirs would have been empty by January, 1966.

New York City, with its 7 million people, relies heavily on the Delaware River flow to augment its municipal reservoir supply. But by late October, 1965, the Delaware was at its lowest ebb in fifty-three years. George Washington would scarcely have recognized this shrunken rivulet as the boisterous stream he once crossed. According to a 1954 decision of the U.S. Supreme Court, New York City had the right to withdraw 490 million gallons a day directly from the Delaware for its own use. In return, however, it was to release enough water into the river from the reservoirs, during periods of low stream flow, to ensure that salt would not back up from the ocean. In a desperate (though illegal) attempt to conserve the dwindling reservoir waters, New York discontinued releasing water into the Delaware. As a result, saltwater intrusion, advancing at a rate of one-half mile a day, corroded expensive industrial equipment, contaminated the underground aquifers of water-thirsty Camden, and became a threat to Philadelphia.

One positive feature of the drought was that millions of Americans were at last awakened from their traditional complacency regarding the intelligent use of their primary natural resource. It is easy for those living in areas with abundant normal rainfall (the Northeast has 40 to 50 inches yearly) to be lulled into the belief that a severe drought will never come. Americans have always waited until their natural resources (whether topsoil, rangeland, forest, or passenger pigeon) have been reduced to a precarious state before they become aroused to constructive action.

But they are aroused now. From the wealthy industrialist whose expensive machines were reduced to worthless, corroded hulks as a result of saltwater contaminants, to the housewife who drew mud-colored water from the faucet, most Americans are united in their determination never again to allow themselves or their children to experience the discomfort and apprehension associated with a severe water shortage.

Floods.   Not only is man plagued by water scarcity, he also is beset with the equally serious problem of too much water from violent rainstorms and floods. Throughout his history man has suffered from destructive floods. (Fig. 5–4)

In 1811, for example, the "Beautiful Blue Danube" was neither blue nor beautiful when it swept over its banks, inundated large sections of Poland and Austria, washed away twenty-four villages, and drowned 2,000 soldiers. In 1877 the Hwang Ho River of China destroyed 300 villages, left 2 million homeless, and took the lives of 7 million people.

The greatest flood frequency in the United States ranges from February in the

Figure 5-4. *Aerial view of California farm inundated by December flood.* [*California Department of Water Resources*]

Southeast to June in the Northwest (6). Floods have inundated the Mississippi River Valley about once every three years. In 1861 the Sacramento River swept 700 people to their death. In 1889 a dam burst along the rain-swollen Conemaugh River of Johnstown, Pennsylvania, releasing a torrent which caused $10 million damage and took over 2,000 lives. Hurricane-spawned floodwaters moved through Galveston, Texas, in 1900, devastated 3,000 buildings, and left 6,000 dead. The Mississippi flood of 1936–1937 extended for 1,000 miles through seven states, drove over 1 million people from their homes, injured 800,000 people, took 500 lives, and caused $200 million worth of property damage. The long-continued flooding of the Columbia lowlands inflicted $100 million damage during the summer of 1942. According to the Army Corps of Engineers, in August, 1955, Hurricane Diane caused $1.6 billion damage along the Atlantic coast from North Carolina to Maine (18).

Paradoxically, however, in some parts of the world, man's very survival may be dependent upon floods. Thus, the flourishing agricultural economy of Egypt had been sustained for millennia by the recurrent flooding of the Nile. Each inundation was eagerly awaited by flood plain farmers, for when the Nile finally receded, it left behind a deposit of extremely fertile topsoil carried from its upstream watershed.

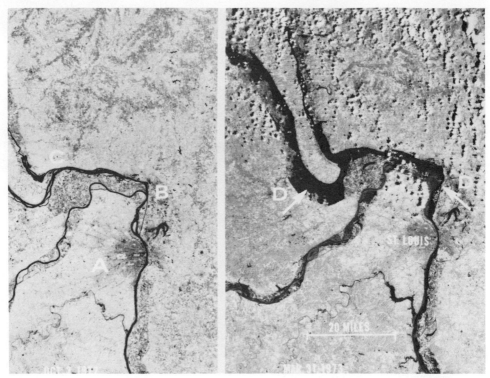

Figure 5-5. *Flooding at St. Louis, Missouri, as revealed by NASA's Earth Resources Technology Satellite. In photograph on the left, taken Oct. 2, 1972, St. Louis can be located by the letter A. North of St. Louis, the Missouri River joins the Mississippi River at point B, and further upstream the confluence of the Illinois and Mississippi Rivers is noted at C. The photograph on the right was taken of the same region on March 31, 1973. It shows areas under water (D) as a result of flooding. In this near infrared wavelength view, the darkest tones indicate areas of deepest water. The Mississippi River was 38 feet deep at St. Louis, the highest level since 1903. In this photo about 300,000 acres are submerged. The flood wave slowly made its way downstream, threatening cities and agricultural lands along the entire length of the Mississippi River.*

So important were these floods to ancient Egypt that the early Egyptian priests kept accurate records of their occurrence.

THE UPPER MISSISSIPPI FLOOD OF 1965. According to the U.S. Army Corps of Engineers, an unusual combination of factors involving excessive rainfall, massive snow melt, and frozen ground set the stage for a "once-in-a-century" flood in the upper Mississippi River Valley. Late summer rainfall, which was about normal in the St. Paul–Minneapolis region in 1964, caused water-saturated soil conditions at the time of the initial autumn freeze. As a result, the ground was frozen solid to a considerable depth. Then came the snow. The 73 inches that fell in the Minneapolis region was 25 inches above the average for a single winter season. The partial snow melt of early March, followed by severe cold, resulted in a 4-inch ice cover. Finally, the combination of mild April weather (of 1965) and heavy rain-

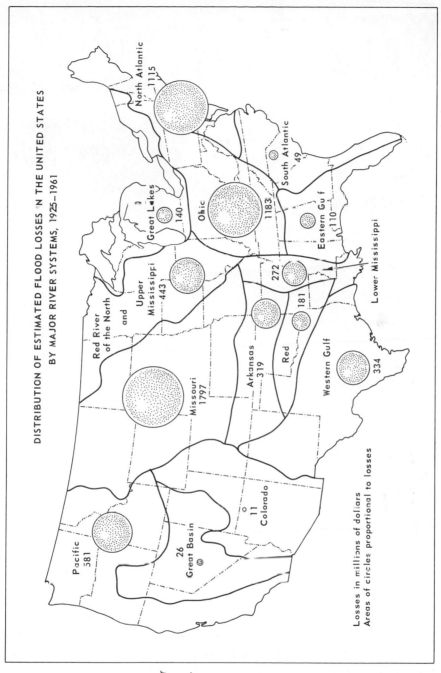

DISTRIBUTION OF ESTIMATED FLOOD LOSSES IN THE UNITED STATES
BY MAJOR RIVER SYSTEMS, 1925–1961

North Atlantic
1115

South Atlantic
49

Great Lakes
140

Ohio
1183

Eastern Gulf
110

Red River
of the North
and
Upper
Mississippi
443

272

Arkansas
319

Red
181

Lower Mississippi

Western Gulf
334

Missouri
1797

Colorado
11

Pacific
581

Great Basin
26

Losses in millions of dollars
Areas of circles proportional to losses

Figure 5-6. *U.S. Weather Bureau estimates of flood damage losses by major river systems, 1925 to 1961. Damage ranged from $11 million (Colorado River system) to $1,795 million (Missouri River system). High losses in the North Atlantic and Ohio regions reflect industrial and residential encroachment on the river flood plains. [Adapted from Guy-Harold Smith, Conservation of Natural Resources (New York: John Wiley & Sons, Inc., 1965). After U.S. Weather Bureau records.]*

Figure 5-7. *Flood damage in Harrison, Arkansas, caused by the storm of May 7, 1961. Four lives were lost. Damage was estimated at $5,278,000. [U.S. Department of Agriculture, Photo by* Harrison Daily Times]

Figure 5-8. *Flooded residential area in a Wisconsin town on the banks of the Mississippi River. Note sandbagging. [Wisconsin Natural Resources Department, Madison, Wis.]*

storms (5 inches fell in one area in 24 hours) contributed to flood conditions. Swollen with spring run-off waters, the Mississippi River surged over its banks from Minneapolis south to its junction with the Missouri at Hannibal, Missouri. Thousands of acres of winter wheat were devastated. It submerged 90,000 acres of cropland in Illinois alone. The Milwaukee Road's crack streamliner the *Hiawatha* was forced to halt its Minneapolis-Milwaukee run for the first time in history. Merchandise in river-front shops was damaged. At Hannibal, a few resolute shop owners hung out "business as usual" signs, even though much of Main Street was open to motor boat traffic only. At Mankato State College in Minnesota, hundreds of student volunteers erected a sand-bag barrier to restrain the flood waters. When the sand gave out at Savage, Minnesota, resourceful volunteers filled their bags with wheat. Despite such emergency measures, the rising waters drove 40,000 people from their homes. After a helicopter survey of the stricken area, President Johnson gave this terse, three-word summary of his impressions, "It was terrible." Eventually the waters receded. A thick, smelly deposit of brownish ooze covered the exterior and interior of many river-front homes. Thousands of fish were stranded in stagnant backwaters. The official toll taken by the greatest flood in upper Mississippi River history read 16 drowned, 330 injured, and $140 million in property damage.

Flood Control

Although man cannot prevent all floods, he can prevent some of the lesser ones and can restrict the magnitude and destructiveness of others. Flood-control measures include protection of the watershed, measurement of snow pack to predict flood conditions, levees, dredging operations, and dams.

Protection of the Watershed. A *watershed* may be defined as the area drained by a single water course. It may range from less than 1,000 acres to more than 1 million. The largest watersheds, such as those of the Ohio, Missouri, Colorado, or Mississippi rivers, are known as drainage basins. All watersheds, large or small, have the basic function of converting precipitation into stream flow (14). Even during a light shower, 0.1 inch of rainfall would be "converted" by a 1-acre watershed into 11.3 tons of stream flow, whereas a watershed of 1 square mile would convert it into 1.74 million gallons of stream flow.

Recently, Congress enacted the Watershed Protection and Flood Prevention Act, usually referred to as the "Small Watershed Act." The small watershed program is administered by the USDA's Soil Conservation Service. Protection of large watersheds is primarily the concern of the Bureau of Reclamation, the U.S. Army Corps of Engineers, or the Tennessee Valley Authority (TVA). Although the primary objective of the act is flood control, it is operated under a multiple-purpose concept, and where possible it embraces problems of erosion, water supply, wildlife management, and recreation. According to the USDA, 8,000 (61.5 per cent) of the 13,000 small watersheds (of less than 250,000 acres) in this country have flood and erosion problems (23).

Any type of vegetational cover on the watershed will impede flow velocity and hence will be of value in flood and erosion control. This, is well illustrated by the following incident. On December 31, 1933, merry celebrations ushering in the New

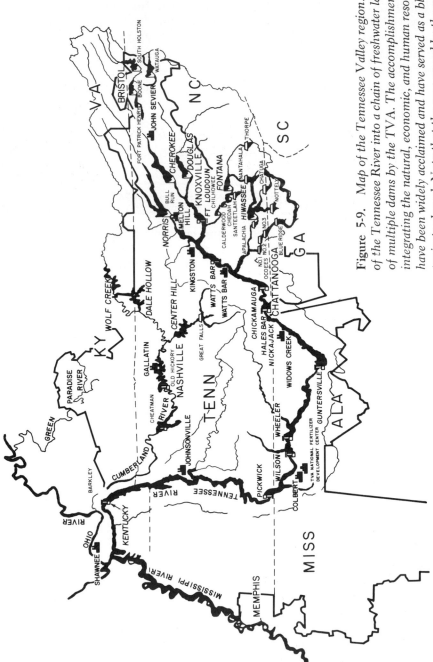

Figure 5-9. Map of the Tennessee Valley region. Note the conversion of the Tennessee River into a chain of freshwater lakes by the construction of multiple dams by the TVA. The accomplishments of the TVA in integrating the natural, economic, and human resources of the valley have been widely acclaimed and have served as a blueprint for similar projects abroad. Note that the area served by the municipal and cooperative distributors of TVA power extends far beyond the Tennessee state border into Kentucky, Virginia, North Carolina, South Carolina, Georgia, Alabama, and Mississippi. Over 65 per cent of the electrical power produced in the TVA project is generated by steam plants. [Map from the Tennessee Valley Authority]

Figure 5-10. *Brush fire working down Bear Canyon in the Los Padres National Forest, California. Once vegetation is destroyed, the burn area becomes susceptible to soil erosion, and flash floods in the lowlands become more frequent.* [U. S. Forest Service]

Year at LaCrescenta, California, were abruptly ended when floodwaters rushed down from the adjacent hillsides of the San Gabriel Mountains, inflicting $5 million in damage and killing thirty citizens. When flood-control experts investigated the watershed above LaCrescenta, they discovered that the floodwaters originated from a 7-square-mile area in the San Gabriel Mountains that had been burned over only a short time before. The unburned watershed, with its vegetational "sponge" of chaparral, herbs, and grasses, served to restrain the downhill rush of run-off waters; peak flows were roughly 5 per cent of those of the burned areas. Whether it is California chaparral, Alabama alfalfa, or Wisconsin woodlands, any type of vegetational cover is to some degree useful in restraining floods.

Measurement of Snow Pack to Predict Flood Conditions. In recent years the U.S. Geological Service has employed snow surveys to make measurements of the area and depth of the snow pack at more than 1,000 snow courses in the western mountains. Equipped with snowshoes, skis, and snowmobiles, these hardy men compile data that can be useful in flood prediction. For example, several years ago a survey predicted that the imminent spring snow melt would crest the Kootenai River at 35.5 feet, sufficient to cause extensive flooding at Bonner's Ferry, Idaho. Alerted by this forewarning, federal troops evacuated all residents and reinforced the dikes. On May 21, the river did indeed crest at 35.5 feet as predicted. However, flood damage was minimized and not one life was lost.

Figure 5-11. *Snow surveyors viewing Ward Creek, a tributary to Lake Tahoe. [Soil Conservation Service, U. S. Department of Agriculture, Photo by Frank M. Roadman]*

Levees. *Levees* are dikes constructed of earth, stone, or mortar that are built at varying distances from the river margin in an effort to protect valuable residential, industrial, and agricultural property from floodwaters. Levees along the Arkansas, Red, White, and Ouachita rivers have given a measure of protection to more than 2 million acres of fertile alluvial land. In the last 150 years a mammoth system of over 3,500 levees and dikes has been constructed along the lower Mississippi River. Levee systems occasionally create special problems. For example, after a protracted rainfall, the drainage of diked lowlands requires pumping the water up over the levees back into the main channel.

Dredging Operations. Because of the huge soil deposits that are washed into a stream from the surrounding watershed, the channel tends to accumulate sediment, which increases the probability of a flood. Because of the force of the current of a river or stream, a portion of the bank may crumble and be washed into the stream. Thomson King describes such a bank cave-in near Point Pleasant, Missouri, where the Mississippi River eroded a strip of bank 10 miles long and 2 miles wide and carried soil, trees, and homes downstream. The enormity of this problem can be appreciated when we realize that the Mississippi River, for example, transports roughly 2 million tons of sediment daily. To cope with this situation (as well as to deepen channels for navigation), our major river channels are periodically dredged by the U.S. Army Corps of Engineers.

The importance of periodic dredging is emphasized by the 1852 Yellow River catastrophe in China. As the channel of this river became choked with silt, levees were built higher and higher, until the Yellow River was flowing above the roof tops! Inevitably, a massive surge of floodwaters crumbled the retaining walls and drowned 2 million people.

Dams. Dams have been used by man since long before the Christian era. The ancients checked the surging waters of the Euphrates and Nile with massive barriers of earth and masonry. The ruins of numerous concrete dams erected by the Romans many centuries ago in northern Africa and Italy may still be observed.

Even though there have been serious criticisms because of their expense and siltation-abbreviated life span, the United States has committed itself to a vast program of superdam construction. As of late 1966 the Bureau of Reclamation alone had constructed 248 dams, with an impoundment capacity of 129.5 million acre-feet. As of 1960 the United States had 1,300 large reservoirs, which occupied an estimated area of 11 million acres. By the year 2000, 10 million additional acres of land will be covered by reservoir waters.

Are these dams effective in flood control? According to Brigadier General W. P. Leber, Ohio River Division Army Engineer, the Ohio River flood of March, 1964, would have caused additional damage of $290 million had it not been for the coordinated system of 30 flood-control reservoirs, plus 62 flood walls and levees. He stated that flood crests were reduced by up to *10.5 feet by these flood-control* facilities (18). The water retained by the Shasta dam and others in northern California aids in the prevention of flash floods that formerly harassed the region. Partial flood control is also effected by such dams as the Santee in South Carolina, the Grand Coulee on the Columbia, and the Hoover on the Colorado. In 1965 Los Angeles County, which has experienced repeated floods from rain-swollen rivers, established a coordinated complex of control structures costing nearly $600 million. It involves 60 headwater dams in the mountains, 14 retention reservoirs in the Los Angeles and San Gabriel Rivers, and 6 major flood-control dams. This system has proved to be very successful in protecting 325 million acres from flooding.

Disadvantages of Dams. The mammoth downstream dams have been constructed largely by the U.S. Army Corps of Engineers, the Bureau of Reclamation, and the TVA. They are extremely expensive and the costs, running into many millions of dollars, would be prohibitive if it were not for the fact that these dams, in addition to providing flood control, also generate hydropower, improve navigation, provide irrigation waters, and establish recreational facilities. It should be pointed out, however, that for effective flood control there must be frequent "drawdowns," so that the reservoir capacity is great enough to accommodate flood waters. Such drawdowns will adversely affect both the hydropower generators and recreational functions of the dam (16). Furthermore, such drawdowns would be highly detrimental to fish that might spawn amid the vegetation in the shallows along the reservoir margin. The receding waters would leave millions of eggs "high and dry."

Big dams have other negative features, in addition to cost. The reservoir that forms behind the dam may inundate thousands of acres of once fertile agricultural land. In coastal regions the blocking of stream flow may result in *salt water* intrusion, which would ruin the productivity of agricultural lands and pollute fresh water aquifers. Dam construction on rivers emptying into the ocean may cause such reduction in water flow that the delicate salt water–fresh water balance of the estuaries (region where river meets ocean) is upset, resulting in more saline conditions. Any marked salinity change might have disastrous effects on many valuable species of fish and invertebrates (shrimp, oysters) that might use the estuary as a breeding and "nursery" grounds, since most of them are adapted to survive in a narrow salinity range. Big dams may abuse natural beauty. Thus, the magnificence of the Rainbow Bridge National Monument in northern Arizona is being jeopardized by the encroachment of the Colorado River's Glen Canyon Dam reservoir. Some big-dam critics maintain that several smaller dams on headwater tributaries would be equally effective in flood control and would be considerably less expensive than one big dam downstream. Thus, Elmer Peterson has compared a large mainstream reservoir plan with an alternate plan for smaller headwaters reservoirs proposed for the same watershed. The single large mainstream dam would cost $6 million and would have 52,000 acre-feet of flood storage. The fourteen smaller headwaters dams would have 59,100 acre-feet of flood storage and would cost only $1.9 million (17).

Figure 5-12. *Night view of switchyard at Glen Canyon Dam on the Colorado River near Page, Arizona.* [*Bureau of Reclamation, U.S. Department of the Interior*]

Siltation Problem. Another drawback associated with the construction of big dams is the speed with which their reservoirs are filled with sediment. The rate of filling depends, of course, on the soil types in the drainage basin and on topography. Since the Columbia River is relatively sediment-free, such dams as the Grand Coulee and Bonneville might have a storage life of 1,000 years. However, the life span of dams constructed across more turbid streams, may be quite short. For example, the huge Lake Mead Reservoir behind Hoover Dam in Arizona is filling at a rate of 137,000 acre-feet of silt per year, sufficient to destroy the operation of this multimillion-dollar structure in less than 250 years. Many of our nation's lesser reservoirs have a life expectancy of less than fifty years. California's Mono Reservoir, which was theoretically designed to provide a permanent water source for Santa Barbara, filled up with sediment within two decades. In addition, biological succession proceeded so rapidly that a thicket of shrubs and saplings became firmly established. For all practical purposes, Mono Reservoir is dead, and buried!

Reservoir Evaporation Losses. Evaporation losses from reservoirs in hot, arid regions, where winds are prevalent, can be considerable. Lake Mead, for example, loses 893 million gallons daily. The top 7 feet of the lake are evaporated annually. The evaporation problem is not applicable to detention reservoirs, which are waterless except during flood time. However, because loss is roughly proportional to water area exposed, more water is lost from several small shallow reservoirs than

Figure 5-13. *The "death" of a reservoir. Lake Ballinger, Texas. Although the original depth of this lake was 35 feet, it eventually had to be abandoned because of siltation. [Soil Conservation Service, U.S. Department of Agriculture, Photo by John McConnell]*

from a single deep reservoir, even though the capacity of the latter was equivalent. A study of Wyoming's Cheyenne River basin has shown that evaporation losses from numerous small stockwater ponds reduced average annual run-off from the basin by more than 30 per cent. About 6 million acre-feet are lost annually from 1,250 large western reservoirs and the loss from all water bodies (lakes, ponds, and reservoirs) in the West amounts to 24 million acre-feet, sufficient to supply all the domestic needs of 50 million people. Although such losses are reduced on small reservoirs in the West with roofs and floating covers, they still are quite substantial. Although the use of a monomolecular film of hexadecanol will reduce evaporation losses by almost 20 per cent, the technique has some drawbacks. First, it is quite costly, since the film tends to disperse and therefore must be repeatedly applied. Second, it has adverse effects on fish and other aquatic organisms because levels of dissolved oxygen decline as a result of increased water temperatures and the sealing off of the reservoir from its atmospheric oxygen supply.

The Aswan Dam Controversy. The United Arab Republics gigantic Aswan Dam is a classic example of a technological boondoggle. Its main purpose was highly desirable: the storage of the Nile's excess water during flood time, and its gradual release during the dry season to permit extensive irrigation and year-round crop production. The architects of this grandiose project were hopeful that massive starvation and grinding poverty might be alleviated. Unfortunately, since the dam became operational in 1971, many unforeseen problems have developed.

Perhaps the most serious disadvantage of the Aswan Dam has been its adverse effect on the health of villagers in the irrigated areas. With water now present in the irrigation ditches on a year-round basis, extensive breeding areas have inadvertently been formed for malaria-transmitting mosquitos and tiny black flies that act as hosts for worms that can burrow into the human blood stream and cause "river blindness." Most importantly, permanent irrigation has resulted in a marked population increase of certain kinds of snails that serve as temporary hosts for the larvae of certain flatworms that cause "snail fever" (*schistosomiasis*) in man. The larval flatworm develops briefly inside the snail, emerges, swims through the water, burrows into the skin of a farmer working barefooted in an irrigation ditch, enters the blood stream, and is carried to the bladder and/or intestine where it becomes established and grows to sexual maturity. Eggs produced by the adults pass from the body with urine and feces. According to William Keeton, snail fever "is characterized initially by a cough, rash, and body pains, followed by severe dysentery and anemia" (10). Even if the disease does not prove lethal, it may exact a tremendous toll in human suffering and impaired working efficiency—something struggling Egypt can ill afford.

Before the construction of the Aswan Dam, the irrigation canals carried water only during the relatively brief period of Nile River flooding. Once the river receded and the summer drought period began, the canals ran "bone dry," thus effectively eliminating any adult snails that might have become temporarily established. Since the construction of the dam the incidence of "snail fever" has risen dramatically from a few per cent to 80 per cent of the villagers in the irrigated area. *One of every ten deaths in Egypt is caused by this disease.* Experts believe that almost 100 per cent of these people will eventually contract snail fever. (About 200 million people the world over are now afflicted with this disease, largely as a result of year-round irrigation in tropical regions.)

Figure 5-14. *Construction of the Aswan Dam, April 1968. [F.A.O. Photo by P. A. Pittet]*

Figure 5-15. *Irrigation canal being built in Egypt. With the completion of the Aswan Dam, it has been possible to cultivate one million acres under a system of perennial irrigation. Formerly, this land was dependent on the seasonal flooding of the Nile for irrigation water. The new irrigation system has made it possible to increase crop production by 40 per cent, because at least one additional crop can be grown. Unfortunately, however, there are many adverse features associated with the Aswan Dam. [F. A. O. Photo by H. Null]*

Although snail fever can be controlled to some degree with drugs, the best method would be *sanitation*—proper disposal of human feces so that the flatworm egg cannot enter the water. A reversion to the practice of *seasonal* irrigation probably would be considered unthinkable by the Egyptian government. After all, you just don't "junk" a technological marvel that cost $1.5 billion and took eleven years to build!

The final disadvantage of the Aswan Dam, as with all dams, is its silt-abbreviated life span. Some experts believe that the dam will be as functionless as the pyramids in 100 to 300 years. And who knows, like the pyramids, the dam may be admired by archeologists of a future era as an eloquent testimonial to the creative genius of a bygone civilization!

The Stream Channelization Controversy. As mentioned previously, the Soil Conservation Service has built up a splendid reputation during many years of valuable service in the area of soil erosion and flood control. However, in the past few years a storm of criticism has swirled around its recently developed *channelization* program—the deepening and straightening of streams for the purpose of flood control. The stated objectives of the program is to prevent the flooding of croplands located in the flood plains of small watersheds. The flood plains, of course, are the low areas on either side of a stream that are frequently subject to spring flooding.

THE METHOD. There are two main steps in channelization. First, all vegetation (including trees) is bulldozed away on either side of the stream to a distance of 100 feet, leaving nothing but bare soil. (By agreement with the landowner, the denuded area is then planted to a cover crop and repeatedly mowed.) Second, bulldozers and drag lines then deepen and straighten the channel; in essence the stream is converted to a water-filled ditch.

THE BENEFITS. The actual benefits that result are minimal. First, we must concede that cropland on either side of the channelized portion of the stream *is* protected from flooding. Second, small lakes with considerable recreational and wildlife potential are constructed by the SCS as an adjunct to the main channelization process.

THE DISADVANTAGES. Unfortunately the disadvantages are multiple:

1. With the removal of its food and cover, the diverse bottom-land fauna (raccoon, mink, otter, bear, wood ducks, songbirds) is either eradicated or forced to emigrate.
2. Stream banks erode because of the removal of the tree roots that formerly stabilized them.
3. Removal of the overarching trees that formerly intercepted the sunlight results in increased water temperatures (thermal pollution) and a host of associated problems discussed in the next chapter on water pollution.
4. Removal of stream-skirting trees means that stream enrichment from leaf fall is considerably reduced.
5. Fish food, in the form of insects that formerly fell into the stream from overhead tree canopies, will be diminished.
6. Much valuable hardwood timber, already in short supply, will be destroyed.
7. The deep pools in which game fish take cover, and the shallow riffle where valuable fish food in the form of aquatic insects flourishes, will be eliminated.

8. Many streams may become "bone dry" during summer drought, when previously their flow was continuous. The effect on aquatic life would be highly adverse.
9. The increased speed of the current undercuts stream banks and causes them to slump into the channel.
10. Pesticides and herbicides applied to farm crops in the watershed may now drain into the stream more quickly and abundantly. The result: heavy fish mortality downstream.
11. The conversion of a picturesque, meandering stream to an ugly eroding "ditch."
12. Lowering of the water table, causing wells to run dry and permitting salt water intrusion in coastal regions. Such intrusion contaminates aquifers and reduces farm land productivity.
13. As the river bottom habitat is removed by channelization, in like manner are removed the opportunities for such recreational activities as canoeing, hiking, swimming, bird watching and hunting for wildflowers. Such simple pleasures are already becoming less available because of the population crush and land development squeeze.

It would seem, therefore, in any cost-benefit analysis that the SCS and its channelization program are found wanting. Just why then does the SCS persist in this ecological boondoggle? George W. Folkerts,[1] aquatic ecologist at Auburn University (Alabama) and former consultant to the National Resources Defense Council, has suggested that the SCS has done its soil erosion and flood control work so well in the past 35 years that it has placed itself in the position where it has to "dream up" more projects or find its budget and staff sharply reduced. According to Folkerts, the project should be terminated not only because of its environmental impact, but also because of its profligate use of public funds. He states:

In one Alabama project costing $4,417,312, the cost per acre to reduce flooding amounts to $405.02. The highest value of the land protected was $300.00 per acre. In other words, money used in the project could have purchased the land and a sizable chunk of funds would have been left. In this project 105 landowners were supposedly benefitted. This means that each landowner was, in effect, receiving over $42,000 in tax monies. If this were merely a gravy train it would be disturbing, but when the damages of the project are considered, it becomes appalling (8).

In their long-range plans the SCS proposes to channelize (and hence wreak gross environmental abuse on) nearly 9,000 small watersheds by the year 2000! That means degradation of nearly half of our nation's small watersheds. It is inconceivable that the public will permit this bureaucratic ambition to be realized. In the long run, an informed citizenry, mounting pressure on vote-sensitive legislators, most certainly will prevail. The sooner the better.

Irrigation

New England and other normally humid regions of the United States have experienced intermittent drought, but an extensive area of the desert biome and the more arid portion of the grassland biome are characterized by more or less permanent drought. Here, through long eons of interaction with the environment,

[1] Much of the material for this section on channelization was derived from Folkerts' excellent article "Stream Channelization: How a Bureaucracy Destroys a Resource" (8).

animal residents have evolved moisture-securing and moisture-conserving adaptations that have promoted their survival. Modern man, however, a relative newcomer to this austere region, has not had to depend on long evolutionary processes to "adapt" to the environment. Instead, with the aid of his mental powers, he has "shaped" the environment to fit his own design. The most significant and dramatic example of man's habitat-shaping talents in this region is modern irrigation.

History of Irrigation. Perhaps the first use of transported water in arid land farming in what is now the United States was made in A.D. 700 by Indians living in the valleys of the Salt and Gila rivers of Arizona (2). Employing crude digging tools, they were able to construct 125 miles of canals sufficient to irrigate 140,000 acres of food plots. By A.D. 1400, these early agriculturists, known as the Hohokam ("Those who have gone"), mysteriously disappeared along with their irrigation economy (2). In the seventeenth century, under the influence of Spanish priests, irrigation systems were established in California and Texas adjacent to Catholic missions. In 1847 the Mormons of Utah, faced with possible starvation during the ensuing winter, channeled water from City Creek to their parched potato and grain fields.

The Imperial Valley Story. The story of the Imperial Valley is one of America's greatest success stories in irrigation. The Imperial Valley, which is 110 miles long and 50 miles wide, lies in the Colorado Desert in southern California, just east of Los Angeles, with San Diego in its southwest corner. In prehistoric times this area was submerged by salt water from the Gulf of California. Gradually, however, it was built up with millions of tons of fertile soil released by overflow of the Colorado River during its flow to the sea. At the turn of the century this valley was a hot

Figure 5-16. *Central Valley, California. Aerial view of the Contra Costa irrigation canal. Mount Diablo is on the horizon.* [*Photo by A. G. D'Alessandro*]

desert wasteland. Annual rainfall, which is almost immediately vaporized because of hot, drying winds, is a paltry 1.5 to 3 inches, hardly enough to settle the dust. The Imperial Valley, however, is wasteland no more. Where once there were lizards and cacti, there now flourish fruit and vegetable farms from which lettuce, tomatoes, watermelons, sugar beets, onions, asparagus, oranges, and dates are shipped to all parts of the United States. This has been made possible by the 1940 completion of the 200-foot-wide All-American Canal, which conveys water from the Colorado River eighty miles away to 0.5-million acres of fertile valley soil. The potential of this area for crop production had always been there. There was an abundance of sunshine and a long growing season (up to ten cuttings of alfalfa have been made). The limiting factor was water, and that was overcome with imagination, resourcefulness, and engineering skill.

Dams and Irrigation.　When Theodore Roosevelt signed the Reclamation Act of 1902, the federal government, through the Bureau of Reclamation, assumed responsibility for conserving, developing, distributing, and most effectively utilizing the limited water resources of the arid West. This objective has been implemented in part by the imaginative construction of a series of dams and reservoirs. During the first decade of the bureau's existence, over 97 per cent of its program was irrigation-oriented (21). The first dam constructed, appropriately named the Roosevelt Dam, was constructed on the Salt River near Globe, Arizona, in 1911. The largest dam constructed is the Hoover Dam, on the Colorado River. The Colorado drains almost one thirteenth of the United States. In order to control the river, prevent flooding, and provide irrigation water and cheap electrical power for thousands of farmers in the arid Southwest, the bureau constructed this 6.5-million-ton concrete dam. Standing as high (726 feet) as a 60-story skyscraper, the

Figure 5-17.　*Scenic view of Flaming Gorge Dam on the Colorado River from a point along transmission line road about 1 mile from dam. [Bureau of Reclamation, U.S. Department of the Interior]*

Figure 5-18. *Delta, Colorado. Irrigating a field planted to sugar beets with siphon tubes drawing water from a concrete head ditch. [Bureau of Reclamation, U.S. Department of the Interior]*

Figure 5-19. *San Joaquin Valley, California. Aerial view of sprinklers in Belridge Irrigation District. [California Department of Water Resources]*

Hoover Dam contains enough concrete to form a 2-lane highway from Chicago to San Francisco. The impounded water forms Lake Mead, the largest man-made lake in the world. One hundred nineteen miles long, it has an area of 246 square miles. Its storage capacity of nearly 30 million acre-feet would be adequate to meet all the water requirements of New York City's 12 million residents for 20 years.

Although, as a result of increasing urbanization, Bureau of Reclamation projects have recently become geared to domestic and industrial functions, about one third of all impounded water is still used in irrigation. In fiscal 1966, the Bureau achieved the greatest construction record in its 64-year history, completing 11 dams with an aggregate storage capacity of 2.8 million acre-feet of water (21). In addition, the Bureau completed 733 miles of canals, pipelines, and laterals for effective distribution of impounded water to farmlands, towns, and industries located many miles from reservoir sites (21). At the end of 1966, 17 additional dams were being constructed with a combined impoundment capacity of 5 million acre-feet, and 248 Reclamation dams have been completed that were capable of impounding 129.5 million acre-feet of water, sufficient to cover New York state to a depth of 4 feet (21).

Irrigation Problems

Water Loss During Transit. Some irrigated fields receive their water from reservoirs or streams located hundreds of miles away. The fruit-raising Central Valley of California, for example, gets its water from the Colorado River, 300 miles to the east. During transit considerable amounts of water are lost. According to the United States Department of Agriculture, only 1 of every 4 gallons drawn for irrigation is actually absorbed by crop root systems. The remaining 3 gallons are lost to evaporation, to water-absorbing weeds, or to ground seepage. Seepage losses

Figure 5-20. *Construction of irrigation canal. Note plastic lining to prevent water loss during transit. Earth has been placed on the plastic for temporary protection against wind-ballooning. [Soil Conservation Service, U.S. Department of Agriculture]*

through unlined, porous dirt canals may amount to 10 per cent per mile, so that reduction to a negligible volume would occur after only 10 miles of transit. Such loss can be minimized by lining canals with water-impervious materials, such as wax coatings or plastic and butylrubber membranes. Asphalt and "shotcrete" (cement mortar applied under air pressure) have also proved valuable in reducing seepage.

Salinization. Would you believe that bringing fresh water to a desert might be destructive to crops? Sounds incongruous, doesn't it? However, even fresh water is slightly salty—having acquired dissolved sodium chloride (table salt), carbonate, and sulphate salts as it flowed down mountain slopes and through valley bottoms. When such water is brought by irrigation canals to hot deserts where the evaporation rate is very high, the water passes into the atmosphere, and the salts precipitate out forming a whitish film on the ground. Additional salt may be deposited because of the evaporation of ground water that has been "sucked" to the surface by *capillary action* (15). As time passes the salt gradually builds up to the point where it becomes toxic to plants. Even in California's Imperial Valley, where crop harvests has been so bountiful, this process of *salinization* has caused many farms to be abandoned. In order to flush the salt from the surface, large quantities of water are required (supplies of which are already critically deficient in some regions). Over 1,800 miles of drainage canals have already been constructed for this purpose. Eventually this salty flushing water flows into a river and dramatically increases its salinity. The Colorado River receives such salty water that has been flushed from thousands of irrigated farms. The Colorado becomes progressively more salty as it flows southwestward across the Mexico border toward the Gulf of lower California.

Figure 5-21.   *Leemore, California. Note the salt crust on this range caused by excessive evaporation combined with poor drainage conditions. Such land is worthless for crop production or for the growing of range grasses.* [*California Department of Water Resources*]

Figure 5-22. A 4,000 gallon per minute irrigation well near Carlton, Colorado. The concrete-lined ditch is designed to carry 20 cubic feet per second. [Soil Conservation Service, U.S. Department of Agriculture, Photo by Harry R. Steele]

As a result of irrigation the salinity of the lower Colorado increased 30 per cent in the last twenty years (15). The Colorado's saltiness has jeopardized cotton production in the Mexicali district where farmers have used the river as a source of irrigation water for several decades. The economy of the region was threatened to such an extent that in 1962 the Mexican president conveyed his concern directly to President Johnson (3).

Georg Borgstrom, of Michigan State University, has described additional problems caused by salinization in this region: "The salt also goes up in the air in the form of brine spray. The corrosion on agricultural machinery is ferocious. Machines used in the cotton plantations must be greased anew every second hour to avoid their rapid destruction by corrosion" (3).

Depletion of Ground Water. Sources of irrigation water vary greatly among the seventeen western states. Although the mountain states (Montana, Wyoming, Colorado, and Idaho) receive over 80 per cent of their irrigation water from surface sources (reservoirs, farm ponds, and rivers), many areas in the high plains secure over 75 per cent of their water supplies from ground sources. In west Texas, much irrigation water is derived from wells. In 1946 there were only 2,000 wells in the entire south plains region of west Texas (25). By 1966 the number had increased 15-fold, to 30,000. West Texas grows 25 per cent of our nation's cotton with this well water (25).

In one part of Arizona, overdraft of ground water lowered the water table by 400 feet, resulting in the loss of 320,000 acres of cropland because of the prohibitive cost of irrigation. Irrigation-induced lowering of water tables has also occurred in California's San Joaquin Valley, where the ground water overdraft in the Arvin-Edison Water Storage District is nearly 65 million gallons (200,000 acre-feet) annually (21). In coastal areas such overdraft may result in salt water intrusion.

As a result of the rapid ground water depletion for irrigation purposes many regions of the United States have been forced to make a choice between using the dwindling supplies either for agriculture or industry—there just isn't enough for both. Borgstrom is convinced that "ground water reserves *never* should be used for regular crop production but be held in abeyance for drought relief in critical times" (3). This intensive and extensive "mining" of our nation's aquifers cannot continue for long, for we are annually withdrawing *twice* as much water as is put back in circulation by the hydrologic cycle (3).

Consumptive Use of Water. Some conservationists criticize irrigation in the semiarid West as a profligate use of water. From their viewpoint, irrigation-based crop production is not needed to satisfy America's food requirements. Farmers annually draw four times as much water for irrigation as is used by municipalities. Irrigationists use 60 per cent as much water as our nation's industries. Moreover, although almost 97 per cent of the water drawn for municipal or industrial use may largely be used again (in some cases only after proper treatment), much irrigation water is *consumed* and cannot be reused. Over 60 per cent of all irrigation water is lost by transpiration, evaporation, and seepage during transit. Furthermore, it is estimated that 10,000 to 50,000 tons of irrigation water must be brought to a farm for every ton of food actually produced (3). In the opinion of some experts, a higher standard of living might be possible for more people if water currently consumed by irrigation were diverted to industrial and municipal use.

BIBLIOGRAPHY

1. Ackerman, Edward A., and George O. G. Lof. *Technology in American Water Development.* Baltimore: Johns Hopkins, 1959.
2. Barnes, Kenneth K. "Water Makes the Desert Bloom," *Outdoors USA: The Yearbook of Agriculture.* Washington, D.C.: U.S. Department of Agriculture, 1967.
3. Borgstrom, Georg. *World Food Resources.* New York: Intext, 1973.
4. Clapham, W. B., Jr. *Natural Ecosystems.* New York: Macmillan, 1973.
5. Clark, George L. *Elements of Ecology.* New York: Wiley, 1954.
6. Cunningham, Floyd F. *1001 Questions Answered About Water Resources.* New York: Dodd, 1967.
7. Hunt, Cynthia A., and Robert M. Garrels. *Water: The Web of Life.* New York: Norton, 1972.
8. Folkerts, George W. "Stream Channelization: How a Bureaucracy Destroys a Resource," in William H. Mason and George W. Folkerts, *Environmental Problems,* Dubuque, Iowa: Wm. C. Brown, 1973.
9. Jones, E. Bruce, Richard Lee, and John C. Frey. "Land Management for City Water," *Outdoors USA: The Yearbook of Agriculture.* Washington, D.C.: U.S. Department of Agriculture, 1967.
10. Keeton, William T. *Biological Science,* 2nd ed. New York: Norton, 1972.
11. Leopold, Luna B. *Water.* New York: Time, 1966.

12. ———, and Walter B. Langbein. *A Primer on Water*. Washington, D.C.: U.S. Department of the Interior, 1960.
13. Lull, Howard W. "How Our Cities Meet Their Water Needs," *Outdoors USA: The Yearbook of Agriculture*. Washington, D.C.: U.S. Department of Agriculture, 1967.
14. Mattison, C. W., and Joseph Alvarez. *Man and His Resources in Today's World*. Mankato, Minn.: Creative Educational Society, 1967.
15. Moran, Joseph M., Michael D. Morgan, and James H. Wiersma. *An Introduction to Environmental Sciences*. Boston: Little, Brown, 1973.
16. Odum, Eugene P. *Fundamentals of Ecology*, 3rd ed. Philadelphia: Saunders, 1971.
17. Peterson, Elmer T. "Insoak Is the Answer," *Land*, 11 (1952), 83–88.
18. Smith, Guy-Harold, ed. *Conservation of Natural Resources*. New York: Wiley, 1965.
19. Smith, Robert L. *Ecology and Field Biology*. New York: Harper, 1966.
20. Southwick, Charles H. *Ecology and the Quality of Our Environment*. New York: Van Nostrand, 1972.
21. U.S. Department of the Interior. *The Third Wave*. Washington, D.C., 1967.
22. Van Riper, Joseph E. *Man's Physical World*. New York: McGraw-Hill, 1971.
23. White, Gilbert F. "Flood Plain Safeguards: A Community Concern," *Outdoors USA: The Yearbook of Agriculture*. Washington, D.C.: U.S. Department of Agriculture, 1967.
24. Wilson, Ralph C. "Small Watersheds Make a Big Splash," *Outdoors USA: The Yearbook of Agriculture*. Washington, D.C.: U.S. Department of Agriculture, 1967.
25. Wright, James Claud. *The Coming Water Famine*. New York: Coward, 1966.

6.

Water Pollution

Jack and Jill went up the hill
To fetch a pail of water;
Jack came down with hepatitis,
And Jill came down soon after.

"Polluted Mother Goose,"
The Ecology Papers, *Sewanee, Tennesee*

The Potomac River was once a beautiful stream. Originating in the Appalachians of West Virginia, its cool waters cut their way through the Blue Ridge Mountains in a spectacular 1,000-foot water gap, then play over a series of falls, some of them up to 35 feet high, before flowing past our nation's capitol and emptying into Chesapeake Bay. Many early explorers used the Potomac as a water pathway into the interior. One called the Potomac "the sweetest and greatest river I have seen." Mount Vernon, the home of George Washington, a mansion of great dignity and beauty,

Figure 6-1. A sign of the times. Throughout America swimming beaches have been closed because of pollution, as was this lake front beach at Hammond, Indiana, July 1, 1962. [Hammond Times]

with its white columns and lush green lawns, overlooks the Potomac from a high bluff. Arlington National Cemetery, with its thousands of white tombs and crosses, is not far from the Potomac's shores. This great river, over 358 miles long and draining a basin of roughly 14,000 square miles, is closely associated with events important in American history. Many great battles of the Civil War were fought near its banks and along tributary streams.

But the river has changed. Once a thing of beauty, it is now an "open sewer." Once a delight to the eye, it is now offensive; its waters smell of decomposing garbage and human excrement and are stained with discharge from industrial plants. President Johnson remarked to Congress on October 2, 1965:

> Two hundred years ago George Washington used to stand on his lawn down here at Mount Vernon and look on a river that was clean and sweet and pure. In our own century, President Theodore Roosevelt used to go swimming in the Potomac. But today the Potomac is a river of decaying sewage and rotten algae. Today all the swimmers are gone. They have been driven from its banks.

The history of the pollution of the Potomac is similar to that of many other American rivers and streams.

Categories of Pollution

Water pollution may be defined as "any unreasonable contamination of water that lessens its value to man and nature." The problem of water pollution was recognized by Hippocrates (450 B.C.), who suggested filtration and boiling as remedial measures. For purposes of simplification we shall consider water pollutants under the following seven categories, though they are not all mutually exclusive: (1) nutrients and eutrophication, (2) oxygen-demanding organic wastes, (3) thermal pollution, (4) disease-producing organisms, (5) sediments, (6) radioactive materials, and (7) industrial toxins.

Nutrients and Eutrophication

All aquatic organisms require carbon, hydrogen, oxygen, nitrogen, phosphorus, sulfur, and many other elements for survival. As we have learned earlier in our study of ecological principles, when any essential element occurs in minimal amounts, it forms a *limiting factor*, that is, restricts the population growth of the organisms concerned. Of these elements, nitrogen and phosphorus are most frequently found to be limiting. Nitrogen usually becomes available to the aquatic ecosystem in the form of nitrate ions ($- NO_3$); phosphorus usually becomes available as phosphate ions ($- PO_4$). Since phosphorus is usually less abundant, it is more important as a limiting factor than nitrogen.

On the basis of productivity, the ecologist recognizes two major types of lakes: the *oligotrophic* ("nutrient-poor") and the *eutrophic* ("nutrient-rich"). A summary of the characteristics of each lake type is found in Table 6-1. The oligotrophic type is represented by Lake Superior, Lake Huron, the Finger Lakes of central New York, and many glacial lakes in northern Minnesota, Wisconsin, Michigan, and New York. Many glacial lakes (which were "scooped out" by glacial action thousands of years ago) were oligotrophic in their "youth." However, with the passage of time, tributary streams gradually increased lake fertility by depositing nutrient-rich loads of sediment. This permitted the production of larger quantities of phytoplankton and other aquatic vegetation, which in turn provided a more

Table 6-1.

Comparison of the characteristics of oligotrophic and eutrophic lakes.

Oligotrophic Lake	Eutrophic Lake
1. Poor in nutrients	1. Rich in nutrients
2. Deep basin	2. Shallow basin
3. Gravel or sandy bottom	3. Muddy bottom
4. Clear water	4. Turbid water
5. Plankton scarce	5. Plankton abundant
6. Rooted vegetation scarce	6. Rooted vegetation abundant
7. Cold water	7. Warm water
8. Characteristic fish: lake trout, whitefish, ciscoes	8. Characteristic fish: sunfish, yellow perch, carp, bullheads

ample food supply for herbivorous crustaceans, insects and fish. When these plants and animals died, their bodies would settle to the lake bottom and accumulate along with the stream-born sediment. The plant and animal remains would gradually decompose, thus releasing nutrients that would be "channeled" into the living bodies of future generations of organisms. It is apparent that in this way the original oligotrophic lake was gradually converted into a eutrophic lake, by purely natural processes operating for thousands of years. This process of lake enrichment is known as *eutrophication.*

When this process is accelerated by human activity, it is called *cultural eutrophication*—a condition that represents one of the more serious and extensive forms of water pollution besetting mankind today. According to David Ehrenfeld, "as much as eighty per cent of the nitrogen and seventy-five per cent of the phosphorus added to surface waters in the United States now comes from man-generated sources" (7). This man-generated nutrient input is derived from several sources, including domestic sewage, livestock waste, agricultural fertilizer, detergents, and industrial waste. When the average ion concentration of inorganic nitrogen exceeds 0.30 ppm, and the inorganic (soluble) phosphorus content exceeds 0.01 ppm, algal populations may become excessive. Usually occurring during summer, such algal "blooms" convert the once-clear water into "pea soup," with visibility frequently being restricted to a depth of 1 foot! Such a "bloom" is often caused by just a few species of green (*Chlorella, Spirogyra,* and so on) or blue-green (*Anabaena, Cladophora,* and so on) algae.

Adverse Effects of Algal Blooms. The adverse effects of such a bloom are multiple. First, it destroys the aesthetics of the lake, rendering it repulsive to swimmers and other sports enthusiasts. Canoe paddles, motorboat propellers, water skies, and fishing lines (as well as human arms doing the crawl stroke) get fouled up in the green slime. Second, the bloom impairs water quality by importing unpleasant taste and odor. If the lake is a source of municipal water supply, considerable expense may be involved in improving its quality. Third, as a result of wind and wave action huge masses of algae (and even rooted plants that have been torn loose from the lake bottom) will pile up in dense windrows along the windward shore and gradually decompose. Hydrogen sulfide (H_2S) gas is given off. Not only does this gas smell like rotting eggs, but it will tarnish silverware and discolor painted houses. Fourth, some of the blue-green algae emit materials toxic to both fish and man. Some individuals are undoubtedly more susceptible to these toxins than others. For example, there is the case of a physician who accidentally slipped off a dock into "pea soup" water. Although he was in the water for only a few seconds before getting back to the dock, he developed severe gastric disturbances a few hours later —apparently the result of algae-generated toxins. Fifth, the masses of algae eventually die off, sink to the lake bottom, and form a dense organic ooze. The billions of bacteria that then decompose this material utilize oxygen dissolved in the surrounding water. As a result the oxygen concentration in the deep water (hypolimnion) may be severely depleted, dropping rapidly from 7 ppm to 2 ppm or less. Consequently, any fish adapted to cold water, such as a lake trout, would be in danger of asphyxiation. (The "winterkill" of fish in such lakes may be excessive if a heavy snow cover intercepts the sunlight required for photosynthesis and hence oxygen regeneration.) Eventually the dead fish float to shore, decompose, generate odors, attract flies, and further contribute to aesthetic degradation.

Figure 6-2A. *Eutrophication caused this dense growth of algae in Lake Tahoe, Nevada, May 1972. [E.P.A.-Documerica—Belinda Rain]*

Figure 6-2B. *A Huey helicopter used in E.P.A.'s National Eutrophication Survey lands on lakes to take measurements and water samples. [U.S. Environmental Protection Agency, Photo by Mike Gordon]*

Adverse Effects of Rooted Weeds. Eutrophication is characterized not only by algae growths but by excessive populations of rooted weeds as well. Turk, Turk, and Wittes have nicely summarized the detrimental effects of this problem not only for the United States, but on a global basis as well.

> In many areas of the world, especially in the great rivers and lakes of the tropical and subtropical regions, aquatic weeds have multiplied explosively. They have interfered with fishing, navigation, irrigation, and the production of hydroelectric power. They have brought disease and starvation to communities that depended on these bodies of water. Water hyacinth in the Congo, Nile and Mississippi rivers and in other waters in India, West Pakistan, Southeast Asia and the Philippines, the water fern in southern Africa, and the water lettuce in Ghana are a few examples of such catastrophic infestations. Man has always loved the water's edge. To destroy the quality of these limited areas of the earth is to detract from his humanity as well as from the resources that sustain him (17).

Stream Eutrophication. Although eutrophication can occur in streams as well as lakes, the effects are usually not quite so severe. Many rivers are naturally oligotrophic at their headwaters, the waters flowing clear and cold and probably supporting trout. Such is the case of the small northern streams feeding into the Mississippi. However, by the time the water has neared the stream's mouth, it has received

Figure 6-2C. *Municipal sewage runs into a South Dakota stream through this culvert. Many thousands of gallons of untreated sewage daily bypassed the city's sewage treatment plant. Since this picture was taken (1962), the city has constructed a modern sewage treatment plant and the problem has been resolved.* [*Rapid City* Daily Journal]

such a cumulative load of nutrients, either from natural or man-generated sources, that it becomes turbid, warm, muddy, and weedy, harboring bullheads and carp rather than trout. Stream eutrophication is more easily reversed than lake eutrophication, since once the nutrient input is arrested, the current will eventually wash the nutrient-rich sediments into the ocean.

River eutrophication has been described in the Bible: "And the fish that was in the river died; and the river stank, and the Egyptians could not drink of the water of the river; and there was blood throughout all the land of Egypt" (Exodus 7:21). This is an account of the first plague God visited upon Egypt. According to Charles E. Warren, "the 'blood' in the water was most probably a heavy bloom of blue-green algae, imparting to the water the red color, the foul smell, and the noxious quality" (20).

Sources of Nutrients. Obviously, man-accelerated eutrophication is objectionable. What are the sources of the added nutrients for which man is responsible? There are four major sources: agricultural fertilizers, domestic sewage, livestock wastes, and phosphate detergents.

AGRICULTURAL FERTILIZERS. As we learned previously, commercial fertilizers are effective in promoting crop production because they are rich in nitrates and phosphates. Regrettably, however, as our nation's farmers strive to feed a rapidly increasing human population, they inadvertently also feed population explosions of aquatic weeds. Thus the amount of agricultural fertilizer used in the United States zoomed from 6 million tons in 1935 to almost 30 million tons in 1967 and has increased 12-fold during the period 1945–1970. Eventually the fertilizer (which is not absorbed by crop roots) is washed by run-off waters into lakes and streams. It is estimated that over 1 billion pounds of agriculture generated phosphorus enters America's aquatic ecosystems yearly (10). Recently, Donald E. Wilkinson, secretary of the Wisconsin Department of Agriculture, emphasized the gravity of fertilizer pollution and suggested that the use of high phosphate and nitrate fertilizers by Wisconsin farmers may be restricted in the near future to "alleviate the algae problems in our waters," even though the fertilizer curb would temporarily reduce crop production.

DOMESTIC SEWAGE. Some components of domestic sewage, such as human waste and detergents, contain a considerable amount of inorganic nitrogen and phosphorus, and hence "enrich" the lakes and streams into which they are discharged. Domestic sewage contributes an estimated 200–500 million pounds of phosphorus to aquatic ecosystems yearly (10). Even a modern secondary sewage treatment plant removes only about 50 per cent of the nitrogen and 30 per cent of the phosphorus from domestic sewage. This means that there is roughly 5 to 15 ppm of nitrogen and 4 to 14 ppm of phosphorus in the sewage effluent discharged into stream or lake. The rapid increase of water milfoil, sea lettuce, and algae in the lower Potomac River below Washington, D.C. has been attributed to the 45 tons of nitrogen and prosphorus compounds contained in the domestic sewage it daily receives.

ANIMAL WASTES. Each of the more than 20 million cattle in the United States excretes *ten* times as much waste per day as a human being. It is apparent that

Figure 6-3. *Aerial view of huge cattle feed lot at Coalinga, California, May 1972. Runoff from such feedlots contributes to eutrophication of American lakes and streams.* [E.P.A.-Documerica—Gene Daniels]

cattle in this country produce the waste-equivalent of 200 million people. And that doesn't even include the waste produced by all other types of livestock, including sheep, pigs, goats, chickens, ducks, and turkeys. It is apparent that if all this waste were washed into lakes and streams, its eutrophication potential would be enormous. During the winter it has long been the farmer's custom in the northern states to spread animal manure on the frozen ground. When spring comes, of course, some of the nitrogen and phosphorus is absorbed by crop root systems. Unfortunately, however, a considerable portion is also washed by spring run-off into aquatic ecosystems. Barry Commoner, well-known environmentalist, has emphasized the seriousness of the recent trend to crowding livestock in *feedlots*, where food is brought to the animals, instead of permitting them to forage for their own food in the open pasture. One large feedlot, accommodating 10,000 cattle, would accumulate 200 tons of cow manure daily. According to Commoner:

> in 1966 more than ten million cattle were maintained in feedlots before slaughter, an increase of 66 per cent over the preceding eight years. This represents about one half of the total U.S. cattle population. Because of the development of feedlot techniques —much of it in the Midwest—the United States is confronted with a huge waste disposal problem, one considerably greater than the human sewage we are attempting to handle with grossly inadequate treatment. The result is predictable—massive, still unresolved, pollution problems exist, especially in the surface waters of the Midwest (5).

And, of course, eutrophication is prominent among these problems.

Figure 6-4. *Sandy Run Creek in Montgomery County, Pennsylvania, forms foamy clouds because of its heavy detergent load.* [*U.S. Department of Agriculture*]

PHOSPHATE DETERGENTS. After World War II the old-fashioned soaps were gradually replaced by synthetic detergents available in a bewildering array of brand names. Soaps were readily decomposed by bacterial action (that is, they were *biodegradable*) shortly after their discharge into municipal sewage lines or rural septic tanks. On the other hand, the widely used detergents, of the ABS (alkyl-benzene-sulfonate) type, were nonbiodegradable, remaining intact sometimes for several years.

Occasionally these ABS detergents would clog water-treatment plants and percolate into ground water aquifers, thus contaminating community water supplies. At Kearney, Nebraska, ABS detergents moved 4,000 feet in fourteen months and eventually contaminated a family's well. Several years ago a survey by William Walton, of the University of Minnesota, revealed that 50 per cent of the private wells in the Minneapolis–St. Paul region were contaminated with ABS detergents. Sometimes ABS detergent contamination of water supplies was so high that the water would actually foam up like beer when drawn from the tap.

Under mounting pressure from an indignant public and scathing indictments from Congressmen, the detergent industry ultimately switched from the ABS formula to the LAS (linear-alkylate-sulfonate), which decomposes much more readily. By 1969 the industry was producing 5 billion pounds of phosphate annually. However the $1.2-billion-a-year industry was soon faced with another formula revision. For in December, 1969, Representative Henry Reuss of Wisconsin informed the House Subcommittee on Conservation and Natural Resources that the detergent industry was the principle cause of accelerated eutrophication. The percentage of phosphate occurring in seventeen leading brands in 1969 ranged from 21.6 per cent (Fab) to 43.7 per cent (Axion). Although sewage treatment plants that would remove the phosphate from the waste effluent can be built, their construction would impose a formidable burden on the tax payer. (Arthur Godfrey, well-known radio-TV personality, and a dedicated environmentalist, resisted doing commercials for a leading detergent manufacturer when he became aware of the product's role in eutrophication.) Finally, in the early 1970's, many detergent manufacturers made yet another formula revision, switching from a phosphate "builder" to NTA (nitrilo-triacetic acid). Although the NTA detergents have minimal eutrophication effects, they have posed still another problem. They are extremely caustic, some physicians having warned that blindness may result were the detergent to accidentally get in one's eyes.

Oxygen-demanding Organic Wastes

We are well aware that if the garbageman fails to make a pick-up for several days the accumulating debris will begin to decay and give off vile odors. The same would be true of the rabbit remains left by a fox. What is happening here? Bacteria are at work, using oxygen from the air to break down (oxidize) the complex energy-rich compounds in the garbage. The energy that is released during decomposition is then used by the bacteria to sustain life. Since there is a superabundance of atmospheric oxygen, bacteria do not compete for oxygen with other terrestrial organisms.

Now, organic matter may also accumulate in aquatic environments, as, for example, when an autumn leaf fall almost blankets a woodland stream, or when a massive fish kill occurs, or when slaughter house debris is discharged. The extent to which a stream may be polluted with such oxygen-demanding waste was revealed recently by Richard Madson, of Jamestown, North Dakota. He made a canoe survey of pollution along a 750-mile stretch of the James River from Bowden, North Dakota, to Yankton, South Dakota. He counted a total of 158 dead animals "including one dog, four deer, fifteen sheep, twenty-seven hogs, thirty-three cattle, and the bones, hides and intestines of twenty slaughtered steers." He also found "raw manure from feedlots, . . . untreated human sewage, including lavender toilet paper" (2).

The process by which this material eventually is decomposed by bacterial action may be summarized as follows:

$$
\begin{array}{c}
\text{(aerobic bacteria)} \\
\text{high energy organic} + \text{oxygen} \rightarrow \text{low energy carbon dioxide} + \text{energy} \\
\text{molecules (fats,} \qquad + \qquad \text{(used by} \\
\text{carbohydrates,} \qquad \text{low energy water} \qquad \text{bacteria} \\
\text{proteins)} \qquad + \qquad \text{to} \\
\text{nitrate ions } (NO_3) \qquad \text{sustain} \\
\text{phosphate ions } (PO_4) \qquad \text{life)} \\
\text{sulphate ions } (SO_4)
\end{array}
$$

However, the amount of dissolved oxygen (DO) in the water is not nearly as abundant as atmospheric oxygen. As a result the bacteria actively *compete* with other oxygen-demanding aquatic organisms (fish, crustaceans, insect larvae, and so on). If sufficient organic food is available, and if other conditions such as water temperature are favorable, the oxygen-using bacteria will multiply rapidly. Levels of DO will, of course, decrease proportionately, sometimes from 10 ppm down to *less than 3 ppm*, to the detriment of aquatic insects, crustaceans, and fish.

Organic wastes with a high biological oxygen demand (BOD) include the peelings and cores from fruit- and vegetable-processing plants; cheese factory and creamery wastes; the excrement, blood, and discarded tissues from slaughterhouses; distillery residues; the hair and fleckings from tanneries; and the sulfite liquors of paper and pulp mills. Many of the wastes have BOD levels ranging from 5,000 to 15,000 ppm. In the late 1960's seven paper and pulp mills in the state of Washington discharged 210 million gallons of sulfite waste liquor into Puget Sound. In terms of BOD, this was equal to the domestic sewage from a population of 8.4 million people, which is remarkable when one considers that there are only 2.8 million people in the entire state of Washington (22).

The BOD Test. Now, how does one measure the BOD of organic waste? Let us suppose that the health authorities of a certain town are suspicious that the effluent from the local sewage disposal plant contamination has an excessive BOD. One might assume that the easiest and most direct procedure would simply be either to filter the organic material from the water or scoop it from the stream or lake bottom and weigh it. Then one might determine that there are x number of pounds of organic matter in y gallons of sewage effluent, or z gallons of river water. Unfortunately, some organic material (fish carcasses, human feces, and so on) de-

Figure 6-5. *Biologists examining fish destroyed by oxygen-demanding cheese factory wastes discharged into stream near Loganville (Sauk County), Wisconsin.* [*Wisconsin Natural Resources Department, Madison, Wis.*]

composes rapidly and some (pesticides such as DDT) are virtually nonbiodegradable. It is apparent, therefore, that the direct method of measuring the degree of organic pollution will not work. The amount of oxygen required by a given load of organic waste is known as its *biological oxygen demand,* or BOD. Degree of pollution can be measured by the BOD test, in which a sample of polluted water whose DO content has been determined is placed in a container from which all air and light is excluded) and incubated for five days at 20° C. The amount of oxygen consumed is then determined by comparing the amounts present before and after incubation. Everytime you flush your toilet you are making it a bit more difficult for black bass or sunfish in the stream near your town to survive, for there is about 250 ppm of BOD in the waste water going down the pipe.

Effect of High BOD on Stream Animals.   Does sewage effluent with a high BOD have any noticeable effect on aquatic animal populations? The answer, of course, is of vital interest to fishermen, nature lovers, stream-side property owners, resort operators, as well as biologists. The answer to such a question is frequently sought by an aquatic biologist working for a state environmental protection agency. He could get the answer simply by determining the kinds and numbers of organisms occurring immediately above, and at several sites below the discharge point, as indicated in Figure 6–6A. Note that at site A just above the outfall the river found is characteristic of an unpolluted stream. However, at point B, immediately below the outfall, DO levels drop rapidly because of the high organic component of the waste effluent. In some streams the DO may drop to 3 ppm or less, insufficient to support the oxygen requirements of *quality* fish such as black bass, walleyes or trout, which the angler enjoys catching. Instead, only *trash* fish, such as carp, bullheads, and garpike, which have low oxygen requirements, can survive. The larvae of may, stone, and caddis flies, which require higher oxygen levels, are virtually absent. The DO concentration is so drastically reduced at C that even carp and garpike cannot survive. The most typical bottom-dwelling animals at C are reddish sludge worms (*Tubifex*), of which there may be 20,000 per square foot of stream bottom, and the bright red larvae (*chironomids*) of midges. These animals are sometimes used as *index* organisms, their occurrence indicating that a particular stretch of stream is highly contaminated with organic waste. (The only reason these organisms can survive is because of the abundance of oxygen-bearing haemoglobin occurring near the animal's body surface.) Unpolluted aquatic ecosystems usually have a much greater *species diversity* than their polluted counterparts. Rather surprisingly, however, the total *biomass* in severely deoxygenated areas might approach that of unpolluted stretches of the stream because each of the few highly specialized species that *can* survive are represented by *huge populations* (13).

At point D the amount of oxygen removed by the sewage bacteria is more than counterbalanced by the oxygen entering the stream from the atmosphere (for example, because of wind action or the stroke of a canoe paddle), or that being generated by the photosynthetic activity of stream-dwelling plants. As a result the DO level rises, permitting once again the occurrence of carp and garpike. Finally, still further downstream at point E, most of the organic material discharged from the sewage plant has been decomposed; consequently the DO curve rises to its original level and permits the occurrence of animals (trout, mayflies, and so on) characteristic of a nonpolluted stream (13).

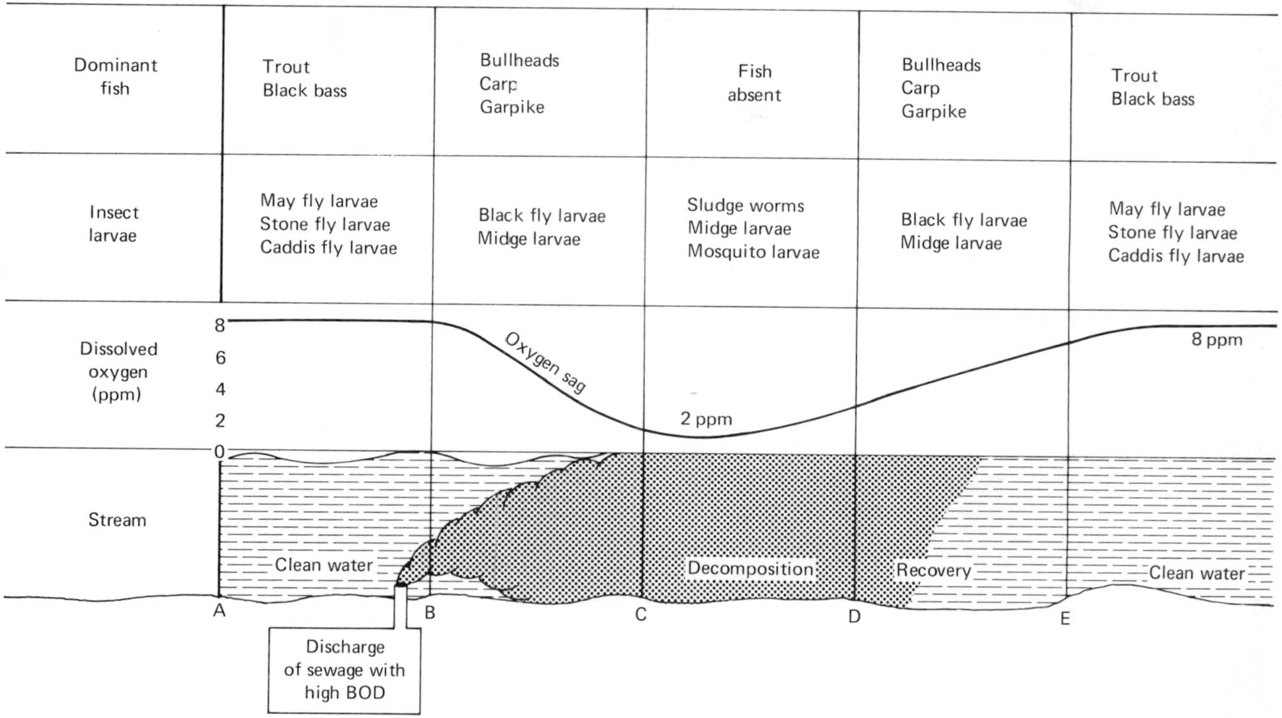

Figure 6-6A. *Effect of sewage discharges (with high BOD) on the oxygen levels and aquatic life of a stream.* [After *An Introduction to Environmental Sciences* by James M. Moran, Michael D. Morgan, and James H. Wiersma. Copyright © 1973 by Little, Brown and Company, Boston]

Figure 6-6B. *Fish by the thousands, most of them of the "rough" species, which became victims of a massive fish kill in a polluted stream in Illinois in September 1967.* [*U.S. Environmental Protection Agency, Office of Public Affairs*]

The characteristic dip of the oxygen curve at points B and C is known as the *oxygen sag*. The slope of the DO curve, which is highly variable, is dependent upon the amount of organic material in the sewage and the rates at which oxygen enters the stream, either from atmospheric or photosynthetic sources. Even *with* efficient waste treatment methods, which most American municipal and industrial sewage plants do *not* have, by 1980 our organic waste load (domestic plus industrial) will be sufficient to consume all the DO in the dry weather stream flow of our nation's twenty-two river basins (13).

Thermal Pollution

An acceptable definition for *thermal pollution* would be: "the warming up of an aquatic ecosystem to the point where desirable organisms are adversely affected." Although thermal pollution may result from both natural (excessive heating by the summer sun) and industrial causes, the latter are by far the most significant. Many industries take water from a lake or stream for cooling purposes; by the time the water is returned it may have been warmed up considerably. According to the Federal Water Pollution Control Administration, the electric power, steel, and chemical industries are the most important users of cooling water, with electrical power plants forming 81 per cent of the total.

Remember the second law of thermodynamics? It states that "whenever energy is converted from one form to another, a certain amount is dissipated as heat." In actuality there are several energy conversions involved in a power plant fired by fossil fuel. The chemical energy in coal or oil is converted into heat to generate

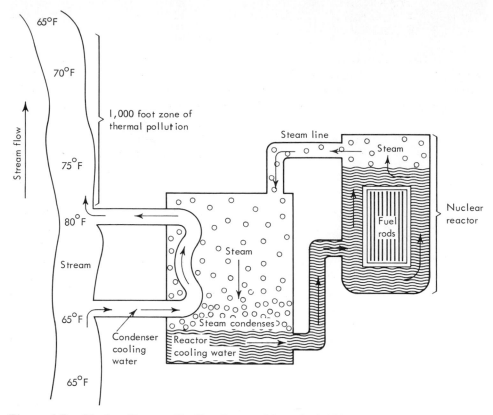

Figure 6-7. *Nuclear Reactor Cooling System. Note the 1,000 foot zone of thermal pollution caused by the discharge.*

steam to turn the turbine. This mechanical energy is then converted into electrical energy by the generator. In order to condense the steam back to water for return to the boiler, the steam is passed over coils that carry cold water withdrawn from a stream or lake. As a result the steam is condensed and the heat is transferred to the coolant water whose temperature may be raised 20° F.

Coal-fired power plants are objectionable because they contaminate air with sulfur dioxide and particulate matter. Nuclear-fired plants are "clean" as far as atmospheric pollution is concerned, but for each kilowatt of power produced, they produce *40 per cent more heat* than the coal-fired plant. Since the power industry appears committed to conversion to the nuclear type plant, and since the nation's electrical power demands are expected to double with each succeeding decade until the year 2000, it would appear that thermal pollution might become much more extensive than it is at present. In fact by 2000 our industries will require the disposal of about 20 million billion BTU's [1] of waste heat per day. To accomplish this they will have to use fully one third of the dry season stream flow for cooling purposes exclusively.

[1] BTU—the amount of heat required to raise the temperature of one pound of water from 63 degrees Fahrenheit to 64 degrees Fahrenheit. One BTU is equal to 252 calories.

Adverse Effects. Thermal pollution has multiple adverse effects on aquatic ecosystems. Let us consider some of them.

REDUCTION IN DISSOLVED OXYGEN. When water is warmed its capacity for dissolving oxygen is *decreased*. Unfortunately this decrease occurs at the same time that the *need* for oxygen by aquatic organisms (fish, crustaceans, and so on) *increases*. For example, even the lowly carp, which requires only 0.5 ppm of oxygen at 33° F, needs at least 1.5 ppm at 95° F. if it is to survive (8). It is apparent that cold water fish such as trout and salmon, which require about 6 ppm to survive could not tolerate the high water temperatures that would prevail at the point where the warmed-up coolant water is discharged. If they remained in the area they would become asphyxiated.

INTERFERENCE WITH REPRODUCTION. Fish and other "cold-blooded" animals whose body temperature (and activity level) varies with that of the external environment are extremely sensitive to slight thermal changes. Some fish, in fact, with the aid of numerous microscopic temperature-sensitive organs in their skin, can detect water temperatures shifts of only 0.05° F. Many species of fish are instinctively "tuned" to certain thermal signals that trigger such activities as nest building, spawning, and migration. For example, the maximum temperature at which a cold water fish such as a lake trout will successfully spawn is 48° F (8.9° C). The corresponding temperature for a large-mouthed black bass is 80° F (26.7° C). Not only will warmed water disrupt spawning, and in some cases prevent it altogether, but it may also destroy the eggs, once they are laid. Thus, according to the Oregon Fish Commission, a mere 5.4° F increase in temperature of the Columbia River could have disastrous effects on the eggs of the Chinook salmon (20). A lake trout will perish if the water temperature is much higher than 50° F. The lethal temperature for trout in Minnesota and Wisconsin is 77° F, for walleye is 86° F, and for yellow perch is 88° F. What actually causes death at these high temperatures? According to John R. Clark, of the Sandy Hook Marine Laboratory (New Jersey), the direct cause is unknown, although "various investigators have suggested that the final blow may be some effect of heat on the nervous system or the respiratory system, the congulation of the cell protoplasm or the inactivation of enzymes." It is apparent that since the discharge of warmed coolant water may raise stream temperatures 20° F above the ambient water temperature, (in other words well into the 90° F range in summer) any cold water fish (lake trout, salmon, and so on) would have to emigrate in order to survive. Several years ago the heated effluent from power plants and other industries raised the temperature of part of the Mahoning River to 140° F (19). Although no data are available, we would logically assume that at that temperature the Mahoning River was beyond the heat tolerance range for *all* species of fish in the area.

ADVERSE EFFECTS ON ALGAE. As Richard Wagner states, each of the three major groups of algae—diatoms, green, and blue-green—have distinct water temperature preferences. Thus, the greatest species diversity for diatoms, green algae, and blue-green algae occurs at 58° F, 90° F, and 104° F, respectively. The most valuable algae, as far as direct crustacean food and ultimate fish food is concerned, are the cool water preferring diatoms. The warm-water-adapted blue-green algae are *least desirable* as aquatic animal food. Not only that, they emit toxic materials and cause multiple problems already discussed under nutrient pollution. (It is apparent that high water temperature is an important factor in promoting blue-green algal "blooms.") One can readily see how aquatic food chains might be disrupted by thermal effluents. As Wagner states, "A water flea, for example, which might be able to tolerate the thermal extreme of 95° F., would probably starve to death if the diatoms on which it fed were unable to survive at that temperature. In turn, fish feeding on water fleas would be similarly hard pressed to survive, regardless of their tolerance or adaptibility to the high water temperature" (19).

DESTRUCTION OF ORGANISMS IN THE COOLANT WATER. It should be emphasized that the volume of water removed from a stream for cooling purposes is enormous, sometimes involving a substantial fraction of a stream's total flow. Some of the larger power plants withdraw *500 million gallons per day.* One may well ask what is the fate of the myriad tiny (1 millimeter or less in length) plants and animals (*plankton*) that not only represent the base of aquatic food chains, but also, in the case of algae, serve as a source of oxygen. Unfortunately, the answer is

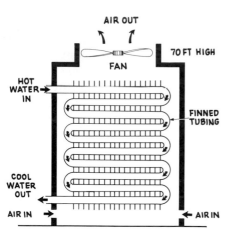

Figure 6-8. *Dry cooling tower, which works very much like a large automobile radiator. Rather than evaporation, cooling takes place as large currents of air are drawn over finned tubing through which high-temperature condenser water circulates. To date, the only installation of any size is at a 200,000 kilowatt power plant in South Africa. This is far too small for use at today's one-million-plus generating stations.* [Pennsylvania Power and Light]

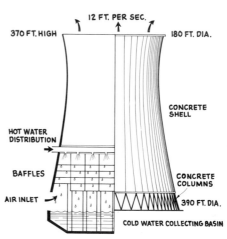

Figure 6-9. *Natural-draft cooling tower removes heat from condenser water by evaporation or direct contact with air rising up through the hollow concrete shell. Its large size is necessary to provide sufficient surface area and draft to cool thousands of gallons of water each day. The hyperbolic shape channels the air flow and yields great structural strength with less material.* [Pennsylvania Power and Light]

Figure 6-10. *Cooling towers in operation. Note the clean water vapor being discharged into the atmosphere by one of the twin "wet" cooling towers. This $260 million power plant, located near Danville, Pennsylvania, has a 1.5 million kilowatt capability.* [Pennsylvania Power and Light]

that many of them are destroyed, either by the thermal shock, as they move through the coils of the condenser, or by the chlorine (applied to kill microorganisms that might form slimy growths in the coolant pipes). The plankton mortality in the coolant pipes is highly variable, ranging from 0 to 95 per cent.

Abatement.   After being prodded by state and federal environmental protection agencies, the power industry has attempted to mitigate the thermal pollution problem with cooling towers and lagoons. Cooling towers are mammoth parabola-shaped structures, about 400 feet tall. As illustrated in Figure 6–9, the heated water is piped to a high level in the tower and then directed downward in a thin sheet over a series of baffle plates. During this time a portion of the water evaporates, a process facilitated by the upward flow of fan-propelled air. The coolant water is then either (1) discharged into the stream, lake, or ocean from which it was drawn, (2) into a lagoon for further cooling, or (3) channeled back to the plant's condenser.

Although cooling towers do abate the thermal pollution problem somewhat, certain undesirable features attend their use. First, when the air temperature is 32° F or lower, the towers generate a considerable amount of fog; further, if the fog comes in contact with a solid surface, a thin layer of ice is formed. It is apparent, therefore, that when cooling towers are sited near highways their operation can greatly increase traffic hazards. Second, the water that is evaporated (amounting to 25,000 gallons per minute for a 1,000-megawatt plant) is consumed; in other words, it is lost to the aquatic ecosystems (rivers, and so on) from which it came. This quantity of water loss is equivalent to a daily rainfall of 1 inch on an area of 2 square miles! Third, toxic materials such as chlorine, used to prevent the growth of pipe-clogging bacterial slimes, must be removed from the collant water before re-entry to the aquatic ecosystem. Fourth, although the towers are remarkable engineering accomplishments, they are 400-foot-tall masses of concrete and steel that dominate the skyline and detract from environmental aesthetics. Finally, the towers are quite expensive, costing about $2 million each. Such an expenditure, of course, is eventually passed along from the utility to the consumer in the form of increased electric rates, amounting perhaps to $5 per customer annually. This cost, however, is negligible, when weighed against the advantages of thermal reduction in our aquatic ecosystem.

Benefits Derived from Warmed Water. Although artificially heated water is generally considered deleterious to aquatic ecosystems, it may have certain limited redeeming features. Thus, in the northern states, the warmed-up water downstream from power plants may serve as an ice-free wintering area for waterfowl or may permit northward range extensions of fish. In 1969 the Water and Electric Board of Eugene, Oregon, announced the results of an experiment in which the warm water discharged from a paper mill was sprayed on fruit trees and prevented frost damage. Experimenters plan to distribute the heated water through subterranean pipes to determine whether the resultant soil temperature increase would permit an extended growing season and allow double harvests of certain crops.

It has been suggested that coolant water, bearing a thermal load, and domestic sewage effluent, bearing a nutrient load, might be combined in specially created lagoons (8). In this scheme, *both the nutrient and thermal pollutants could be put to constructive use.* For example, fast-growing Asiatic milkfish could be stocked in these lagoons. Since they are of tropical origin and adapted to warm waters, the relatively high lagoon temperatures would pose no problem. Moreover, during winters in the northern states the warm water would prevent ice from forming and permit the milkfish to feed and grow on a year-round basis. Furthermore, since the fish are plant eaters, not only would the nutrients be efficiently converted into fillets, but the weed problem commonly associated with eutrophic ponds would be under control. Since milkfish have prodigious growth rates (increasing from 5 inches to 25 inches in a single year), thousands of such "fish factories" distributed throughout the country might to some degree compensate for the progressive loss of prime food protein-producing land to highways, parking lots, and shopping centers.

Disease-producing Organisms

Disease-producing organisms include protozoa, bacteria, viruses, and worms that can live inside or on the human body as parasites. The causative organisms of cholera, amoebic dysentery, polio, typhoid fever, and infectious hepatitis are capable of transmission by sewage discharge and stream flow for many miles from their point of origin. One cup of water randomly taken from the Connecticut River near Hartford recently contained *twenty-six different species of infectious bacteria that typically occur in human fecal matter*. Infectious organisms may have their origin in the wastes discharged from hospitals, private homes, and even slaughter-houses. They may be unsuspectingly taken into the human body via contaminated drinking water. The nineteenth-century cholera epidemic in London was caused by cholera germs originating from a single sewage-contaminated well. In this modern era of ultrasanitation and ultrasterilization, one takes germ-free tap water for granted. However, there are public water systems in this country today contaminated with injurious microorganisms that can cause chills, fever, pain, nausea, malaise, paralysis, and even death.

Paul Ehrlich has underscored the problem that existed in the late 1960's in some of the nation's cities:

> Did you live in Grand Junction, Colorado, Fort Myers, Florida, or Bayonne, New Jersey? Your water in those cities did not come from the purest possible source. In Savannah, Georgia, or North Platte, Nebraska? Your water was not checked frequently enough for dangerous bacteria. Fairbanks, Alaska? Your local regulations were not adequate to prevent health hazard. Pueblo, Colorado? Surveys to detect potential health hazards were too infrequent. Wilmington, North Carolina? The bacterial level in your water was too high. Charleston, South Carolina? Your water department used non-approved tests. . . . These facts were revealed in a Public Health Service Provisional List, in which water supplies of more than 60 American cities were rated as "unsatisfactory" or "potential health hazard." Don't be startled, but that last glass of water you drank may already have passed through the bodies of eight people, especially if you live in a densely populated region. This fact concerning the "toilet-to-mouth" pipeline has been the subject of some humor. Thus, scrawlings on the walls of public bath rooms along the Mississippi River say: "Flush the toilet, they need the water in St. Louis (8)!"

Recently, Kabler surveyed the research on this problem for the span of time from 1922 to 1959. In this survey domestic sewage wastes were analyzed for infectious organisms before and after sewage was exposed to various treatment processes. To his surprise, almost all infectious bacteria, fungi, and viruses occurring in the untreated sewage also could be identified in the treated samples, although their numbers were reduced. Among the organisms that pass through the treatment processes were the bacteria of typhoid, paratyphoid, cholera, salmonellosis, tuberculosis, anthrax, and tetanus. All viruses, including the polio virus and such parasitic worms as hookworm, roundworm, and tapeworm, were present.

State and municipal health departments take frequent samples of drinking water supplies to ensure that disease-causing bacteria are held to an absolute minimum. Since the number of kinds of pathogenic bacteria are so numerous, however, it is not practical to make counts of each type. Instead counts are made of the *coliform* bacteria, relatively harmless bacteria that live in the human gut. These bacteria pass from the human gut with the feces and hence occur in sewage contaminated waters. A low coliform count indicates a low number of pathogenic bacteria in the water. A high count of coliforms (that is, more than 25 per quart) indicates an excessive number of disease-causing bacteria and that the water should be more heavily chlorinated. One drawback to this method is that it is extremely difficult to distinguish human coli from those occurring in the digestive tracts of other mammals such as sheep and cattle.

In 1916 and 1924, two major typhoid epidemics along the Atlantic coast were traced to contaminated clams and oysters. Fifteen hundred people were infected; 150 people died in the 1924 epidemic. After the 1924 outbreak the shellfish companies formed a compact with the Public Health Service whereby interstate health controls and standards were established (22). In the early 1960's some youngsters were playing along the Hudson River into which 400 million gallons of human sewage was discharged daily. They ate a watermelon they found floating in the river. Later, eight of these children contracted typhoid fever. From May to July, 1965, 18,000 of the 130,000 residents of Riverside, California, were stricken with fever, diarrhea, and vomiting. Three died. The causative organism was *Salmonella typhimurium*, a bacterium related to the typhoid organism. Chlorination of the municipal water supplies brought the epidemic under control. In each of the preceding cases, the disease could be traced to sewage-contaminated waters.

Over 166 strains of viruses were discovered by Kelly and Sanderson in treated sewage as recently as 1957. Many kinds of disease-causing viruses have been found in sewage even after chlorination, a process expressly designed to destroy microscopic agents of infection. From time to time we all complain of vague pains, headache, and stiffness. Sometimes we go to a doctor for diagnosis, only to have him say, "You probably have some kind of virus." Where did the virus come from? It is quite possible, as John A. Zapf, Jr., told a recent national conference on water pollution, that "water may be implicated in viral diseases as yet not recognized."

One well-known virus that may be lethal to man is infectious hepatitis. From 1844 to 1956 there were at least six outbreaks of water-borne infectious hepatitis in the United States. Another extensive outbreak of this disease occurred in 1961 in New York and New Jersey. During an ensuing investigation, it was revealed that each disease victim had eaten clams harvested from Raritan Bay, off the Jersey coast. The clams had taken the virus into their bodies during the process of filtering food from the sewage-contaminated waters (22).

Sediments

It is a curious paradox that the very soil that makes the production of life-sustaining food possible on American farms, when washed into a stream or lake, suddenly may be transformed into our nation's most destructive water pollutant. Every day the American people lose about $1 million as a result of silt-polluted water. Silt inflicts damage on our public water supplies, on our reservoirs, and on hydropower plants. It clogs up the irrigation canals of the western farmer and impedes the progress of coal and ore barges along the Mississippi River. Beds of aquatic vegetation on Lake Erie that were once important breeding grounds for fish have literally been smothered by river silt as a result of poor land use methods in the watershed. Suspended clay particles cloud the water to such a degree that submerged aquatic plants (*Chara, Potamogeton,* and *Elodea*) and floating phytoplankton die because of their inability to photosynthesize organic food. Cessation of photosynthesis in turn reduces the oxygen level in the water and results in extensive mortality of game fish and invertebrate food organisms.

Over 2,000 billion gallons of silt-polluted water must be filtered annually so that

Figure 6-11. *Sedimentation of watercourses frequently has its origin at highway construction sites. Soil erosion may be severe unless special precautions are taken. Note the huge area within the "cloverleaf" that must be covered with vegetation as soon as possible. [Department of Housing and Urban Development]*

one can draw a glass of water that is clear rather than the color of diluted mud. Over 3,000 reservoirs in the United States provide water for roughly 25 per cent of our population. However, the reduced reservoir capacity caused by their rapid siltation is equivalent to the daily water requirements of 250,000 people.

Negligent land use practices at urban-suburban construction sites have resulted in severe sedimentation of nearby streams. For example, after one big construction project had exposed the soil along Mill Creek near Washington, D.C., the turbidity of the stream rose from 11.5 ppm to 13,000 ppm within one hour after the start of a rainstorm. The Federal Water Quality Administration has estimated that sediment loads washed from sites of highway, airport, and building construction are 2,000 times greater than that from wooded land, 200 times greater than that from pasture, and 10 times greater than that from cultivated cropland.

Maximum daily concentrations of silt of up to 130,000 parts per million have been recorded in the turbulent waters of the Colorado River at Grand Canyon, and up to 270,000 parts per million have been recorded in certain muddy Iowan streams. This represents the work primarily of accelerated erosion. In some areas up to 9,000 tons of soil per square mile per year are washed downstream. According to the Soil Conservation Service, which recently made a survey of 157 watersheds, 70 per cent of the silt is attributable to sheet erosion and 10 per cent to gully erosion. The Mississippi River alone washes 400 million tons of sediment into the Gulf of Mexico annually. To freight one year's load would require a train of boxcars 63,300 miles long—sufficient to extend around the world more than two and one-half times at the equator. It is apparent that the best way to control siltation is to employ sound land use practices—such as contour farming, cover and strip cropping, and gully reclamation—on the watersheds.

Radioactive Materials

Such elements as uranium and radium possess highly unstable atomic nuclei. This disintegration results in radiation emissions that may be highly injurious, and even lethal, to man. These elements are said to be *radioactive*. Once the mushroom-shaped cloud has dissipated following a nuclear blast, radioactive dust may circle the globe, at altitudes of 10,000 feet or more, several times before being washed to the earth by rain. With each new nuclear weapon test, more of these materials are released into the environment. Eventually some of the radioactive material, such as strontium-90 (which can cause bone cancer), percolates down through the soil into our ground water reservoirs or is carried by run-off waters into streams and rivers. In either case, public water supplies may be contaminated. Radioactive rain 200 times higher than the standard set as safe for drinking, fell in the San Francisco Bay region following nuclear bomb tests. Although some radioactive wastes are discharged from nuclear reactors at university research centers, and some from hospitals employing cobalt radiation for cancer cases, by far the most important source for the remainder of this century will be nuclear power plants. The number of such plants is expected to increase from about 25 in 1973 to about 200 by the year 2000. The construction of a number of large nuclear reactors and the increasing use of radioactive materials in medical research represent other potential contamination sources. Radioactive cobalt, for eaxmple, has been widely used in cancer therapy in recent years.

Low-level radioactive waste is commonly removed by diluting it in water. The Atomic Energy Commission reported several years ago [2] that the 9 billion gallons of liquid waste being discharged annually in the United States primarily into large rivers, the sea, and the soil have 2 million curies [3] of radioactivity. How diluted must these wastes be? Let us suppose, for example, that a radioactive waste solution is discharged from a nuclear-reactor research center and that the 1 ppm concentration of strontium-90 gives off 0.002 curie per milliliter. This may seem quite dilute. However, this concentration of strontium-90 is 2.5 *billion times* the maximal concentration permitted by the National Committee on Radiation Protection. Each teaspoon of this contaminated solution would have to be diluted with about 2.5 million gallons of water before its release into a river would be permitted. The crucial problem is that minute amounts of water-borne strontium may accumulate to extremely high concentration levels in living tissue. For example, the level of radiostrontium-90 in the skeleton of a perch living in water contaminated by seeps from an adjacent liquid atomic waste disposal area was 3,000 times greater than that of the lake water (16). The whole problem of radioactive pollution—sources, effects, and methods of control—is discussed in detail in Chapter 18.

Although biological agents such as bacteria can decompose organic wastes, *the only agent capable of "destroying" radioactive material is time itself*. Given enough time, all of the unstable nuclei of the element will decay. However, it would be theoretically possible for some radioactive materials to remain in underground aquifers for over 1,000 years before the potentially harmful emissions finally ceased.

---

[2] The volume discharged today is much greater.

[3] Curie = the amount of radioactive material in which 37 billion atoms disintegrate each second.

Sewage Treatment and Disposal

All the types of water contaminants we have described thus far—sediments, infectious organisms, detergents, human excrement, organic material, and so on—are all components, to a greater or lesser degree, of municipal sewage. In order to minimize the potentially harmful effects of these pollutants, domestic sewage is usually treated at municipal *sewage treatment plants* before being discharged into lake, stream, or ocean.

During the Middle Ages, in some of the densely populated cities of Europe, such as London and Paris, human waste was often disposed of simply by opening a window and sloshing it into the street below. The stench that assaulted the nose when one strolled along those streets was so vile that refined gentlemen would carry sweet-smelling spices as deodorants. Before the advent of indoor plumbing in the United States, human waste was crudely disposed of by means of the backyard privy—a method still in use today in some back-country areas and in poverty-stricken regions such as Appalachia. A few years ago it was estimated that raw sewage from 11 million people living in 1,342 communities was being discharged directly into streams and lakes without undergoing any treatment whatsoever. As late as 1968 major American cities such as St. Louis, Omaha, and Memphis were in this category. Seventeen million people in 1,337 communities require either new or enlarged sewage treatment systems. The federal government is making a strenuous effort to aid towns in upgrading their sewage systems by providing cost-sharing grants.

Figure 6-12. *"The solution to pollution is dilution" is the false concept shown here. Water pollution in Yancey County, North Carolina, May 15, 1969. Note the privy that has been built over the edge of this mountain stream, an extremely primitive method of disposing of human wastes. [Soil Conservation Service, U.S. Department of Agriculture]*

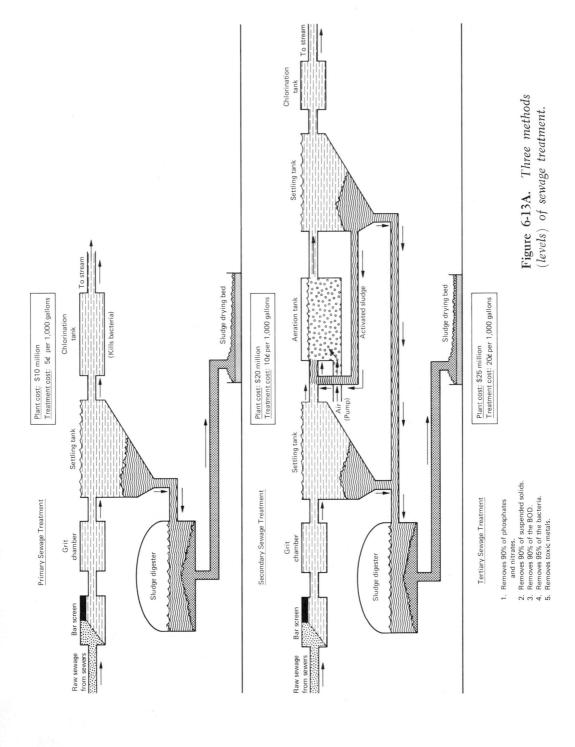

Figure 6-13A. *Three methods (levels) of sewage treatment.*

Primary Sewage Treatment

Plant cost: $10 million
Treatment cost: 5¢ per 1,000 gallons

Raw sewage from sewers

Bar screen

Grit chamber

Settling tank

Chlorination tank

(Kills bacteria)

To stream

Sludge digester

Sludge drying bed

Secondary Sewage Treatment

Plant cost: $20 million
Treatment cost: 10¢ per 1,000 gallons

Raw sewage from sewers

Bar screen

Grit chamber

Settling tank

Air (Pump)

Aeration tank

Activated sludge

Settling tank

Chlorination tank

To stream

Sludge digester

Sludge drying bed

Tertiary Sewage Treatment

Plant cost: $25 million
Treatment cost: 20¢ per 1,000 gallons

1. Removes 90% of phosphates and nitrates.
2. Removes 90% of suspended solids.
3. Removes 90% of the BOD.
4. Removes 95% of the bacteria.
5. Removes toxic metals.

164

Treatment Methods.   Domestic sewage treatment may be *primary* (rudimentary), *secondary* (more effective), and *tertiary* (most effective but rather expensive). Let us briefly examine these methods.

PRIMARY TREATMENT.   About 30 per cent of our nation's treatment plants provide primary treatment. The domestic sewage (from homes, schools, hospitals, stores, and so on) containing human waste, ground-up garbage, wastepaper, soap, detergents, and a variety of debris flows through a network of street sewer pipes. On its way to the sewage treatment plant this sewage may be joined by rain storm run-off (which has flowed down street gutters into storm sewer pipes) carrying sediment, gravel, sticks, and even livestock waste. The combined flow of domestic sewage and storm run-off eventually enters the sewage plant. With occasional reference to Figure 6–13A, we shall describe the major steps in primary treatment.

1. *Screening.*   A series of screens remove large objects from the inflowing sewage —everything from rocks to rats, baseballs to bananas!

2. *Grit chamber.*   Any fairly large objects that may have gotten through the screen are ground up to facilitate processing.

3. *Sedimentation tank.*   The sewage is then piped into sedimentation tanks, where it is detained for several hours so that sand, silt, and suspended organic (BOD) material can settle to the bottom. The fluid is then discharged into a lake or stream.

4. *Sludge digester.*   The sedimented solids are then piped to a sludge digester, where the organic material is decomposed by bacteria in the *absence* of oxygen. One decomposition product, *methane gas*, is frequently used by the plant to serve up to 90 per cent of its power needs—a highly desirable use in this era of fuel scarcity.

Figure 6-13B.   *Close-up of sedimentation tanks at a New York state sewage treatment plant. The sewage is detained in these tanks for several hours. The heavier material settles to the bottom and forms a "sludge," which is removed from the tanks. The lighter greasy materials that rise to the surface are eventually skimmed off the top. [N.Y.S. Health Photo by M. Dixson]*

Figure 6-14. *Des Moines, Iowa. Aerial view of the huge Des Moines Sewage Treatment Plant on the bank of the Des Moines River (left). Two groups of six large round-spoked basins are trickling filters; above the grease tanks is the administrative and pump building, where the city's huge outfall sewer enters the plant. The treated sewage flows into the river just to the left of four final clarifiers, on the river bank at center, whose raised walls are between two groups of trickling filters. New roughing filters (square) and intermediate clarifiers (round) are being built at bottom. Six primary clarifiers are grouped at right between the twelve filters. Above and to the left of domed buildings are eight sludge digesters. At top of photo are sludge drying beds. [U.S. Environmental Protection Agency, Photo courtesy Des Moines (Iowa) Register]*

The solid material that remains after decomposition, collectively known as *sludge,* is removed to *drying beds.* (Occasionally the hard seeds of various fruits and vegetables may pass through the entire primary treatment process intact and eventually develop into mature plants in the sludge drying beds. I know one sewage treatment plant in western Wisconsin where some delicious melons and tomatoes have been harvested.) The sludge may be used as soil conditioner in lawns and flower gardens. The Milwaukee sewage plant processes its sludge and sells it as the commercial product called "Milorganite."

The handling and disposal of sludge can be a costly headache for many treatment plant operators—sometimes using up almost 50 per cent of the budget. Another problem is the "simple" question of where to put the mounting piles of material. Take Chicago, for example. Its sewage plants generate 1,000 *tons of sludge daily*. Until recently about half of this material was dumped into huge excavations near the plant at a cost of $60 per ton; the remainder was sold to fertilizer companies and to citrus ranchers in Florida. However, in the early 1970's the plant experienced a dire shortage of suitable disposal sites. Faced with this dilemma, sanitary district superintendent Vincent Bacon conceived an ingenious scheme that would not only solve the disposal problem and reduce costs, but would reclaim nonproductive Illinois land as well. The sludge would first undergo bacterial digestion to remove odors and eliminate the health hazard. It would then be pumped through a 24-inch pipe to strip-mined barrens and marginal farmlands 60 miles southwest of Chicago. As Bacon says, "It's the perfect marriage. That land needs our sludge as much as we need the land." The most astounding feature is that the disposal cost would come to only $20 per ton, only one third the cost of the original disposal method.

It might seem repugnant to the reader to increase the fertility of farmlands with sludge derived from human excrement. However man's wastes have been employed for this purpose throughout history. Such "night soil" was commonly spread on agricultural fields by the Chinese and many European countries as well. In *Les Miserables*, published in 1862, the famous French novelist Victor Hugo provides both an eloquent and an ecologically correct reference to this practice:

> Do you know what these piles of ordure are, collected at the corners of streets, those carts of mud carried off at night from streets, the frightful barrels of the nightman, and the fetid streams of subterranean mud which the pavement conceals from you? All this is a flowering field, it is green grass, it is mint, thyme, and sage; it is game, it is cattle, it is the satisfying lowing of heavy kine; at night it is perfumed hay, it is gilded wheat, it is bread on your table, it is warm blood in your veins, it is health, it is joy, it is life.

About one third of the plants in the United States provide primary treatment only. It is primarily a *mechanical* process in which most of the settleable solids are removed. Although it makes the sewage *look* a lot better, it still contains a substantial amount of organic material, nitrates, phosphates, and bacteria—some of which may cause human disease. Federal and state governments, with the aid of cost-sharing grants to municipalities are striving to replace primary treatment plants with secondary plants as soon as possible.

SECONDARY TREATMENT. About 60 per cent of the municipal sewage treatment plants in the United States provide secondary treatment. It is a more advanced treatment, primarily biological in nature, involving intensive use of bacterial activity. Its main function is to remove much of the suspended organic material that remains in the effluent after primary treatment.

Figure 6–13A indicates that fluid from the first sedimentation tank is piped to an *aeration tank* in which air is bubbled to provide a maximal supply of oxygen. This enables the aerobic (oxygen-using) bacteria to act with optimal efficiency in decomposing the organic compounds. It is apparent that the greater the amount of atmospheric oxygen used here in oxidizing this material, the less the demands on the limited supply of DO in the stream once the effluent is discharged. In other words, the BOD of the sewage is being greatly reduced. The liquid that accumulates at the top of sedimentation tank 2 is then chlorinated and discharged. However, the sludge that settles to the bottom of tank 2 is now called *activated sludge* because it bears a high number of bacteria that have become conditioned to the unique environment of the system. Only a part of this activated sludge is piped to the sludge digester. The remainder is *recycled* back to the aeration tank and sedimentation tank 2, in turn activating the inflowing nonactivated effluent.

Secondary treatment removes 90 per cent of the BOD and 90 per cent of the suspended solids. However, fully 50 per cent of the nitrogen compounds and 30 per cent of the phosphorus compounds (the chemical "culprits" responsible for eutrophication) still remain. Tertiary treatment is required to remove them.

TERTIARY TREATMENT. In this rather costly, most advanced method of sewage treatment, the effluent is rapidly mixed with lime in order to remove the phosphate by precipitation. The nitrogen, which occurs in sewage primarily as ammonia, is "stripped" from the effluent in a "stripping tower," where large amounts of air are blown through the sewage.

Lake Tahoe, an isolated beauty in the High Sierras on the California-Nevada border, provides a classic example of the effectiveness of tertiary treatment in reducing the eutrophication problems caused by sewage. Once it was an aquatic "jewel," with gravel bottom, clear cold water, abundant trout populations—a swimmer, angler, tourist delight. However, in the early 1960's definite symptoms of

Figure 6-15. *"Scenic" Lake Tahoe. Note boatmen trying to make headway through barrier of algal growths caused by eutrophication.* [E.P.A.-Documerica—Belinda Rain]

Figure 6-16. *Tertiary sewage treatment plant at South Lake Tahoe, California. The capacity of this plant is about 7.5 million gallons per day. It effectively removes such nutrients as nitrogen and phosphorus from the sewage. As a result the eutrophication process, which threatened to destroy the beauty of Lake Tahoe and impair its recreational potential, has been arrested.* [California Department of Water Resources]

eutrophication appeared—weedy growths, slimy algal mats, bottom ooze, increased turbidity, declining game fish, and all the rest. Eutrophication was a direct result of the accelerated influx of both tourists and permanent residents to the area. An increase in people meant an increase in the amount of inadequately treated sewage discharged into the lake. Alarmed at seeing their "jewel" tarnished, the residents, who fortunately were rather affluent, decided to do something about their effluent. With the aid of expert technical advice they installed a 7.5-million-gallon tertiary treatment plant, which incorporates the most sophisticated developments in treatment technology. The cost of tertiary treatment at Tahoe is 30¢ per 1,000 gallons of effluent, compared with only 12¢ for secondary treatment. In a few years the eutrophication problem gradually lessened, and today the original beauty of the lake has been restored. What happens to the effluent? Instead of being discharged into the lake it is piped over the mountains rimming the lake to agricultural areas for use in irrigation.

While it would theoretically be advisable for all communities in the United States to follow Tahoe's example and provide tertiary treatment, the financial burden for the taxpayer would be somewhat increased. However, here again, as in other environmental dilemmas, the citizen must make a cost-benefit analysis. A few extra pennies on his yearly tax bill might mean the difference between an unsightly, smelly, carp-infested river or lake and an attractive aquatic resource. Are the extra pennies worth it?

Water Pollution and Industry

Industry's water use is increasing daily. It increased from 77 billion gallons per day in 1950 to 140 billion gallons per day in 1960. Estimated use for 1980 is 363 billion gallons per day and for 2000 is 662 billion gallons per day. Water is industry's most important raw material. It is used as a solvent, as a cleansing agent, as a mineral extractant, as a coolant, as a waste-removal agent, and so on.

The chemical industry is an important pollution source. Rate of pollution has kept pace with this industry's growth, which is one of the most rapidly growing industries in America. By 1963 total sales had increased 500 per cent since 1939, and by 1975 they are expected to have increased 1,000 per cent. Sales of synthetic organic compounds have zoomed. Thus, plastics sales increased from 20 million pounds in 1928 to 6 billion pounds in 1961, synthetic rubber increased from zero in 1928 to over 2 billion pounds in 1961, nylon (and other noncellulose fibers) increased from zero in 1928 to 800 million pounds in 1961.

Industrial pollution of water is much in evidence. Dyes from a factory stain a Mississippi tributary green. Oily scums spread over the Rouge River near Dearborn, Michigan. The Merrimack River bubbles with nauseating gases. Water from a Minnesota iron mine stains a trout stream. Partly because of industrial pollution the Niagara Falls emanate foul odors. Parts of the Missouri run red with slaughterhouse blood. Because thousands of industrial plants are employing the Mississippi River as an "open sewer," conservationists have renamed it the "colon of mid-

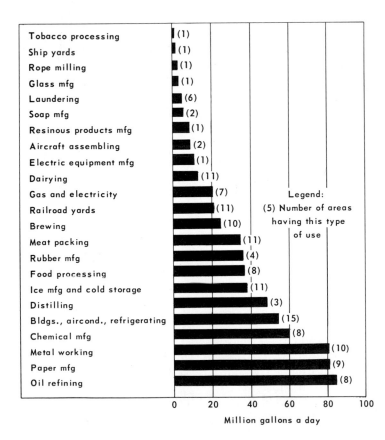

Figure 6-17. *Industrial use of ground water in the United States. Based on a sample of twenty urban areas. (Water from municipal systems is not included.)* [From Conserving Natural Resources *by Allen and Leonard. Copyright © 1966 by McGraw-Hill, Inc. Used by permission of McGraw-Hill Book Company.*]

Figure 6-18. *Aerial view of pollution along harbor front, Ashtabula Harbor, Ohio, in 1963.* [*U.S. Public Health Service*]

America." There is certainly little resemblance between its clear, sparkling head-waters at Lake Itasca (Minnesota) and the foul-smelling broth of domestic and industrial waste that spews into the Gulf at New Orleans.

Industrial wastes are destructive in many ways. Some have a high BOD, some have foul odors, some impart an ugly appearance to a stream, some are toxic to aquatic life, some curtail photosynthesis, and of course all industrial wastes help render the stream water unfit for human use.

Industrial pollutants may be severely toxic to aquatic vertebrates. Some wastes that are harmless alone may be lethal in combination with other contaminants. This phenomenon is called *synergism*. Heavy metal salts are an example. Thus, 8 parts per million of zinc or 2 parts per million of copper alone will not be injurious to game fish; however, only 1 part per million of the two combined will eradicate the fish. Spectacular fish kills have been caused in this way (16).

The effective treatment of industrial wastes, in particular those from chemical industries, is exceedingly complex and in many cases methods of treatment are unknown. Thanks to the Federal Water Pollution Control Act, which now provides more muscle than ever before to bring industrial offenders in line, a number of plants are studying possible methods of either reducing the amount of discharged waste or at least rendering it less toxic before release. They are finally beginning to accept the principle elucidated by the Environmental Protection Agency that pollution control is part of the expense involved in operating their plants. Some industries have effectively reduced pollution by converting their waste into commercially valuable by-products. Thus, the sugar beet industry has found a market for desiccated pulp and other former wastes. One company received a gross return on a single by-product that amounted to one tenth of the payment

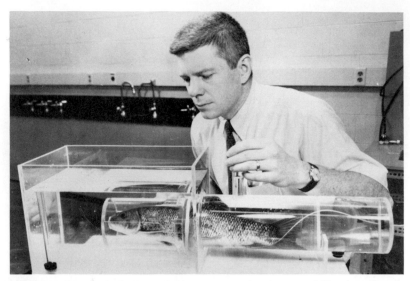

Figure 6-19. *A fisheries biologist uses a sucker in a specially constructed metabolism chamber at the E.P.A. National Water Quality Laboratory near Duluth, overlooking Lake Superior. This device simultaneously samples excretory products from three anatomical sites, furnishing clues to sub-lethal effects of toxic materials, such as copper and zinc. [U.S. Environmental Protection Agency, Office of Public Affairs]*

Figure 6-20. *Industrial pollution. Note surface films caused by effluent from factory in background. [Wisconsin Natural Resources Department, Madison, Wis.]*

received for the beets. Tanneries have similarly discovered that hair and fleckings have value and that their reclamation reduces the putrescence of a stream.

A few years ago an American-Canadian International Joint Commission reported that pollution in the Rainy River at International Falls, Minnesota, was a menace to health. It further stated that this pollution was largely caused by the effluent from a large paper and pulp plant located on the river's shore. Twelve years of dealing with this plant by the Minnesota Water Pollution Control Commission produced no improvement in the situation. Eventually, however, several studies were launched by the company to abate pollution. One of them involved a "dry-barking" process, in which the bark from poplar and aspen trees is removed without water. Other projects included a mill that would reduce the sulfite liquors so characteristic of pulp mill wastes.

Recently, the Kimberly-Clark Corporation planned to construct a giant pulp and paper mill in northern California. However, a state statute required that the effluent discharged into the Sacramento River have no poisonous effect on newly hatched salmon and steelhead trout. These fish are an important wildlife resource that attract anglers to California from all over the United States. The problem was finally solved after many technical difficulties, with the construction of a $2 million waste-purifying plant capable of treating 12 million gallons of mill waste daily.

Wastes from food-processing plants pose a special problem. The effluent, containing suspended inedible plant fibers, is rich in organic content and has an extremely high BOD. One of the most successful techniques for removal of this type of waste has been developed at Seabrook, New Jersey, where wastes are sprinkled on the floor of a forest. Some areas of the forest have received up to 4,000 inches of water in four years, with no apparent reduction in infiltration capacity.

On the other hand, some of the waste disposal schemes employed by industry have not been so well conceived. Take *injection wells*, for example. Certain wastes, such as arsenic compounds, cyanides, radioactive materials, and so on, are potentially so harmful to man that to discharge them directly into lakes and streams would be unthinkable. Furthermore, these wastes are not amenable to treatment by conventional waste disposal plants. Instead, many industries (oil refineries, pharmaceutical plants, chemical manufacturing companies, uranium mills, and photographic processing plants) have injected these wastes into wells ranging from 300 feet to over two miles in depth! For example, in order to dispose of strong acid wastes resulting from a steel-cleaning process, one company drilled a well 0.80 mile deep into an 1,800 foot thick layer of porous sandstone. In theory the wastes would then "stay put" because the waste-holding sandstone was completely walled-off by impervious rock. As of 1975 about 130 such wells were already in use and the prospect is for the construction of many more in the near future. However, suppose there is an earthquake. The wastes might then be released from their sandstone "prison," move laterally, and eventually contaminate an aquifer used by a community as a source of drinking water. In fact, there is evidence which suggests that the deep well injection technique may actually *cause* earthquakes. Thus, scientists have demonstrated a well-defined correlation between the volume of waste injected by the U. S. Army chemical plant near Denver, Colorado, and the frequency of earthquakes in the immediate region (19). Certainly, the injection well technique is similar to "sweeping pollution under the rug." It may be a stopgap answer for our generation, but the final effective solution is simply being postponed for our descendants, who might have a dire need for these aquifers in the next century.

Enforcement of Pollution Laws

In his State of the Union message to Congress in January, 1970, President Nixon proclaimed, "Clean air, clean water, open spaces—these should once again be the birthright of every American. . . . If we act now, they can be. . . ." He vowed that pollution standards would be more strict and more stringently enforced.

One of Nixon's most constructive accomplishments was the establishment of the Environmental Protection Agency, under the vigorous and courageous leadership of William Ruckelshaus. Before its formation the job of environmental "watchdog" had been splintered among several agencies. The results were chaotic, the action of one agency negating the program of another. Now, however, the campaign against environmental degradation has unified direction and integration. Its record, thus far, has been commendable. A direct result of the federal government's firmed-up posture against water polluters were the criminal charges filed by the U.S. Attorney General's office against seven industrial firms in New York City and New Jersey for contaminating the tributary waters of New York harbor. Among the concerns named for discharging oil and waste into the harbor were: E. I. duPont de Nemours, Texaco, Central Railroad of New Jersey, and the General Aniline and Film Corporation. They were prosecuted under a law enacted in 1898. Upon conviction the violators are subject to a $2,500 fine for each offense.

Affirming the stricter attitude of the federal government toward pollution, U.S. Attorney Frederick B. Lacey proclaimed, "Our rivers can no longer be used as a dump for garbage and waste. Water pollution is a serious health hazard and a threat to our environment." In a further demonstration of the stringent new policy,

Figure 6-21. *"Clean water . . . should once again be the birthright of every American." Water is essential to the life of all organisms, including children. Children drinking water from a fountain in Socto, California.* [California Department of Water Resources]

the U.S. Attorney General announced that thirteen Chicago area firms (including International Harvester, Pure Oil, and Procter and Gamble) were being charged with water pollution. After an intensive investigation by the U.S. Corps of Army Engineers, they were being accused of discharging such wastes as soybean oil, solvent, cyanide, grease, gasoline, ground limestone, fuel oil, suspended solids, and kerosene into Chicago area rivers, some of which empty into Lake Michigan. The litigation is an expression of the Environmental Protection Agency's efforts to arrest pollution of Lake Michigan. According to U.S. Attorney Thomas A. Foran, the action is "only the first step" in a "new program to enforce vigorously the federal criminal law against pollution."

Despite mounting public opinion against the environmental degradation caused by pollutants from industrial sources, many concerns still drag their feet. This attitude was prevalent at a recent conference of businessmen and government officials convened to consider the pollution problem. A representative from International Harvester maintained, "Industry can spend nothing [on pollution abatement] it does not first earn in profits." In a similar vein a U.S. Steel official voiced his opposition "to treatment for treatment's sake."

In order to prod industry into more effective pollution control, Senator Proxmire of Wisconsin has suggested that legislation be enacted that would compel industry to pay "by the pound" for their discharged pollutants. Total annual revenue from this source would amount to $1.5 billion. In an address at Memphis State University a few years ago, economist Walter W. Heller, of the University of Minnesota and former adviser to President John F. Kennedy, contended that industry must pay for the use of water and air just as it pays for raw materials, machinery, and labor. According to Heller:

> This is good sound economics and sound social policy. . . . It has to be done by tough national regulations and penalties, regulations that treat all competitors alike. Giving special tax incentives and rewards to those who install pollution-abatement facilities is the wrong road to take. . . . It imposes the costs on the public . . . instead of on the users of the product where they belong.

In any event, effective water pollution control programs, whether instituted by federal, state, or municipal governments or by private industry, will be expensive. Experts are largely agreed that adequate control of water pollution on a nation-wide basis will cost a minimum of $30 billion during the five year period 1975–1980. Ultimately, of course, the consumer will finance any industrial projects by paying higher prices for goods, while the taxpayer will support governmental programs. Considering the resultant environmental gains, however, the costs per capita would be minimal. It has been estimated, for example, that a mere 25¢ per month increase in most consumers' electric bills would finance the annual $700 million expense to curb industrial and power plant pollution.

New Sources of Water

It is apparent that as our population continues to increase, as more and more sewage must be diluted and transported, as Americans acquire more leisure time for recreational use of water resources, as more water-using gadgets—such as garbage grinders, automatic washers, and air conditioning units—proliferate, the per capita water use in this country will inevitably increase. The per capita average daily use of water, which was only 600 gallons in 1900, increased to 1,500 gallons in 1960 and is expected to be 2,300 gallons by 1980 and 2,700 gallons by 2000. The U.S. Public Health Service has estimated that the total municipal water use was only 21 billion gallons per day in 1960, but it estimated that needs will rise to 29 billion gallons per day by 1980 and to 43 billion gallons per day by 2000.

Where will this additional water come from? Not from the skies. Total annual rainfall in the United States has remained fairly constant for many centuries, except for occasional wet and dry spells, and probably will remain so for many centuries to come. Possible methods for alleviating the impending water shortage problem include reclamation of sewage water, development of ground water sources, use of asphalt pavements to catch and retain rainfall in desert areas, the desalination of seawater, eradication of moisture-wasting plants, forest removal, rain making, and the transfer of surplus water supplies to water-deficient areas.

Reclamation of Sewage Water. Although it might seem repugnant to utilize treated sewage water, sewage effluent is 99 per cent water, and when the 1 per cent of pollutant is removed, the final water product may be purer than the original substance (12). The advanced Waste Treatment Research Program was launched by the U.S. Public Health Service to explore and develop effective methods of processing sewage waste water for direct and deliberate use. Its major objectives are twofold: to separate pollutants from the water and dispose of them harmlessly and to recover the purified water product. Thus, in one process both the problem of sewage pollution and of water shortage would be solved. Several conversion processes have recently been investigated. The most promising processes in an operation treating 10 to 20 million gallons per day, together with the estimated cost of purifying 1,000 gallons, follow: foam separation process (2¢), coagulation-solids removal (4¢ to 8¢), adsorption (14¢ to 18¢), electrodialysis (40¢ to 50¢). Pilot plants have been established at Washington, D.C., Lebanon, Ohio, and three California sites (10). These laboratory-scale operations probably could become engineering realities by 1976.

Processed sewage water is already being utilized for a variety of functions. The Bethlehem Steel plant at Baltimore, Maryland, employs 150 million gallons of sewage effluent daily for steel-cooling purposes (9). Golf greens are sprinkled with it in San Francisco, Las Vegas, and Sante Fe. Treated sewage water is used to irrigate crops in the San Antonio area (12), and ornamental shrubs along highways in San Bernardino, California, are watered with it (1). For many years the Pennsylvania State University discharged sewage effluent directly into a stream. In 1962, however, it distributed the treated sewage water to nearby croplands and woods. Within three years multiple benefits were derived. Not only was crop production increased 300 per cent, but crops showed an increased protein content. Moreover, the annual lowering of the water table was reduced from 75 feet to just a few feet, tree growth was accelerated, and forest-dwelling wildlife benefited (12).

As a result of its location in a semiarid region, Los Angeles has been plagued with a perennial water shortage problem. The city daily discharges 600 million gallons of sewage water into the Pacific Ocean. Reclamation of this water would be considerably more economical than sea water desalination. The big problem besetting water engineers, however, has been the elimination of virus-contaminants that might be disseminated throughout the city and cause epidemics. Recently, Albert Bush, of the University of California at Los Angeles, devised a method of virus removal that would permit the reclamation of 50 per cent (300 million gallons per day) of the Los Angeles sewage waters. The reclaimed water could theoretically be used against brush fires, for irrigation, or for swimming and boating.

Los Angeles daily discharges 17 million gallons of processed sewage water over "spreading beds" at the edge of town. Eventually, this water seeps into aquifers that supply the town's wells. This water is of higher quality than water piped 200 miles from the Colorado River. Treated sewage water has also been employed in southern California to form a barrier to salt water intrusion. By the early 1960's water table levels had been dropping steadily in the coastal region, in some areas to a point 25 feet below sea level. As a result, salt water encroachment progressed at the rate of 1 mile per year. To check this intrusion, a freshwater wall was erected by injecting sewage water into a series of coastal wells (1). The use of reclaimed sewage water in Los Angeles alone is expected to quintuple during the period 1970–1990.

Development of Ground Water Resources.   Ground water forms 97 per cent of the world's freshwater supplies. In the 48 contiguous states there are 53,000 cubic miles of fresh water in the aquifers located in the upper half-mile of the earth's crust. This is 100 times the volume in the total run-off in all of our nation's water courses. Almost any 20-foot well in New England will deliver 2 to 5 gallons per minute; 50-foot wells near Miami frequently yield 1,000 to 1,500 gallons per minute.

However, most of the wells in the United States are at present too shallow and yield less than 400 gallons daily. In an effort to alleviate the impending water deficit, aquifers will be tapped to depths of 500 to 2,000 feet. Utilization of the increased supplies must be carefully planned from the long-range economic viewpoint. In some situations the proper decision may be to "mine" the water until the supply is exhausted; in other cases it may be better to draw the water on a sustained-yield basis (15).

The U.S. Geological Survey has embarked on at least fifty computer studies of surface and ground water resources as part of a nation-wide project to determine America's future water needs. Intensive efforts are being made to locate and develop new aquifers. Location determinations can be made by charting the earth's varying electrical sensitivity, by seismographs (15), by sampling cores taken during well drilling (6), by the study of geological features at the surface, and by aerial photography to determine the nature of ground water sources at or near the surface (14). Hydrologists are also employing radioactive tracer techniques to determine the pattern and rate of aquifer water flow. Such data will enable them to predict how withdrawal from one site will affect water tables at other points. These studies are already yielding results. Water-rich strata have been located in the southern California and Arizona region, which should markedly enhance the agricultural potential of this notoriously water-deficient area. Another was found at Salisbury, Maryland. A recent aquifer discovery under glacial Passaic Lake in northern New Jersey is capable of yielding 30 million gallons daily. After a hurricane had disrupted conventional water supplies, a 2,000-foot well shaft drilled under brackish Lake Pontchartrain in Louisiana provided emergency water for washing and drinking (18).

Use of Asphalt Coatings in Desert Regions.   Many desert plants possess remarkably flattened root systems that lie just a few inches below the desert floor; they permit utilization of rainfall before it vaporizes. Recently, the U.S. Geological

Survey developed a "human adaptation" that might be equally efficient in securing rainfall in desert regions. The technique involves coating the desert floor with water-impervious asphalt. Collected rainfall could be channeled into large water-holding pits from which it could be drawn off periodically either for irrigation or to raise the water table. On an experimental 9-acre asphalt-coated area near White Sands, New Mexico, 60 per cent of the rainwater was salvaged, compared with 3 per cent on a control plot. The survey estimates that up to 130,000 gallons of rainwater would be available from each asphalt-coated acre. Based on an annual precipitation of 15 inches, a 6- by-9-mile area would collect over 8 billion gallons yearly, sufficient to meet all the water requirements of 100,000 people (18).

Desalination. "Water, water everywhere, Nor any drop to drink" wailed the sailor in the *The Ancient Mariner*. It is a curious paradox that 70 per cent of the earth's surface is covered by oceans, in some places up to 6 miles deep, yet a water shortage harasses man from New York to New Delhi. Deeply concerned with this dilemma, in 1952 Congress authorized a research and development program for the improvement of *desalination* processes. Various types of desalination plants have been constructed, including *electrodialysis, flash distillation, solar distillation,* and *nuclear power*.

ELECTRODIALYSIS.[4]   Coalinga, California, was the first city in the United States to provide a community supply of fresh water by desalination. Electrodialytic methods there reduce the mineral salt content of the well water from 2,200 to 300–350 parts per million and yield 28,000 gallons daily (1). Webster, South Dakota, which initiated operation of an electrodialytic plant in October, 1961, has a capacity of 250,000 gallons per day and reduces salinity from 1,800 to less than 275 parts per million (1). At Port Mansfield, Texas, where saltwater intrusion from the Gulf of Mexico contaminates artesian well sources, an $827,000 plant was dedicated in December, 1965, with a 250,000-gallon capacity (22). Although electrodialytic conversion is suitable primarily for smaller communities because of limited capacity, it could be profitably employed in at least 1,000 American communities where water sources are at least 1 per cent salt (22).

FLASH DISTILLATION.   The federal government established a flash distillation plant in Freeport, Texas, which utilizes water from the Gulf coast. The water is superheated to 250° F, vaporizes, condenses in cool coils, and is conveyed to storage tanks. The resultant product, which is produced at the rate of 1 million gallons per day, tastes so flat that salt must be added to enhance palatability. Some authorities predict that by 1986 huge flash distillation plants with capacities of 500 million gallons per day will be constructed in critically water-short urban areas.

The multistage flash distillation plant that was constructed at San Diego, California, in 1962 has received considerable publicity. This plant can convert 1 million gallons per day at a cost of 97¢ per 1,000 gallons. It provided San Diego with 1.33 per cent of its water supply (1). In 1963, when Castro threatened to choke off the water supply used by American marines at the Guantanamo Naval Base, the San

---

[4] Electrodialysis—a desalination process involving a series of parallel membranes placed between two electrodes. As salt water flows between the membranes, the sodium ions and chlorine ions are progressively removed.

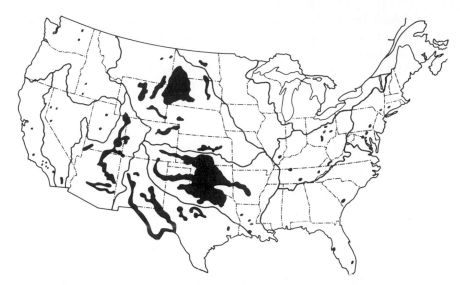

Figure 6-22. *Regions of brackish water in the United States. Because this water is not potable, it must be desalinated. This map was based on a survey by the Office of Saline Water, U.S. Department of the Interior.* [*From* Conserving Natural Resources *by Allen and Leonard. Copyright © 1966 by McGraw-Hill, Inc. Used by permission of McGraw-Hill Book Company.*]

Figure 6-23. *Desalination plant at Chula Vista, California.* [*California Department of Water Resources*]

Diego plant was dismantled and shipped to Cuba to ensure a continuing source of fresh water.

SOLAR DISTILLATION. In addition to conducting its own research in solar distillation, the federal government is heavily subsidizing investigations at universities and institutes. The sea water conversion Solar Research Station set up at Daytona Beach, Florida, in 1958 pumps sea water from the mouth of the Halifax River. This water, which has a salinity of 35,000 parts per million, is channeled into a glass-roofed basin to a depth of 7 to 12 inches. The water absorbs solar energy, vaporizes, and condenses on the glass roof from which it is collected. This station also has two stills with plastic roofs. The total yield of the three stills is 500 gallons of fresh water daily. When there is adequate sunshine, roughly 1 pound of fresh water is secured per square foot of basin surface per day.

NUCLEAR POWER. The federal government has published a report in which it proposed the construction of mammoth nuclear-powered plants that would not only provide fresh water but would also yield electrical power. One of these plants would be capable of producing 620 million gallons per day, enough water to supply the needs of a major city. However, the water would cost 25¢ per 1,000 gallons even before delivery. Householders would have to pay perhaps 40¢ per 1,000 gallons for delivery to their homes. More recently a plant has been proposed for southern California that not only would produce 150 million gallons per day at a cost of 22¢ to 30¢ per 1,000 gallons but would provide the Los Angeles region with 1.8 million kilowatts of electricity.

This program, however, has certain drawbacks. According to John C. Maxwell, Department of Geological Engineering, Princeton University, these plants would inevitably produce enormous quantities of heat, concentrated brine, and radioactive wastes. Certainly the destruction of oysters, crustaceans, and fish in estuaries would be severe. If not properly dissipated, the warmed-up ocean waters near the plant might trigger such a "bloom" of marine plants that a thick green algal "soup" could some day smother the California coast. Moreover, the radioactive waste, which remains potentially injurious for up to 1,000 years, would have to be contained in some manner that would remove its threat to human well-being.

Eradication of Moisture-wasting Plants. *Phreatophytes* are undesirable plants that occur primarily in the arid Southwest. They absorb and transpire exceptionally large volumes of water, roughly 50 to 100 per cent more than agricultural crops (14). Among the most important phreatophytes, which cover about 16 million acres, are salt cedar, cottonwood, willow, greasewood, rabbitbrush, cattail, and tule. The salt cedar, whose roots extend down to the water table, inflicts a 20-trillion-gallon water loss in a 900,000-square-mile area of western United States (10). Hydrologists of the U.S. Geological Survey determine the volume of water loss with delicate moisture-sensitive infrared film that is exposed while flying at low altitudes over a given salt cedar stand. The data are then radioed back to a computer on the ground (10).

Herbicides have superseded mechanical control methods because of superior effectiveness and lower cost ($25 to $43 per mile) (9). One to 6 million acre-feet of water can be saved annually, according to the Senate Select Committee on National Water Resources, if the phreatophytes are properly controlled. This salvaged water could be pumped into irrigation systems (1).

Forest Removal. It has been estimated that the daily domestic requirements of 100,000 people can be satisfied with 12 million gallons of water. Were this water spread over a 10-square-mile watershed, it would form a layer only 0.1 inch deep. However, in a single day the root systems of a growing stand of timber on that same 10-square-mile watershed could absorb *twice* this amount of water. It is apparent, therefore, that as water-demands increase, responsible officials must eventually determine whether a given watershed acreage is more valuable for water collection and storage than for timber, wildlife habitat, scenic beauty, or some other function. It could well be that in some areas timber, with its high water requirements, should be replaced with grass or some other vegetation with lesser water needs. Watershed research in humid West Virginia and North Carolina has shown that clearcutting has produced maximal annual increments of 12 to 16 inches, or 326,000 to 434,000 gallons per acre. Increases were smaller in partial cuttings. In North Carolina the clearcutting of oak stands growing in deep soil resulted the following year in sufficient increment per square mile to supply the needs of 6,800 people (9).

However, such techniques will not be invariably successful. It depends upon the individual climate, topography, forest, and soil. For example, the thinning of lodgepole pine stands in the Rockies of Colorado did not substantially increase overall water yield (9).

Rain Making.   Rain making is a novel approach to increasing man's water supplies. One technique involves seeding clouds with crystals of dry ice and silver iodide, with the hope that these crystals will serve as condensation nuclei around which moisture droplets will collect until a drop of rain is formed (15). A few years ago a presidential Advisory Committee on Weather Control concluded that although seeding had no clearly defined influence in increasing precipitation in nonmountainous areas, seeding of winter storm clouds in the mountainous western states resulted in a 10 to 15 per cent increase in rainfall. However, because of the high cost of rainmaking ventures, the employment of this technique is perhaps ill advised except under emergency conditions of water storage. One drawback is the lack of control over the volume and distribution of induced precipitation. For example, a late July rainfall might benefit the corn farmer but might be damaging to cut alfalfa awaiting the bailer (6). Increased rainfall may improve forage for cattle but may be deleterious to fruit orchards. Even more serious, induced rainfall might contribute to flooding, as has been suggested by Virginia Brodine:

> The danger of an experiment at the wrong time and place was demonstrated when a rainmaking experiment in the summer of 1972 was carried out near Rapid City, South Dakota, while a storm was gathering. Experimenters claimed that the cloud-seeding had no effect on the subsequent 14-inch rain and the flood that followed, but this is impossible to prove—just as it is impossible to prove that the experiment augmented the rain. It is clear, however, that there was inadequate understanding of the weather conditions and poor judgment in seeding clouds which *could* contribute to the severity of the rainfall (2).

According to the U.S. Geological Survey, rain making probably could be used to greatest advantage in the West, where increased mountain snowfall can be used to boost water supplies for valley ranches during the ensuing arid summer. The potential of cloud-seeding for increasing water supplies is under continuing study at the National Center for Atmospheric Research, which was established at Denver, Colorado, in 1961 (1).

Long-Distance Transport: The California Water Project.   Looking down on the planet Earth, a shrinking bluish sphere far below, America's moon-bound astronauts could identify only two man-made structures—one was the Great Wall of China, the other the main aqueduct of the California Water Project (CWP). California has long been victimized by the curious fact that 70 per cent of the state's potentially usable water has its source in the northern third of the state (in the form of relatively abundant rainfall and the snow melt of the High Sierras), while 77 per cent of the demand is located in the semiarid southern two-thirds, occupied by 10 million people, where only 5 inches of rain falls per year. Voted the nation's outstanding civil engineering project of 1972, the most complex and expensive water-moving project in the history of the world, it includes 21 dams and reservoirs, 22 pumping plants, and 685 miles of canals, tunnels, and pipelines. A pretty expensive "faucet," the project cost well over $2 billion—enough money to build two St. Lawrence Seaways or six Panama Canals (4).

The keystone to the system is the Oroville Dam (as tall as a 77-story skyscraper), which blocks northern California's Feather River to form 15,800 acre Lake Oroville. With a depth of 700 feet, the lake could feed all the household faucets in California for a full year before finally going dry. The water is alternately moved by pumps

Figure 6-24. *Focal point of the California Water Plan System is Oroville Dam and Lake pictured here. The lake provides multiple benefits, including recreational facilities such as swimming, boating and fishing, scenic beauty, a source of water power for the production of electrical power, and is released to arid regions for irrigation purposes. [California Department of Water Resources]*

Figure 6-25. *California Water Plan. Aerial view of the Tehachapi Range in California. At bottom left of photo is the Edmonston Pumping Plant, which pumps water upward to an elevation of 1,400 feet above the plant. The water is then transferred by aqueducts across the range to the valley seen at top of photo. [California Department of Water Resources]*

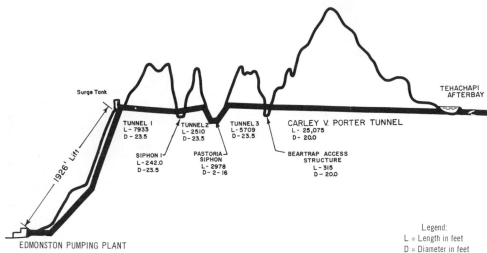

Figure 6-26. *Diagram showing the path of the water across the Tehachapi Mountains. Note that the water is pumped upward 1,926 feet to Tunnel 1 before moving across the mountain range* [*California Department of Water Resources*]

and gravity toward southern California, the main aqueduct being sufficiently wide and deep to float an ocean-going steamship. Eventually the water is channeled to the foot of mile-high Tehachapi Mountain, a seemingly impassable barrier. However, with the aid of fourteen 80,000-horsepower pumps the water is pushed up to the 3,000-foot level. From here it rushes downslope to the fertile San Joaquin Valley and the densely populated cities of Los Angeles and San Diego. From beginning to end the system extends a distance equal to that from New York City to Columbia, South Carolina (4).

The CWP is a classic example of a multiple function project:

1. It provides water for the lower San Joaquin Valley, converting a 250,000 acre cactus-jackrabbit-rattlesnake wasteland to lush, crop-productive farmland that may eventually gross $75 million per year. It was estimated that in 1970 alone the crop production made possible by CWP produced 800,000 tons of oxygen, sufficient to supply the annual requirement of 1 million people.
2. It will raise the dangerously low water table in a 600,000-acre area of the San Joaquin Valley, which had receded because of overdrafts from irrigation wells.
3. Through 1973 it had already generated 9.2 billion kilowatt hours of electricty. The Devil Canyon Power Plant unit harnesses the energy derived from a water level drop of over 1,400 feet.
4. Its complex system of dams serves to curb the surging waters of the Feather and Sacramento rivers when swollen with spring rains and mountain snow melt, thus minimizing property damage and loss of human life. During the severe winter storm period of 1964–1965, the Oroville Dam alone prevented an estimated $30 million in downstream flood damage.
5. It provides a variety of recreational opportunities for millions of vacationists seeking refuge from the noise and bustle of the urban environment. Through 1971, 14.4 million visitors enjoyed such activities as swimming, fishing, water-skiing, sailing, and hiking. The cane poles of youngsters as well as the fiberglas rods of adults are arching to the scrappy fight of a variety of game fish, from rainbow and brown

Figure 6-27. *Aerial view of the California Aqueduct in Antelope Valley. [California Department of Water Resources]*

trout to black bass and catfish—all well stocked by the California Department of Fish and Game (4).

Despite the obvious benefits derived from this colossal project, certain aspects have drawn heated criticism from environmentalists. They argue that the proposed $208 million forty-three-mile auxiliary canal that would transport water from the north around San Francisco Bay would reduce the volume of fresh water flowing into the bay. The result would be salt water intrusion and attendant destruction to fish and wildlife habitat. Environmentalists also criticize the proposal to dam up other free-flowing "wild" rivers in northwestern California such as the Eel, Klamath, and Trinity. In their view too many of such unharnessed streams have already been "sacrificed" on the altar of irrigation and power production.

Notwithstanding these criticisms, and the enormous cost to the people of California, CWP is an accomplished fact and seemingly will do much to solve southern California's recurring water-shortage crises.

BIBLIOGRAPHY

1. Allen, Shirley W. and Justin W. Leonard. *Conserving Natural Resources.* New York: McGraw-Hill, 1966.
2. Anonymous. "River of Junk in North Dakota," *Audubon* (May 1972), p. 103.
3. Brodine, Virginia. *Air Pollution.* New York: Harcourt, 1973.

4. California Department of Water Resources. *The California Water Plan*. Sacramento, Cal., 1973.
5. Commoner, Barry. "Salvation: It's Possible," *Progressive* (April 1970), 12–18.
6. Cunningham, Floyd F. *1001 Questions Answered About Water Resources*. New York: Dodd, 1967.
7. Ehrenfeld, David W. *Biological Conservation*. New York: Holt, 1970.
8. Ehrlich, Paul R., and Anne H. Ehrlich. *Population, Resources, Environment*. San Francisco: Freeman, 1970.
9. Jones, E. Bruce, Richard Lee, and John C. Frey. "Land Management for City Water," *Outdoors USA: The Yearbook of Agriculture*. Washington, D.C.: U.S. Department of Agriculture, 1967.
10. Leopold, Luna B. *Water*. New York: Time, 1966.
11. Lull, Howard W. "How Our Cities Meet Their Water Needs," *Outdoors USA: The Yearbook of Agriculture*. Washington, D.C.: U.S. Department of Agriculture, 1967.
12. Mattison, C. W., and Joseph Alvarez. *Man and His Resources in Today's World*. Mankato, Minn.: Creative Educational Society, 1967.
13. Moran, Joseph M., Michael D. Morgan, and James H. Wiersma. *An Introduction to Environmental Sciences*. Boston: Little, Brown, 1973.
14. Peterson, Elmer T. "Insoak Is the Answer," *Land*, 11 (1952), 83–88.
15. Smith, Guy-Harold, ed. *Conservation of Natural Resources*. New York: Wiley, 1965.
16. Smith, Robert L. *Ecology and Field Biology*. New York: Harper, 1966.
17. Turk, Amos, Jonathan Turk, and Janet T. Wittes. *Ecology, Pollution, Environment*. Philadelphia: Saunders, 1972.
18. U.S. Department of the Interior. *The Third Wave*. Washington, D.C.: 1967.
19. Wagner, Richard H. *Environment and Man*. New York: Norton, 1971.
20. Warren, Charles E. *Biology and Water Pollution Control*. Philadelphia: Saunders, 1971.
21. Wilson, Ralph C. "Small Watersheds Make a Big Splash," *Outdoors USA: The Yearbook of Agriculture*. Washington, D.C.: U.S. Department of Agriculture, 1967.
22. Wright, James Claud. *The Coming Water Famine*. New York: Coward, 1966.

7.

Rangelands

All flesh is grass.

Isaiah XL, 3

It was mid-August, 1973, during the height of the meat shortage. The little old lady entered a Midwest supermarket and strode briskly to the meat counter, and stared! The rows of sterile, gleaming meat trays were empty, except for one scrawny chicken that was selling at $1.39 per pound. Where were the sirloins? The T-bones? The lamb chops? These were the days when the lowly hamburger and hot dog suddenly enjoyed "luxury" status, the days when housewives the nation over acquired the "beans-pancakes-spaghetti" habit—to the distress of their families. It wasn't much gastronomic fun to move down to the second link of the food chain —even though it was an ecological position held by most of the world for millennia. These were the days when meat-hungry citizens, who had hitherto been law-abiding, began poaching deer; when cattle-rustlers, long relegated to TV westerns, were suddenly being recorded "live" on ranches throughout the nation. Regrettably, it is only during periods of acute shortage such as this that Americans really appreciate their enviable life style and their abundant resources—that they trace, for example, the energy flow from a veal cutlet or sirloin backward to those most unusual, highly specialized plants, the *range grasses*, which make the livestock industry possible in the first place.

Thousands of years before the Christian era, man had learned to cultivate species of the grass family as a food source. The Indo-Chinese culture was based on rice, the Mediterranean culture on wheat, and the culture of early America on maize, or corn.

The leaves of grasses, from big bluestem to blue grama, convert solar energy to a form usable by animals—including cattle, sheep and men. Carnivorous man secures this energy in the form of veal, beef, mutton, or lamb. On the other hand, grazing herbivores—such as cattle, sheep, and goats—obtain this energy directly by chewing and digesting the grasses. In a very real sense, therefore, the Biblical statement, "All flesh is grass," is true.

Figure 7-1. *San Antonio, Texas. Close-up of big bluestem —a native perennial bunchgrass. March is the optimal planting time. Abundant in true prairie climax.* [Soil Conservation Service, U.S. Department of Agriculture]

The 109 million beef cattle on farms and ranches in the United States (at $149 per head) are worth $12.6 billion, and the 18.1 million grazing sheep (at $19.20 per head) represent a total resource worth $365 million. The cattle and sheep industry in the United States produces about $12 billion worth of meat and other products yearly—roughly 7 per cent of our nation's gross national product. This industry, which dwarfs even the steel and automobile industries, produces over 18 billion pounds of dressed beef yearly (90 pounds for every man, woman, and child in the United States), in addition to 1 billion pounds of veal and 715 million pounds of lamb and mutton.

Rangeland Depletion

The cattle industry's phenomenal expansion during the nineteenth century was responsible for much of the settlement of the West. For this we can thank thousands of courageous, hard-working ranchers and farmers. However, we cannot thank them for the ruthlessness with which they abused a once bounteous grassland resource.

Cattlemen severely depleted the ranges in many areas. Where a given pasture could have supported only 25 cattle, many were trying to graze 100. As a result, the big bluestem, the bluegrass, and the buffalo grass were gnawed down to the roots. Once the grass plant's metabolic reserve had been eliminated, the vitality of the root system became severely impaired and death was the inevitable result. Many of these nineteenth-century stockmen were so engrossed in *numbers* of range animals that they disregarded the fact that *four* head of livestock, sick and scrawny from

Figure 7-2. *Texas longhorns being unloaded at a railhead in Dodge City, Kansas, about one century ago.* [*U.S. Department of Agriculture*]

Figure 7-3. *New Mexico. Comparison of root systems of blue grama (left) and a shrub. The dense root system of grama is much more effective in binding soil and preventing erosion.* [*Soil Conservation Service, U.S. Department of Agriculture*]

undernourishment, would not have as much market value as *one* head in prime condition after grazing on good forage.

We must not be too severe in our criticism, however. These ranchers could not take a course in range management or plant ecology and learn about the principles of plant succession, limiting factors, and tolerance ranges.

In a desperate attempt to increase our food production during the emergency caused by World War I, our federal forest authorities in 1918 permitted an additional million animals to graze on forest ranges despite the already overly severe grazing pressure. In addition, much valuable rangeland was ripped up and turned face down by the newly developed "goliath" plows and then was seeded to wheat. Many of these farming enterprises were ill fated. Thus, except for one bumper crop year, the average annual income for a 640-acre wheat farm in western Kansas over a twenty-one-year period was only $35 (2).

Finally, in 1932, the seriousness of the range problem prompted Congress to request the U.S. Forest Service to make a survey of the overall range condition. The survey showed conclusively that rangeland productivity had been reduced by 50 per cent. On some Utah ranges, rice grass (a valuable forage species during the critical winter period when most pasture is covered with snow) was reduced almost 90 per cent under the intense grazing pressure. The survey further revealed that the removal of extensive grass cover had exposed 80 per cent of the range to erosion of varying degrees of severity (1).

Figure 7-4. *A lightly grazed pasture consisting of a dense growth of tobosa with some sacation, on the right of this fence. At the left is overgrazed rangeland where the vegetation has become sparse; there is a growth of worthless soleropogon and some sacation. [Soil Conservation Service, U.S. Department of Agriculture]*

Taylor Grazing Control Act

As a direct consequence of the Forest Service report on the condition of our western range, Congress enacted the Taylor Grazing Control Act in 1934. This represented the successful culmination of a long struggle on the part of conservationists to place our ailing public rangelands under effective federal control. The act had three major objectives: (1) the checking of deterioration, (2) the institution of projects designed to maintain and improve the range, and (3) the stabilization of the rangeland economy. Although only 80 million acres of rangelands were included in the original provisions, the acreage was increased to 160 million acres by 1959. Since the end of World War II, the administration of these rangelands has been charged to the Bureau of Land Management. The lands included in these grazing districts were, at one time, among the most badly depleted in the nation. Even in 1951, after several years of protection under the Taylor Grazing Control Act, the Bureau of Land Management estimated that 50 per cent of the land was severely eroded and 32 per cent was suffering from moderate erosion; on only 18 per cent was erosion damage slight or nonexistent.

The basic organizational and operational unit in the scheme is the *grazing district*, which is roughly analogous to the soil conservation district. The grazing district is run by a local committee of ranchers in collaboration with representatives of the federal government. As of 1959 the grazing lands were divided into 59 districts (primarily in Utah, Nevada, Arizona, New Mexico, Colorado, Wyoming, Idaho, Montana, Oregon, and California) ranging in size from 3 million to 9 million acres. By 1959, over 7.7 million head of livestock were being grazed in these districts by roughly 17,000 ranchers. Each rancher was charged a fee for the privilege of grazing his animals on these federal lands. Typical fees have been 22¢ for five goats or sheep, 22¢ per head of cattle, and 44¢ per horse. During the 1956–1964 period alone, almost 11.5 million acres of rangeland was reseeded, and 11,835 acres of shelter belts were established within the framework of the grazing district.

Grass Plant Biology

In order to appreciate certain aspects of rangeland management, we should first briefly examine the grass plant's remarkable root system, its highly specialized leaves, and its methods of seed dispersal.

Roots. Unlike the simple *taproot* system of many rangeland weeds consisting of a single main root, the *fibrous root* system of a grass plant has a number of major roots, each of which may have many primary, secondary, and tertiary branches. (Fig. 7-5) A plant with a taproot can be easily uprooted with a rather negligible amount of earth clinging to it. Conversely, a grass plant is exceedingly difficult to uproot, and it comes free with a big clump of earth adhering to it. Howard Dittmer, of the University of New Mexico, has estimated that the fibrous root system of a 21-inch rye plant may bear 14 million branches, over 300 miles long. He further estimated that 1 cubic inch of soil taken from under a Kentucky bluegrass plant may contain up to 2,000 root branches. It is no wonder that grass is the cover par excellence in controlling soil erosion.

Leaves. A unique feature of the leaf is its *basal* rather than *apical* growth zone. Most plants, such as alfalfa, clover, sage, or mesquite, have leaves with apical (toward the leaf tip) growth zones. Were a jackrabbit or steer to clip off such a leaf tip, leaf growth would be terminated, thereby reducing the vigor of the plant, which was dependent upon that leaf to manufacture a certain quota of food. But when a leaf tip of rangeland grass is clipped, as long as the basal zone remains intact, the leaf can grow in a short time to its original length. In fact, the grass leaf can be grazed again and again without adverse affects, thus providing a continuous food reservoir for the grazing animal. Range ecologists generally regard the upper 50 per cent of the grass shoot (stem and leaves) as representing a "surplus" that can be safely eaten by livestock or wild herbivores (deer, antelope, elk, and so on) without damaging the plant. The lower 50 per cent, known as the *metabolic reserve*, is required by the plant for survival, for this minimum of photosynthetic equipment is needed to manufacture foods required by the roots. When a range is badly overgrazed, the herbivores "bite" into the metabolic reserve, frequently clipping the grass to the bare ground, causing starvation and death of the root system and rendering that particular site vulnerable to erosion.

Seed Dispersal. An embryo is formed when the egg is fertilized by the sperm in the pollen grain. This embryo, together with a food reservoir and an enclosing protective seed coat, composes the *seed*. Seeds may simply drop to the ground at the base of the parent plant and germinate the following spring, thus entering into competition with the parent for sunlight, moisture, and soil nutrients. The seeds of other species may be dispersed by wind, washed down slopes by run-off waters, or carried away by animals. Some grass seeds have sharp spines that readily adhere to the wool of a sheep, or the hide of a steer or antelope, only to drop off many yards or even miles from the parent plant. Rodents such as pocket mice and kangaroo rats may transport grass seeds to their burrows. A number of grasses have successfully invaded the United States from abroad as seeds. Thus, Kentucky bluegrass, which is considered a top-quality forage species, apparently was accidentally introduced from Europe as a grain contaminant by early colonists.

During protracted drought grass seeds may remain dormant near the ground surface for several years. Then, as soil moisture gradually accumulates during a wet year, they may germinate and cause a drab straw-colored rangeland to turn green within a few days.

Effect of Drought on Range Forage

Drought is perhaps the rancher's greatest environmental problem. He can to some degree control rodents, poisonous plants, brush and weeds, predators, disease-causing insects, and soil chemistry, but there is absolutely nothing he can do (except for cloud seeding) about controlling drought. He can adjust to it, but that is all. Moreover, drought is unpredictable.

Deterioration. Through processes of evolution operating over many centuries, western range plants developed a variety of drought adaptations (described in Chapter 2) that enable them to survive as a species, even though individual plants may succumb.

Nevertheless, a severe drought may effect a drastic deterioration of the range plant community, regardless of severity of grazing pressure. Three examples follow. (1) In the Snake River plains of southern Idaho, the 1934 drought caused an 84 per cent reduction from the range plant cover of 1932, even though livestock had been excluded from the study plot. (2) During a thirteen-year period marked by an aggregate eight years of drought, the black grama (*Bouteloua eriopoda*) cover of an ungrazed plot was reduced 89.1 per cent (14). (3) In western Kansas, the 1934 drought killed 74.8 per cent of plants on study areas that were overgrazed and 64.6 per cent on pastures that were grazed in moderation (3).

Range Recovery. Once the dry spell has ended, range recovery may be fast or slow, depending upon precipitation. Thus, a lightly grazed Montana pasture required eight years to return to good condition after the 1934–1936 drought.

The close correlation between rainfall and range plant growth was strikingly evident in a study conducted in southwest Utah on the Desert Experimental Range of the U.S. Forest Service. Dry herbage production in October ranged from 95 pounds per acre when total rainfall the preceding year was under 4 inches, to more than 450 pounds per acre when precipitation the preceding year was 10.5 inches. Moreover, the relationship between rainfall and forage weight was so precise that it could be expressed in terms of a mathematical formula.

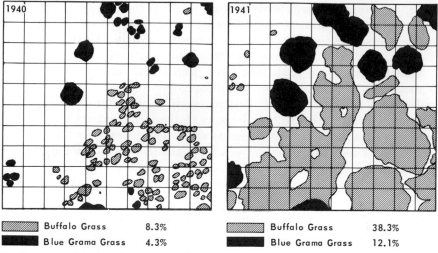

	Buffalo Grass	8.3%			Buffalo Grass	38.3%
	Blue Grama Grass	4.3%			Blue Grama Grass	12.1%

Total coverage of quadrat 12.6 per cent and 50.4 per cent.

Figure 7-5. *Recovery of drought-depleted range following a period of adequate rainfall. Basal cover of range vegetation near Ness City, Kansas, had been reduced to only 12.6 per cent of the area of a sample meter quadrat by the autumn of 1940. Overgrazing had contributed to the deterioration. However, within one year after the return of adequate rainfall, range grasses responded sufficiently to cover 50.4 per cent of the sample plot. [Adapted from Ruben L. Parsons,* Conserving American Resources *(Englewood Cliffs, N.J.: Prentice-Hall, Inc., 1956). After Albertson and Weaver,* Ecol. Mono. 14 *(January 1944), pp. 1–29.]*

Range Management

Range management has been defined by Stoddard and Smith as "the science and art of planning and directing range use so as to obtain the maximum livestock production consistent with conservation of range resources" (14). In the context of range management we shall here consider methods of maintaining the range in good condition, such as varying the grazing pressure, manipulating stock, using fire, and reseeding. We shall consider the selection and development of cattle breeds. Finally, we shall describe problems posed by rangeland pests and how they can best be controlled.

Management of Range Grasses.

ASSESSMENT OF RANGE CONDITION. The term *range condition* may be defined as "the current condition of the range site in relation to its theoretical potential." It refers to the health or productivity of the range.

CLASSES. Various criteria are employed as a basis for establishing categories of range condition. Among them are (1) the species composition of the plant community in terms of the plant succession, (2) the vigor of the plants, (3) the amount of plant residue or mulch on the ground, (4) the condition of the soil with regard to structure and erodibility, and (5) the number of animal units that can be supported per acre. Four range condition classes are recognized on the basis of these criteria: excellent, good, fair, and poor. It must be emphasized that in comparing range conditions, one must always deal with ranges belonging to identical or very similar range sites. It is apparent that a range in the arid sagebrush region of Wyoming may be in "excellent" condition and still be much less productive than a "good" ranch in the semiarid short grass region of Nebraska. We shall now describe the range condition in terms of the preceding criteria.

Composition of the Plant Community. Ranchers frequently classify the various range plants in three categories with respect to the dynamics of plant succession: *decreasers, increasers,* and *invaders. Decreasers* are highly nutritious, highly palatable members of the climax community that generally decrease under heavy grazing pressure. Representative decreaser species are big bluestem, little bluestem, blue grama, wheat grass, and buffalo grass. *Increasers,* on the other hand, are generally less palatable but are still highly nutritious climax species that tend to increase (at least temporarily) when a range is heavily grazed. Apparently this increase is the result of reduced competition with the decreasers, whose numbers have lessened. When severe grazing pressure continues over a long period of time, even the increasers begin to decrease, apparently not being able to withstand trampling by hoofs of grazing animals, and are replaced by invaders. The *invaders*—such as ragweed, cactus, and thistle—may be considered as undesirable weed species, low in nutritional value, and not very desirable for grazing animals. Invaders frequently are annual forbs or herbs that thrive best under sunlight intensities much higher than the 1 to 2 per cent of full sunlight occurring under a dense stand of climax grasses. Because their roots are simple taproots instead of the dense fibrous roots of a typical grass, these invaders are not very effective in binding the soil. A range in excellent condition has a high percentage of decreasers and no invaders. Conversely, a range in poor condition characteristically has a low percentage of high-forage-value decreasers and a relatively large component of low-forage-value invaders. As a result of this forage differential, an excellent range may require only 1 acre per *animal unit month,*[1] whereas 5 or even 10 acres may be required on poor range.

Plant Vigor. Reduction in plant vigor usually precedes change in the composition of the range plant community. Thus, if decreased vitality of forage species can be detected quickly enough, reduction in size of the herd may allow the range to regain its original vigor by natural processes. Recognition of reduced vitality is based upon plant color (dark green or yellow), number of leaves, seed production, and plant size and weight.

Plant Residue, or Mulch. Mulch is herewith defined as "dead plant material that accumulates on the ground surface." It represents a very reliable indicator of range condition (12). Mulch represents a link between the forage plants and the organic content of the soil. When mulch decreases in quantity, soil fertility ultimately will decline and the range will deteriorate. Mulch serves to increase the porosity (and hence drainage and aeration) of the soil; it may prevent seed

---

[1] Animal unit month = the forage necessary to keep one head of cattle well fed for one month.

transported by wind and water. The amount of mulch on a range varies with the temperature, moisture, plant composition, grazing pressure, and other conditions. A study of a California range dominated by wild barley (*Hordeum leporinum*) showed 1,500 pounds of mulch per acre where forage was considered in excellent condition as compared with only 400 pounds for range in poor condition (13). In humid regions the per-acre weight of mulch on excellent range may reach 0.5 ton and equal the current annual forage production.

Condition of Soil. As might be expected, an excellent range would have a relatively thick layer of fertile, spongy, erosion-resistant soil. Run-off water would be clear and minimal. The soil of a poor range, on the other hand, would characteristically be shallow and infertile. Moreover, because of the considerable area of bare ground and because of the fact that the simple taproots of the annual weeds that invade the poor range are inadequate soil binders, the land is highly susceptible to erosion. Frequently the range is dissected with gullies. Run-off water is brown with silt and is excessive.

PLANT INDICATORS. Any rancher capable of identifying the major plant components of his range could, in this way, determine range condition. Sometimes he only needs to identify a single species. The use of plants as indicators of range condition is based upon the ecological concept that a plant is the expression, or product, of its total environment, whether it be soil, moisture, temperature, light, animals, or even other plants. In other words, a given plant represents the effect of a certain *environmental cause*, and simply by identifying the presence of a particular species of plant the ranch manager can assume certain charactcristics of the environmental cause. It is true that any plant may thus serve as an indicator. However, the best (most precise) indicators would be plants having an extremely narrow *range of tolerance* for certain environmental factors. Some species indicate certain soil types. In southern Arizona, for example, salty soils are indicated by saltgrass (*Distichlis stricta*), alkaline soils by alkali sacaton (*Sporobolus airoides*), and heavy alluvial soils, subject to periodic flooding, by tobosa (*Hilaria mutica*) (12). Of greater immediate concern to the rancher than soil type is the question of whether his pastures are deteriorating under heavy grazing pressure. Plants whose presence indicates overgrazing include snakeweed, rabbitbrush, cactus, bullthistle, locoweed, pigweed, sunflower, wild daisy, plantain, goldenrod, tarweed, creosote bush, and dandelion (14).

SHIFTING STOCKING-LEVEL POLICY. The rancher must be prepared to make adjustments to the severe drought years that will inevitably occur. Two methods of adjustment may be employed. First, he may employ a shifting stocking-level plan in which grazing pressure is adjusted to forage capacity. Thus, if a pasture that originally supported 100 head is reduced by drought to only 25 per cent of its original carrying capacity, the rancher obviously may run only 25 head on that depleted pasture, thus necessitating sale of 75 excess head, possibly at very low prices. When a wet year recurs, the pasture may once more support the original 100 head, thus necessitating purchase of 75 additional cattle to keep that pasture grazed to capacity. This "shifting-numbers" technique involves many economic problems. Frequently a rancher starts out with good intentions of reducing his herd. However, because of a poor market he retains his full herd even during the height of the drought. The result may be disastrous, not only for the range, because

Figure 7-6. *New Mexico. This range during season of best growth barely provides sufficient forage to keep livestock alive. Cattle must cover a large area to get feed. Range deterioration will continue until livestock pressure is relieved.* [Soil Conservation Service, U.S. Department of Agriculture]

of the combination of drought and overgrazing, but also for the herd, which may incur wholesale malnutrition and even starvation. The sight of gaunt cattle moving lethargically in search of a few sprigs of green grass in a well-trampled field of thistles and cactus is the unpleasant aftermath of such mismanagement.

STABLE STOCKING-LEVEL PLAN. Second, to adjust to drought a stable stocking-level technique may be followed. Many authorities advise ranchers in the arid western plains to stock their pastures permanently to only 65 per cent of average capacity (14). For example, if 100 head of cattle is average capacity on a given pasture, the rancher would stock only 65 head, even though the pasture may be slightly overgrazed during a wet spell. The "surplus" growth of forage during the wet season will by no means be wasted, for the foods manufactured by this green herbage will provide a nutrient reserve, which the plant, if a perennial, will draw upon during the next drought.

STOCK MANIPULATION: WATER AND SALT DISTRIBUTION. Another range management problem is to ensure a proper herd distribution pattern so that livestock will make uniform use of available forage. Because cattle, for example, concentrate in wet meadows and along stream margins and avoid ridges and slopes, part of the range may become severely overgrazed while another part, of equal food value, may be completely ignored. Livestock distribution can be directly controlled with barbed-wire fencing and herding, both of which are rather costly. Indirect methods, much less expensive but highly effective, involve the strategic distribution of water holes and salt blocks. Because cattle and sheep normally congregate around water sources (one cow requires 10 gallons per day), the salt blocks should be placed roughly 0.50 mile from the nearest water source, preferably on ridges, gentle slopes, or openings in brush or forest, to induce the livestock to frequent areas they normally would avoid.

Salt is essential to the vigorous health of range animals. Sheep, for example, require 0.25 to 0.50 pound per month. Within three weeks after being deprived of salt, cattle develop an unusual craving for it. When salt deprivation continues, the animals show loss of appetite, emaciation, roughening of the coat, extreme weakness, and ultimately complete collapse. In some ranges where the soil is naturally high in phosphate and sulphate salts, livestock may partially satisfy their salt requirements by grazing on salt-absorbing vegetation. An analysis of the leaves and stems of range plants in New Mexico showed the equivalent of about 0.28 per cent salt for saltgrass (*Distichlis*) and 1.83 per cent salt for greasewood (*Sarcobatus*).

DEFERRED GRAZING SYSTEM. When livestock are allowed to graze in a pasture continuously throughout the grazing season, the more palatable (and usually more nutritious) range plants frequently are so seriously overgrazed that they incur a reduction in vitality and reproductive potential. To remedy this problem, several range management experts advise *deferred grazing* (14). The main features of this system are represented in Figure 7-7. Note that the ranch is divided into three

Figure 7-7. *Deferred grazing.* [*Adapted from Ruben L. Parsons*, Conserving American Resources, *(Englewood Cliffs, N.J.: Prentice-Hall, Inc., 1956). After A. W. Sampson*, Range Management, *(New York: John Wiley & Sons, Inc., 1952).*]

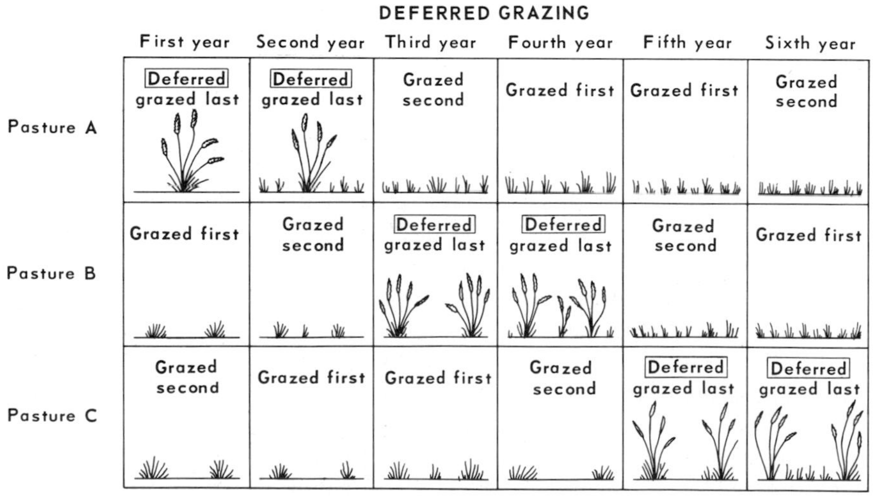

DEFERRED GRAZING

	First year	Second year	Third year	Fourth year	Fifth year	Sixth year
Pasture A	Deferred grazed last	Deferred grazed last	Grazed second	Grazed first	Grazed first	Grazed second
Pasture B	Grazed first	Grazed second	Deferred grazed last	Deferred grazed last	Grazed second	Grazed first
Pasture C	Grazed second	Grazed first	Grazed first	Grazed second	Deferred grazed last	Deferred grazed last

pastures, A, B, and C, and that each of them is deferred for two successive years within a six-year period. During years 1 and 2, forage plants in pasture A are allowed to reach maturity and drop their seeds before livestock are permitted to graze on them late in the season. Even though the grasses become rather dry at this time, they still are highly nutritious. A certain amount of grazing after the seeds have been produced may be advantageous to the pasture, because with their foraging activity cattle not only scatter the grass seed, but by trampling the seeds underfoot thrust them into the ground and enhance germination success. The net result of deferred grazing is the increased size, density, weight, vitality, reproductive potential, and nutritional value of the deferred forage species. Note that in Figure 7-7, pasture A is deferred the first and second years, pasture B the third and fourth years, and pasture C the fifth and sixth years. Thus, for this hypothetical ranch all three pastures, within a six-year rotation plan, receive temporary release from grazing pressure.

USE OF FIRE.   In addition to the employment of grazing pressure, a rancher may utilize fire to control the species composition and growth rate of his pastures. Admittedly controversial, this technique has both positive and negative features. According to Jack R. Harlan, agronomy professor at Oklahoma Agricultural and Mechanical College, range burning has the following deleterious results: many plants are either destroyed or incur depressed vitality because of food reserve depletion; weed invasion is facilitated; soil erosion is promoted because of loss of

Figure 7-8.   *Destructive burning of bluestem grass pasture in Kansas. [Soil Conservation Service, U.S. Department of Agriculture]*

Figure 7-9. *Controlling grass fire with portable firefighting units on western Oklahoma rangeland.* [*Soil Conservation Service, U.S. Department of Agriculture*]

vegetational cover; effectiveness of rainfall is reduced because of decreased permeability of the mulch-deprived, sunbaked soil; and much valuable organic nitrogen is destroyed. The positive features of range burning are listed by Harlan as follows: old plants of low forage value are removed; new growth may develop earlier because it is not shaded by old straw and is of greater nutritional value than it would be were the range left unburned. In general, range burning, from the short-term viewpoint, is probably good for cattle and is favored by cattlemen who are leasing rangeland. However, on a long-term basis, burning is probably deleterious to the range and is usually disparaged by the landowner.

ARTIFICIAL RESEEDING OF RANGE. Through ignorance, greed, or incompetence almost 80 million acres of America's rangelands were virtually destroyed. If these acres are to be restored within the next few decades, they will have to be reseeded by artificial methods. Natural reseeding alone will not accomplish the job fast enough. Although initial grass-planting experiments were conducted as early as 1895, almost all of the 1,500 experimental seedings resulted in failure. Since these early days of frustration, however, much progress has been made.[2]

METHODS OF RESEEDING RANGE.

1. Broadcasting. Seeds may be broadcasted by hand or airplane. Unless some provision, however, is made for covering them, the project will probably fail. Uncovered seeds may be blown away by strong winds, may succumb to protracted winter cold, may be consumed by birds and jackrabbits, or may be washed away

[2] The following material has largely been obtained from the fine paper "Restoring the Range by Reseeding," by Pearse, Plummer, and Savage (9).

Figure 7-10. *Seeding California rangeland by helicopter.* [*Soil Conservation Service, U.S. Department of Agriculture*]

during heavy spring rainstorms. Sometimes ranchers may drive a herd of cattle over the area to trample the seeds into the ground. If seeding is done in recently burned-over timberland, the loose covering of ashes may ensure reseeding success. Similarly, if reseeding is synchronized with autumn leaf fall, the leaf litter may provide sufficient seed cover for successful germination.

Airplane broadcasting, the only feasible method in rough, mountainous areas, can be both inexpensive and effective. Thus, in the fall of 1944, a burn in a Douglas fir and ponderosa pine stand in the Cabinet National Forest of Montana was seeded by airplane at a cost of only $1.20 per acre. Only two years later the burn area was cloaked with a dense stand of timothy, Kentucky bluegrass, and orchard grass, which not only gave full erosion protection, but also provided a ton of food per acre for grazing animals. Although much rather sensational publicity has been given to the technique of encasing seeds in pellets of prefertilized mud and broadcasting them from airplanes, this method has almost universally met with failure or poor results, partly because of poor germination.

2. Drilling. When rangeland is fairly even, not too rocky or brush-covered, the use of a mechanical drill that may plant seeds at a uniform depth is preferable to either hand broadcasting or broadcasting by plane. Row spacing of about 1 foot is desirable on most ranges. The density of seeds planted should be sufficient to make use of the available moisture; too great a density would reduce seedling vigor because of competition for nutrients, light, and moisture; underseeding would permit invasion by weeds.

3. *Selection of Appropriate Species.* Not all species of native grasses have the same tolerance for such environmental factors as heat, cold, drought, acid soils, stony soils, infertile soils, trampling, grazing pressure, and parasites. Moreover, because our rangelands extend for almost 1,500 miles from the Canadian border to Mexico, encompassing a great variety of climatic conditions and soil types, for a reseeding operation to be successful species must be adaptable to the specific range site to be reseeded. Thus, cool-season grasses such as wheat grasses, fescues, bromes, and bluegrasses would be appropriate for the cool growing season regions of the western intermountain region. On the other hand, in the warm Southwest, where summer temperatures commonly exceed 100° F, warm-season plants such as grama grass and buffalo grass are more appropriate. In recent years the U.S. Department of Agriculture has introduced a great number of species from abroad and has grown them on an experimental basis to determine their adaptability to the American range. A few have proved their ability to establish themselves thousands of miles from their origin. Thus, Russian wild rye (from Siberia) grows vigorously in our northern rangelands, being quite resistant to the bitter winter cold; on the other hand, the heat-tolerant Bermuda grass, imported from the semitropics, fares well in the deep South.

VALUE OF RESEEDING. Although we still have a long way to go, there is little doubt that by artificial methods of reseeding we shall eventually be able to reclaim most of the 80 million acres of rangeland we once so disgracefully destroyed. Most

Figure 7-11. *Cattle food at Woodward, Oklahoma. A close-up of buffalo grass—a perennial, highly palatable, drought-resistant species. Thrives on clay and loam soils. Best adapted to regions having 15 to 30 inches of rainfall. Best pasture results from deferred grazing. [Soil Conservation Service, U.S. Department of Agriculture]*

reseeding can be accomplished for less than $5 per acre; the direct value of increased food supplies may amount to 50¢ per acre annually. In general, ranges that have been properly reseeded will support a greater number of livestock in better condition over a longer period than equivalent ranges that have not been reseeded. Many plantings in the West, for example, have been grazed for fifteen successive years and still produce from three to twenty times as much forage as they did before seeding. A classic example of how artificial reseeding can improve rangeland is provided by a 500-acre plot in the Fish Lake National Forest in Utah. Before seeding, this area supported a vigorous cover of sagebrush and rabbitbrush, which provided forage for only eight head of cattle. However, only three years after it was seeded to wheat grasses and bromes (at a nominal cost of $3.22 per acre) it was able to sustain 100 head.

Selection of Cattle Breeds. For greatest efficiency in rangeland use, the proper breed of herbivore, in the form of cattle or sheep, is just as important as having the proper type of forage plant. The food chain is only as strong as its weakest link. Without an efficient second link (herbivore), the efficiency of the first link (producer) in converting solar energy to food energy is more or less dissipated.

The Texas longhorn, introduced to the United States by the Spaniards in the sixteenth century, and once grazed by the millions, is now found only in wildlife preserves and zoos. It has been replaced by a large variety of breeds, either imported from abroad or developed on our own western range.

HEREFORD. This large, powerfully built breed, its "white face" contrasting handsomely with its red-brown body, is perhaps the favorite of our western range-

Figure 7-12. *Texas longhorn steer on the King Ranch at Kingsville, Texas. [U.S. Department of Agriculture]*

Figure 7-13. *Cowboy riding herd on Herefords. This powerfully built breed yields steaks of high quality. Its ability to rustle food under adverse conditions is unsurpassed. Note the excellent condition of both range and cattle.* [U.S. Department of Agriculture, Photo by B. C. McLean]

lands. Its meat is of high quality. It is able to withstand the severe winter cold. It is unsurpassed in its ability to find enough food to survive even under the adverse conditions of drought and heavy snow. (The rustling ability of western cattle was severely tested during the winter of 1886–1887, when temperatures dropped to −60° F and forage was sealed off with snow. Some ranges experienced 90 per cent cattle mortality.) However, when it comes to milk production, the Hereford ranks poorly.

SHORTHORN. Numerically, the shorthorn ranks second to the Hereford on our western range. When forage is plentiful, its flesh is unexcelled. However, under adverse grazing conditions, as when forage is concealed by snow, the shorthorn might starve where the Hereford might survive. Evenly tempered and easily managed, the shorthorn is the best milk producer among our beef cattle.

ABERDEEN-ANGUS. The handsome, black Aberdeen-Angus is an excellent beef animal. However, because of its nervous temperament it is difficult to herd and to manage in the feed lot.

BRAHMAN. The large, light-colored Brahman, introduced from India about 1849, is ungainly and has long, drooping ears and loose folds of skin hanging from the neck. Although extremely excitable, these excellent rustlers are unsurpassed in their ability to withstand heat, drought, and bloodsucking fleas and ticks. Because certain ticks may transmit the causative organism of Texas cattle fever, a potentially lethal disease, its tick-resistant ability is highly regarded in the South.

SANTA GERTRUDIS.   Research geneticists of the U.S. Department of Agriculture and cattlemen themselves are continuously conducting breeding experiments in an effort to develop superior breeds. A cross between two different breeds, known as a *crossbreed* or *hybrid*, will sometimes combine the better traits of each parent and lack their undesirable characteristics. One of the most successful hybrids ever developed on American rangelands in recent years is the Santa Gertrudis. This breed was developed by geneticists on the world-famous King Ranch at Kingsville, Texas. It was developed after a series of crossings, the original of which involved a Brahman bull and a shorthorn cow (5). As the King Ranch geneticists hoped, the dark red Santa Gertrudis hybrid combined the beefiness, milk-producing ability, and docility of the shorthorn with the drought, heat, and tick resistance of the Brahman. As a result, the Santa Gertrudis is a breed par excellence for the hot, arid rangelands of the Southwest.

Proper Livestock Nutrition.   Of the roughly 100 elements in the physical universe, only about 30 or so actually become incorporated into living substance. This is true not only of man, but of all living members of the rangeland community, from blue grama to Black Angus. A steer or antelope secures these elements from range plants; these plants, in turn, obtain their elements from the soil, air, or water. In the final analysis, therefore, the availability of an essential element to a range

Figure 7-14. *Rio Grande City, Texas. A two-year, four-month-old Santa Gertrudi bull, and other members of the herd, are shown on the Everett Bell ranch. This breed was developed from Brahman and short-horn cattle.* [U.S. Department of Agriculture]

animal depends, to a large degree, upon its abundance or scarcity in the soil. Proper nutrition of livestock is just as important a facet of range management as pest control, deferred grazing, or artificial reseeding. As an illustration we shall consider the role of *phosphorus* in livestock nutrition, the nature of deficiency symptoms, and the way in which the phosphorus deficiency can be remedied.

Most rangeland soils are to some degree phosphorus deficient. For U.S. soils as a whole, maximal soil deficiencies occur in the coastal area from Texas to Maryland (6). Even though soil has relatively abundant amounts of phosphorus, if bound up in insoluble compounds (iron, aluminum), it will not be available for plant and (later) animal use. A large percentage of phosphorus derived from range forage is concentrated in bones, hair, wool, and horns. Robert Humphrey cites one authority as estimating that 6 boxcars of fat cattle would contain the equivalent of all the phosphorus contained in the upper 6 inches of an acre of soil, and because many cattle have been raised and shipped away from some ranges for almost a century, the loss of soil phosphorus has been considerable (6). Phosphorus may also be removed by erosion. Up to 37.75 pounds per acre may be eroded annually from plowed land with no vegetational cover. On the other hand, the loss from land of the same type continuously covered with blue grass is only 0.16 pound per acre.

Phosphorus and calcium are essential for the proper development of a sturdy skeleton. When both calcium and phosphorus are deficient in an animal, the bones lose their rigidity and are easily broken. The animal loses its normal appetite for food and virtually starves when surrounded by abundance. It develops instead a bizarre appetite for wood, bones, hair, tin cans, and rotting flesh. The deficiency may be remedied by supplying phosphorus in drinking water or by feeding the animal ground bone meal. The soil could also be fertilized with a compound containing phosphorus, so that ultimately the cattle would secure the element through their forage.

It is apparent that soil chemistry is basic to the chemistry of producers grown in that soil, and ultimately to that of livestock. Although slight deficiencies of phosphorus and other elements such as cobalt and iodine may not be limiting to range vegetation, the effect on livestock may be lethal. The rancher should make soil chemistry a basic consideration in range management and should realize that it is as important as terrain, rainfall, pest control, and the composition and condition of range plants.

Range Pests and Their Control

Plant Pests. The rancher is periodically confronted with invasion of his pasturage by woody, low-value shrubs, such as mesquite, sagebrush, juniper, burroweed, creosote bush, and many others. In Texas alone, mesquite and juniper cost the livestock industry $20 million annually (10). Unless effective control methods are established, aggressive spread of these weed species may seriously lower the livestock-carrying capacity of the range. Within the limited scope of this text we shall consider this problem in terms of a single species, the mesquite.

MESQUITE. The mesquite (*Prosopis juliflora*) is a thorny desert shrub, sometimes attaining the form of a tree, with relatively small, leathery leaves. Like all representatives of the pea family (Leguminosae), it produces large, pulpy seed pods. The extensive root system in older plants may have a 100-foot circumference and penetrate to a depth of 50 feet.

Of all woody plant invaders of the southwestern grasslands, mesquite ranks first in terms of distribution, abundance, and aggressive encroachment of rangeland pastures (12). Many plant ecologists believe that for millennia mesquite invasion was prevented by periodic grassland fires probably ignited by lightning strikes or by Plains Indians (as an aid in hunting). Even though grasses were consumed in the conflagration along with mesquite, many grasses can mature and produce seeds within two years, whereas mesquite requires a longer period. As a result of this time differential for maturation and reproduction, were there recurrent fires at intervals of, say, two years, the mesquite would be at a reproductive disadvantage and, therefore, would be prevented from spreading (6). Ecologists also believe that before the introduction of domestic grazers, the vigorously growing climax vegetation of the grassland biome, with the aid of deep fibrous root systems, was able to compete successfully with mesquite for sunlight and limited soil moisture. However, when the white man drove off the Indians, introduced cattle and sheep by the millions, and instituted new methods of effective fire control, the two main factors responsible for confining mesquite were no longer operative. The frequently overstocked range herds caused serious pasture deterioration. The deeply and extensively rooted climax species declined and were replaced by increasers, which in turn were replaced by invaders with shallow, simple taproots that were competitively

Figure 7-15. *Mesquite covers millions of acres of southern Great Plains rangeland.* [*U.S. Department of Agriculture*]

inferior to mesquite. The mesquite invasion was facilitated by a curious reciprocal relationship with cattle. The late-summer-maturing mesquite pods, some up to 8 inches long, provide cattle with nutritious food. After digesting the pulp, cattle eventually void the seeds with their excrement, frequently a considerable distance from the parent plant. The seeds, still viable and well fertilized, show a surprisingly high germination success. Kangaroo rats also play a role. They often facilitate mesquite dispersion when they permit forgotten mesquite seed caches to germinate (14). By such means, mesquite encroachment has been facilitated until this thorny invader has blighted 50 million acres of Texas prairie alone.

METHODS OF CONTROL. Like other woody, shrubby invaders of the rangeland community, mesquite may be controlled more or less successfully by fire and mechanical devices.

Fire. Dense, mature mesquite stands can be controlled to some degree by flame torches, thus duplicating in the twentieth century the natural type of control that operated for thousands of years before the white man restructured the arid grassland ecosystem. Major disadvantages of this method are that older trees tend to sprout vigorously from the upper branches after the fire and that much valuable grass may be consumed along with the mesquite. Moreover, unless a very hot fire can be obtained sufficient to destroy the mesquite, burning will place the grasses at a competitive disadvantage and aggravate the problem.

Grubbing and Plowing. Grubbing the plants out of the ground or plowing them up are effective control measures. However, this is extremely costly, up to $25 per acre; the ground is torn up and disturbed by the operation; it is necessary to repeat the operation periodically to remove new seedlings and sprouts; and in the case of plowing, the whole area must be carefully reseeded with nutritive forage grasses (14).

Herbicides. The growth and development of plants is regulated by special chemicals called auxins, or growth hormones. The plant is very sensitive to the concentration of these hormones, and too little or too much of the hormone will result in arrested growth and even death. Within the last decade, biochemists have been able to synthesize a compound (2,4–D) that duplicates the characteristics of growth hormones in broad-leafed plants but has no effect on narrow-leafed plants such as grasses. When 2,4–D is sprayed in sufficient concentrations on mesquite foliage, "top kills" are easily accomplished. Aerial spraying, being one third as costly as ground spraying, is the method of choice (14).

POISONOUS PLANTS. Each year death from plant poisoning claims 4 per cent of all livestock grazing in our western ranges. In some years one out of every seven Wyoming sheep die from this cause. At Harper, Oregon, 1,000 out of 1,700 sheep died from greasewood poisoning in 1930. There are over 400 plant species in the United States that are poisonous to livestock.

Because most poisonous plants do not occur in the climax community but have rather the status of "weedy invaders," control can largely be effected simply by the prevention of overgrazing. Moreover, because most poisonous plants are unpalatable to livestock, they normally will be avoided unless they are the only plants available to half-starved animals. Although only 2 ounces of water hemlock root will kill a sheep and only 8 ounces will destroy a cow, most poisonous plants are quite harmless unless large quantities have been ingested.

Figure 7-16. *Las Cruces, New Mexico. A spoonful of 25 per cent fenuron pellets will kill a medium-sized mesquite bush. This method, shown at the Jornada Experimental Range, is very effective on bush stands up to 70 per acre. [U.S. Department of Agriculture]*

The white loco and its close relatives (the purple loco and blue loco) are responsible for the deaths of great numbers of range animals annually. Because they are extremely abundant, widely distributed, and lethal to all range livestock, including horses, cattle, sheep, and goats, some authorities consider them the most destructive of all poisonous plants. (Curiously, the white loco is a member of the pea family, Leguminosae, which also includes some of the rancher's most beneficial species, the nitrogen-fixing alfalfa and clover.) The white loco, which may bear either white or red flowers, ranges from western Minnesota to Montana in the north, to Arizona and Mexico in the south.

Seriously poisoned animals get the "blind staggers," characterized by loss of weight, erratic gait, inability to see clearly, weakness, extreme nervousness, and crazed behavior. (*Loco* is Spanish for "crazy.") Apparently the toxic effects are caused by the element *selenium*, which frequently occurs in the tissues of the locoweed in high concentrations. In fact, the plant is dependent upon selenium for maximal growth, so that it may be used as an indicator of selenium-bearing soils. Selenium is distributed widely in the shales of many Western states. South Dakota and Arizona have relatively high concentrations. Even if soil content is negligible, the locoweed can absorb enough to build up high levels. In one study one species of loco growing in topsoil having a selenium content of only 20.4 parts per million was able to build up a selenium concentration of 2,590 parts per million in its tissues, a 125-fold increase. In another study *Astragalus bisulcatus* had 4,300 ppm of selenium in its tissues, whereas 50 plants of *Andropogon scoparius* (little bluestem) growing in the same general region averaged only 0.8 parts per million.

Most livestock tend to shun locoweed and other selenium-bearing plants, possibly because of their characteristic garliclike smell. Therefore, if the range is kept in good condition, locoweed poisoning will be reduced to a minimum.

Competitors with Livestock. Within the rangeland community a number of herbivorous animals such as grasshoppers, jackrabbits, and prairie dogs compete intensively with livestock for forage.

GRASSHOPPERS. Of the 142 species of grasshoppers collected in western range vegetation, the most destructive and widely distributed are the lesser migratory grasshoppers. During periods of peak abundance they may gather in swarms and migrate several hundred miles. For several years of cool, wet weather, the grasshopper populations may remain small, so that the rancher may barely be aware of

Figure 7-17. *A grasshopper infestation on a western range, June 1971. Note the partially devoured stalk.* [U.S. Department of Agriculture]

their presence. Then comes the year of severe drought, with perhaps only 5 inches instead of the usual 15 inches of rainfall. With environmental factors now at the optimum of the grasshoppers' tolerance range, the populations rapidly increase until it is almost impossible to take a single step through a grama grass pasture without flushing several of them. During a peak year, grasshoppers may so deplete forage that livestock either must move to other pastures or starve. The havoc wrought by hordes of grasshoppers has been eloquently recorded in the Bible (Joel 2:3), "The land is as the Garden of Eden before them, and behind them a *desolate wilderness,* yea, and nothing shall escape them."

During the drought year of 1937, grasshoppers inflicted an aggregate forage damage of about $66 million in 24 states. Morton estimated that in 1936 there were roughly 25 grasshoppers per square meter in his Montana rangeland study area and that they consumed or destroyed 67 per cent of the total forage production. He estimated that 3 acres of grasshoppers consumed as much forage as one cow. J. R. Parker, of the U.S. Department of Agriculture, has estimated that one large adult grasshopper consumes 30 milligrams of vegetation (dry weight) daily, as compared with the cow's daily requirement of 20 pounds. In other words 301,395 "hoppers" would eat as much as one cow (8).

One interesting facet of the grasshopper-rangeland relationship is that these insects are much more populous in overgrazed ranges than in moderately grazed fields. A study in southern Arizona revealed that the insect order Orthoptera (largely represented by grasshoppers) had a population of 180,000 per acre on overgrazed lands compared with only 20,000 per acre on range in average condition —a 9:1 population differential. It may be, therefore, that an effective method of

Figure 7-18. *Colorado, June 1971. Planes are spraying malathion on a Colorado rangeland for grasshopper control. The U.S. Department of Agriculture does not undertake or cooperate in any program until departmental scientists evaluate the environmental, biological, and economic impact of applying available pest control methods as opposed to not taking any action at all. Vehicles on the road belong to the U.S. Department of Agriculture personnel who are keeping tabs on the operation. [U.S. Department of Agriculture, Photo by Jim Strawser]*

controlling grasshopper plagues is to ensure that the range is not being subjected to excessive grazing pressure.

Investigators for the U.S. Department of Agriculture are continuously searching for an effective biological method of grasshopper control. Thus in 1949 two species of predatory flies belonging to the family Nemistrinidae were discovered in Montana (7). Female flies may lay eggs in crevices of tree trunks or in fence post fissures at the rate of roughly 1 per second over a 15-minute period, until a total of 1,000 have been deposited. Within about 10 days, tiny wormlike maggots emerge from the eggs, are borne aloft and whisked away by the wind for a considerable distance, and eventually are dropped among the range grasses. When a squirming maggot comes into contact with a grasshopper, the parasite burrows its way into the host and feeds on its soft, living tissues until the grasshopper succumbs. In some foci of grasshopper infestation, up to 80 per cent of a single species have been victims of predation by nemestrinid flies. Because the females are such efficient egg producers and because the minute eggs can be easily transported to regions of grasshopper infestations, nemestrinid flies may someday serve as agents of biological control.

JACKRABBITS. Under conditions of excessive drought jackrabbits seriously compete with cattle and sheep for high-quality forage. On the basis of stomach analyses and appraisal of fenced quadrats, 75 antelope jackrabbits consume as much forage as 1 cow, and 15 eat enough food to sustain 1 sheep. During their investigation researchers estimated that the jackrabbit population numbered 7,500 animals on 50,000 acres, or a density of 1 jackrabbit per 7 acres. The aggregate weight of the rabbits was roughly 7 per cent that of the cattle with which they were competing. They concluded that the dense rabbit population was a major *limiting factor* in keeping the rangeland plant community at a low or retrogressive successional stage. The overall effect of the heavy grazing pressure was to prevent re-establishment of highly nutritious decreaser species and to favor intrusion by low-value increasers, as well as invaders such as mesquite, cacti, and weeds.

KANGAROO RATS. The intriguing pocket-sized kangaroo rat of the southwestern United States digs extensive burrow systems. During nocturnal foraging, it stuffs its cheek pouches with seeds and deposits them in its burrow, to be utilized later during food scarcity. In one study an average of 3.7 pounds of plant material was discovered in each of 24 burrows examined. With a kangaroo rat density of 2 per acre, this would mean a per acre decrement of 7.4 pounds of forage. In addition, many forage plants suffer from retarded growth because of foliage depredations by kangaroo rats too early in the growing season. These rodents may also be effective passive dispersal agents of undesirable "invader" species such as mesquite. This occurs when caches of mesquite seeds in underground burrows are forgotten and later germinate.

CONTROL OF COMPETITORS BY PROPER STOCKING. The rangeland pest, whether grasshopper, jackrabbit, prairie dog, or kangaroo rat, becomes a serious problem only during population peaks, and these peaks usually coincide with rangeland deterioration. It should be emphasized that these pests do not *cause* the initial depletion of pasture. The high pest populations represent *symptoms* rather than causal factors of range deterioration. E. R. Kalmbach has compared range abuse to a wound (7). The "wound" was initially inflicted by excessive stocking, and the ensuing rodent build-up merely served to irritate the wound and prevent it from healing properly. Just why a range in good condition (well-stocked with climax plants) should be unsuitable habitat for certain rabbits and rodents has never been fully explained. It may be that the tall vegetation obstructs the vision of these relatively defenseless animals and makes them more vulnerable to predation. In any event most rangeland experts agree that shooting, trapping, and poisoning campaigns are really only stopgap procedures; the best long-term solution to the pest problem seems to be simply a four-strand barbed-wire fence—for keeping excess cattle off the deteriorating range.

The Predator Problem. Livestock losses of over $1 million are annually inflicted by a variety of livestock predators such as coyotes, cougars, bobcats, and bear. Through millennia of pre-Columbian time, there existed large herds of herbivores, such as buffalo, elk, and bison, which satiated the appetites of grassland carnivores. (The cougar is capable of killing ten to twenty deer monthly.) Beginning with the sixteenth-century introductions of Spanish livestock, however, the wild grazers declined in numbers or were displaced westward to semimountainous wilderness retreats. The carnivores persisted, however (much to the ranchers' vexation), finding domesticated herbivores fully as savory and nutritious, and probably somewhat more vulnerable, than the wild grazers.

Of all rangeland predators, the coyote perhaps poses the most serious problem. This wily, resourceful brush wolf has become a romantic symbol of the western plains—and a thorn in the side of the rancher. Where the coyote has become numerous, sheep ranchers have waged all-out extermination campaigns—poisoning, trapping, shooting, even pursuing the animal and killing it in its own den. (In 1972 the trapping and poisoning of predatory animals on leased Federal grazing lands was banned by executive order of President Nixon.) When a rancher destroys a coyote that has been killing, say, ten sheep a year, simple arithmetic might suggest that this rancher will be ten sheep richer each year thereafter. However, it is not quite that simple. For one thing the coyote feeds on other animals besides sheep. Thus a study of coyote feeding habits revealed livestock (actually killed by coyotes) formed only 14 per cent (by volume) of its diet as compared to the 49.5 per cent represented by range-grass-consuming rabbits and rodents. It is apparent, therefore, that the value of the few sheep saved by destroying a coyote may be considerably less than the value of forage consumed by rodents and rabbits, which the coyote would have removed from the rangeland community.

Case of the Peccary. The javelina, or collared peccary, is a favorite game animal among many sportsmen of the Southwest. Up to 4,000 of these snorting rooters of the desert shrub community are taken in a single year. Although their range in the United States is restricted to Texas, southern New Mexico, and southern Arizona, they range southward through Mexico into South America. Because this herbivorous "wild pig" occupies marginal rangeland, on which harassed ranchers strive to support a few head of livestock, it has long been regarded with a jaundiced eye. In years past ranchers have shot these creatures on sight. Because the peccary is gregarious, the kill in certain areas has been high. Concerned by this persecution of an intriguing game animal, wildlife biologists have made thorough studies of its feeding habits. Their findings have completely exonerated the peccary. Neal, in

Figure 7-19. *Coronado National Forest, Arizona. A peccary shown in its natural habitat. Note gravel pavement of desert floor and the cactus in the background.* [*U.S. Department of Agriculture, Photo by Ray Manley*]

Arizona, for example, found that 84.5 per cent of stomach contents analyzed consisted of the roots, stems, and fruit of the relatively worthless prickly pear cactus, whereas nutritive range grasses, preferred by livestock, formed an insignificant 8.6 per cent of the diet. According to Humphrey, moreover, it may well be that the peccary has been instrumental in *improving* range condition rather than causing its deterioration (6). In rooting up fleshy weed plants, it not only makes room for preferred grasses but also by stirring the soil unwittingly prepares their seedbed. The case of the peccary points up the need for a critical study of all aspects of an ecological problem before taking impulsive action that may be poorly conceived.

BIBLIOGRAPHY

1. Bennett, John B., F. R. Kenney, and W. R. Chapline. "The Problem: Sub-Humid Areas," *Soils and Men: The Yearbook of Agriculture*. Washington, D.C.: U.S. Department of Agriculture, 1938.
2. Carter, Goodrich, Bushrod W. Allin, and C. Warren Thornthwaite. *Migration and Economic Opportunity: The Report of the Study of Population Redistribution*. Philadelphia: University of Pennsylvania, 1936.

3. Chapline, W. R. "Grazing on Rangelands," *Grass: The Yearbook of Agriculture*. Washington, D.C.: U.S. Department of Agriculture, 1948.
4. Corner, E. J. H. *The Life of Plants*. Cleveland: World, 1964.
5. *Encyclopaedia Britannica*. Vol. 5. Chicago: Benton, 1973.
6. Humphrey, Robert R. *Range Ecology*. New York: Ronald, 1962.
7. Kalmbach, E. R. "Rodents, Rabbits and Grasslands," *Grass: The Yearbook of Agriculture*. Washington, D.C.: U.S. Department of Agriculture, 1948.
8. Parker, J. R. "Grasshoppers," *Insects: The Yearbook of Agriculture*. Washington, D.C.: U.S. Department of Agriculture, 1952.
9. Pearse, C. Kenneth, A. Perry Plummer, and D. A. Savage. "Restoring the Range by Reseeding," *Grass: The Yearbook of Agriculture*. Washington, D.C.: U.S. Department of Agriculture, 1948.
10. Pechanek, Joseph F., Charles E. Fisher, and Kenneth W. Parker. "How to Control Noxious Plants," *Grass: The Yearbook of Agriculture*. Washington, D.C.: U S Department of Agriculture, 1948.
11. Platt, Rutherford. *This Green World*. New York: Dodd, 1943.
12. Sampson, Arthur W. *Range Management*. New York: Wiley, 1952.
13. Smith, Guy-Harold, ed. *Conservation of Natural Resources*. New York: Wiley, 1958.
14. Stoddart, L. A., and A. D. Smith. *Range Management*, 2nd ed. New York: McGraw-Hill, 1955.
15. Weaver, John E., and F. W. Albertson. *Grasslands of the Great Plains*. Lincoln, Neb.: Johnsen, 1956.

8.

Man And
the Forest

A tree is a monument to a seed.

Earl Calverley Owen

From early colonial days, when the straight, sturdy trunks of New England spruce and pine were fashioned into masts for the Royal Navy, until today, fully three centuries later, American forests have been the source of a variety of products useful to man. Today our forests provide the raw materials for over 5,000 products worth $23 billion annually (3). They support an industry that employs 1.3 million people and has an annual payroll of over $6 billion.

To help maintain the world's highest standard of living America uses more wood per capita than any nation on earth. Each year, every man, woman, and child in the United States uses about 204 board feet [1] of

[1] A board foot is a unit of measurement used in the lumbering industry to refer to a volume of wood 1 foot square and 1 inch thick.

Figure 8-1. *Gun stocks, samples of veneer, and other products derived from walnut. [Forest Service, U.S. Department of Agriculture]*

lumber. (Much of this is imported from Scandinavia and Canada.) In 1962 Americans used 37.3 billion board feet, enough to build 3.5 million 6-room cottages, or build a 4-foot-wide boardwalk long enough to bridge the distance to the moon at least 70 times. Americans eat, sleep, work, and play in a world of wood. Whether it be toothpicks, telephone poles, photographic film, maple syrup, acetic acid, or cellophane, we depend heavily on wood and wood-derived products. Each year we use over 0.5 million barrels of turpentine to thin our paints, over 30 million railroad ties to cushion our trains, over 200 million fence posts to fence our lands. Each year, well-fed Americans use over 232,000 tons of napkins, buy over 1 million tons of paper bags, use 2 million tons of newsprint, and purchase 2 million tons of writing paper.

The Tree: A Living Organism

To develop a better appreciation of the importance of our forest resource, the operation of destructive environmental factors, and how the forest can most effectively be managed, we shall briefly examine the anatomy and physiology of a tree.

Roots. Roots have three major functions: anchorage, absorption, and food storage.

ANCHORAGE. The root system of a tree is much more elaborate than most people realize; it forms a complex branching and rebranching arrangement of "living cables" adapted for holding the tree firmly in the soil. An oak tree 37 feet high may

Figure 8-2. *"Mountain" of pulp logs at a pulp mill in New York.* [*New York State Conservation Department*]

have a root system which thrusts downward with rock-splitting force to a depth of 14 feet, and may extend radially 60 feet from the base. The roots of a large mesquite, representatively of arid soil, penetrate downward to a depth of 75 feet for precious water. On the other hand, hemlock and tamarack, found in coniferous forests, are notoriously shallow rooted. Some authorities believe that the valuable stands of even-aged white pine, which were highly prized by the nineteenth-century lumber industry and which extended from New England west to Minnesota, became established as a subclimax stage after the climax spruce and firs were uprooted by an extensive hurricane.

ABSORPTION.   In an earlier section we mentioned that a tiny rye plant only 20 inches high may have a water-absorbing system composed of 14 million root hairs. No one has ever been able to uproot a living 100-foot-tall Douglas fir to count its root hairs, but Platt has suggested that, end to end, these might extend around the globe at the equator. It is through these root hairs that the tree absorbs water, oxygen, and soil nutrients such as nitrate and phosphate salts. The tree's roots may have to absorb 200 pounds of water for every pound of sugar photosynthesized in the canopy.

FOOD STORAGE.   Most roots serve as storehouses for surplus foods transferred from the canopy. During periods of stress, when photosynthesis is reduced by drought, cold, or leaf-consuming insects (such as gypsy moth larvae and spruce bud worms), the energy-rich starches held in the roots are converted into soluble sugars and transported upward through the trunk to food-deficient organs.

Trunk.   The tree trunk is the most valuable tree part to the forest industry. It is primarily from the trunk that wood for construction materials, furniture, plywood, and paper pulp is derived. Proper forest management requires knowledge of the architecture and design of a trunk, its functional organization, the manner and rate of growth, and many other characteristics. (Reference to Fig. 8-3 will be helpful in the following discussion.)

OUTER BARK.   The outer bark, or "cork," of the tree is composed of dead cells and greatly thickened walls that have become impregnated with waterproofing materials. As the tree trunk grows in diameter, the pressure generated by the trunk's interior causes the bark to break up into a pattern of ridges, scales, or plates that

Figure 8-3.   *The biology of a tree.* [*U.S. Forest Service*]

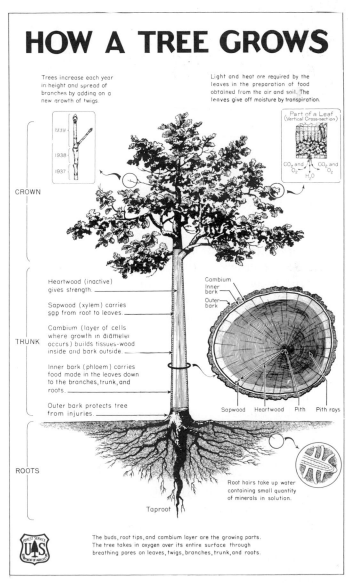

is species characteristic (18). One can often identify the species simply by an examination of the bark's texture, surface pattern, and color. Thus, in the mature shag bark hickory (*Carya ovata*), long, shaggy dark patches tend to slough off; in the paper birch (*Betula papyrifera*), on the other hand, the attractive cream-white bark tends to peel off in thin paperlike layers—a characteristic exploited by the Indian in fashioning birch-bark canoes. In addition to "locking" moisture inside the trunk, the outer bark serves as the tree's first line of defense against wood-boring insects, fungous growths, fire, and herbivorous vertebrates, such as rodents, rabbits, and deer (13).

INNER BARK, OR PHLOEM. Just inside the outer bark is a thin sheath of bark composed of elongate phloem cells. Arranged end to end in long vertical columns, these cells form pipe lines for the rapid transport of sugar, photosynthesized by the leaves, downward to the roots, either for immediate use or for storage. When their usual food supplies are covered with snow, such herbivorous animals as mice or rabbits may girdle a tree by removing a section of phloem and outer bark all the way around the trunk. Because this effectively cuts off food supplies to the roots, the tree's death is inevitable.

CAMBIUM. The cambium is a delicate sheath of embryonic cells occurring just inside the phloem. These cells continue to reproduce throughout the life of the tree; cells displaced to the outside of the cambium differentiate into phloem, and those forming on the inner cambial surface transform into xylem cells (13). Growth in thickness of the trunk from seedling to patriarch is dependent exclusively upon cambial activity.

WOOD. The xylem cells that are continuously proliferated from the cambium may appear in the form of relatively long cylindrical vessel elements or as much shorter tracheids, which taper at either end. Wood from deciduous trees may have either vessel elements or tracheids; in coniferous woods the vessel elements are lacking (11). Ultimately the vessel elements and tracheids die, lose their proto-plasm, and become water-conducting "pipes." Up to 900 gallons of water may be conducted through the xylem of a large oak daily. Because of their thick, rigid walls, the xylem cells form the "skeleton" of the tree, firmly supporting the combined weight of branches, twigs, leaves, flowers, and seeds. Because the woods of most deciduous trees are hard and dense, they are commonly called hardwoods. Most coniferous woods, which are relatively soft and porous and which yield much more readily to the saw, are popularly known as softwoods. However, these classes are not mutually exclusive, for some "softwood" species, such as hemlock, actually have harder wood than such "hardwood" species as basswood and poplar.

Perhaps you have cut down a tree in your backyard and have examined the stump's cross section. The wood is readily distinguishable into a darker, drier, more dense central core, known as the heartwood, and a lighter, moist, more porous layer immediately ensheathing it, known as the sapwood. Sapwood is composed of dead, hollow xylem cells that actively transport water and soil nutrients. As they get older, these "pipe" cells gradually become so clogged with gums and resins that they lose their conducting function; they then become part of the heartwood. In some species the striking color of the heartwood (as in the case of black walnut, red cedar, and redwood) adds greatly to its value. The heartwood of an overmature

Figure 8-4. *A forester measures width of newly felled tree. Note the narrow light-colored band of sap-wood on the outer part of the trunk. The darker "core" of heartwood is much thicker and is composed largely of resin-filled xylem cells. [Minnesota Conservation Department]*

Figure 8-5. *Cross-section of a pine trunk. Note the annular rings. [U.S. Department of Agriculture]*

tree frequently becomes vulnerable to heart-rot fungus. Such trees quickly become hollow and are completely valueless to the forest industry. On the other hand, such stubs frequently make good breeding dens for opossums, flying squirrels, and raccoons, as well as suitable nesting cavities for owls and woodpeckers; thus, they serve to increase the forest's capacity for wildlife.

AGE DETERMINATION. Xylem cells formed by the cambium during seasons when adequate moisture is available are relatively large in diameter and have thin walls. On the other hand, the xylem formed without adequate moisture usually are small in diameter and have thick walls. In the north temperature zone of the United States, where a wet period alternates with a dry period, the wood is laid down in the form of easily distinguishable concentric *annular rings*. A forester may quite accurately determine the tree's age by counting these rings. However, instead of felling a tree and examining the stump, he uses a device called an increment borer, by means of which he can withdraw a core sample from the trunk (13). With this technique tree longevity may be determined. Birches are old at 40, maples at 50 to 70; but oaks, hickories, and walnuts may live 200 to 300 years. Conifers usually live longer than hardwoods, because their resins render them more resistant to insect and fungus attacks. Some specimens of Douglas fir, ponderosa pine, and western hemlock along the Pacific coast are 500 to 1,000 years old. Some California redwoods are more than 3,000 years old. Three bristle cone pines (*Pinus aristata*)

Figure 8-6. *Large redwoods in Del Norte State Park, California. Interesting light patterns are created by sunlight filtering through dense fog. Some California redwoods are more than 3,000 years old.* [*U.S. Forest Service*]

Figure 8-7. *Inyo National Forest, California. William F. Fischer stands under a 4,000 year old bristlecone pine and looks over the typical White Mountain habitat of the bristlecones-high, rolling treeless areas on the volcanic soils, and sparse, scrubby stands of bristlecones on the limestone sites.* [*U.S. Department of Agriculture*]

growing in the White Mountains along the southern California-Nevada border germinated from seeds produced over 4,000 years ago. They are the oldest living organisms known to science.

Any marked variation in the width of the annular rings may reflect abnormal environmental conditions. Thus, extremely narrow rings may suggest to the forester that the tree's growth was severely limited during that particular year because of drought, insect attacks, or parasitic fungi. It could also mean that growth was impaired because of intensive competition for sun, moisture, and soil nutrients. Variations in the width of annual rings in ancient redwoods have enabled experts to reconstruct patterns of West Coast climate dating back to 1,000 B.C.

Leaves. The anatomy and function of a tree leaf was described in the section on photosynthesis in Chapter 2.

Reproductive Organs of Deciduous Trees. The sexual organs of a tree are found in the flower. In deciduous trees such as the apple, cherry, tulip, catalpa, and magnolia, these flowers may be large and brightly colored, whereas in the elm,

Figure 8-8.
Staminate and pistillate flowers of the Allegheny chinkapin growing at Silver Spring, Maryland. [*U.S. Department of Agriculture, Photo by W. D. Brush*]

willow, cottonwood, birch, and maple they are much reduced in size and inconspicuous. The fragrance and bright colors of the large flowers serve to attract insects, which inadvertently become dusted with mature pollen grains during their feeding activities. When such insects fly to another flower these pollen grains may accidentally be transferred to the sticky surface of a pistil, thus effecting pollination. Species with minute, drably colored flowers (such as the willow, aspen, and birch) are usually pollinated by wind or falling rain. The pollen grain eventually develops a pollen tube, which grows down the neck of the pistil toward the ovary, which houses the eggs. After the tip of the pollen tube has dissolved a "sperm" moves through the open end of the tube to unite with an egg and effect fertilization.

Eventually the fertilized egg develops into a seed. A seed may be defined as the embryo, together with a supply of stored food, which is enclosed by a protective wall or seed coat. The coat protects the embryo against desiccation, insects, and fungal parasites. Seeds vary in weight from 40 per pound in the black walnut (*Juglans nigra*) to 414,000 per pound in the western red cedar (*Thuja plicata*). Large, heavy seeds may be disseminated by squirrels, birds, or other animals. A robin may digest the pulp of a cherry and then void the pit several miles from the parent tree. Frequently such voided seeds show better germination success than seeds that have not been so "processed." Cottonwood seeds are provided with cottony tufts that facilitate wind transport. Maple seeds are provided with "blades"

Figure 8-9.
Staminate flowers of the Eastern white pine. [*U.S. Department of Agriculture, Photo by W. D. Brush*]

that revolve like miniature propellers as they drop to earth. By such agents of dispersal competition among seedlings for moisture, sunlight, and soil nutrients is reduced to a minimum. Sunlight intensity plays an important role in seedling survival. Climax species, such as sugar maples and basswood, can grow well in shade and are said to be shade tolerant. On the other hand, the white oaks, willow, white birch, and quaking aspen, all subclimax species, develop best in full light and die in dense shade. These species are said to be intolerant to shade. We shall see that the cutting method used by the logger depends in part upon whether he proposes to harvest tolerant or intolerant timber species.

Reproductive Organs of Coniferous Trees.   The United States derives 75 per cent of its paper pulp from coniferous trees, of which there are 570 species in the world (18). In conifers, flowers are extremely minute and are enclosed between the scales of cones. Unlike flowers of most deciduous trees, which are bisexual, the flowers produced by conifers are either pollen-producing male flowers or egg-producing female flowers. The pollen cones are usually much smaller than the seed cones. The latter may vary in length from the 0.5-inch cone of the jack pine to the 20-inch cone of the sugar pine.

In spring and early summer millions of tiny dustlike pollen grains are dispersed by the wind for a distance of a few feet to several miles. Were these pollen grains

Figure 8-10. *Leaves and cone of the long-leaf pine collected at Gainesville, Florida.* [*U.S. Forest Service*]

to fall on concrete highways, rocky outcrops, rooftops, or lakes and streams, they would perish; a very small percentage, however, come to rest, purely by chance, on the female cone of the same tree, or another tree of the same species and thus ultimately effect fertilization and the generation of a winged pine seed. In most pines two years are required for the seed cone to mature. When maturity is attained, at the end of the second summer (13), the scales (which protected the seed during development) open up, releasing large quantities of dry, light seeds, which may be dispersed by wind, by such seed-eating birds as grosbeaks and siskins, or even by woodland mice and squirrels. Many species of wildlife are dependent upon pine seeds for food. They form almost 70 per cent of the red crossbill's (*Loxia curvirostra*) diet. Even the American Indian of the Southwest supplemented his diet with the nutritious and highly edible seeds of the pinyon pine (*Pinus edulis*).

The seed cones of jack pine (*Pinus banksiana*) occasionally may remain tightly closed for several years with the mature, viable seeds within. However, when these cones are heated by a forest fire they open wide releasing seeds in much greater numbers than usual. A recent study in Minnesota has shown that 15,000 jack pine seedlings had sprung up in the ashes of a fire that had warmed the seed cones of only six mature trees. Usually considered highly destructive, fire may actually favor reproduction in the jack pine and other conifers.

History of Exploitation

The Colonist and the Forest. When the first white man arrived in America dense forests covered half the land (3), an area of 950 million acres (10), equivalent to all of Norway, Sweden, Italy, Germany, Spain, and France put together. This forest extended westward to the Appalachian summit and beyond into the uncharted wilderness of mid-America. Historians will never learn the name of the settler whose ax sent the first ill-fated tree crashing earthward, nor will they identify the species of tree, nor the place and time of the event. We do know, however, that the death of that first tree initiated the most ruthless and accelerated exploitation of a forest resource this earth has ever witnessed. (Fig. 8–11)

Not all of the timber was squandered. Colonists chopped down trees to provide logs for their cabins and firewood to burn. From the trees they fashioned handles for axes with which to chop down more trees. Showing great resourcefulness, they worked logs into tables and chairs, wagons, fence posts, and bowls. Many a turbulent Appalachian stream was bridged with timbers carved from the forest. Colonists erected wooden stockades around their tiny settlements to deter the savage. Much of the forest resource, however, was destroyed simply to get it out of the way (1). The woods had to be removed to make way for corn hills, squash, beans, pumpkins, and livestock pasture. Moreover, because hostile Indians lurked in the forest, security from attack was in some cases almost directly proportional

Figure 8-11. *Distribution of major forest types in the United States.* [*Adapted from Richard M. Highsmith, J. Granville Jensen, and Robert D. Rudd,* Conservation in the United States (*Chicago: Rand McNally & Company, 1962*).]

MAJOR FOREST REGIONS OF THE UNITED STATES

Rocky Mountain — Ponderosa, sugar and western white pine

Northern — Spruce, fir
White, red and jack pine
Beech and maple in southern portions

Southern coniferous — Longleaf, loblolly and slash pine

Central hardwood — Oak, hickory, yellow poplar

Pacific Coast — Douglas fir (Wash. and Oregon)
Sugar and ponderosa pine
and redwoods (California)

Tropical

Nonforested

0   250   500
Scale in miles

to the distance between the forest edge and the cabin door. Gradually at first, then faster, the virgin forest yielded to ax and torch.

Depletion of the Softwoods. Early in colonial history the king's foresters reserved the tallest and straightest white pines in New England for the British navy by marking them with a "broad arrow." For many decades the position of the British navy as the world's mightiest was in part dependent upon its American source of white pine (3). After the Revolutionary War, American logging companies fed white pine into the boat-building industries dotting the north Atlantic coast from Portland to New Bedford. These early logging outfits probably never heard the word *conservation* or the phrase *sustained yield*. For these men a forest had no future, only a present and a past. Why should they worry about tomorrow? There would always be more timber, somewhere. So they "cut out and got out." In their haste, they wasted 25 per cent of the harvest. Many logs were floated downstream to sawmills. When jams formed, logs were blasted loose with dynamite— a crude technique that rendered large numbers of valuable logs worthless (15). During the "cut out" operations, branches, twigs, bark, and other "slash" were left on the forest floor. After becoming tinder dry, this material occasionally became ignited and quickly blazed into a full-scale forest fire. The Peshtigo, Wisconsin,

Figure 8-12. *Extensive stands of white pine once occurred in Minnesota, Wisconsin, Michigan, and New York. These stumps were left after the last big white pine stand in Michigan was cut at DeWard, 1900–1908. A few of these huge stumps should be preserved.* [U.S. Department of Agriculture]

Figure 8-13. *Waupaca County, Wisconsin. Logging crew and sled load of pine logs, 1890–1910 (?). Note old-fashioned saw in center of picture.* [State Historical Society of Wisconsin]

fire of 1871, which started in this way, destroyed over 1 million acres of forest and claimed 1,500 lives (6).

By 1900 the pine stands of Minnesota and Wisconsin were so badly depleted, that the loggers again were forced to leave. They now split into two groups, one moving to the Pacific Northwest in quest of the Douglas fir, western hemlock, western red cedar, and redwood, the other moving to the South for the pines located there. Much of the southern pine had become established as a stage in the ecological succession that followed the abandonment of soil-depleted tobacco and cotton farms. The lumber interests were so dedicated and efficient in their "cut outs" that by 1940 the once magnificent stands of long-leaf, short-leaf, loblolly, and slash pine were being reduced to remnants (3).

Depletion of the Hardwoods. As was mentioned, the extensive deciduous forest biome originally embraced a variety of communities ranging from the elm-maple-basswood stands of Minnesota and Wisconsin to the beech-maple forests of Michigan and Ohio, from the oak-chestnut mantling of the Appalachians to the oak-hickory groves of Indiana. Although of considerable potential value, these stands posed a difficult and frustrating harvesting problem to the commercial timber men; for the more desirable species, such as walnut and oak, frequently occurred in mixed stands, which included a number of relatively worthless "weed" species, quite unlike

Figure 8-14. *Train load of huge logs on way to California sawmill, 1910–1920(?).* [U.S. Department of Agriculture]

Figure 8-15. *Allegheny National Forest, Pennsylvania. A 120-acre stand of virgin forest was logged over in the late 1920s. Although many of the standing trees in old stands continue to grow slowly, some of the overmature trees die and fall, so net growth in such stands is often zero. Eventually the fallen trees rot and contribute to the organic content of the soil. Note rotting trunk.* [U.S. Forest Service]

the uniform single-species stands of white pine in the North. Instead of being able to "clearcut," much more laborious "hunt and pick" methods were required. These methods were too slow for ambitious men engaged in a head long "rush to riches." As a result, although commercial loggers did thin out many deciduous forests, and although many a cabinet was fashioned from black walnut, many a chestnut was converted into fence posts, and many a maple did find its way into a parlor floor, the impact of the commercial logger on our original hardwood stands was relatively slight.

If not the lumberman, then what was the factor that reduced our virgin hardwoods to today's pathetic handful of wood lots? For farmers, road and dam builders, and enterprising industrialists, the deciduous forest formed a block to progress. It had to be removed. The retreat of this vast biome, which once extended from the Atlantic to the Mississippi, continues unabated to this day.

U.S. Forest Service

Four federal bureaus are charged with the administration and management of our nation's forested areas. They include the Soil Conservation Service, which is concerned with farm-management-associated forests; the Tennessee Valley Authority, charged with timberland management in the vicinity of the numerous dam-reservoir sites along the Tennessee River and its tributaries; and the Fish and Wildlife Service, which is interested in improving forest habitat for game and fish. However, the Forest Service, a bureau of the Department of Agriculture, has the primary responsibility of managing our nation's forests so as to promote "the greatest good for the most people" over the long run. Although the Service has headquarters in Washington, D.C., it is highly decentralized, with ten administrative regions, each of which embraces several states. (Thus, the North Central Region, based in Milwaukee, includes Ohio, Michigan, Indiana, Illinois, Iowa, Wisconsin, Minnesota, Missouri, and North Dakota.) A tropical forestry unit has headquarters in Rio Piedras, Puerto Rico.

Figure 8-16. *Theodore Roosevelt and Gifford Pinchot (to left of Roosevelt) standing at the base of a giant redwood called "Old Grizzly." Pinchot was America's first Chief Forester.* [U.S. Department of Agriculture]

The first Chief Forester was Gifford Pinchot, appointed by Theodore Roosevelt in 1905. Pinchot was a zealous crusader for resource conservation and infused the Service with a spirit that persists to this day (6). The Forest Service divides its attention now among three major areas: (1) administration and protection of the national forests; (2) research on forest, watershed, range, and recreation management; on wildlife habitat improvement; on forest product development; and on fire and pest control; and (3) cooperation with the state and private forest owners in the fifty states, Puerto Rico, and the Virgin Islands in promoting sound forest management.

The Forest Service protects and manages 154 national forests and grasslands embracing 182 million acres with 990 billion board feet of timber. Included under its supervision are the grazing lands of 6 million head of livestock and habitat for one third of America's big game animals. In a single year the Forest Service extinguishes almost 10,000 fires. It annually grasses about 180,000 acres.

Forest Management

We shall now consider various aspects of forest management as practiced by the Forest Service, many state forestry departments, and an increasing number of enlightened private owners, with respect to sustained yield, clearcutting, selective cutting, reforestation, multiple-use management, and pest and fire control.

Sustained Yield. Today's lumbermen are a different breed from the "cut-out-and-get-out" loggers of the late nineteenth and early twentieth centuries. After studying German silvicultural techniques, American foresters learned that a forest can be managed in such a way that a modest timber crop may be harvested indefinitely year after year without being depleted if annual decrements are counterbalanced by annual growth increments. This is called the sustained-yield concept. (Fig. 8-17)

Annual measurement of a timber crop is somewhat different from measurement of a crop of corn. The latter matures in a single growing season, whereas an aspen may require 20 years and a Douglas fir 100 years to attain a harvestable age.

To determine the volume of the annual forest crop of a given acreage, the volume lost to destructive agencies is subtracted from the growth for that year. A comprehensive nationwide forest inventory, conducted by the U.S. Forest Service in 1952, revealed growth rate of western forests to be about 1 per cent of the growing stock of 273 billion cubic feet. However, because each year about 3.75 billion cubic feet was harvested, our forest stocks incurred an annual decrement of about 1 billion cubic feet. It is encouraging to note that by 1965, because of intensified forest management, for the first time in many decades, timber growth exceeded timber cut, even though much of the growth was not of excellent quality.

Clearcutting. The *clearcutting method* of timber harvest, which is the standard logging practice in the Northwest in both private and public forests, is employed on even-aged stands composed of only a few species and is applicable only to trees whose seedlings thrive best in full sunlight. The Douglas fir on the Pacific coast is harvested by this method. Perhaps the most valuable timber species in the world, it has been imported to Europe, where it has proved superior to native species. Some

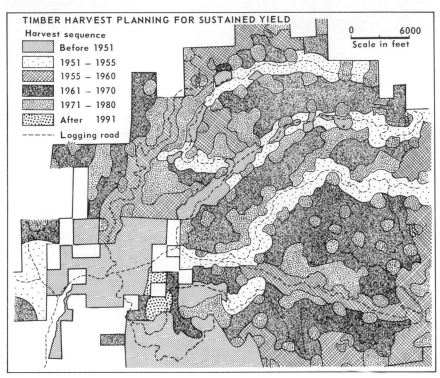

Figure 8-17. *Sustained-yield plan. This map of a timber tract owned by the Weyerhaeuser Company demonstrates the type of long-range planning required for successful sustained-yield forestry. Symbols indicate areas that will mature and should be harvested within a given decade. Note the large number of well-distributed logging roads providing fire protection and serving as logging facilities as well. [Adapted from Richard M. Highsmith, J. Granville Jensen, and Robert D. Rudd,* Conservation in the United States *(Chicago: Rand McNally & Company, 1962). Weyerhaeuser Company map]*

Douglas fir in Washington and Oregon stand over 200 feet high and are over 1,000 years old.

A Douglas fir, unlike a beech or maple, is not a climax tree and is not shade-tolerant as a seedling. Therefore, this species would not be amenable to selective cutting, because its seeds would not germinate in the reduced light intensity of the forest floor. Moreover, its place in the forest would rapidly be appropriated by shade-tolerant species. In addition, a 100-foot Douglas fir weighing several tons could not be removed without badly bruising and killing younger growth. With the clear-cutting technique an entire patch of evenly aged mature trees, possible forty acres in area, is removed, leaving an unsightly rectangular "scar" in the midst of the forest. Because a large number of such blocks may be removed, when viewed from the air a clearcut forest resembles a giant green-and-brown checkerboard. In addition to its use on Douglas fir in Oregon and Washington, the clearcutting method has been used effectively in harvesting even-aged stands of southern pine and subclimax aspen forests in northern Minnesota, Wisconsin, and Michigan.

Figure 8-18. *Felling a large Western red cedar in the Wenatchee National Forest, Washington. A wedge is employed to prevent the tree from binding the chain saw.* [U.S. Department of Agriculture]

Figure 8-19. *Clear cutting of old-growth Douglas fir in the Gifford Pinchot National Forest, Washington. Mt. St. Helens in background.* [U.S. Forest Service, Photo by P. F. Heim]

Figure 8-20. *The slash in this clear cut area in the Kootenai National Forest, Montana, has been piled in windrows by a bulldozer to reduce the fire hazard. [U.S. Department of Agriculture]*

Let us see now why this method of harvest may result in a *sustained yield*. Suppose that a Wisconsin farmer who owns 15 acres of aspen woods wishes a yearly harvest of pulpwood logs. He could log off a 1-acre block year after year for 15 successive years. At the end of this period, if each block removed had been successfully reseeded, he would have 15 age classes, all 1 acre in area, ranging from 1 to 15 years in age. At the end of this 15-year period, he could harvest 1 acre of 15-year-old pulpwood stock, year after year for an indefinite period, as long as he ensures successful reseeding. The length of the cutting cycle or rotation depends upon the species of tree and on its intended commercial use. For aspen and birch, to be used as pulpwood, it varies from 10 to 30 years; on the other hand, the rotation for Douglas fir, to be used as lumber, may be up to 100 years.

THE CLEARCUTTING CONTROVERSY. The clearcutting practices of the Forest Service became a storm center of considerable controversy in 1971. Much of the criticism focused on the ponderosa pine logging in the Bitterroot National Forest of Montana. Let us examine some of the criticisms:

1. Clearcutting resulted in accelerated water run-off. Theoretically, this water could be used for irrigation and for watering livestock in nearby valley ranches.

Figure 8-21. *A sample slash pine plantation in Miden, Louisiana. Trees average 50 feet in height. The stand has been thinned by removing every other row.* [*Soil Conservation Service, U.S. Department of Agriculture*]

However, as one rancher from Sleeping Child, Montana, stated, "Nature previously controlled the run-off and regulated it naturally. Now the water is coming down in early spring, at the least desirable time . . . if they keep this up we might as well forget about farming . . ." (5).

2. The wildlife carrying capacity of an area that has been clearcut is greatly diminished, at least temporarily.[2] How many grouse or deer can be supported by a bare patch of ground?

3. Clearcutting destroys the scenic beauty of the region, converting it into an ugly, desolate scar.

Perhaps some of this criticism is valid. In any event, it certainly has served as a catalyst for a series of self-examination studies on the part of the Forest Service. The chief of the service has emphasized that in the future the service will make more strenuous efforts to protect environmental quality. The record of the Forest Service,

---

[2] It is true that in the third or fourth year after clearcutting, such early successional species such as aspen, birch, and various shrubs may provide more wildlife food than was actually available in the mature forest before the clearcutting.

TOO MANY TREES
YEARLY GROWTH—NONE
SPACING — 5 FT. X 5 FT.
(1700 TREES PER ACRE)

NOT ENOUGH TREES
YEARLY GROWTH—ONE CORD PER AC.
SPACING — 15 FT. X 15 FT.
(170 TREES PER ACRE)

RIGHT NUMBER OF TREES
YEARLY GROWTH—2 CORDS PER AC.
SPACING — 10 FT. X 10 FT.
(425 TREES PER ACRE)

THE ABOVE TREES WERE CUT WHEN TEN YEARS OLD

Figure 8-22. *The effect of thinning on timber growth. These pines came from a stand growing near Magnolia, Arkansas. [U.S. Department of Agriculture]*

over the long haul, has been an admirable one. It has been vigorously defended by William E. Towell, in *American Forests,* official magazine of the American Forestry Association, as follows:

Clearcutting most certainly has been abused in some areas. But it is a necessary tool in the professional forester's kit. It is the only way of regenerating forests of desirable species in certain regions. It is the only way to control some diseases and insects which can destroy the forest in a much more unsightly way. Clearcutting can be just as important to the forester as amputation is to the surgeon who must use it to save a life, but unlike human amputation, the forest will grow again. Foresters are learning to use the clearcut more sparingly, in smaller units and away from public view, just as they are giving greater priority to esthetics, to recreation, to wildlife, to water quality and other amenities of forest lands. Let's not rob him of the essential tools of his profession, but rather demand that they be used with greater discretion in the public interest. The forester is a professional who will rise to the challenges of today as he has in the past. Let's give him that chance . . . (19).

Selective Cutting. It is apparent that clearcutting will not work in timber stands composed of unevenly age trees, or in mixed stands, composed in part of valuable timber species and in part of "trash" species. Under such conditions trees are harvested by *selective cutting,* a sort of "hunt-and-pick" method in which mature trees of quality species are harvested after being marked in advance with spray paint or some other method. Selective cutting has been employed extensively in mixed coniferous hardwood stands and in deciduous forests (oak, hickory, butternut, walnut, and so on). It is obviously a more costly and time-consuming method than clearcutting. However, such environmental abuse as land scarring, accelerated runoff, soil erosion, and wildlife depletion is reduced to a minimum.

Audubon magazine has reported on a case where "selective cutting" has been carried to extremes:

Walnut veneer is so popular that tree "rustlers" range the Great Plains states, making off with any rare old black walnuts that remain. One thief sawed down and carried off a handsome specimen from a city park in broad daylight. Another took a prized tree from a farmer's front yard while he was attending church services! The best old trees can be sold for up to $25,000 and buyers come all the way from West Germany and Japan to bid for them . . . (16).

Reforestation. The sustained-yield concept dictates that whenever timber is removed, either by clearcutting or by selective cutting, the denuded area must be reforested. This may be done by natural or artificial methods. Similarly, any forested land that has been destroyed by fire, insects, disease, hurricanes, or strip-mining activities also should be reforested, even though timber may not be its ultimate primary use.

After clearcutting a few mature wind-firm trees may be left intact on a ridge within the otherwise logged-off site as a seed source. Scattered by wind and to a lesser degree by birds, rodents, and run-off water, the seeds will eventually become dispersed throughout the denuded area. Natural reseeding, however, is usually not

Figure 8-23. *One-year-old pine seedling protected by good litter and duff. Still thrifty and vigorous in late September, following a dry season. Huntsville, Texas.* [*Soil Conservation Service, U.S. Department of Agriculture, Photo by John McConnell*]

completely adequate. One reason is that some tree species, such as loblolly pine, may have only one good seed-producing year out of every two-to-five-year period. (In a good year seed production may be ten times that in a poor year.) Another reason is that the dispersed seeds must reach mineral soil to develop properly. Because of these drawbacks, natural reseeding is usually combined with aerial, hand, or machine seeding.

In rugged terrain aerial seeding is the method of choice. Seeds arc sown from planes flying slowly just above treetop level. Unfortunately, many aerially sown seeds fall on infertile soil or are consumed by birds and rodents. To minimize loss to animals, the seeds are frequently coated with a toxic deterrent. Except in the case of exceptionally small seeded trees, such as hemlock (*Thuja*) and spruce (*Picea*), rodent eradication is virtually a prerequisite to successful seeding.

If the logged-off site is of even topography, power-driven seeding machines may be advantageously employed, as has been done in the cut-over land of Wisconsin and Michigan. Not only are these machines capable of planting up to 8 acres per day, but simultaneously they fertilize the soil and apply a herbicide to prevent weed encroachment.

Figure 8-24. *Winter Green, Florida. Soil conservationist Donald E. Vandergrift is looking at a young planting of slash pine on cold spot. Pines are planted on land that would otherwise remain idle.* [*Soil Conservation Service, U.S. Department of Agriculture, Photo by W. G. Diamond*]

In addition to the bird and rodent problem, a major disadvantage to seeding is the high number of first-year seedlings killed by frost, drought, hot weather, insects, and autumn leaf fall. As a result, seeding, even by artificial methods, is less effective than planting young trees from plantation stock. In the South and in the lake states, trees can be planted at a rate of 150 per man-hour. Open fields in the Midwest have been planted with the aid of an ordinary moldboard plow. On flat land, three men, a tractor, and a planting machine can set 1,000 to 2,000 trees per hour.

STRIP-MINE AREAS.   Reforestation frequently is required in areas denuded by strip mining. This has been the case in the coal-mining regions of the Appalachians. A few years ago extensive open-pit and shaft mining operations in the anthracite regions of northeastern Pennsylvania left 112,928 acres defaced with barren spoil banks and waste dumps. In 1961, with the cooperation of the Northeastern Forest

Figure 8-25.   *Sullivan-Green State Forest, Indiana. Fishing in a lake created by strip mining. The trees planted along the formerly denuded banks not only enhance the beauty of the region but also provide valuable wildlife cover. [U.S. Department of Agriculture, Photo by G. A. Linstrom]*

Experiment Station, the Pennsylvania Power and Light Company initiated and financed "Operation Trees" in an attempt to rehabilitate the despoiled areas. The company donated $100,000 and furnished 625,000 seedlings of the 100 million eventually required. From 1963 to 1966, 3 million seedlings were planted under the supervision of the Pennsylvania Department of Mines. Moreover, between 1928 to 1966 the U.S. Forest Service planted 6.625 million trees. These plantings were not done in a haphazard manner. Intensive studies were conducted by the Forest Experiment Station to determine the tree species best suited to the extremely acid conditions. Of ten conifers, three hardwoods, and one hybrid poplar tested, the European white birch appeared best adapted to the acid sites. Reforestation in this region has not only reduced erosion and minimized acid drainage, but has partially restored the original beauty of the area and has shown that some spoil banks may have at least a modest timber and wildlife producing potential.

TREE FARMS.   A tree farm is a private land area used for growing timber for profit. The tree farm movement was started by the Weyerhacuser Company at Montesand, Washington, in 1941. It is currently sponsored by the American Forest Products Industries, composed of the timber, paper, pulp, and plywood industries and private owners of forest lands. In applying for certification the owner must demonstrate to an inspecting forester that he is employing sound forest management practices such as sustained yield and effective pest and fire control. When a state tree farm certification committee has approved the forester's report, the tree farm owner is awarded the official roadside tree farm sign as recognition of his achievement. This movement has grown from 8,086 tree farms embracing 39 million acres in 1956, to 29,000 farms covering 66 million acres in the mid-1960's.

Multiple-Use Management.   A primary objective of the United States Forest Service is to make the greatest number of forest resources available to the greatest number of Americans. This principle is graphically portrayed in the multiple-use tree, the official National Forest symbol, which is enclosed by a ring bearing the legend "National Forest—Lands of Many Uses." The trunk of the tree represents the American people, who benefit from the varied resources of our forests—timber, water, forage, wildlife, and recreation. These five major forest-derived resources are in turn symbolized by the five branches of the multiple-use tree. The single line used to inscribe the tree suggests the ecological interactions not only between the resources, but between them and the people who use or abuse them (26).

Multiple-use management of forests looks simple on paper. In actual operation, however, it is an extremely complex ecological problem with a veritable thicket of coalescing cause-and-effect relationships. For example, the Forest Service is frequently forced to utilize a given forest acre primarily for one resource while sacrificing its potential for other values. A given acre of forest cannot be all things to all people. If a given acreage of Douglas fir is to be developed for high-quality timber, then clear cutting of this acreage would certainly be a perfectly valid management procedure. However, at the same time, the wholesale removal of a timber block would greatly impair the value of that particular acreage in terms of flood and erosion control, wildlife habitat, and recreation. Sound multiple-use management must weigh the needs of the people, and these vary both in time and place. Thus, timber production may have top priority in the valuable Douglas fir and western hemlock stands of Washington and Oregon, but in the low-value, second-growth forests of populous New York, where many city dwellers require occasional doses of "wilderness tonic," recreational values would have high priority.

We shall now briefly examine some examples of how the Forest Service has managed our forests in terms of such uses as flood and erosion control, rangeland, and wildlife habitat.

USE OF FORESTS IN FLOOD AND EROSION CONTROL. Ever since the late nineteenth century many of our western valley towns situated at the base of steep mountain slopes have been periodically battered by brief but damaging flash floods spawned by sudden summer storms. One hour a valley stream would be placid, the next it might be transformed into a churning torrent, bearing soil, rocks, uptorn shrubs, and debris washed from the slope of a mountain. Surging down the valley, the swollen stream might cause considerable property damage and loss of life.

One of the regions hardest hit by this type of flash flood was Davis County, Utah, at the eastern margin of Great Salt Lake. Harried citizens, beleaguered by recurring disasters, finally asked Congress for federal assistance. In his book *Land, Wood and Water*, the late Senator Robert S. Kerr of Oklahoma describes the work of the Forest Service in dealing with the problem (11). Kerr describes how, during their meticulous survey, investigators discovered that much of the flood-triggering run-off originated from areas that had been depleted of their vegetational cover. These denuded parts of the watershed had either been burned over, overgrazed, or plowed up and converted into marginal croplands. In some areas the run-off waters carved gullies 70 feet deep. During one rainy period up to 160 times as much water ran off an abused plot than ran off an undisturbed one. In 1936, with the aid of bulldozers, the gullies were filled in, slopes were contoured, the bare soil was carefully prepared

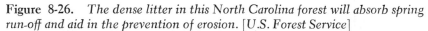

Figure 8-26. *The dense litter in this North Carolina forest will absorb spring run-off and aid in the prevention of erosion.* [*U.S. Forest Service*]

as a seedbed and planted to rapidly growing shrubs and trees. Only eleven years later, in 1945, severe August rainstorms put the rehabilitated watershed to the test. An investigation revealed that fully 93.5 per cent of the rainfall was retained by the newly forested area. Moreover, soil erosion was reduced from the pretreatment figure of 268 cubic feet per acre to a mere trace (11).

USE OF FORESTS AS RANGELAND.   Our forests frequently include, in addition to timber, considerable areas of high-quality livestock forage. Thus, of the 186 million acres comprising our national forests and national grasslands, 100 million acres (over 53 per cent) provide forage for 6 million cattle and sheep belonging to 19,000 farmers and ranchers. (Most of this is in the West. In the lake states and central states most forest grazing occurs on farm woodlots.) Graziers pay fees for the privilege of grazing their livestock in national forests. In a typical year, grazing fee receipts amount to $3.7 million, of which 25 per cent (about $947,000) is returned to state coffers for the improvement of highways and schools in the counties where the fees were levied (23).

In 1963 the Forest Service conducted a study on the Front range in the Rockies to determine what effect the introduction of high-quality exotic forage grasses would have on beef production. Thus, calves were grazed part time on native bunch grass range and than transferred to an adjacent range composed of such exotics as Sherman big bluegrass (*Poa ampla*), crested wheat grass (*Agropyron desertorum*), and Russian wild rye (*Elymus junceus*). When weaned the calves raised on the integrated grazing plan were 17 pounds heavier and worth $4 more per head than calves raised exclusively on native range (23).

Another Forest Service study in the low-timber-value post oak and blackjack oak

Figure 8-27.
Sheepherder and two sheep dogs watch over sheep grazing in a high meadow within the Plumas National Forest, California. Some 18,000 sheep graze the summer ranges of the Plumas under paid permit. [U.S. Forest Service, Photo by Daniel O. Todd]

forests of the Ozark Mountains revealed how these areas can be converted into high-value rangeland. By spraying herbicides to kill the scrubby trees, preparing the forest floor as a seedbed by fertilizing and setting carefully regulated fires, and then seeding heavily with small bluestem and fescue grass, cattle forage per acre could be increased 100 times (22).

During a typical year rangeland improvements made in our national forests by the Forest Service include reseeding 100,000 acres, applying rodent-control measures on 25,000 acres, checking the growth and spread of undesirable noxious weeds on 162,000 acres, constructing more than 2,000 miles of fence, and developing more than 1,900 livestock-watering sites.

USE OF FORESTS AS WILDLIFE HABITAT. Our nation's 154 national forests and nineteen national grasslands embrace 186 million acres, almost 1 acre for each American. Two thirds of the sportsmen visiting this vast public hunting ground seek big game; the remainder seek upland game and waterfowl. In a typical year hunters spend about 15 million visitor days in the national forests and grasslands and bag about 600,000 big-game animals, 95 per cent of which are deer and elk.

The U.S. Forest Service attempts to manage our national forests in such a way as to provide the best possible habitat for wildlife. Sometimes best management involves increasing the forest "edge" habitat, frequented by many game animals such as deer, rabbit, and pheasant. Forest edge improvement for game may be integrated with timber harvesting and the construction of fire lanes and logging trails. Because game food and cover are more abundant in seral than in climax stages, retardation of succession by prescribed burning may be beneficial to wildlife. In a typical year the Forest Service seeds and plants game food on 45,000 acres, protects 35,000 acres of key wildlife habitat, and employs regulated burning to improve the wild-game carrying capacity of 45,000 acres (24). We shall briefly describe two game habitat development programs recently initiated by the Forest Service, one for turkeys and the other for deer.

Improvement of Turkey Habitat. In an attempt to improve wild turkey habitat on the Jefferson National Forest in Virginia, a number of clearings were made in the otherwise dense timber and were then heavily seeded with ladino clover and bluegrass. Once these plants had become well established, the turkeys in the region made heavy use of the openings as feeding areas, consuming not only large quantities of grass, clover, and weed seeds, but also insects attracted to the newly introduced vegetation. As a direct response to the modified forest environment, the turkey population increased from 12 birds to 125 birds within a 6-year period (22, 25).

Solving the Deer Versus Forest Reproduction Problem. A sizable deer herd generally poses such a browsing menace to young hardwood seedlings that in many situations there are two alternatives, to maintain the deer herd and sacrifice the seedlings, or vice versa. For example, basswood and hemlock have been completely eliminated by deer browsing in certain mixed hardwood-hemlock forests of the North, with only sugar maple and red maple being able to survive. In Rocky Mountain National Park mule deer (and elk) have prevented aspen stand establishment. It was of considerable interest, therefore, when Forest Service researchers, working in an Appalachian hardwood stand in North Carolina, discovered at least a local solution to the problem (24). Three years after a heavy cutting had been made in the study area, deer showed a rather surprising preference for old stump sprouts to seedlings; they consumed 60 per cent of the sprouts but only 10 per cent of the seedlings. Therefore, by cutting down hardwoods of little commercial value, such as weed species, misshapen or fire-scarred trees, the volume of stump sprout food could be deliberately increased to the point where a fairly large deer herd could be sustained while concurrently assuring vigorous regeneration of valuable hardwoods (24).

USE OF FORESTS AS RECREATIONAL AND WILDERNESS AREAS. In this polluted age when urban dwellers from Seattle to Miami and from San Diego to Boston are being

Figure 8-28. *Multiple use of the forest. A logger and a fisherman greet each other along the Santeetlah Creek in North Carolina's Nantahala National Forest. The logger is transporting part of the timber harvested annually from the surrounding watershed, and the angler is anxious to fill his creel.* [U.S. Department of Agriculture]

crowded together shoulder to shoulder, when air is weighted with soot and odious with industrial gases, when drinking water tastes of chlorine, and when the tyranny of noise assaults the ears from all compass points, it is somehow reassuring to know that "way out there" somewhere in the great forests of America is wilderness country. And once you get there, you can hike for miles without even getting near a human shoulder; you can actually inhale unadulterated fresh air; you can drink clear, cold water from a tumbling brook, and the only sounds are pine boughs sighing in the evening breeze, or the dusk chant of a whippoorwill. Regrettably, despite the strenuous efforts of such organizations as the Sierra Club, Friends of the Earth, the Wilderness Society, and the Audubon Society, our nation's wilderness areas have been steadily diminishing. In their valiant attempts to preserve wilderness habitat, the environmentalists frequently draw the ire of the big timber interests. Recently, for example, the Western Timber Association brought a $20 million suit against four environmentalist groups because they secured a restraining order that tempo-

Figure 8-29. *Angeles National Forest, California. Use of the forest as a recreational area. A family of hikers studies a map of the forest before starting a wilderness trip in order to escape the tensions of day-to-day living. [U.S. Department of Agriculture]*

rarily barred commercial logging on any federal lands being considered for wilderness status (17). In the name of "progress" wilderness country has gradually receded under the onslaught of timber and mining interests, highway engineers, and land developers. Even the U.S. Navy has gotten into the act with its controversial Project Sanguine, an electronic system for communicating with submarines, which, as initially proposed, would have converted 20,000 square miles of Wisconsin backwoods country into a gigantic "electric waffle!"

In order to preserve as many wilderness areas as possible, Congress passed the National Wilderness Preservation Act in 1965. Among the officially designated wilderness areas are the Boundary Waters Canoe Area in northern Minnesota. Under the terms of this act such obtrusive activities as logging, mining, and the use of automobiles, motorboats, and snowmobiles are prohibited. In some areas even aircraft is not permitted to descend below a designated altitude. In the officially designated wilderness area, every attempt is made to permit the forest ecosystem to operate without human interference. If an overmature pine, riddled with bark beetle galleries, blows down during a wind storm, it remains where it falls. Barring a major catastrophe, such as a crown fire, the official policy is, "Let nature take its course." As a result, these areas have considerable scientific as well as recreational value. In such an area, many a university researcher can make observations, collect data, and formulate hypotheses, and many an eager college student can acquire valuable field experiences in such areas as geography, entomology, mammalogy, ornithology, ecology, field natural history, and game management, as well as forestry.

Pest Control. The most serious agents of forest destruction are disease and insect pests. Under the authority of the Forest Pest Control Act of 1947, surveys are annually conducted in both private and public forests to permit early detection of pest population increases so that they may be arrested before reaching disastrous levels. In a typical year Congress appropriates $10 million for pest control and an additional $3 million for research.

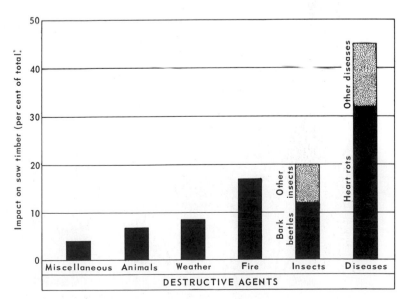

Figure 8-30. *Impact of destructive agents on saw timber (indicated in per cent of total impact).* [*Adapted from Guy-Harold Smith,* Conservation of Natural Resources *(New York: John Wiley & Sons, Inc., 1965). Data from* Timber Resources Review, U.S. Forest Service.]

DISEASES. Forest diseases resulting from parasitic fungi, rusts, mistletoes, viruses, and nematodes cause roughly 45 per cent of the total saw timber destruction. Young seedlings are especially vulnerable to nematode infections. Heart-rot fungus (*Polyporus* and *Fomes*) alone is responsible for about 33 per cent of the total forest damage. (This fungus, however, may be beneficial as an important agent in the decay of fallen logs, dead stubs, and slash, thus recycling elements and removing flammable debris). The remaining 12 per cent of disease damage may be attributed primarily to white pine blister rust (*Cronartium ribicola*), dwarf mistletoe (*Arceuthobium*), oak wilt (*Chalara quercina*), Dutch elm disease (*Ceratostomella ulmi*), elm phloem necrosis (caused by a virus), and oak wilt (*Certocyster fagacearium*). The most injurious disease pests are exotics, accidentally introduced to the United States, that have suddenly been released from environmental factors that ordinarily keep them in check.

OAK WILT. The oak wilt fungus is threatening extensive oak forests of the southern Appalachians and upper Mississippi Valley. The parasite enters the host tree via roots or bark wounds. Healthy trees may become infected by root grafts with an adjacent diseased tree or by the disseminating agency of nitidulid beetles (*Glischrochilus* and *Colopterus*), which acquire the fungus while consuming mats of fungus spores just under the bark of diseased trees. Squirrels and possibly birds may also serve as disseminating agents. The fungus spores are transmitted throughout the host by water flowing through xylem tissue. Eventually the fungus clogs the xylem vessels and causes leaf death. Characteristic symptoms include discolored leaves, premature defoliation, and cracked bark (caused by the spore mats).

Figure 8-31. *Oak wilt. Harrisonburg, Virginia. Close-up view of young tree tops and branches affected with oak wilt. Note that the leaves and stems die progressively from the top downward.* [U.S. Forest Service]

CHESTNUT BLIGHT.   At the turn of the century, the American chestnut (*Castanea dentata*) was a conspicuous, attractive, and valuable member of the deciduous forest in the eastern United States; in some areas, such as the Appalachians, it formed over 50 per cent of the stand. Both man and beast found its nuts nutritious and palatable. Tannin, a substance of prime importance in the leather-tanning process, was derived from its bark; from its straight trunk were fashioned durable fence posts and rails. Today, however, only the leafless "skeletons" of these trees remain. You can tramp the Appalachians for weeks without finding a single living mature tree. In New England a few living sprouts from native stumps may be found.

The near extinction of the once abundant chestnut was caused by a parasitic fungus (*Endothia parasitica*), inadvertently introduced along with nursery stock from China. The parasite was first reported in New York City in 1904. Once established, the fungus spread rapidly, virtually eliminating the chestnut as a commercial species by 1914. After gaining access through a bark wound (possibly caused by fire, insects, or rodents) the fungus invades the cambium and phloem, spreads rapidly, and ultimately plugs the food-conducting phloem tissue, causing the leaves to turn brown and wither. Eventually, when the malnourished roots no longer can absorb soil moisture and nutrients, the tree dies. Trunk and branches swell at foci of infection and form cankers that produce tiny reproductive spores. During dry seasons light spores are formed that are wind disseminated. During wet seasons, heavy, sticky yellowish-brown tendrils of spores ooze from the cankers and adhere to the bodies of bark beetles, squirrels, or bills and feet of woodpeckers. (Up to 1 billion spores have been washed from the feet of one woodpecker.) During migrations

Figure 8-32.   *These American chestnut trees in the mountains of North Carolina have been killed by the chestnut blight.* [*U.S. Department of Agriculture*]

woodpeckers may fly 20 miles or more daily, thus serving as superb dispersal agents.

In recent years Oriental chestnuts, which are quite resistant to the blight, have been introduced. Although these trees do well when given solicitous care under nurserylike conditions, they are unable to survive in the wild. Forest geneticists have been crossing the resistant Oriental chestnut with the American chestnut in an attempt to develop a blight-resistant hybrid. If successful, the chestnut may yet again be an important component of our deciduous forests.

WHITE PINE BLISTER RUST. The blister rust parasite (*Cronartium ribicola*) has primarily infected the white pines of New England and lake states and the western white pine and sugar pine of the Pacific coast. Many of these stately trees, over 200 years old and 150 feet tall, have withstood wind, storm, hail, sub-Arctic cold, drought, fires, and insect attacks only to succumb to this microscopic fungus. The blister rust was introduced accidentally from Germany, first being found in North America at Geneva, New York, in 1906. When new infections were introduced on the West Coast, hope for its eradication was abandoned.

The first signs of the infection, which attacks all five-needle pines, are the yellowish spots that speckle the needles. Within three years the parasite spreads to the branches and main trunk, causing the tree's death when it girdles the inner bark. Numerous minute, orange spores are released during spring and summer from

Figure 8-33. *Tree infected by white pine blister rust.* [*U.S. Department of Agriculture*]

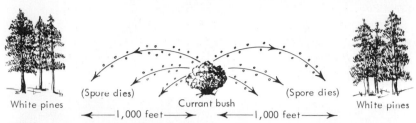

Figure 8-34. *Dissemination of blister rust spores. Because the spores can be dispersed a maximum of 1,000 feet from the currant or gooseberry hosts, removal of all such hosts within a radius of 1,000 feet from a stand of white pine would protect the pine from infection with blister rust.*

elongated yellowish blisters. When wind-borne these spores may be carried 100 miles. Although more than 99 per cent eventually die, a few may alight and germinate on the leaves of domesticated or wild gooseberry or currant (*Ribes*) bushes, which will serve as an alternate host. The infected leaves of the new host present a frost-white appearance. Eventually, after a period of development, a new type of spore is produced, which may be wind-blown for a maximum distance of 1,000 feet. If some of these spores alight upon white pine needles, they will in turn germinate, thus completing the parasite's life cycle.

ERADICATION OF HOST. Because the blister rust requires two hosts to complete its life cycle, it can be eradicated simply by depriving the rust of one of them. White pine timber is much more valuable than jam; hence, all gooseberry and currant bushes within a 1,000-foot radius of a white pine stand are destroyed. These thorny shrubs may be grubbed out by hand or bulldozer, burned, or treated with a herbicide. The U.S. Forest Service surveys about 3 million acres in its blister rust control operations and eradicates *Ribes* from about 234,000 acres annually.

USE OF ANTIBIOTICS. Several antibiotics have been developed recently that have proved effective in blister rust control. One antibiotic, phytoactin, has been successfully used on infected western white pine. Another, cyclohexamide, has given promising results on parasitized white pine seedlings without having any harmful residual effect on the beneficial root-associated mycorrhizae (24). The U.S. Forest Service treats over 100,000 acres of infected pine with rust-killing antibiotics annually.

DEVELOPMENT OF RESISTANT PINES. In recent years Forest Service geneticists have succeeded in developing rust-resistant hybrids. By 1980 a 100-acre seed orchard of resistant hybrids will have developed a mass quantity of seeds suitable for use in planting several hundred thousand acres to rust-resistant pine (22). The extension of this program of "genetic control" may ultimately eliminate the blister rust as a major agent of forest destruction in this country.

INSECTS. Insects account for 20 per cent of all timber destroyed, ranking second only to diseases as a destructive agent. Each year insects ruin 5 billion board feet of

Figure 8-35. *A young Western white pine stand in the St. Joe National Forest (Idaho) is being sprayed with the antibiotic fungicide phytoactin to arrest the damage being caused by the white pine blister rust.* [*U.S. Department of Agriculture, Photo by Miller Cowlin*]

timber, roughly equivalent to 10 per cent of our total annual timber harvest. Each tree species has its own unique assemblage of insect pests. An oak tree may be ravaged by over 100 species. No part of a tree's anatomy is spared.

Timber-valuable pine trees are under insect attack from the top of the terminal shoot down to the roots. Terminals may be killed or deformed by grubs of the white pine weevil (*Pissodes strobi*) or by larvae of the ponderosa pitch moth (*Dioryctria ponderosae*). The small pine bark aphid (*Pineus strobi*) consumes needles. Leaves may be stripped and skeletonized by the nearly hairless caterpillars of the spruce budworm (*Choristoneura fumiferana*). Sawfly (family Diprionidae) larvae cause defoliation. Fresh green pine cones may be attacked by cone beetles (*Conophthorus*); mature dry cones may be attacked by the slender white cone borer larvae of the family Cerambycidae. Seeds are susceptible to the mining activities of the minute, legless white larvae of the seed chalcids (Chalcidae). Several species of bark beetles (*Dendroctonus*) consume the inner bark. Wood of living and dying trees is ravaged by flat-headed borers (Buprestidae); sawed lumber and seasoned wood are devoured by the black-horned pine borer (*Callidium antennatum*). Even the finished wood products may be riddled by soft white and brown termites (*Reticulitermes*) (7).

GYPSY MOTHS.   In 1869 pupae of the gypsy moth were shipped through the mails from France to Medford, Massachusetts, at the request of a young scientist who was conducting silkworm research. Unfortunately, a few of the insects escaped from his laboratory and soon became established in nearby woodlands. Released from the controls exerted by its native European predators, the gypsy moth population rapidly

Figure 8-36. Aerial photo taken with infrared film readily reveals the extent of an insect infestation of Oregon timber. Damaged trees appear darker; healthy trees appear lighter. [NASA]

Figure 8-37. Leaf-eating caterpillars of the gypsy moth damage hundreds of thousands of dollars worth of forest and shade trees in the Northeastern states annually. They hatch in April from eggs laid the previous year. [U.S. Department of Agriculture]

increased. An early writer describes an infestation in an eastern town as follows, "The street was black with them [caterpillars] . . . they were so thick on the trees that they were stuck together like cold macaroni . . . the foliage was completely stripped from all the trees . . . presenting an awful picture of devastation." Although the larvae prefer oak leaves, they will also consume birch and ash foliage, and when full grown will even eat pine needles. An intensive attack will kill a white pine. Even though defoliation may not kill some trees directly, it may increase their vulnerability to fungus infections, windstorms, and drought.

Currently the gypsy moth is widely distributed throughout 40 million acres of forest in northeastern United States (15). Ever since 1890 federal and state agencies have made strenuous efforts to curb its range extension and check population increases. Descriptions of some of these measures follow:

1. *Quarantine.* The federal government has imposed a quarantine on all materials such as branches, bark, and soil in the infected area. (Unscrupulous individuals have periodically attempted to violate the quarantine. Some have even mailed uncertified evergreen boughs in boxes labeled laundry.)

2. *Parasites.* A parasitic fly (*Compsilura concinnata*) has been successfully imported from Europe for gypsy moth control. After alighting on a moth larva, the female fly injects her young directly into its body, whereupon they rapidly consume their host's tissues. The U.S. Forest Service has also successfully employed viral spray as a control (25). It is applied at concentrations of 1 trillion polyhedra virus to 1 gallon of water. A larval moth becomes infected when it feeds on viral-contaminated foliage.

3. *Use of Sex Attractants.* Shortly after emergence from their pupa cage, the strong-winged male moths are attracted to the weak-flying female by a species-specific chemical attractant known as gyptol. Within the past few years the U.S. Department of Agriculture researchers have succeeded in synthesizing a chemically related substance, gyplure, from a constituent of castor oil. Gyplure has proved equal to gyptol as a sex lure. Under laboratory conditions male moths may be deluded into "mating" with small wood chips impregnated with gyplure. Large

Figure 8-38. *Cape Cod, Massachusetts. This is a typical gypsy moth trap picked up in the field. It contains captured gypsy moths lured into the trap by gyplure, a synthetic attractant that confuses male moths into thinking a female is inside the trap. Once inside, the moth becomes entangled in a sticky substance and is unable to extricate itself.* [*U.S. Department of Agriculture*]

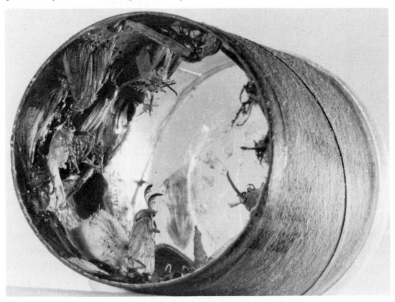

numbers of such impregnated chips could be released from airplanes over badly infested areas. Male gypsy moths might be induced to copulate with the chips and squander their sperm, thereby curtailing reproduction (2).

4. *Sterilization.* In 1965 Forest Service researchers sterilized a number of male moths with radioactive cobalt-60 in an attempt to duplicate the screw worm fly eradication success. However, because sterilized males do not compete successfully for females with fertile males, certain refinements in this avenue of control will have to be made (24).

BARK BEETLES. Almost 90 per cent of insect-inflicted timber mortality is caused by bark beetles. They destroy roughly 4.5 billion board feet annually. Adult beetles attack a tree by boring through the bark and then tunneling out egg chambers and galleries with their powerful jaws. The tiny grubs that hatch from the eggs consume the phloem and cambium, and if sufficiently numerous (1,000 per large tree) may actually girdle the tree and kill it within a month. The bark beetle group includes a large number of destructive species. The western pine beetle (*Dendroctonus brevicomis*) killed 25 billion board feet of ponderosa pine along the Pacific coast between 1917 and 1943. The mountain pine beetle (*Dendroctonus monticolae*) has killed an aggregate 20 billion board feet of sugar pine, western white pine, and lodgepole pine in California alone. The Black Hills beetle, (*Dendroctonus ponderosae*), which feeds on ponderosa pine in the Rocky Mountains, destroyed 2.5 billion board feet of timber from 1895 to 1946.

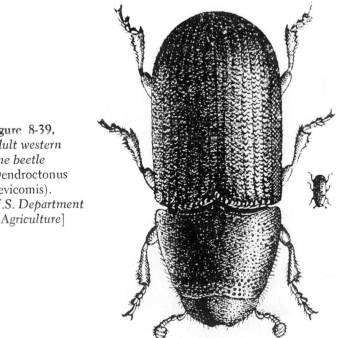

Figure 8-39.
*Adult western
pine beetle*
(Dendroctonus
brevicomis).
[*U.S. Department
of Agriculture*]

Figure 8-40. *Englemann spruce bark beetle larvae located just under the bark of a tree in the White River National Forest, Colorado. These beetles have destroyed over 2 billion feet of Englemann spruce timber on the White River.* [U.S. Forest Service]

The fluctuating populations of the Englemann spruce beetle (*Dendroctonus englemanni*) in the higher elevations of the Rockies form an interesting ecological study. For many years before 1942, these beetles were at least partially held in check by predatory insects and birds; woodpeckers were especially well adapted for feeding on them. Woodpeckers have extremely long sticky tongues with which they can probe the beetle galleries and snare their bean-sized prey. Whenever the beetle population increased, an influx of woodpeckers would soon check the incipient build-up, thus keeping the population in dynamic equilibrium. During this pre-1942 period the spruce beetles had concentrated on moisture-deficient trees, or on trees in which the sap flow was not sufficiently vigorous to protect them from beetle intrusions. However, in 1942, a violent windstorm uprooted thousands of spruce. The fallen trees formed a food bonanza for the spruce beetles. Because they were protected from woodpeckers by the interlocking branches of the prostrate trunks and probably also as a result of the superabundant food supply, the beetle population increased sharply. They now could more fully realize a reproductive potential in which a single pair could theoretically give rise to 10,000 progeny in a single breeding season. In 1949 a portion of the beetle population drowned in a small lake and drifted ashore, forming a solid drift of beetles 1 foot deep, 6 feet wide, and 2 miles long (20). The beetle hordes were now so numerous that they successfully attacked even young, vigorously growing trees (heretofore protected by their sap flow), as well as overmature trees and wind-blown timber. Within a 6-year period (1940–1946), the spruce beetles had destroyed 20 per cent of the Engelmann spruce in Colorado, a volume of 3 billion board feet—sufficient to provide homes for a city of 2 million people. The rate of timber destruction by beetles in the region was 75 times the rate of destruction by fire.

An inexpensive but effective method of controlling bark beetles is to fell infested trees, then peel and burn the bark; the peeled logs may then either be kiln-dried, heated to 125° F for an hour, sun-dried, or scorched with a flame thrower. Egg galleries of standing trees may be cut out with a chisel and the wound painted with pruning paint. In some cases egg galleries may be injected with ethylene dichloride or carbon disulfide. On a long-term basis, perhaps the best method of "control" is to prevent infestations from occurring in the first place. This may be done by sanitation techniques, by burning all potential bark beetle breeding sites such as senile and wind-blown trees, logging-accumulated slash and debris, and the stubs of lightning and fire-killed specimens.

Fire Control. Even before the white man's coming, North American forests have been consumed by flames. Annual ring sequence studies on giant redwoods indicate that these trees have been exposed to fire about once every twenty-five years over the past ten centuries. Early Spanish and French explorers write of traveling through dense clouds of smoke issuing from flaming forests. Every three minutes a forest fire starts somewhere in the United States. During the 1940–1950 period, fires consumed an average of 21.5 million acres of timber yearly, which is the equivalent of sending the entire state of Maine up in smoke (13). From 1955 to 1964, 1,175,664 forest fires, at an average rate of 322 per day, burned 76,000 square miles of forest range and watershed. Although fire may not kill a tree outright, it may cause distorted growth and impair its timber value. Fire annually is responsible for 17 per cent of saw timber destruction from all causes. Because of the better fire-control techniques that have been developed recently, the total acreage of destroyed timber has gradually been reduced. For example, the 125,371 forest fires that broke out in 1968 succeeded in burning only 4.2 million acres, roughly 20 per cent of the 1940–1950 annual average of 21.5 million acres.

MAJOR FIRES. A few of the forest fires that have been destructive of timber, property, and/or human life are listed.

1. The Miramichi, Maine, fire of 1825 consumed 3 million acres of coniferous forest.
2. The Peshtigo, Wisconsin, fire of 1871 killed 1,500 people and devastated 1.25 million acres of timberland.
3. The Hinckley, Minnesota, fire of 1894 consumed 160,000 forested acres and killed 418 men, women, and children. Many more would have been engulfed by the flames had not a warning been given by Father Lawler, a Catholic priest, who ran down the main street of Hinckley shouting, "Run for your lives." Some of the villagers found safety by crouching up to their armpits in the water of a gravel pit; others escaped by boarding a moving freight train.
4. The Cloquet, Minnesota, fire of 1918 took a toll of 432 lives, destroyed $30 million worth of timber and property, and advanced to the outskirts of Duluth, Minnesota, before being checked (6).
5. The Tillamook, Oregon, fire of 1933 ravaged 270,000 acres and destroyed 12 billion board feet of timber (10).

6. The Bar Harbor, Maine, conflagration of October, 1947, devastated the famed resort area, consumed 400 homes, including many plush estates, and put 3,500 vacationists to flight (18). This was only one of a series of Maine forest fires during October, which burned 240,000 acres and caused several million dollars' worth of property and timber damage.

FIRE CLASSES. Forest fires may be classified as surface, soil, or crown, according to the substratum being consumed.

1. *Surface Fires.* The surface fire is the most common type. It moves along the forest floor, fed by tinder-dry pine needles, crisp leaf litter, twigs, vines, shrubs, logs, leathery mushrooms, and the leaf-woven homes of ground-nesting birds. Driven by the wind, these fires may burn intensely but are of short duration. An occasional tree will have its bark singed, making it susceptible to insects and fungus growths. The most destructive aspect of the surface fire is that in consuming millions of germinating seeds and seedlings, it destroys the forest of the future.

2. *Soil Fires.* Surface fires may develop into soil fires, which consume the humus and peat content of the forest soil immediately underlying the leaf litter. Some penetrate to a depth of 6 feet. Because soil fire fuels rarely dry sufficiently to burn, they are uncommon. Largely deprived of access to oxygen and wind, the soil fire burns slowly but continuously, sometimes for months, issuing a considerable amount of smoke, but little flame. Low-lying smoke clouds from soil fires may form serious traffic hazards. In October, 1966, smoke-blinded motorists speeding along a Wisconsin freeway near Mauston were involved in a chain-reaction wreck that claimed four lives and destroyed several cars. The tremendous heat generated by soil fires may destroy timber in an insidious, underground attack on their heat-sensitive roots. Soil fires are extremely destructive to the organic content of podzol soil and hence reduce its water-absorptive role. Moreover, in killing billions of soil fungi and bacteria, the soil fire impairs the soil's role in recycling nitrogen and other essential elements in the forest ecosystem. Soil that nature required centuries to build may be consumed by a soil fire in a matter of hours and be converted into an inert, sterile medium, largely incapable of supporting life.

3. *Crown Fire.* The highly spectacular and destructive crown fire may also originate from a surface fire. The crown may be ignited by wind-blown sparks. Flames from burning litter may find a combustible pathway to the canopy by way of pendant dried moss streamers or via resin flowing down a conifer trunk. Heat from a surface fire may ignite dry crown needles. In a strong wind the crown fire may jump from crown to crown with a speed of up to 40 miles per hour. Wind-driven sparks and brands may be carried far in advance of the original fire and ignite "spot" fires, thus making it extremely hazardous for man or beast to remain in the crown fire's path. A crown fire at Freeman Lake, Idaho, devasted 20,000 acres within a twelve-and-a-half-hour period. When the fire started the relative humidity was only 10 per cent and the air temperature was 90° F. Although the wind was of only moderate velocity, a 350-acre spot fire was ignited fully 3 miles ahead of the parent blaze (9). (Fig. 8–43)

CAUSES OF FIRES. A study of the causes of forest fires reveals the average American's irresponsibility with regard to forest conservation. Roughly 90 per cent of all forest fires are started by man. Only 10 per cent are triggered by natural causes such as lightning (25).

There is not much that we can do to prevent lightning-caused fires. Even before

Figure 8-41. *Ochoco National Forest, Oregon. Forest fire burned approximately 100 acres in August 1951. [U.S. Department of Agriculture]*

the Pilgrims settled at Plymouth Rock, destructive fires originated in electrical storms. During the period 1900–1963 over 58 per cent of the 68,400 forest fires that occurred in the Rocky Mountains and along the Pacific coast were ignited by lightning. In 1910 over 1,100 lightning-originated forest fires occurred in the national forests of Idaho and Montana within a two-week period. Currently research is being conducted on seeding thunder clouds with dry ice in an effort to dissipate the electrical charges causing lightning.

We definitely can do something about 91 per cent of the forest fires that we have ignited ourselves. Many fires are caused by careless people:

The tourist who deftly flicks a lighted cigarette stub into a bed of dry pine needles, while thinking only about getting to the motel in time for supper.

The fisherman who is in such a frenzy to "snag those big bass" that he forgets to drown the dying coals of his campfire.

The brush burner "cleaning up" in the wake of a logging operation who is so intent on the cottage he is building for his family that one of his brush fires gets out of control and flares into a holocaust, consuming enough timber to build a thousand homes.

As John D. Guthrie, former fire inspector for the U.S. Forest Service has written so well, "To stage a forest fire you need only a few things—a forest, the right

Figure 8-42. *Payette National Forest, Idaho. The aftermath of a forest fire. Much life is destroyed, even many of the soil organisms.* [U.S. Department of Agriculture, Photo by Bluford W. Muir]

Figure 8-43. *Forest fire victim. Charred carcass of deer provides mute testimony of the wildlife-destroying potential of a forest fire. Although deer can attain speeds of about 35 miles per hour, a raging forest fire can move even faster.* [U.S. Department of Agriculture, Photo by Paul S. Bieler]

260

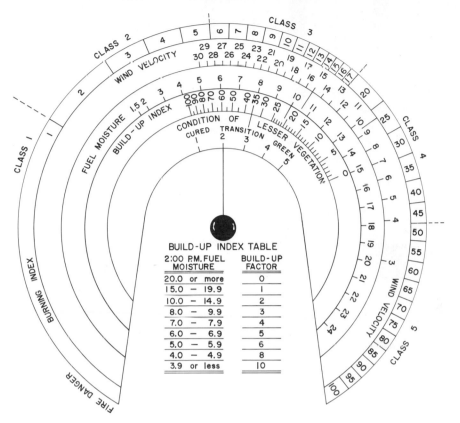

Figure 8-44. *Forest fire danger meter developed by the U.S. Forest Service.*
[*U.S. Forest Service*]

atmospheric conditions, and a spark either from a lightning bolt or a match in the hands of a fool or a knave. The formula is simple . . . the larger the forest, the drier the air, the bigger the fire you will have."

FIREFIGHTING.   Even during the first three decades of this century, firefighting was a poorly organized, haphazard operation that relied primarily on hand tools and the ineffectual efforts of bucket brigades. The technique of modern forest fire suppression, however, is an intensively organized, well-coordinated operation that employs the latest technological developments, from infrared scanners to heli-copters (21). In 1965, 113,685 forest fires consumed 2.6 million acres of timber. Only 0.12 per cent of the forest land protected with a modern fire suppression system was burned, whereas 4.28 per cent of unprotected timber was destroyed (25). In other words, only 1 acre of protected forest was burned for every 34 acres of unprotected forest. We shall describe fire suppression in sequential order: fire detection, dispatching and transport of fighters, and fire suppression.

Figure 8-45. *A fire control worker employs the fire-finder alidade to make a fix on a smoke. Olympic National Forest, Washington.* [*U.S. Department of Agriculture*]

FIRE DETECTION. Fire detection is frequently made by observers stationed in look-out towers. Most well-forested states have a network of such spotting towers in operation. During seasons of severe fire hazard, this detection work is frequently supplemented with airplane patrols. Once the fire is spotted, the precise position is determined and radioed to the dispatcher.

DISPATCHING AND TRANSPORT. The dispatcher immediately alerts one or more firefighting teams. Over 2,000 fighters have been used in major conflagrations. The fighters rush to the scene of the fire by truck or jeep if roads are accessible. In rugged mountainous country, "smoke jumpers" may parachute into the area of the fire. They are equipped with lightweight parachutes capable of slow descent and provided with steering slots that facilitate pinpoint landings. The national forests of mountainous regions in Washington, Oregon, California, Montana, Idaho, and New Mexico are protected by a corps of 350 U.S. Forest Service smoke jumpers. Forest fire suppression is most effective at night, when fire intensity is reduced and fighters find the heat less oppressive. To exploit the possibilities of nocturnal fighting, special lights and markers have been developed by the U.S. Forest Service for reducing hazards attending the night transport of helicopter-borne fighters. With the help of smoke jumpers, many remote blazes that in 1930 might have flamed out of control may now be extinguished within a matter of minutes.

FIRE SUPPRESSION. The actual suppression or attack pattern employed by fighters varies greatly depending upon the size of fire, terrain, fire class, wind direction, location of roads, availability of water supplies, and relative humidity. We shall describe just a few of the techniques, devices, and materials used in modern forest fire suppression.

1. *Fire Lanes.* The fire lane is a 10-foot-wide strip that is plowed up around the periphery of the fire with the aid of special fire plows, bulldozers, and gasoline-powered brush and sapling cutters. In well-managed forests these lanes usually have already been systematically carved out of the forest at regular intervals. Because a fire lane is denuded of all combustible material, it effectively checks the fire's advance.

2. *Back Fires.* Occasionally, in an effort to head off an advancing fire, the intervening forest between the fire head and a fire lane may be set on fire. If wind conditions are right, the back fire will burn its way toward the major fire; when both fires meet they will die from lack of fuel. This technique may boomerang if the wind suddenly shifts direction.

3. *Water.* Water may be sprayed from a portable back-tank or tank truck. Portable motor pumps may take water from a nearby stream or lake. Some fighter teams have special well-drilling equipment with which they can sink a shallow well shaft within fifteen minutes. In rough country helicopters have laid 1,500 feet of fire hose in less than a minute. Some planes have special water tanks that can skim water from a lake for use in dousing the fire.

Figure 8-46. *Helicopters are employed to scout fires, transport men, and deliver urgently needed supplies to firefighters.* [*U.S. Forest Service*]

4. *Fire-Retardant Chemicals.*   Fire-retardant chemicals almost three times more effective than water can be sprayed from back-tank and tank truck or may be dropped on the blaze from a plane in the form of chemical bombs. Huge air tankers with up to 4,000 gallons capacity were first employed in 1956, when 124,000 gallons of fire-retardant chemicals were released on twenty-four fires. A variety of such retardant chemicals as viscous water, sodium borate, bentonite clay, and ammonium compounds have been applied to forest fires in recent years.

5. *Aerial Photography.*   Aerial photographers may take pictures of the fire, develop them in a darkroom aboard the plane, and within minutes parachute them down to the firefighters below. The pictures will show the fire boss the overall pattern and status of the fire. They may suggest to him how best to deploy his men, not only for most effective suppression, but also to prevent possible encirclement by flames.

Figure 8-47.   *Smoke jumpers in action. Some thirty-five miles north of the Arctic Circle, three smoke jumpers drift toward a spruce forest far below. The fire, racing through moss-laden spruce and parched peat, has a headstart on the fire-fighters.* [Bureau of Land Management]

Figure 8-48. *Fire suppression in the Angeles National Forest, California.* [*U.S. Forest Service*]

Figure 8-49. *Ozark National Forest, Arkansas, April 1966. A U.S. Forest Service plane drops a chemical slurry to suppress a fire.* [*U.S. Department of Agriculture, Photo by Robert W. Neelands*]

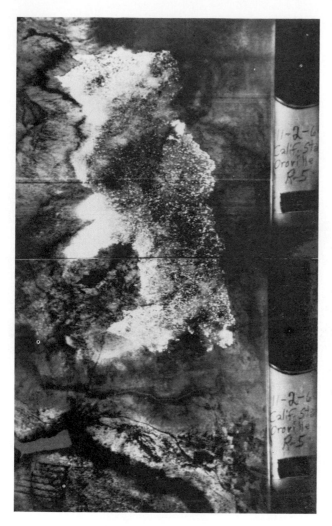

Figure 8-50. *Oroville, California. This is a photograph of a forest fire made with an infrared scanning device, Fire Scan, being tested by the U.S. Forest Service. The white areas show where the fire is burning. The darker spotted area within the fire ring has already been burned over. Details of the terrain can be seen, even though the picture was taken through dense smoke that would hide the burning area from the fire fighters in the plane. With such a picture of the fire, flame extinguishing chemicals can be dropped by air on the actual burning area, rather than being wasted on trees not yet touched by the flames or already burned out. Under Project Fire Scan, a high-flying airplane employs an infrared device to pinpoint small fires when visibility is obscured by darkness, smog, haze, or dense drift smoke from other fires. The system was used during a recent forest fire emergency in the Northwest to detect more than 150 fires. [U.S. Department of Agriculture]*

6. *Prescribed Burning.* Not all forest fires are destructive. Ecologists are generally agreed that a number of our nation's valuable timber stands may be established and maintained because of fire. Examples include the giant sequoias in California, the old-growth, even-aged stands of Douglas fir in the Northwest, of red pine in northwestern Minnesota, and of white pine in northwestern Pennsylvania and southwestern New Hampshire. Certain less valuable species, such as pitch pine on sandy soils near the mid-Atlantic coast and jack pine in the lake states, are also considered to be "fire types" or "fire climaxes."

Today foresters employ prescribed burning to improve quality of timber, livestock forage, and wildlife habitat. Prescribed burning may be defined as surface burning according to a plan in which the utmost precaution is taken in terms of (1) dryness of fuel, (2) wind velocity (3 to 10 miles per hour preferred) and direction, (3) relative humidity, (4) type of fire (head, flank, or back), and (5) composition and combustibility of fuel. The long-term effect on the forest in terms of

Figure 8-51. *Marion County, South Carolina, February 1969. The prescribed (controlled) burning of a 28-year-old stand of slash pine. [Soil Conservation Service, U.S. Department of Agriculture, Photo by Al Crouch]*

multiple use receives top priority. Prescribed burning has been employed with considerable success in southern stands of long leaf-slash pine and more limited success on short-leaf loblolly-hardwood stands. At the Alapaha Experimental Range in Georgia, prescribed burning is conducted only in the afternoon under damp conditions, and the low fire is usually extinguished by ensuing night dewfall (20). Any pine stand 8 to 15 feet tall may be prescription burned, whereas the highly fire-resistant long-leaf pine (whose terminal bud is protected by a group of long needles) may be burned without ill effect already at the grass stage.

In the long leaf-slash pine stands of the South, prescribed burning may serve (1) to reduce crown fire hazard by removing highly compustible litter, (2) to prepare the forest soil as a seedbed, (3) to increase the growth and quality of livestock forage, (4) to retard a forest succession leading to a low-value scrub oak climax and maintain the high-timber-value pine subclimax, (5) to promote legume establishment and resultant soil enrichment, (6) to increase the amount of soluble mineral ash (phosphorus, potassium) available to the forest plants, (7) to stimulate the activity of soil bacteria, (8) to control brown spot needle blight (*Scirrhia acicola*) of seedling long-leaf pines, and (9) to improve food and cover conditions for wild turkey and quail.

Richard J. Hartesveldt and his coworkers at San Jose State College (California) have found that recurrent fires are absolutely essential to successful regeneration of the magnificient sequoias. (Many of those now standing developed from seeds that fell on the forest floor about the time of Christ!) In the event that fires do not periodically occur, plant succession progresses to the point where it is almost impossible for sequoia seedlings to become established. The San Jose group found that sequoia reproduction in burn areas was best where incineration temperatures penetrated deeply into the soil. The researchers feel that the elevated soil temperatures "probably aided in sterilization against pathogenic fungi, reduced competition with established plants, [and] improved the soil wettability and structure . . ." (8). As Hartesveldt et al. observe:

> The concept of fire as a natural environmental factor before the advent of man has been a most difficult one to establish. Perhaps this has been due to man's role in starting forest fires and perhaps to the fact that man has too long been inclined to see trees as individuals rather than dynamic communities in which fire has always played a significant role . . . (8).

Forest Conservation by Efficient Utilization

During the "cut-out-and-get-out" logging operations of the 1890's, lumbermen were interested only in logs. The rest of the tree—stump, limbs, branches, and foliage—was left in the forest as worthless debris that frequently served as tinder for a catastrophic fire. Further waste occurred at the sawmill, where square timbers were fashioned from round logs. Slabs, trimmings, bark, and sawdust were hauled to the refuse dump and burned. Even today, three fourths of a century later, almost 25 per cent of the forest harvest is squandered (8). It is apparent that unless we also practice conservation after a tree is finally harvested and removed from the forest, all the solicitous effort devoted to protecting it from destructive diseases, insects, and fires during the 30 to 100 years before the harvest seems futile.

Although we are still much too wasteful of our timber resource, a definite trend toward more efficient utilization is under way. The U.S. Forest Products Laboratory at Madison, Wisconsin, is the world's largest institution dedicated to the study of the mechanical and chemical properties of wood and how this resource can most effectively be used by man. Whereas early in the timber industry wood had primarily only two uses, as lumber or as fuel, through the efforts of the Forest Products Laboratory and similar research centers, a number of ingenious methods have been developed for utilizing almost every part of the tree, including the bark.

The forest industry has become much more diversified. Whereas in 1890 almost 95 per cent of the forest harvest was converted into lumber, by 1962 only 37.3 billion board feet, or 54 per cent, of the 68 billion board feet of forest products consumed by the American people were fashioned into boards and timbers (1). In the last few years techniques have been developed for making extremely usful products from scrap boards, shavings, wood chips, bark, and sawdust. A few of these technological triumphs follow:

1. The development of superior, waterproof glues that can cement together an in-indefinite number of short boards (originally discarded as scrap) into sturdy structural beams of almost unlimited length or thickness (20). (Fig. 8-52)
2. The development of methods for compressing small particles, such as wood chips and shavings, into "chipboard" or "hardboard" construction materials (20). An increasingly important method of harvesting timber is to chip all the timber in the woods. A mechanical shearer clips the tree off with hydraulic pinchers and stacks the trees in piles. Large rubber-wheeled vehicles drag the piles to a chipper, which chips the entire trunk, limbs, bark, and leaves and blows them into a large truck.

Figure 8-52.
Testing the tensile strength of glued-laminated beams, 50 feet long and 31 inches deep, at the U.S. Forest Products Laboratory, Madison, Wisconsin. [U.S. Forest Products Laboratory, U.S. Forest Service, U.S. Department of Agriculture]

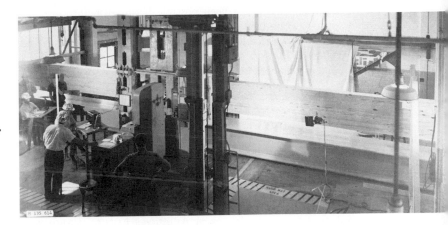

Figure 8-53. *A single man here operates equipment that cuts and removes a number of pulpwood trees and then places them in a chipper machine. The chips can then be trucked to a plant and converted into either paper pulp or "chipboard." [Morbark Industries]*

Up to 200 per cent greater yield per acre has been achieved over conventional logging methods. The chips then can be used in producing compressed "chipboard." It is intriguing to reflect that the handsome cabinet for your stereo, or even the walls of the room in which you are sitting this moment at one time may have existed as a nondescript heap of wood scraps.

3. The development of a great variety of bark-derived products. Not too long ago bark either was left lying on the forest floor gradually to disintegrate under the multiple assault of weather, insects, and fungi, or bark residues were put to the torch at the sawmill's refuse dump. This lowly bark, which for decades had been considered by the lumberman as an irritating nuisance, has suddenly achieved status in the forest industry. Today modern man comes face to face with bark-derived materials almost every way he turns. The successful drilling of an Oklahoma "gusher" may have been possible because of an oil-well-drilling compound derived in part from bark; the leather in your belt, shoes, and wallet may have been tanned with bark-derived tannin; your Thanksgiving turkey may have been raised on shredded bark litter. Bark is even the source of quercitin, which is used in checking hemorrhaging during surgery (4).

Meeting Future Timber Demands

Demographers predict that by the year 2000 our population will reach 332 million, roughly a 75 per cent increase over the 1966 figure of 190 million. The nation's demands on its timber resources will increase accordingly. The amount of forest per capita will decrease from the 3 acres of 1958 to 1.75 acres by 2000. In a scholarly survey, *Resources in America's Future*, Landsberg, Fischman, and Fisher (12) review the present status of our nation's resources, future demands, and the methods by which these demands might be met. Much of the following material is derived from this source.

The projected total lumber consumption by 2000 will be 98 billion board feet, a 164 per cent increase above the 1960 figure of 37 billion board feet; by 2000 plywood utilization will be 133 billion square feet, a 504.5 per cent increase above the 22 billion square feet consumed in 1960; pulpwood use will rise 307.4 per cent from the 27 million short tons of 1960 to the 110 million short tons projected for 2000 (9). In aggregate, the overall projected domestic timber demand for the year 2000 is 29 billion cubic feet, 17 billion cubic feet in excess of the projected annual growth of slightly over 12 billion cubic feet.

These demands may be met in the following ways:

1. By upgrading and extending forest management in all forests, public and private, large and small. Where can the greatest gains be made? Primarily on the small, privately owned woodlots. This is true for two principal reasons. First, the small ownerships (under 5,000 acres) embrace 55 per cent of our forest land, comprise one third of our saw timber, and contribute about 40 per cent of our annual timber harvest. Of the 4.5 million small forest ownerships in the United States over 50 per cent are under 30 acres. Yet these small owners, primarily farmers, control twice as much timberland as is included in the entire National Forest System. Second, the small forest owner has until now sadly botched his forest management responsibilities. According to Richard E. McArdle, former chief of the U.S. Forest Service, the small forest owners can meet the projected demand for the year 2000, if they:

a. Reforest their lands three and one-half times more rapidly than they are at present.
b. Improve the quality of their timber stands at nine times the current rate.
c. Convert much more rapidly from wasteful cutting to sustained-yield harvesting.
d. Increase forest protection so that damage by disease, insects, and fire is reduced at least 50 per cent.

Perhaps greater incentives for upgrading forest management among small land-owners may be supplied by consolidating several small stands under one management, by providing better insurance against timber losses, by providing reforestation assistance, and by discouraging premature cutting through liberalized tax assessments. Let us hope that the small owners, with encouragement and technical and financial assistance from both federal and state agencies, will shoulder their full forest management responsibility.

2. By increasing the tempo of harvesting mature western timber. Eastern stands, primarily under private ownership, are generally poor-quality, understocked second- or third-growth hardwoods located on small farm woodlots. Because timber growth rates are highest when trees are young and lowest in mature trees, the eastern forest growth rate is quite high roughly six times that of western stands. However, total volume is low because of much commercial forest land that is either poorly stocked or barren. Western forests (including those in coastal Alaska), primarily under public ownership, have almost 50 million acres of old-growth saw timber (that is, timber 10 inches or more in diameter at chest height), over 20 million acres of which is unutilized virgin forest. Because of the high inventory of mature timber, annual growth increments are low. These mature western stands should be more intensively harvested, together with the upgrading of our eastern forests (9).

3. By increasing our forest acreage. Because our timber deficit by 2000 will be 17 billion cubic feet, and because one forest acre can annually produce only 55 cubic feet of timber, 300 million more forest acres (in addition to the current 484 million acres) would be sufficient to remove the projected deficit. However, it is not realistic to expect such forest extensions. Rather, because of the acute need for more agricultural, urban, and industrial lands, the total forested acreage probably will decrease by 2000 (9).

4. By more effectively controlling destructive forest agents. The combined impact (mortality plus impaired growth) of diseases, insects, grazing, fire, and storm is roughly 75 per cent of the annual harvest.

5. By increasing utilization of wood residues and of weed species.

6. By developing superior (faster-growing; better-grained; disease-, insect-, fire-, and drought-resistant) trees through the techniques of grafting and hybridization.

7. By increasing use of wood substitutes. Plastics and aluminum foil might be used in packaging; fiberglas, concrete, bricks, and aluminum might replace construction timber; bagasse from sugar cane could be employed instead of pulp in paper manufacture (12).

8. By increasing imports. As of 1963 we were already importing 5 to 6 million tons of newsprint annually, as well as 10 to 15 per cent of our timber consumption. The best we can expect from our Canadian source by 2000 is a fourfold increase of our 1960 imports, or 3 billion cubic feet of softwood annually. This would tax Canadian supplies to the limit. Current imports of hardwood plywood from Japan and the Philippines may be expanded. In addition, by 2000 the tropical and sub-tropical hardwood forests of certain developing nations in South America and Africa might be tapped (12).

BIBLIOGRAPHY

1. Allen, Shirley W., and Justin W. Leonard. *Conserving Natural Resources.* New York: McGraw-Hill, 1966.
2. Carson, Rachel. *Silent Spring.* Boston: Houghton, 1962.
3. Cheyney, E. G., and T. Schantz-Hansen. *This Is Our Land.* St. Paul: Webb, 1950.
4. Clepper, Henry E., and Arthur B. Meyer. *American Forestry: Six Decades of Growth.* Washington, D.C.: Society of American Foresters, 1960.
5. Craig, James B. "The Clearcut Crisis," *Amer. Forests,* 77 (March 1971), p. 11.
6. Dasmann, Raymond F. *Environmental Conservation.* New York: Wiley, 1959.
7. Forbes, R. D. *Forestry Handbook of the Society of American Foresters.* New York: Ronald, 1965.
8. Hartesveldt, Richard J., H. Thomas Harvey, Howard D. Shellhammer, and Ronald E. Stecker. "Sequoia's Dependence on Fire," *Science,* 166 (October 31, 1969), 552–553.
9. Hawley, Ralph C., and Paul W. Stickel, eds. *Forest Protection.* New York: Wiley, 1948.
10. Highsmith, Richard M., Jr. *Conservation in the United States.* Chicago: Rand McNally, 1962.
11. Kerr, Robert S. *Land, Wood and Water.* New York: Fleet, 1960.
12. Landsberg, Hans H., Leonard L. Fischman, and Joseph L. Fisher. *Resources in America's Future.* Baltimore: Johns Hopkins, 1962.
13. Northen, Henry T. *Introductory Plant Science.* New York: Ronald, 1953.
14. Odum, Eugene P. *Fundamentals of Ecology,* 3rd ed. Philadelphia: Saunders, 1971.
15. Parson, Ruben L. *Conserving American Resources.* Englewood Cliffs, N.J.: Prentice-Hall, 1956.
16. Sayre, Roxanna. "Econotes," *Audubon* (May 1972), p. 103.
17. ———. "Econotes," *Audubon* (September 1972), p. 110.
18. Smith, Guy-Harold, ed. *Conservation of Natural Resources.* New York: Wiley, 1958.
19. Towell, William E. "Let's Not Scuttle Professional Forestry," *Amer. Forests* (March 1971), p. 10.
20. U.S. Department of Agriculture. *Insects: The Yearbook of Agriculture.* Washington, D.C.: 1952.
21. U.S. Forest Service. *Annual Report, 1962.* Washington, D.C.: U.S. Government Printing Office, 1963.
22. ———. 1963. Washington, D.C.: U.S.G.P.O., 1964.
23. ———. 1964. Washington, D.C.: U.S.G.P.O., 1965.
24. ———. 1965. Washington, D.C.: U.S.G.P.O., 1966.
25. ———. *Forest Fire Statistics.* Washington, D.C.: U.S.G.P.O., 1965.
26. ———. *Multiple Use Management.* Washington, D.C.: U.S.G.P.O., 1966.

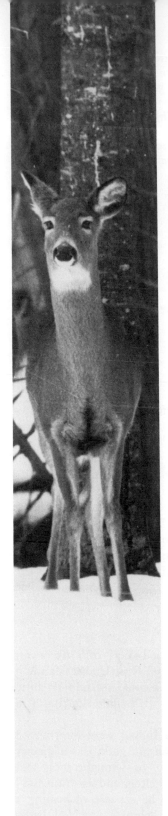

9.

Wildlife

For one species to mourn the death of another is a new thing under the sun. The Cro-Magnon who slew the last mammoth thought only of steaks. The sportsman who shot the last (passenger) pigeon thought only of his prowess. The sailor who clubbed the last auk thought of nothing at all. But, we, who have lost our pigeons, mourn the loss. Had the funeral been ours, the pigeons would hardly have mourned us. In this fact, rather than in Mr. DuPont's nylons or Mr. Vannevar Bush's bombs, lies objective evidence of our superiority over the beasts. . . .

Like winds and sunsets, wild things were taken for granted until progress began to do away with them. Now we face the question whether a still higher "standard of living" is worth its cost in things natural, wild, and free. For us of the minority, the opportunity to see geese is more important than television, and the chance to find a pasqueflower is a right as inalienable as free speech.

Aldo Leopold,
A Sand County Almanac,
New York, Oxford University Press, 1949.

Figure 9-1. *Flushing a pheasant on an Indiana hunting preserve. The game-farm-reared birds were released in patches of good wildlife cover such as the sargo in this picture.* [Soil Conservation Service, U.S. Department of Agriculture]

America's wildlife resources provide aesthetic, scientific, recreational, and economic benefits. Often the recreational and economic values are closely related. For example, sport fishing and hunting are big business. Over $1 billion are spent annually by hunters alone. In 1974 the needs of hunting and shooting sportsmen were being supplied by 1,400 manufacturers. Sporting arms and ammunition sales reached $350 million in 1974. The sporting firearms industry has over 20,000 employees and a payroll of more than $100 million. Each year at least $5 million are spent on hunting dogs. America's hunters travel 5 billion miles annually. Whether it be muskellunge fishing in Wisconsin or antelope shooting in Wyoming, the quest of quail in Georgia or pheasant in the Dakotas, sportsmen are attracted from considerable distances to pursue their favorite pastime.

History of Abuse and Depletion

Bison. It is estimated that up to 60 million bison roamed the North American prairies in the late eighteenth century. An observer, Colonel R. I. Dodge, standing at the summit of Pawnee Rocks in Arkansas, stated that he could see 6 to 10 miles in all directions and the entire panorama was "covered with buffalo, looking at a distance like a compact mass."

For centuries the culture and economy of the Plains Indian were intertwined with the bison. He depended on buffalo meat (pemmican and jerky) as a dietary staple. From sinews he fashioned bowstrings. From bone he wrought tools and ornaments. Hides were used in bedding, garments, and shelters and as "canvases" by Indian artists. The rare albino hides were thought to be capable of healing a variety of ills. Even the dried feces, known as buffalo "chips," provided badly needed fuel.

Figure 9-2. *Cow buffalo suckling her calf. Note patches of molting hair. Kaibab National Forest, Arizona.* [*U.S. Forest Service*]

For many years the prairie grasses, buffalo, and Plains Indians represented the major living components of a balanced ecosystem. The unmounted Indian made slight impact on the buffalo hordes with his lances and arrows. When the herds immigrated to new range, the Indian quickly broke camp and followed, for the herd represented his food, clothing, and shelter—on the hoof.

When the Civil War ended, a ruthless campaign of bison butchery was launched that brought this animal to the brink of extinction. Apparently the U.S. Army believed that the subjugation of the fierce Plains Indian would be assured once the buffalo was exterminated. It has been estimated that during 1871 and 1872 about 8.5 million buffalo were slaughtered, about one seventh of the peak population. Such butchery was facilitated by the westward extension of several railroads into the prairie country. These railroads employed professional buffalo hunters to provide their crews with food. One hunter, the celebrated Buffalo Bill Cody, sometimes was able to kill 200 "shaggies" in one day. During the winter of 1872–1873 almost 1.5 million hides were shipped via three railroads to eastern markets and sold for $3 per hide. However, less than 1 per cent of the meat was marketed and much of it went to waste. Over 100,000 animals were killed just for their tongues, which were considered a delicacy. Once the tongue had been sliced off, the rest of the carcass was left to rot. "Bone pickers" collected skeletal remains and shipped them by the ton to fertilizer plants in Kansas and Minnesota. Kansas plants paid $4.5 million for bones over a period of thirteen years. The long facial hair was used for stuffing mattresses. A buffalo wool company was even established in the Red River Valley. However, after shipping a few yards of wool cloth to England, this enterprise collapsed. Inevitably the buffalo hordes dwindled to scattered bands. By 1889 only 150 bison survived in the wild; in 1894 the last wild buffalo was shot by a rancher in Parke County, Colorado. Sound management practices have successfully built up the herd in several wildlife refuges from the 250 animals that still survived in captivity.

Waterfowl. When Captain Howard Stansburg explored the Bear River marshes of Utah in 1849, he was amazed by the immense numbers of waterfowl. "Thousands of acres, as far as the eye could reach seemed literally covered with them." Other explorers used phrases like "clouds of ducks" and "thunderlike sounds" to indicate the waterfowl abundance. The redhead duck (*Nyroca americana*) occurred in dense rafts, several miles long, numbering up to 50,000 birds. Eventually, however, the waterfowl populations dwindled. The decline was due in part to marsh and pothole drainage for agricultural purposes and in part to frontal assaults by market hunters and so-called sportsmen. Live decoys and multiple-gun rigs were employed. One Maryland hunter used a 100-pound gun to slaughter and cripple large numbers

Figure 9-3. *Two "sportsmen" at the turn of the century exerted considerable predatory control during a single day of hunting. At least thirty-five birds were shot, most of them mallards.* [State Historical Society of Wisconsin]

of birds with a single shot. Albert M. Day documents some of the early carnage: One "sportsman" killed 64 broadbill, 98 black duck, and 1 gadwall in four hours; a Connecticut hunter bagged 127 birds in one day. During the winter of 1893–1894 over 120,000 mallards were sent to market from Big Lake, Arkansas. One Minnesota market hunter boasted of slaughtering 6,000 ducks in one season. Waterfowl flesh was considered gourmet fare in the metropolitan areas. The Palmer House in Chicago featured a menu that included a dozen species of wild game. In the 1880's wild mallards sold for $3 a dozen, teal for $2, wild geese for $4.50, and canvasbacks for $6 per dozen. William J. Hamilton reports that dead ducks littered the platforms of North Dakota railroad stations in the 1890's; during hot weather it was not uncommon for many carcasses to spoil and be hauled away by the wagon load to the dumping ground (25).

Whooping Crane. The 4-foot whooping crane (*Grus americana*) is the tallest bird on the North American continent. Snow white, except for its scarlet crown and black wing tips, it resembles a flying cross as it passes overhead, with its graceful neck projecting forward and sticklike legs trailing behind. In the early nineteenth century its breeding range extended throughout the grassland biome from the prairie provinces of Canada south through the Dakotas to Iowa. It wintered along the Gulf coast from Mexico east to Florida. As of 1970, however, it was known to nest only in Wood Buffalo National Park in northern Alberta, Canada,

Figure 9-4. *These two adult whooping cranes, photographed on the Aransas National Wildlife Refuge, Texas, represent about 4 per cent of the total world population of the species. [U.S. Fish and Wildlife Service]*

and the wintering area was restricted to the Arkansas Wildlife Refuge on the Texas coast. Although very slowly increasing in numbers, only about fifty-five wild and eight captive whooping cranes survived as of 1974.

Among the factors that have contributed to the endangered status of this strikingly handsome bird are the following: appropriation of its prairie nesting habitat by rancher and farmer, intensive shooting, severe storms during migrations, and low biotic potential—only two eggs being laid per clutch.

Avian species that have "flown their last flight" are the great auk of the north Atlantic, which became extinct because of intensive hunting by 1844; the Hawaiian rail, extinct by 1893 because of predation by introduced rats; the Carolina parakeet of the southeastern United States, which became extinct by 1920 because over-hunting and the removal of its woodland habitat; and the Molokai thrush of Molokai Island, Hawaii, which passed into oblivion in 1936 because of the destruction of its habitat and the inadvertent introduction of predatory rats and disease organisms.

Extinction of Wildlife

Extinction is the rule rather than the exception. Perhaps 99 per cent of all plant and animal species that ever existed are now extinct. It has been estimated that the average "life span" of an avian species to be about 2 million years; that of a mammal to be 6 million years. It is assumed that many of these prehistoric organisms such as the dinosaur *Tyrannosaurus rex* and the saber-toothed cat became extinct because of overspecialization or inflexibility—once their environment changed, they were unable to adjust to the new conditions.

Theoretically, one might say that all of the organisms on earth today will some day become extinct, including man! The point is, however, that since man appeared on the scene about 2 million years ago, and especially since the dawn of the Industrial Age, about 1850, he has unwittingly accelerated the process, more than 75 species of birds and mammals having gone down the road to oblivion. Recently the International Union for Conservation of Nature and Natural Resources listed 359 species of birds and 297 species of mammals as being "endangered" (threatened with extinction) the world over. Within the United States, 101 species of wildlife were listed as endangered. Several American species have had their ranks severely depleted. Thus, according to the Bureau of Sports Fisheries and Wildlife, there are fewer than 100 individuals of the Ipswich sparrow left in the world, only 70 whooping cranes, about 40 California condors, about 10 Florida everglade kites, and about 10 ivory-billed woodpeckers.

Causes of Extinction. Now let us consider some of the major factors contributing to the decline (and possible ultimate extinction) of wildlife today.

1. RESTRICTED HABITAT. The Kirtland's warbler is a diminutive blue-gray and yellow creature, small in size (4.5 inches) but large in song. The world population of this species amounts to only about 1,000 individuals. It has perhaps the smallest breeding range of any North American bird—an 85-by-100-mile area in the north-central part of Michigan's lower peninsula. Not only does it nest exclusively in jack pine barren habitat, but more particularly in pine stands ranging in age from 6 to 15 years and from 5 to 20 feet in height. In pines under 6 years of age the lower

branches do not provide adequate nesting cover; in pines older than 15 years, the bottom branches become shaded out and die—again not serving as suitable cover. It is apparent that the natural growth of the pine stand poses a survival threat for the warbler—when the pines mature, the warbler is forced to move out. Michigan conservation officials and the U.S. Forest Service have been employing *prescribed burning* to increase the amount of suitable habitat. The fire destroys the mature pines, and many young pine seedlings eventually become established from the seeds that are released when the seared pine cones "pop" open. Burnings are made in patches of 40 acres or more, since this is the size of the warbler's breeding territory (63).

2. LOW BIOTIC POTENTIAL. Some animal species are extremely vulnerable to environmental vicissitudes (storms, diseases, and so on) because of their low *reproductive potential*. The female polar bear, for example, breeds only once in three years, and then gives birth to only two cubs. The female California condor, of which species there are only 40 individuals left in the world, lays only a *single egg every other year*. Since there are only about 20 females left, even if all of them breed successfully, the world total annual egg production for this species would be only 10 eggs—and probably not all of them would hatch.

3. GENETIC ASSIMILATION. The red wolf (*Canis niger*) and the coyote (*Canis latrans*) are closely related "brush wolves." The highly adaptable coyote is one of the few animals that has actually benefited from the human alteration of terrestrial ecosystems, since its preferred habitat, *brushlands*, has increased extensively in the wake of logging, forest clearing for agriculture, and so on. At one time found primarily west of the Mississippi, it has now extended its range eastward to within a "stone's throw" of New York City. The red wolf, on the other hand, is on the verge of extinction, there being only 150 animals left, all in Texas (18). Now, there are reports that the coyote is crossing with the red wolf to form coyote–red wolf hybrids. It is apparent that if such hybridization continues, it is probable that the red wolf's unique constellation of genes will eventually be absorbed into the coyote gene pool (18). At that point the species *Canis niger* will have ceased to exist.

4. NONADAPTIVE BEHAVIOR. The Carolina parakeet, the only parrot native to the United States, became extinct in 1914 when the last survivor died in a zoo. The parakeet was hunted extensively by fruit ranchers because it descended on their orchards in huge flocks and ravaged the fruit. However, we might still be able to see this fascinating red-yellow-green "paint pot" were it not for a peculiar behavioral trait: When one member of a flock was shot and fluttered to the ground mortally wounded, the remaining birds would fly toward the dying bird and hover over its body—thus forming ridiculously easy targets for the gunners. Of more recent interest, the red-headed woodpecker, whose population has undergone drastic reduction in the past few decades, has the curious tendency of flying along a highway directly ahead of a motor car, with the latter frequently winning the race (18).

5. SPECIALIZED DIET. The Florida Everglade kite is undoubtedly the rarest species of bird in the United States, there being only about ten individuals left. (However, the species is better represented in Mexico and South America.) An important factor contributing to its plummeting numbers is its highly specialized

diet—it feeds almost exclusively on snails of the species *Pomacea caliginosa*. Now that real estate developers are draining considerable portions of the snail's marshy habitat, both snail and kite populations are declining rapidly.

6. PET TRADE. Wasn't it fun taking your little sister and brother to the five-and-dime store and buying them a pet—maybe a white Easter bunny, or a turtle, or baby alligator, or even a horned lizard? That is, it was fun, until the time came to take care of the pets. William G. Conway, general director of the New York Zoological Society, looks at the animal pet trade in general and the horned lizard traffic in particular with a jaundiced eye:

> The trade in horned lizards has been going on for decades. . . . The unforgivably immoral nature of this piece of commercialization is that horned lizards almost invariably starve to death after a few weeks in captivity. This tells us something about the character of the exotic pet trade for it is well known that horned lizards have highly specialized and poorly understood food and temperature requirements, which few pet buyers could hope to meet (18).

The horned lizard is not alone. Many dozens of sensitive species, including the three-toed sloth, Saki monkey, South American parrot, and arboreal anteater, with highly exacting temperature-humidity-dietary-spatial requirements are imported from abroad and end up in ordinary pet shops where their survival is threatened. It is estimated that South American parrots are given such rough treatment during their transport from the Amazon rain forests to New York and Chicago pet shops that only 1 of 50 birds survives the trip. In other words almost 0.5 million parrots died to supply the 10,000 sold by American pet shops in 1968 (63).

According to the U.S. Fish and Wildlife Service, in a single year recently the American pet trade imported 74,304 mammals, 203,139 birds (not including parrots and canaries), 405,134 reptiles, 137,697 amphibians, and 27,759,332 fish (18). One wonders how many of these unfortunate creatures are still alive.

7. INTRODUCTION OF EXOTICS. Although with the best of intentions, man has all too many times introduced exotic species of animals only to discover, too late, that the beneficial objective, such as increased game for the hunter or the effective control of insect pests, never actually materialized. Instead, the ultimate result was the serious depletion of native wildlife. A classic example of this phenomenon was the introduction of the Indian mongoose (a fierce, quick-moving, weasellike predator) to Puerto Rico, for the purpose of controlling rats that had been causing extensive damage to the sugar cane crop. Although the mongoose did kill a few rats, it soon began to destroy many other animals such as amphibians, reptiles, and ground-nesting birds, to the point where some of them became quite scarce.

The rat itself was inadvertently introduced by man from Europe to the United States and many Pacific islands, apparently having dispersed from anchored ships. Rats have been directly blamed for contributing to the extinction of nine species of rails (weak-flying ground-nesting marsh birds) as well as the 1936 extinction of Hawaii's Molokai thrush.

8. DIRECT HUNTING BY MAN. Man has directly destroyed wildlife for a number of reasons: (1) for sport, (2) for food and clothing, (3) to protect crops and live-

stock, and (4) for a variety of novel uses. We have already discussed the first three earlier in this chapter; let us now examine wildlife persecution for novel uses. Some of the bizarre reasons for killing wild creatures have been pithily stated by Richard Wagner in his excellent book *Environment and Man*:

> Killing wild animals for food or for their skins can perhaps be rationalized, but killing a gnu to make a flyswatter out of its tail or an elephant to convert its feet into waste paper baskets is perverse. In the United States, mummified baby alligators or baskets made of armadillo "shells" are as tasteless as a cookie jar made out of a human skull (63).

At the turn of the century it became fashionable for ladies to wear immense hats decorated with egret plumes. These feathers came from the American egret, a tall, long-legged, snow-white wading bird. The plumes brought a price of 500 dollars per pound. Market hunters shot the egret to a feather's breadth of extinction. Fortunately, however, when restrictive laws were passed early in this century, the population responded, and the species is no longer "endangered."

For many decades powdered rhino horn was thought by Asiatics to be capable of improving sexual appetite and vigor. The result of these strange notions was disastrous to African rhino populations (163). Superstitious people have for millennia ascribed magical healing powers to portions of the bodies of wild animals. The use of albino buffalo hides as "big medicine" by the Plains Indians is an example. Perhaps the most "curative" animal in history, however, was the wild mountain goat (ibex) of the Swiss Alps. According to Vinzenz Ziswiler, as quoted by Wagner, the hairy balls rarely found inside the animal's stomach were reputedly "effective against fainting, melancholy, jaundice, hemorrhoids, hemorrhagic diarrhea, pestilence, cancer, and other ills. The ibex's blood was considered a cure for bladder stones; the heelbone helped combat spleen diseases; the heart yielded a strength-giving tonic; and even the droppings were utilized as medicine against anemia . . ." (63). All these supposed medicinal values, however, did not help the "health" of the ibex—in fact, they hastened its ultimate extinction in the Swiss Alps by the seventeenth century (63).

9. USE OF PESTICIDES. The role of chlorinated pesticides such as DDT, dieldrin, and endrin in decimating wildlife populations is described in detail in Chapter 12. We merely wish to mention here that the current alarming decline of the osprey (fish hawk), southern bald eagle and the brown pelican has largely been attributed to chlorinated pesticides. Not only do they impair gonadal function, but they also apparently cause the production of extremely thin-shelled eggs. The eggs are destroyed, along with the contained embryo, by the weight of the incubating female.

An Extinction Case History: The Passenger Pigeon. The passenger pigeon (*Ectopistes migratorius*) was once the most abundant bird on earth. Early in the nineteenth century the renowned ornithologist Alexander Wilson observed a migrating flock that streamed past him for several hours. Wilson estimated the single flock to be 1 mile wide and 240 miles long and composed of about 2 billion birds. (The population of this flock was roughly ten times the total North American waterfowl population of today.) Yet not one living passenger pigeon is left.

What factors contributed to the passenger pigeon's extinction? First, many potential nest and food trees (beech, maple, oak) were chopped down or burned to

Figure 9-5. *Extinction. When the last living passenger pigeon, Martha, died at the Cincinnati Zoo, on September 14, 1918, a unique organism was removed from the human ecosystem forever.* [State Historical Society of Wisconsin]

make room for farms and settlements. The pigeon fed extensively on beech nuts and acorns; the single flock observed by Wilson could have consumed 17 million bushels per day.

Second, disease may have taken a severe toll. The breeding birds were susceptible to infectious disease epidemics, because they nested in dense colonies. Schorger reports that in 1871 a concentration of 136 million pigeons nested in an 850-square-mile region in central Wisconsin. Up to 100 nests were built in a single tree.

Third, many pigeons may have been destroyed by severe storms during the long migrations between the North American breeding grounds and the Central and South American wintering region. Bent cites a record of an immense flock of young passenger pigeons that descended to the surface of Crooked Lake, Michigan, after becoming bewildered by a dense fog. Thousands drowned and lay a foot deep along the shore for miles.

Fourth, the low biotic potential may have been a factor in their extinction. Although many perching birds, such as robins, lay four to six eggs per clutch and ducks, quail, and pheasants lay eight to twelve eggs, the female pigeon produced only a single egg per nesting.

Fifth, the reduction of the flocks to scattered remnants possibly deprived the birds of the social stimulus requisite for mating and nesting.

Sixth, the bird's decline was hastened by persecution from market hunters. They

Figure 9-6. *Shooting "wild pigeons" in Iowa. Copied from Leslie's* Illustrated Newspaper, *September 21, 1867. Note the gunner firing point-blank into the densely massed birds. Over 100 birds are resting on the bare branches of the oak in the background.* [State Historical Society of Wisconsin]

slaughtered the birds on their nests. Every imaginable instrument of destruction was employed, including guns, dynamite, clubs, nets, fire, and traps. Over 1,300 densely massed birds were caught in one throw of the net. Pigeons were burned and smoked out of their nesting trees. Migrating flocks were riddled with shot. Over 16 tons of shot were sold to pigeon hunters in one small Wisconsin village in a single year. Pigeon flesh was considered both a delectable and fashionable dish in the plush restaurants of Chicago, Boston, and New York. Sold for 2¢ per bird, almost 15 million pigeons were shipped from a single nesting area at Petoskey, Michigan, in 1861. The last wild pigeon was shot in 1900. Martha, the last captive survivor, died on September 1, 1914, at the age of twenty-nine, in the Cincinnati Zoo.

Biotic Potential

Biotic potential (BP) may be defined as the theoretical maximum population growth rate of a species. Let us take a hypothetical case. Suppose all American robins lived to be ten years old and that each adult female annually fledged eight young. If the robin population started in 1970 with only a single breeding pair, there would be 1,200 million million million robins by 2000—a population so enormous that the earth could accommodate only 1/150,000 of it (64).

According to Raymond Dasmann, biotic potential varies with size of clutch or litter produced, the number produced annually, the minimum and maximum breeding age of the individual, sex ratio, mating habits, and population density (15).

Clutch size in birds, which is primarily determined by heredity, varies greatly with the species. One-egg clutches were characteristic of the now-extinct great auk and passenger pigeon and may have been a factor in their extinction. Loons, eagles, great horned owls, and whippoorwills lay 2-egg clutches; passerines (thrushes, warblers, sparrows, blackbirds) lay 4 to 6 eggs per clutch; 8 to 15 egg clutches are representative of ducks, pheasants, quail, and grouse. A hen Hungarian partridge may produce 20 eggs per clutch. Clutch size probably is determined by the maximum number of young a species can adequately nourish.

Because it is exceedingly difficult to find mammalian litters, data are frequently indirectly determined by counting embryos in the uteruses of collected specimens or by counting the placental scars if animals are secured after the breeding season. From litter-size data collated by Davis and Golley, there appears to be an inverse relation between litter size and weight of the adult (16). According to S. Charles Kendeigh, the number of young per litter are limited by uterine size and the

Figure 9-7. *Ruffed grouse nest at base of tree with clutch of eleven eggs. Clutch size varies greatly in birds, from two eggs in the bald eagle to twenty eggs in the Hungarian partridge.* [*Wisconsin Natural Resources Department, Madison, Wis.*]

number of the female's mammary glands (33). The average number of embryos found in various species follows: moose, 1.12; black-tailed jackrabbit, 2.30; fox squirrel (Michigan), 3.02; bobcat, 3.20; California vole, 4.30; coyote, 5.54; and muskrat, 7.49. In the widely distributed opossum there is considerable geographic variation in litter size, ranging from 6.50 embryos in Florida to 8.90 in Missouri.

Biotic Potential of Deer. A doe usually gives birth to a single fawn after her initial pregnancy and to twin fawns thereafter. In a study of mule deer fertility rates in Utah, Robinette et al. found that 84 per cent of yearling deer were pregnant and averaged 1.32 fetuses per doe; two-year-olds, with a pregnancy rate of 99 per cent, averaged 1.77 fetuses per doe (52). Triplets and quadruplets occur but are uncommon. In addition to age, the health of a doe may influence the number of young she produces. Thus, a severe winter that leaves the doe in a malnourished condition may cause her to resorb her embryos. In Vermont an estimated 93 per

Figure 9-8. *A buck white-tailed deer in prime condition. Note the erect ears, an indication that the animal has been alerted to possible danger.* [*Wisconsin Natural Resources Dept., Madison, Wis.*]

cent of the mature does over 75 pounds had fawns during a given year (60). However, on a Texas range that had been severely overgrazed by livestock, only 42 per cent of the does had young. An experimental dietary study by Verme on a captive white-tail herd in Michigan revealed that productivity of well-fed does was three times that of inadequately nourished animals (62).

Fawns are usually dropped in a thicket where they are well concealed from predators. Although a young fawn might seem quite vulnerable to wolves, coyotes, and wild dogs, protection is afforded by its dappled coat, which causes it to blend with the shifting shadows, and by its almost complete lack of scent.

When mortality factors are minimized, white-tail populations may increase rapidly. Thus, an initial population of six deer (four does and two bucks) that were introduced in 1928 to the 1,200-acre George Reserve in southern Michigan increased to over 160 head after only six years, when controlled hunting was permitted to protect food and cover. The average increase rate for this six-year period was 60 per cent. A Maryland herd of three bucks and three does increased to an estimated 1,000 head from 1926 to 1941. The average annual increase rate for this sixteen-year period was 37.7 per cent. According to David B. Cook, under optimal conditions a deer herd could double its population annually (60).

Factors Depleting Waterfowl Populations

A variety of environmental influences, both biotic and physical, prevent waterfowl from expressing their high biotic potential. Among those discussed here are pothole drainage and drought, appropriation of duck habitat for recreation, habitat destruction by carp, oil pollution, lead poisoning, and botulism.

Pothole Drainage and Drought. The most productive duck factory on the North American continent is located in the grassland biome of Manitoba, Saskatchewan, Alberta, the Dakotas, western Minnesota, and northwestern Iowa. This region produced 53 per cent of the continent's waterfowl during 1950–1957 (39). The ducks are raised primarily on tiny potholes, 1 or 2 acres in size, where all the basic waterfowl habitat requirements of food, cover, water, and nesting sites are usually met. However, the drainage of considerable pothole acreages for agricultural purpose, some of which, inexplicably, was actually subsidized by the federal government, has long posed a critical habitat impairment problem. In 1948 the government paid $17,285 to 350 farmers of Day County, South Dakota, to dig 43 miles of drainage canals (8). As a result 1,400 potholes representing 6,285 acres were eliminated as duck nesting areas. During 1949–1950 in Minnesota, North Dakota, and South Dakota 64,000 potholes were destroyed, representing a loss of 188,000 acres of waterfowl habitat (39). In 1955 only 56,000 of the original 150,000 square miles of pothole habitat still remained. In Iowa alone, over the last sixty years, 2.4 million hectares of pothole country has shrunk to 20,000 hectares—a reduction of well over 90 per cent. Severe drought in the 1930's and early 1960's compounded the problem by drying up many potholes that hitherto had escaped drainage. In Canada alone during drought conditions, the number of potholes may be reduced from a wet season peak of 6.7 million to 1.7 million, with corresponding reduction in waterfowl populations (58). It should be mentioned here that much drainage has benefited both agriculture and game, other than waterfowl. Thus the

Black Swamp in Wood County, Ohio, which was converted into a profitable agricultural region, now affords some of the best pheasant hunting in the state.

Appropriation of Duck Habitat for Recreation. For many centuries of pre-Columbian time, the weed beds and marshes along the western end of Lake Erie provided optimal habitat for thousands of waterfowl. Today, as a result of a mushrooming human population with increasing amounts of leisure time, the area's waterfowl carrying capacity has been severely impaired. Where once mallards paddled, motorboats churn. The scubadiver has replaced the scaup; the marsh has given way to the marina. Over 3,000 boats are berthed along a 0.5-mile shoreline of Lake St. Clair. They appropriate space once used by waterfowl. During the summer large numbers of motorboats trim the tops of emergent food plants with great efficiency. We would not expect a field of daisies to be capable of reproduction were we to go through them with a power mower; neither can duck food plants survive unless they are permitted to keep their reproductive heads above water to effect pollination. It is apparent that in this confrontation of waterfowl, concerned with survival itself, and man, concerned only with weekend water fun, the interests of man have been served—with catastrophic effect on waterfowl.

Habitat Destruction by Carp. To many a barefooted youngster armed with cane-pole and worms, a carp might seem a prize, but to the sophisticated duck hunter, it is a notorious destroyer of waterfowl habitat. Carp can eradicate dense growths of sago pondweed, water milfoil, and coontail, all favored duck foods (46). By

Figure 9-9. *Aerial view of dried-up potholes near Antler, Saskatchewan. These duck breeding grounds are also utilized by beaver. [Bureau of Sport Fisheries and Wildlife, U.S. Department of the Interior]*

means of enclosure experiments, Threinen and Helm showed that carp could quickly devastate growths of floating-leaf pondweed. Lake Koshkonong in southern Wisconsin was once almost blanketed with rafts of canvasbacks, which fed on the abundant buds of wild celery and pondweed nuts. Late in the nineteenth century, however, carp were introduced to Lake Koshkonong. In a brief time the fish uprooted the choice waterfowl food plants, and the thrilling panoramas of rafting "cans" quickly vanished, except in memory. Hundreds of waterfowl feeding areas throughout the United States have had similar histories. Moreover, recent food analysis studies have shown that young carp will compete directly with ducklings for protein-rich invertebrates, so essential for growth and development. Scuds and water fleas are preferred by carp under 5 inches; 5-inch to 11-inch carp prefer aquatic insects (46).

The turbidity caused by carp, which stir up the bottom muds while searching for plant rootstocks and invertebrates, may restrict photosynthesis sufficiently to eliminate certain duck food plants not actually directly killed by the fish. According to Frederick C. Lincoln, this factor was partially responsible for the impaired waterfowl carrying capacity of the Potomac River and the Susquehanna Flats in the late 1940's (42).

Carp are extremely difficult to eradicate. Once under control, however, a given site may recover its original ability to support waterfowl. This has been demonstrated at the Lake Mattamuskeet Wildlife Refuge (North Carolina), where carp had infiltrated from brackish coastal waters in the 1930's. Because of their deleterious impact on waterfowl, refuge personnel, under the direction of W. G. Cahoon, launched an intensive carp control campaign in 1945. It included the erection of a barrier to prevent further infiltration and an extended seining operation that netted 2.4 million pounds of carp from 1945 to 1960. Already by 1952 water turbidity was markedly reduced and duck food plants were becoming established on the formerly barren lake bottom. As a result Lake Mattamuskeet once again is a celebrated waterfowl wintering ground, currently being utilized by 60,000 to 80,000 Canada geese, 80,000 to 150,000 ducks and teal, and hundreds of whistling swans annually (10).

Oil Pollution. An excess of 100,000 waterfowl are destroyed annually by oil pollution. Oil hazards for marine birds developed about 1925 when oil-burning ships replaced those utilizing coal as fuel (44). Much of this pollution occurs in Atlantic coastal waters. Resolutions to control marine oil pollution proposed at the 1954 International Conference on Pollution of the Sea by Oil were ratified by twenty-eight countries and the United States (30). Nevertheless, as a result of willfulness, carelessness, and accidents, oil pollution continues. Oil kills ducks by matting their feathers and impairing their insulative function. An oil-soaked area the size of a quarter will kill a murre, according to Leslie M. Tuck, of the Canadian Wildlife Service in Newfoundland (44). Oil may also prove lethal if ingested accidentally during preening and drinking. "Accelerated starvation" may frequently occur when oiled ducks exhibit a greatly increased metabolic rate in conjunction with a retarded food intake (27).

In 1954 oil spillage from a shipwreck off the Canadian coast destroyed 1,500 ducks. One quarter million murres, eiders, razorbills, and puffins died off Newfoundland because of jettisoned oil during the winter of 1960. Oil killed 4,000 ducks in Long Island Sound in December, 1960. Another 4,000 ducks, almost 20 per cent

Figure 9-10. *Spring Lake, Minnesota. Oil-coated ducks are piled up on the shore of the Mississippi River, near Spring Lake, victims in 1963 of petroleum- and soybean oil-polluted waters. Collected in 20 minutes, these were a few of the 20,000 ducks killed by the oil.* [U.S. Environmental Protection Agency]

of the wintering population in Narragansett Bay, were destroyed by an oil spill in 1961. In 1969 thousands of waterfowl were destroyed off Santa Barbara, California, because of an oil spill resulting from faulty drilling operations. Oil pollution of freshwater habitats frequently originates in industrial sources. During the spring of 1960, 10,000 ducks, primarily canvasbacks aggregating in a restricted area of open water in the Detroit River, were killed by an oil spill (43).

Lead Poisoning. Lead toxemia resulting from the ingestion of spent shot causes an estimated 2 to 3 per cent annual waterfowl loss in the United States, almost equivalent to the combined duck production of North and South Dakota (3). (Nearly 25 per cent of 8,000 waterfowl investigated in southern France contained lead shot.) From 1940 to 1963 over 1,500 Canada geese died in Wisconsin from lead poisoning. The heaviest duck mortality from lead poisoning has occurred along the Mississippi flyway, especially in Louisiana, Illinois, Missouri, Indiana, and Arkansas. Because there are 280 pellets of #6 shot in one shell, and the average hunter requires five shots to kill one duck, he deposits 1,400 pellets on waterfowl habitat for each bird taken. In 1952 goose hunters at Horicon Marsh (Wisconsin) required thirty-six shots to bag one bird. Sixty thousand pellets per acre were counted in the San Joaquin River marshes of California; 118,048 per acre were

Figure 9-11. *Early hunter in the act of decreasing the mallard population by one.*
[*State Historical Society of Wisconsin*]

recorded from the bottom of Wisconsin's Lake Puckaway (3). Species incurring heaviest losses have been the bottom feeders, such as mallards and pintails, which ingest the shot inadvertently along with food and grit. Ducks may confuse shot with the seeds of certain pondweeds. According to a British study, roughly 70 per cent of mallards bearing a single ingested shot will succumb if they persist in a wild seed diet (30). Nevertheless, up to 179 pellets have been recovered from a pintail and 451 from a trumpeter swan (3).

After ingestion chemical reactions within the digestive tract cause the release of soluble lead salts, which may paralyze the gizzard and cause starvation in a month. In acute cases poisoning of the liver, blood, and kidneys may cause death in one to two weeks. Symptoms include extreme emaciation, protruding sternal keel, absence of fat deposits in the body cavity, hypertrophied gall bladder, and characteristically green-stained gizzard lining and vent (3).

Stopgap measures to reduce mortality include covering the pellet-bearing feeding area with fine gravel. Plastic-coated lead pellets have not proved successful in reducing the toxemia. Perhaps the best long-term solution to the problem would be the substitution of nontoxic iron alloy for lead shot (3).

Botulism.   The prostrate bodies of dead and dying ducks littered the mud flats of a western marsh. Here a mallard feebly fluttered its wings and voided bright green

Figure 9-12.   *Botulism at the Bear River Migratory Bird Refuge. Biologist picks up sick and dead birds. Sick birds are given antitoxin treatments at the duck hospital. Since the hospital was established, the loss of water fowl from this disease has dropped off greatly on the refuge.* [Bureau of Sport Fisheries and Wildlife, U.S. Department of the Interior]

droppings; there a widgeon struggled vainly to lift its head out of the stagnant ooze; a Canada goose was blinded by the yellowish slime that covered its eyes; a blue-winged teal gasped and died. What had happened to these birds? They were the victims of *botulism,* a disease caused by the toxic metabolic wastes of the anaerobic bacterium *Clostridium botulinum,* type C. Although most prevalent in the West, it has been recorded from Canada to Mexico, from California to New Jersey. During the summer of 1910 this tiny organism was responsible for millions of waterfowl deaths. In 1929, and again in 1932, an estimated 100,000 to 300,000 waterfowl in the Great Salt Lake (Utah) died from botulism (29). In 1965 botulism claimed the lives of 20,000 birds in Utah's Bear River Migratory Bird Wildlife Refuge.

The optimal environmental conditions for a population build-up of *Clostridium* include (1) exposed stretches of stagnant alkaline flats, (2) an abundance of "trapped" organic matter such as aquatic vegetation, to serve as food, (3) high water temperatures. These conditions are most likely to occur in late summer during periods of protracted drought. The shallow-feeding dabbling ducks are especially vulnerable because they accidentally ingest the toxic material along with aquatic plants and their invertebrate foods. Apparently, invertebrates serve as a specialized microhabitat for the bacteria where growth and reproduction are favored (29). Once absorbed by the blood stream of the waterfowl, the toxin affects the nervous system, rendering the birds flightless and eventually causing death by respiratory paralysis. At the Bear River Wildlife Refuge many thousands of sick ducks have recovered after receiving antitoxin shots. Such treatment, however, would be prohibitively costly and time-consuming in the event of a major outbreak. Thus prevention seems to be the answer. Kalmbach and Gunderson have suggested that prevention can be effected by rapidly raising the water level of the marsh or mudflat so that *Clostridium* no longer has optimal conditions for reproduction (32).

Figure 9-13. *Unloading botulism-stricken ducks at the Bear River Migratory Bird Refuge, Utah. They will be given antitoxin shots at the duck hospital. A very high percentage of treated birds recover. [Bureau of Sport Fisheries and Wildlife, U.S. Department of the Interior]*

Such flooding would both lower the water temperature and dilute the toxin. Research is currently being conducted to determine whether botulism cannot be controlled indirectly by reducing the invertebrate populations (29).

Factors Depleting Deer Populations

Among the various environmental factors adversely affecting deer populations are malnutrition, accidents, predation, parasites, and disease.

Malnutrition. Winter is a critical season for deer survival in the northern states because available food is extremely limited. Much potential food, such as herbs, mosses, fungi, seedlings, low-growing shrubs, and stump sprouts, is frequently covered with snow. Under such conditions the only available plant materials are buds, twigs, and the foliage of shrubs and trees. If the deer population exceeds the carrying capacity of the habitat (as it has in many of the lake states in the past few decades), deer will consume all the available browse up to the height they can reach when rearing up on their hind legs. As a result, a conspicuous *browse line* will form at a height of 4.5 to 5 feet, a definite warning to the game biologist of deteriorating range. Under these conditions fawn mortality is high, not only because of their restricted "reach," but because the young rank at the bottom of the buck-doe-fawn social hierarchy, as observed by Kabat, Collias, and Guettinger in a Wisconsin deer yard (31). During the winter of 1955–1956 game wardens in Michigan found

Figure 9-14. *Note how deer have browsed the twigs of this young pine. When deer populations are dense in winter deer yards, damage to pine stands may be severe.* [Wisconsin Natural Resources Department, Madison, Wis.]

Figure 9-15. *Michigan deer yard. During the winter season deer tend to congregate in deer yards. These yards frequently are located in cedar swamps where the animals are protected from wind and blowing snow. The compaction of snow in a yard facilitates movement to and from feeding areas. When deer are alerted to possible danger the tail is lifted erect and appears as a white "flag" as the animals bound away.* [Michigan Department of Natural Resources]

large numbers of deer floundering in snow drifts, severely weakened from malnutrition. Over 115,650 deer died that year, at least one third perishing directly from starvation, the remainder from predators and disease that merely finished off the deer after starvation had set the stage.

Emergency feeding of starving deer is not considered sound management by most game biologists. They argue that it permits the survival of deer whose future progeny will exert even greater demands on the available natural browse, thus aggravating the problem. Artificial feeding may facilitate the spread of disease by promoting concentrations of highly susceptible animals. Moreover, it is expensive. During the period 1934–1956 Wisconsin spent over $0.5 million on the purchase and distribution of 7,000 tons of artificial feed. To feed the Michigan deer herds properly for one winter would cost $800,000, or roughly $16 to $40 per head.

Accidents. Dahlberg and Guettinger report at least thirteen types of fatal deer accidents in Wisconsin (13). They include death by auto and train, entanglement in browse trees, falling over a cliff, enmirement in muck, drowning, lightning strike, herbicide poisoning, and antler locking while fighting. A speeding convertible can be a more significant mortality factor than a wolf. During 1944–1960 Minnesota game wardens reported that 7,937 (79.39 per cent) of 9,991 deer deaths were caused by motor cars as compared to only 457 (4.57 per cent) fatalities caused by predation. In 1954 cars killed 1,093 Wisconsin deer. Currently an estimated 3,000 deer are killed annually by Minnesota motorists. According to Taber and Dasmann, most accidents to the black-tailed deer of California's chaparral range were experienced by male fawns (59).

Figure 9-16. *Just a small sample of the thousands of white-tailed deer which starve annually during severe winters (with deep snow cover) in Wisconsin, Minnesota, Michigan, New York, and Pennsylvania.* [*Wisconsin Natural Resources Department, Madison, Wis.*]

Figure 9-17. *Note the dead deer lying on the floor of the car after crashing through the windshield. Several thousand deer are killed by cars annually in Wisconsin. [Wisconsin Natural Resources Department, Madison, Wis.]*

Predation. Among deer predators may be listed wolves, cougars, bobcats, coyotes, and domestic dogs. During 1951–1960 wolves in the wilderness of the Superior National Forest destroyed 1.5 deer per square mile annually. In 1950 wolves killed 6,000 (17 per cent) of the 37,000 deer in the forest. Ninety-seven per cent of 435 wolf scats (deposited fecal matter) collected in northern Wisconsin from 1946 to 1948 contained the remains of deer. Despite much contrary opinion wolves do not cull the weak, sickly, crippled, or senile individuals but simply take any deer regardless of sex, age, or physical condition. However, because hunting pressure in the remote backwoods country of the Superior National Forest is extremely light, accounting for only 0.65 deer per square mile, wolf predation serves to regulate a deer herd that in 1961 was on the verge of exceeding the carrying capacity of the range. Since there were only 350 timber wolves in the entire state of Minnesota in 1965, the impact of wolf predation on deer in that state must be negligible.

Although one cougar may kill an estimated 50 or more deer annually, cougars are unimportant as regulators of deer populations because of their scarcity, except in localized areas of Arizona and other parts of the Southwest. King reports seeing a black bear killing a black-tailed fawn and consuming the entire carcass (34). Bobcats weighing 25 pounds can kill deer weighing 175 pounds, usually attacking when the latter are lying down. Deliberate aggressive responses of mule deer does toward bobcats that have approached fawns have been observed (26). Deer remains were found in only 3.5 per cent of 300 bobcat scats collected in Michigan. Surprisingly, the most serious deer slayer other than man is the dog. Beagles, German shepherds,

Figure 9-18. *Deer killers! Minnesota conservation officer holding two dogs responsible for killing more than fifty deer in St. Croix State Park in one winter. [Minnesota Department of Natural Resources, Photo by Walter H. Wettschreck]*

Figure 9-19. *Yearling deer killed by dogs near Radisson, Wisconsin. Note the slashed throat. [Wisconsin Natural Resources Department, Madison, Wis.]*

and Airedales have been implicated. Pregnant does and young fawns are especially vulnerable. In March 1962, dogs killed 43 deer on the Carlos Avery Game Refuge in Minnesota. Hamilton estimates that during one January dogs killed 1,000 snow-bound deer in New York. In summary, over most of the white-tailed deer's range domestic dogs that have gone astray are the most significant predators; except in local situations wild predators are of little consequence. In remote hunting areas where hunting pressure is light, a higher predator population might be advantageous in preventing disastrous irruptions.

Stable, Irruptive, and Cyclic Populations

Aldo Leopold has classified wildlife populations as being either *stable, irruptive,* or *cyclic* (41). Stable populations are characterized by a saw-toothed curve as a result of random increments and decrements. However, from a long-range stand-point, the population remains at a rather constant level. Most wildlife populations become stable once they have reached the plateau of the sigmoid curve, or, in other words, have reached the carrying capacity of the habitat. Bobwhite quail is a representative species having stable populations. In this species population fluctua-tions are frequently seasonal. Thus, shortly after the young have hatched, popula-tions will be at a peak; in early spring after a severe winter characterized by crusted snow, quail populations will be low. Factors such as disease, predators, climate, cover, and food availability may vary, resulting in slight upward or downward popu-lation swings. Even intrapopulation shifts in age and sex ratios may affect population levels.

After fluctuating mildly for many years, some populations, such as those of deer and house mice, may suddenly increase sharply or *irrupt* and then suddenly crash to a very low level. Irruptions are highly erratic and unpredictable. In some cases they occur when there is an unusually favorable climate for reproduction or an unusually abundant, though temporary, food supply. Perhaps the most celebrated example of an irruption is that involving the mule deer herd in the Kaibab National Forest in the Grand Canyon region of Arizona. For many years in the late nineteenth century a deer population of about 6,000 head lived here in dynamic equilibrium with a biotic environment that included a variety of predators, such as the wolf, coyote, cougar, and bear.

However, in 1906, the same year the area was proclaimed a national forest by Theodore Roosevelt, an all-out predator control campaign was launched in a naive attempt to increase the deer herd for the combined benefit of tourists and hunters. All predators were drastically reduced in numbers. The wolf was eradicated. With the ER reduced, the deer population's BP attained full expression, the herd climb-ing to a peak of 100,000 by 1924, a sixteen-fold increase within sixteen years. Un-fortunately, however, the herd had increased beyond the carrying capacity of its range. A browse line became well-defined on palatable shrubs and trees, such as aspens and conifers. Herbs were grazed down to the bare ground. Thousands of valuable seedlings, representing the timber of the future, were destroyed. Then came the inevitable "crash." Saved from a quick, sudden death from predators, deer now began to succumb to slow, agonizing death by starvation. Within the six-year period from 1924–1930, 80,000 deer starved, their gaunt, emaciated carcasses bearing eloquent testimony to man's heavy-handed and simple-minded solution to an ex-tremely delicate and complex ecological problem.

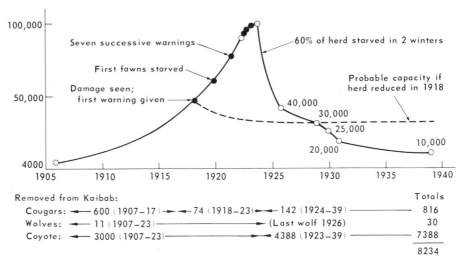

Figure 9-20. *This classic example of a deer irruption occurred in a herd of mule deer on the Kaibab Plateau on the north edge of the Grand Conyon, Arizona. It was caused by an intensive predator removal campaign. Note that repeated warnings of impending disaster were ignored.* [*Adapted from Edward J. Kormondy,* Concepts of Ecology *(Englewood Cliffs, N.J.: Prentice-Hall, 1969). After A. S. Leopold,* Wisconsin Conservation Bulletin, *No. 321, 1943.*]

Cyclic populations show sharp increases, followed by crashes, at rather regular intervals. To some degree the population peaks and troughs can be predicted. The most thoroughly studied cycles occur at three-to-four-year (lemming) or at ten-year (snowshoe hare, lynx, grouse) intervals. The three-to-four-year cycle is characteristic of the brown lemming of the North American tundra biome. Other species in which this cycle has been observed include the northern shrike, red-tailed hawk, meadow vole, martin (mammal), and sockeye salmon. The lemming forms the principal food of the Arctic fox, red fox, snowy owl, and pomarine jaeger; therefore the populations of these predators varies with that of their lemming prey. Apparently these predators have few alternative prey species on which to feed. Although many snowy owls starve during the winters of lemming population troughs, large numbers will emigrate to the United States, some moving as far south as North Carolina. In his study of brown lemming crashes in northern Alaska, Pitelka found that the peak lemming population overgrazed vegetation that had served as protective cover (51). During the ensuing spring's snow melt, the lemmings therefore became highly vulnerable to predation and their numbers were drastically reduced.

The ten-year cycle is not well understood. It is characteristic of the snowshoe hare, an occupant of the northern coniferous forest or taiga, and has been reported for the muskrat (Iowa), ruffed grouse, sharp-tailed grouse, and willow ptarmigan. Also involved in this cycle are quail, partridges, pheasants (in the northern portions of their range), and northern grouse. The Canada lynx, which preys largely on the snowshoe hare, has a ten-year cycle that lags just behind that of the hare. The lynx cycle has been elucidated by Elton and Nicholson by examination of the Hudson Bay Company's lynx pelt returns (20).

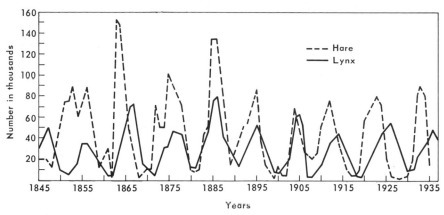

Figure 9-21. *A classic example of a wildlife population cycle. Based on pelt records of the Hudson Bay Company. Note the roughly 10-year interval.* [Adapted from Eugene P. Odum, Fundamentals of Ecology (Philadelphia: W. B. Saunders Company, 1959). After D. A. Maclulich, University of Toronto Studies, Biological Series No. 43, 1937.]

Green and Evans, in a study of snowshoe hare in the area of Lake Alexander, Minnesota, found "shock disease" to have been responsible for the cyclic phenomenon (22). In recent years a number of other workers have implicated "shock disease" in population cycles. The theory is that when populations peak, the increased stress caused by fighting and other physical contacts, in addition to the impaired nutritional value of marginal food supplies and the greater energy expended in searching for food and cover, results in stimulation of the pituitary gland by way of neural pathways and the hypothalamus. The pituitary is stimulated to produce ACTH (adrenocorticotrophic hormone), which in turn causes the adrenal gland to increase its secretion of cortins. These hormones then cause a reduction of the reproductive function. Eventually the pituitary-adrenal system becomes exhausted and death ensues.

A number of other theories have been advanced to explain the immediate cause of the nine to-ten-year cycle. They include variations in weather, fluctuations in solar radiation, depletion of food supply, disease, and changes in nutrient levels of plant foods. It may be that several of these in combination are responsible for the cycles. As yet, however, much of the underlying mechanism remains to be defined.

Habitat Requirements of Wildlife

We may consider habitat to be the general environment in which an organism lives—its natural home. The habitat of a wild animal provides certain essentials: shelter, food, water, breeding sites (den, nest, or burrow), and a fairly well-defined area called the *territory*, in which an animal has psychological dominance over intruders.

Cover. Cover may serve to protect an animal from adverse weather conditions.

Good examples are the dense cedar swamps that protect white-tailed deer herds from winter winds and drifting snow and the leafy canopies of apple trees that shield nestling robins from the heat of the midday sun. Cover may also protect wild animals from predators. Representative of this function is the thicket into which a cottontail plunges when eluding a fox or the marsh grasses that conceal a teal from a hawk. Even water may serve as cover, as for a muskrat or beaver, providing relative security from all landbound predators, from wolf to man.

Food.   On the basis of food habits, vertebrate animals may be classified as herbivores, spermivores, insectivores, frugivores, carnivores, omnivores, and so on. The tendency to eat certain basic food types is inherited but is subject to modification on the basis of experience. There may be considerable variation in food habits within the species, and even in the same individual, depending on such variables as health and age of animal, season, habitat, and food availability. An animal's access to adequate food may be influenced by many factors, including population density, weather, habitat destruction (by fire, flood, or insects), and plant succession.

Because mammals (and presumably birds) must spend 90 per cent of their waking hours searching for food, the importance of food availability is emphasized. Occasionally, when a food occurs in superabundant quantities, an animal will exploit this source, even though it is not a usual dietary item. Consider some examples: Even though the green-winged teal's diet is 90 per cent vegetarian, it avidly consumes the maggoty flesh of rotting Pacific salmon. Although the lesser scaup is not normally a scavenger, the stomachs of ducks that had been feeding at the mouth of a sewer were filled with slaughterhouse debris and cow hair (as well as rubber bands and paper). A house wren, usually insectivorous, fed its nestlings large quantities of newly hatched trout from an adjacent hatchery (64). In a study of winter mink diets in Missouri, Korschgen found that volume percentage of fish increased from 11.9 in 1951 to 27.4 in 1953, apparently because low water levels increased the vulnerability of the prey. Similarly, during periods of drought or high muskrat population densities, muskrat may become the principal mink food, although at other times it forms only 1 or 2 per cent of the mink diet.

Dietary changes are frequently seasonal in character. Thus, although the red fox consumes mice throughout the year, Hamilton describes the following shifts in its diet: winter—carrion, offal, frozen apples; spring and summer—snakes, turtles, and eggs, an occasional fawn, blackberries, and raspberries; autumn—wild cherries, grapes, grasshoppers (25). Joel Welty reports that barn owls near Davis, California, that had subsisted primarily on house and deer mice during spring and summer, shifted to gophers and voles during autumn and winter (64).

Animals that consume a great variety of foods are *euryphagous*. The omnivorous opossum is a classic example. It consumes fruits, blackberries, persimmons, corn, apples, earthworms, insects, frogs, snakes, lizards, newly hatched turtles, bird eggs and young, mice, and even bats. It is apparent that during critical periods when usual foods are scarce, the euryphagous animal is well adapted to survive. Thus, although staple foods for the ring-necked pheasant are corn, sorghum, rye, wheat, barley, soybeans, lesser ragweed, and pigeon grass, Errington found that when its usual foods are covered with ice and snow, the bird shifts to the seeds of bittersweet, sumac, and black locust.

A *stenophagous* animal, which maintains a specialized diet, is more vulnerable to starvation when its usual foods are scarce. For example, a spell of freezing weather in late April that causes a dearth of flying insects will frequently result in considerable starvation losses to chimney swifts and purple martins. Similarly, when a parasite caused 90 per cent destruction of eelgrass along the Atlantic coast from 1931 to 1933, the wintering population of brants, which depends on eelgrass almost exclusively, was reduced by 80 per cent (45).

Water.   Roughly 65 to 80 per cent of wild animal biomass is composed of water. It serves many functions. It flushes wastes from the body. As a major blood constituent it transports nutrients, hormones, enzymes, and respiratory gases. Animals can survive for weeks without food but only a few days without water. Although fed dried pears, a water-deprived domestic pigeon died in five days (56). Mourning doves have been known to lose 15 per cent of their body weight when water-deprived for 24 hours at 39° C (64). Buffalo herds living in arid western grasslands traveled many miles to water holes, leaving trails that are visible to this day. Mourning doves may fly up to 30 miles from nesting site to watering place. Dove and quail populations have been increased in the Southwest by the installation of "gallinaceous guzzlers"—devices that collect rainwater (15). Some herbivores (for example, wild donkeys) may recover up to 25 per cent of water loss in less than two minutes, thus minimizing the predator hazard (16). Birds and mammals may secure their water from dew or may drink it as it drips from foliage and tree trunks after a shower.

Figure 9-22.   *Wildlife habitat improvement. Chukar partridge(introduced from Asia) attracted by a "guzzler," a recently developed watering device employed in arid regions.* [*California Department of Fish and Game*]

During the northern winter, when liquid water is scarce, the author has observed English sparrows and starlings eating snow. The versatile Adelie penguin, according to Robert Cushman Murphy, may drink salt water or fresh water as well as eat snow. Many living in arid regions satisfy their water requirements by consuming water-containing foods. Desert carnivores, such as the rattlesnake, desert fox, prairie falcon, and bobcat, may secure water from the blood and body fluids of prey. The desert-dwelling grasshopper mouse feeds extensively on insects having a 60 to 85 per cent water content (16). Forty-four per cent of the white-throated wood rat's desert diet consists of cacti and other succulent plants. The kangaroo rat may not require ingested water during its entire life span, because it can make effective use of the metabolic water synthesized within its tissues from the breakdown of fats and proteins (49).

Home Range. Smith defines a home range as "the area over which an animal habitually travels while engaged in its usual activities" (54). Home range may be determined by marking, releasing, and recapturing an animal. Animals may be tracked with geiger counters after having been fed radioactive materials. Dyed foods will result in colored feces; the home range can then be determined on the basis of dropping distribution (16). Birds may be individually marked with colored leg bands or spray paints. Small mammals may have their ears notched or toes clipped. Large mammals (buffalo and elk) can be tattooed or marked with colored plastic collars so that visual identification is possible at a distance.

Herbivores usually have smaller home ranges than carnivores. Animals occupying a deteriorated habitat maintain larger home ranges than those in a good habitat. A few home ranges for herbivorous mammals are as follows: field mouse, 0.5 acre; deer mouse, 0.5 acre (good habitat) or 5 acres (poor habitat); porcupine, 1 kilometer; beaver, under 1 kilometer. According to Burt, buck cottontails have a home range of 8 to 20 acres compared to the doe's 3 acres (8). Lowell Adams found the buck snowshoe hare's home range was 25.2 acres compared to the female's 18.9 acres (1). In one study 70 per cent of the released muskrats were retaken within

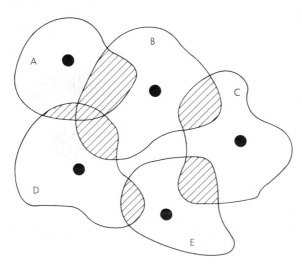

Figure 9-23. *Home range compared with territory. A diagrammatic representation of five home ranges and territories. The large clear areas (A, B, C, D, E) are home ranges. Note the diagonally hatched areas where two adjacent ranges overlap. Territories are indicated by the black spot in the center of each home range. Note that territories never overlap.*

160 feet of original capture (16). Bull moose may have a summer home range of only 100 acres of swamp. After attaching miniature radio transmitters to the bodies of eastern wild turkeys, Ellis and Lewis, with the aid of portable receivers, acquired telemetric data indicating an annual average home range of 1,100 acres for four adult gobblers (19). Although more data are required, the mink appears to occupy a home range embracing 15 to 100 miles of lake or river shoreline.

Kolenosky and Davis determined by telemetric methods that the maximum ranges of timber wolves in east-central Ontario were 3.2 kilometers (with ground receivers) and 9.6 kilometers (with receivers in airplanes) (35). Burt, on the other hand, reports that timber wolves have circular runways 20 to 60 miles in diameter.

Territory.   G. K. Noble defines a *territory* as "any defended area." Territories are usually defended against individuals of the same species. Nice set up the following classification of avian territories in terms of areas defended: type A—entire mating, feeding, and breeding area; type B—mating and nesting area; type C—mating area; type D—nest only; type E—nonbreeding areas such as feeding and roosting sites (48).

Van Tyne and Berger summarize the various functions that avian territorialism might serve: provision of adequate food; a mechanism for establishing and maintaining the pairing bond; regulation of population density (territories are on the average

Figure 9-24.   *Ruffed grouse drumming on log. Drumming sound is caused by the rapid series of air mass compressions resulting from the beating wings. The drumming serves not only in territorial advertisement to competitive males, but also as an attractant to prospective mates. A suitable drumming log (partially decomposed) is an essential component of the ruffed grouses's territory. [Wisconsin Natural Resources Department, Madison, Wis.]*

Figure 9-25. *The golden eagle, like most carnivorous birds, maintains an extremely large territory—in some cases up to 93 million square meters. [Wisconsin Natural Resources Department, Madison, Wis.]*

smaller where food is superabundant); reduction of interference with breeding activities (copulation, nest building, incubation); reduction of predation losses (resulting from familiarity with refuge sites as well as from the population dispersion); and reduction of infectious disease transmission (little evidence) (61).

Average territorial areas (in square meters) for certain avian species follow: black-headed gull in England, 0.3; eastern robin in Wisconsin, 1,200; red-winged blackbird in Wisconsin, 3,000; black-capped chickadee in New York, 53,000; great-horned owl in New York, 500,000; and golden eagle in California, 93 million (64). The varying areas here depend partly on function, partly on size of bird. The black-headed gull's territory is concerned with nest defense only, that of the horned owl and golden eagle with defense of mating, nesting, and feeding area.

Territorial behavior is well developed in many species of fish, including the sunfish, bass, sticklebacks, and minnows. Male black bass and sunfish will defend their nests by rushing toward an intruder.

Territoriality is not readily observed in mammals, because many species are nocturnal or fossorial (burrowing). It appears rather poorly defined. Thus Murie has reported two female wolves with litters occupying a den simultaneously in Mount McKinley National Park, Alaska (47). In a study of the prairie spotted skunk in Iowa, it was found that a den was not the private possession of one skunk, but was coinhabited by the entire local skunk population. However, according to Burt, territoriality occurs in squirrels, beavers, female chipmunks, bull sea lions, muskrats, rabbits, mice, and domestic dogs. There are two fundamental types—defense of nesting site, as represented by the muskrat and beaver, and food store

Figure 9-26. *Black-capped chickadee feeding from hand. These birds respond so readily to human imitation of their territorial song that they will perch on one's head.* [*U.S. Department of Agriculture*]

protection, as in the red squirrel, which may cache and defend several bushels of green pine cones (8). According to Davis and Golley, the social dominance hierarchies of some mammals serve the functions filled for others by territoriality.

Animal Movements

Large-scale movements of animals serve functions for both the individual and the species. Individuals may secure more favorable food supplies, breeding facilities, climate, or simply more living room. A species may benefit if movements result in establishment in a new habitat where the species may persist in the event formerly occupied habitats are destroyed. Movements may also aid the species by increasing the amount of genetic variability upon which natural selection may operate. Three basic types of movements among vertebrates are dispersal of the young, mass emigration, and migrations.

Dispersal of Young. The phenomenon of dispersal occurs in the young of many birds (gulls, herons, egrets, grouse, eagles, owls) and mammals (muskrats, fox squirrels, gray squirrels). In a pine-oak barrens in central Pennsylvania, Chambers and Sharpe found that up to half of the juvenile ruffed grouse emigrated from their nesting areas to all points of the compass, some up to a distance of 7.5 miles (11). Broley reports that young bald eagles banded in Florida moved northward immediately after nesting, some arriving 1,500 miles distant in Maine and Canada by June (6). Van Tyne and Berger postulate that the eagle was a bird of more northern origin whose establishment in Florida may have been relatively recent (61). Therefore, dispersal was adaptive because it enabled eagles to escape the intense heat of the Florida summer. According to Errington, up to 40 per cent of a wintering muskrat population may disperse in spring. They are primarily young animals who have been ejected by the established, more aggressive adults. Such dispersal apparently is an important mechanism for controlling population densities. Many of the dispersing young move into marginal habitats, where they incur heavy mortality from predation and accidents.

Figure 9-27. *Five precocial ruffed grouse young shortly after hatching. A few weeks later some of these grouse may have dispersed up to 7.5 miles from this nest site.* [*Wisconsin Natural Resources Department, Madison, Wis.*]

Mass Emigration. Mass emigrations frequently occur when a population has peaked because of extremely favorable conditions (food, weather) and then experienced a greatly reduced food supply. Under such conditions the only alternatives to starvation are aestivation, hibernation, or emigration. Emigrations of grosbeaks and crossbills into the northern states from the Canadian taiga result from pine seed crop failure. Crossbills are highly erratic in their movements, in terms of season and direction; even time and place of nesting is apparently determined by the availability of an adequate seed supply. Snowy owl emigrations into the United States from the Canadian tundra are correlated with the population crash of their lemming prey. Ornithologists recorded 13,502 snowy owls during the 1945 to 1946 emigration, which extended as far south as Oregon, Illinois, and Maryland. Twenty-four were observed out over the Atlantic. Some were even seen in Bermuda (50).

Latitudinal Migrations. Winter bird densities in the southern latitudes of the United States are high, not only because of the permanent residents but also because of the many individuals that breed in more northern latitudes. For the most part territorialism is relaxed; many species traveling, feeding, and roosting in flocks.

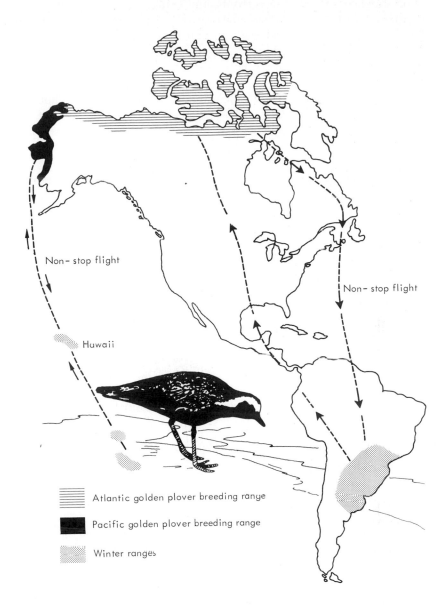

Figure 9-28. *Distribution and migration of the golden plover. Adults of the eastern form migrate across northeastern Canada and then by a 2,400 mile non-stop flight reach South America. In the spring they return by way of the Mississippi Valley. Their entire route is in the form of a great ellipse with a major axis of 8,000 miles and a minor axis of about 2,000 miles. The Pacific golden plover, which breeds in Alaska, apparently makes a non-stop flight across the ocean to Hawaii, the Marquesas Islands, and the Low Archipelago, returning in the spring over the same route.*
[F. C. Lincoln, biologist, and B. Hines, illustrator, in Migration of Birds, Circular 16 (Washington, D.C.: Government Printing Office, 1950).]

Food supplies, such as insects, fruits, and seeds, are more readily available than in northern latitudes. In spring, however, the lengthening photoperiod eventually triggers a neuroendocrine mechanism that causes some birds to migrate northward. Presumably the northern habitats have a higher carrying capacity for the migrants and their future broods. In far northernlatitudes, during the summer there is more time in one twenty-four-hour cycle for feeding young. For example, in northern Alaska (69° north latitude) a robin brood was fed twenty-one hours a day by the female parent. Welty has suggested that the exploitation of two different habitats (winter and summer) may ensure a more balanced supply of vitamins and minerals (64).

Altitudinal Migrations. As Kendeigh has pointed out, the conditions of less snow, higher temperatures, and more available food supplies—which latitudinal migrants secure by moving thousands of miles to the south—are secured by altitudinal migrants simply by moving a few miles down the mountain side (33). The elk herds of the Jackson Hole country in Wyoming ascend the mountains in spring, keeping pace with the receding snow line, and spend the summer at relatively cool upper levels. Murie noted that only when the first snows covered their food supplies, whether in September or November, did the elk move down to the sagebrush valleys for the winter (47). The bighorn sheep of Idaho make similar migrations (in herds of five to fifty animals), which may be 40 miles long. Altitudinal migrations are characteristic of several birds breeding in the Colorado Rockies. Thus the pine grosbeak, black-capped rosy finch, and gray-headed junco all nest at higher altitudes than those at which they winter. Curiously, the blue grouse reverses the usual altitudinal migration; it winters at higher levels than it breeds. Orr has postulated that this arrangement perhaps lessens winter competition with other species for buds and conifer needles (50).

Wildlife Management

Through the years American biologists and legislators have employed a number of techniques for restoring, maintaining, and increasing game populations. They include protective laws, wildlife refuges, predator control, and, most recently, habitat development. In addition, several exotic species have been introduced.

Game Laws. Throughout human history there have been a few farsighted citizens aware of the importance of wildlife to man's happiness and welfare and of the ease with which this resource can be depleted, if not exhausted, by the unrestrained human "predator." Thus, as early as 700 B.C., Moses decreed (Deuteronomy 22:6) that although eggs and nestling birds could be taken for food, the adult breeding stock should be spared "that it may go well with you and that you may live long."

Although game was generally abundant during early colonial times, constant hunting of a few species such as the white-tailed deer prompted some states to enact protective laws. Thus, in 1646 Rhode Island established the first closed season on deer, and by 1694 Massachusetts was also protecting this popular game species. In 1708 New York afforded protection to upland game such as the ruffed grouse, wild turkey, and the heath hen. The first law to protect does was enacted by Virginia in

1738; in 1788 this state prohibited the use of hounds in hunting deer. Rhode Island was the first state to enact legislation barring spring shooting of migratory waterfowl. In 1874 the American people became so aroused over the near extermination of the buffalo that Congress was prodded into passing a protective law; unfortunately, it was vetoed by President Grant. The first game bag limit was set by Iowa in 1878. Kansas, Montana, and Texas all barred sale of protected game in 1897.

During most of the nineteenth century, however, protective game laws were poorly enforced. Very few officials were sufficiently courageous to punish the numerous violators. Nevertheless, greater respect for restrictive game legislation developed by 1878 when New Hampshire and California employed game wardens charged with the responsibility of law enforcement. By the turn of the century, thirty-one states employed wardens.

In 1894, just three years before the last wild bison was shot in Colorado, a bison law was passed that made poaching in Yellowstone Park punishable by fine or imprisonment. Several states in the late 1890's tried to protect the vanishing passenger pigeon by enacting appropriate laws. But by the time these laws were passed the buffalo herds had been reduced to remnants, and the pigeon was well on the road to oblivion.

Introduction of Exotics. Another phase of wildlife development and management involves the introduction of exotic species. They may be brought over to provide game, to serve as predators in controlling some pest, or simply to add color to the native wildlife community. Welty reports that in the late nineteenth century several societies were organized for the explicit purpose of introducing and dispersing exotic species of birds (64). Most of these efforts failed despite an extensive program in which hundreds of thousands of individuals representing over one hundred foreign species were released. Formerly, the Biological Survey and, currently, the U.S. Fish and Wildlife Service have had the responsibility of permitting or barring such imports. Several years ago, according to Gustafson et al. (24), a would-be smuggler tried to bring four exotic finches into the country by tying them around his ankles inside his socks! A few introductions have been successful, notably that of the ring-necked pheasant, which was originally introduced to Oregon from Asia in the late nineteenth century. After several additional plantings elsewhere in the United States, it became the most important upland game bird in much of the agricultural Midwest. South Dakota prides itself on being the pheasant capital of America.

Some introductions have had an adverse affect on the native wildlife community. Notable among such unfortunate importations is that of the English sparrow in 1865 and the European starling in 1880. Both of these aggressive and noisy species have appropriated breeding habitat formerly utilized by more attractive and/or melodic native species such as the bluebird, purple martin, and red-headed woodpecker. It is apparent, therefore, that all aspects of the ecology of the proposed exotic must be thoroughly studied before it is released. With such investigations, future harmful introductions will be held to a minimum. Our experience with the ring-necked pheasant is a convincing demonstration that the right exotic in the right habitat may ultimately form an important component of our wildlife resource. In recent years fourteen exotic species of game birds were being reared in twenty-one states with the objective of ultimate release.

Predator Control. The control of predators assumed a popular and conspicuous role early in wildlife management history. It was only natural for the nimrod, tired and disappointed after tramping the fields in fruitless quest of elusive quail or cottontail, to vent his frustration by blaming the hawk or fox. His thesis was based on grade-school arithmetic. If a fox in a certain meadow eats thirty rabbits a year, a rifle bullet through that fox's brain will mean thirty additional cottontails available for hunters. In the past, pressure has been exerted by sportsmen's organizations on state legislators to enact bounty laws, resulting in the expenditure of funds that could have been used to greater advantage in the acquisition and development of wildlife habitat. Money paid by a state for bounties may be considerable, ranging from $2 for a fox and $15 for a bobcat, to $25 for a coyote and $35 for a timber wolf. Game officials in many states, however, have been re-examining predator control in the last few years. The bounty system has been criticized for several reasons.

Figure 9-29. *Wanted: dead—or alive? Red fox pup peers out from behind a rock at Kettle Moraine State Forest, Wisconsin. Predators add interest and sparkle to the out-of-doors, well worth the few rabbits and other small game they may take.* [U.S. Department of Agriculture, Photo by Tom Beemers]

The possibility for fraudulent bounty claims is well pointed up in an account related by Gustafson et al. Some years ago, a midwestern state had placed a bounty on squirrels. To claim the bounty all that was required was to turn in the squirrel's tail. Some quick-witted youngsters devised a scheme whereby they live-trapped a number of squirrels, cut off their tails, released the animals, and turned in their tails for payment. Because the de-tailed squirrels suffered no reduction in biotic potential, the squirrel population remained at a relatively high level, thus assuring a continuous supply of tails (and bounty payments) for the enterprising youths (24).

Many accusations against predators are ill founded. A good example is the crow, frequently the recipient of the duck hunter's wrath for destroying nests and making a meal of eggs and ducklings. However, an analysis of crow stomachs in Michigan revealed that two thirds of the diet was composed of beetles, grasshoppers, and other herbivorous insects, all of considerable crop-destroying potential. The barn owl is frequently persecuted by the harried farmer for raiding his chicken yard or by the irate hunter for seizing quail and rabbits. However, a three-year investigation by Michigan state biologists have revealed the misdirection of their control efforts. An examination of 2,200 barn owl pellets (regurgitated masses of indigestible bones and fur) showed absolutely no trace of poultry or game birds. Although 1.07 per cent of the owls' diet was indeed made up of birds, the great majority of them were the pestiferous starlings and English sparrows. Further, over 90 per cent of the mammals represented in the pellets were mice, primarily the meadow mouse, a species capable of inflicting serious crop damage.

Most ecologists consider the predator as forming an essential part of the ecosystem. As Dasmann has pointed out, the number of predators in the apex of a food pyramid is dependent upon the number of prey animals at the lower levels, and *not the reverse* (15). Thus, in an analysis of data provided by Errington's fifteen-year study of Wisconsin quail, Lack showed that the greater the quail population in spring, the heavier the mortality (including predation) the following fall (37). In some cases, paradoxical as it may seem, predators may actually promote the welfare of the prey species by culling the aged, crippled, and disease-ridden individuals from the population. Moreover, predators may serve a useful role in keeping the resilient prey population within the limits imposed by the carrying capacity of its habitat. A lack of predatory pressure might release a population explosion resulting in habitat deterioration and culminating in massive death caused by starvation and disease.

Habitat Development. Currently the best prospect for increasing wildlife populations is to increase the amount and quality of suitable habitat. Many game biologists consider habitat development absolutely indispensable. In other words, even with protective game laws, predator control, exotic introductions, transplantations, and artificial propagation, wildlife populations will nevertheless be in jeopardy if at the same time their habitat is usurped, destroyed, or permitted to deteriorate. Conversely, if an abundance of high-quality wildlife habitat is available, game populations will remain relatively high regardless of the lack of predator control, artificial propagation, introductions, and transplantations.

It is not surprising, therefore, that habitat acquisition and development programs are receiving high priority among many state game divisions, as well as wildlife research units administered by the U.S. Fish and Wildlife Service. We shall describe some of these programs later in conjunction with case studies of deer and waterfowl. At this time, however, it may be well to show what can be done by private landowners.

Because over 85 per cent of the hunting lands in the United States are privately owned or controlled, and because it is on the private farms, ranches, and woodlots that most of the grouse, quail, doves, pheasants, and rabbits are produced, the biggest contribution to an abundant and varied game resource (as in the case of forest development) can be made by the private citizen. Fortunately, many of the land practices that are effective in soil and water management may be simultaneously applied toward the goal of wildlife habitat improvement.

LIVING FENCES. Before the advent of barbed wire in 1874, ranchers and farmers resorted to other devices for separating woodlot from pasture, or cropland from marsh. In much of the deciduous forest biome split rail fences were used; in rocky New England crude fences were constructed from boulders removed from the path of the plow; and in the lake states rows of pine stumps were employed. Osage orange was used in midwestern prairies as a "living fence." None of these fences was as "neat" as the barbed-wire fences that replaced them; nevertheless, they were much more picturesque, and they reserved more land between boulders, trunks, stumps, and zigzagging rails for potential use as wildlife habitat. The barbed-wire fence reserved *nothing* for wildlife. Because the farmer could now plow to within inches of his fences, results for upland game were disastrous.

In recent years game biologists have encouraged landowners to replace barbed-

Figure 9-30. *Ingredient for a stew! The cottontail rabbit, shown here on the alert to possible danger, is perhaps the most valuable game animal in the United States.* [*Soil Conservation Service, U.S. Department of Agriculture*]

wire fences with living fences composed of native or exotic shrubs (such as the *multiflora* rose), which may provide food, cover, and travel lanes for pheasants, quail, and cottontails. To date, an encouraging 2,000 such fences are being constructed annually. When planted at 1-foot intervals, the exotic *multiflora* rose, introduced from Asia, produces a thorny livestock barrier within three to five years. Not only is it attractive, but it provides cover for rodent-destroying skunks and weasels. Songbird density in such a fence, according to an Ohio study by Charles Dambach, is thirty-two times that in open crop fields. Other fence shrubs suitable for game use are bayberry, tartarian honeysuckle, silky cornel, and highbush cranberry.

WOODLOT MANAGEMENT. Eighteen per cent of the land in five midwestern states is either wooded or in "waste" areas. A woodlot can be a wildlife desert or a paradise depending on how it is managed by the landowner. It should be properly fenced off to prevent cattle from grazing and trampling herbaceous ground cover that might serve as a suitable bird and mammal habitat. In 1941 a comparative study was made in Ohio of two adjoining woodlots, one grazed and the other protected for ten years from grazing by the erection of a barbed-wire fence. The ungrazed woodlot had 53,000 young trees up to 21 feet tall and the grazed woodlot 1,000 seedlings under 5 inches in height. Nineteen species of birds nested in the ungrazed lot to only 8 for the grazed area. Annual avian density averaged 1.7 pairs per acre in the fenced grove compared to only 0.4 pairs per acre in the unfenced area. Here and there an occasional brush pile could be strategically placed to serve for rabbits. A good number of hollow stubs should be left standing to serve as potential breeding sites for opossums, raccoons, flying squirrels, woodpeckers, and owls. In southern stands of longleaf and loblolly pine, wildlife foods may be provided by planting strips of bicolor lespedeza. Wild grape, bittersweet, Virginia creeper, and blackberry bushes planted at the woodlot margin will enhance its wildlife value. Occasionally the undigested seeds in the droppings of birds that have used brush piles as refuge or roosting sites will germinate and develop into a thicket of vines and berry bushes.

ECOLOGICAL SUCCESSION. In our earlier discussion of ecological succession, we indicated that both plant and animal communities change as the physical environment (available sunlight, moisture, wind velocity, soil fertility) changes. Dasmann (15) has classified a number of game species according to the successional stage of which each is characteristic, as follows: *climax species*: bighorn sheep, caribou, grizzly bear, musk ox, passenger pigeon; *mid-successional species*: antelope, elk, moose, mule deer, pronghorn antelope, ruffed grouse, sage grouse, white-tailed deer; *low-successional species*: bobwhite quail, dove, hare, rabbit, ring-necked pheasant. From the preceding classification, it is apparent that the game biologist can regulate the abundance of these species by manipulating ecological succession. Thus, he could permit a succession to proceed on its natural course to a climax, or, by employing such artificial devices as controlled burning, controlled flooding, herbicides, plowing, and logging, he could retard the succession or even revert it to the pioneer stage.

Because climax-associated or wilderness species such as caribou, bighorn sheep, and grizzly bear will flourish only in relatively undisturbed climax communities, their survival depends to a large degree on the establishment of state and national refuges. Without such protected islands in the oceans of successional disturbance

Figure 9-31. *Prescribed burn area at the Agassiz Wildlife Refuge in Minnesota for the purpose of developing suitable habitat for sharp-tailed grouse.* [*Minnesota Department of Natural Resources, Photo by Walter H. Wettschreck*]

caused by man, these climax-associated species would face decline and extinction—a fate already met by the passenger pigeon.

Mid-successional species such as the moose, white-tailed deer, and ruffed grouse, according to Dasmann, must be regarded as purely temporary phenomena, as temporary as the vegetational community on which these herbivores depend for food. In northern Minnesota, for example, moose are not found in the dense, well-shaded spruce-fir climax forest, but in mid-successional thickets of willow, aspen, and birch. Inevitably, when these thickets are shaded out by climax spruce and fir, the local moose, a highly sedentary species, will gradually decline in numbers and ultimately die out. On the other hand, such devices as logging or controlled burning may open up a dense climax forest and permit the eventual establishment of sun-tolerant birch and aspen as well as the moose that utilize them as a primary food source. In any event, these mid-successional species are disturbance-dependent, and without the intervention of game biologist, lumberman, or forest fire (ignited by lightning or man) they will vanish.

The low-successional species such as the rabbit, quail, and dove are greatly dependent on major disturbances of the ecological succession by man. All these species, for example, find food and cover in the weedy pioneer plants that invade an area that has been denuded by human activity. Such vegetation may become established when a cotton or corn field is abandoned or when a fresh road cut becomes exposed to invasion by wind or animal-borne seeds.

In many southeastern states the natural climax is composed of oak-dominated hardwood stands, a community of inferior timber value and poor carrying capacity for quail. Controlled burnings have been used periodically in this region to hold the succession in a subclimax stage. These fires effectively destroy the heat-vulnerable oak seedlings but promote the establishment and survival of fire-tolerant and timber-valuable long-leaf pine, as well as a great variety of herbs and shrubs that provide top-quality food, cover, and nest sites for quail. Here, then, we have a good example of how succession can be regulated by a single device, controlled burning, to promote the twin objectives of high-value timber and wildlife.

Figure 9-32. *Wildlife habitat improvement. Aerial view of Horicon Wildlife Refuge, Wisconsin, showing ditching made to raise carrying capacity for muskrats. [Wisconsin Natural Resources Department, Madison, Wis.]*

Some Methods of Deer Management

Determination of Movements and Range of Marked Deer. Live-trapped deer may be marked in various ways to permit individual recognition after release. Aluminum ear tags, dyes, and reflecting collars (visible by day and night) have been used. Individual deer may be identified by various color combinations of plastic collars and markers or by some natural deformity such as a misshapen antler. Nyon-base vinyl collars have been used by Hawkins, Autrey, and Klimstra on Illinois white-tails, on which symbols can be seen at 300 yards with 7 x 35 binoculars (28). In Texas deer have been affixed with bells to permit records of nocturnal movements. More recently, deer have been equipped with miniature transistorized radio trans-mitters by means of a special harness; their movements are then recorded by port-able receiving sets. With such techniques data can be secured to answer questions of importance to sound deer management. How long does a deer live? What is its growth rate in wilderness habitat as compared with a semiagricultural environment? How rapidly and how far does a deer disperse from its fawning site? Do deer on

Figure 9-33. *Group of twelve deer photographed from plane during an aerial census in the Upper Souris Refuge, Foxholm, North Dakota. [U.S. Fish and Wildlife Service]*

Figure 9-34. A deer is released from deer trap after being tagged. Re-trapping of this animal would provide information concerning range mobility and longevity. [New York State Conservation Department]

overbrowsed ranges disperse more rapidly than deer on good range? Are there sexual differences in mobility? Age differences? What are the dimensions of a deer's home range?

Recapture of marked deer has provided much interesting data. In many cases the home range of the Columbian black-tail is less than 1 square mile in area. The black-tail's attachment to its home range is so strong that an animal will prefer to starve within its own home range rather than sustain itself on an abundance of food available just outside. A small percentage of black-tails, for some unknown reason, will wander beyond the home range limits only to return at a later time. A. S. Leopold et al. observed that the Jawbone herd on the western slope of the California Sierras maintained a summer home range of 0.50 to 0.75 mile, whereas the winter home ranges were under half the summer area (40). The home ranges of pregnant does or those with young fawns were considerably smaller than the average. Regardless of size, however, each deer home range contains the essentials of bedding areas, watering sites, food, and cover.

A study by Hahn and Taylor revealed that most white-tailed deer in Texas spend their lives within a radius of 2 miles. After having been transported from their original home range, individual Texas bucks have traveled considerable distances to get back to their original locality, one traveling 340 miles in nine months.

Browse Improvement. Many species of deer food plants are utilized only at an early developmental stage when the more succulent young twigs and stems are at browse level. As these plants mature the basal portions become lignified, tough, and unpalatable, while the preferred portions become unavailable to deer because they

Figure 9-35. *Browse cutters on the trail in Minnesota. Snow cover was deep so browse was provided at selected spots in order to reduce winter starvation losses to a minimum.* [*Minnesota Department of Natural Resources*]

have grown out of reach. Game biologists have discovered that the browse value of such plants can be maintained simply by *topping*, or cutting back, the old growth. In a study by Ferguson and Basile on the winter range of mule deer in southwestern Idaho, tops of bitterbrush were cut off at the 3-foot level. The following year growth was 900 per cent that of controls (21). Krefting, Stenlund, and Seemel conducted a similar study on mountain maple in Minnesota (36). To simulate varying browsing pressures, 20, 40, 60, 80, and 100 per cent of the annual growth was clipped on experimental plants. A high degree of browsing pressure tolerance by mountain maple was indicated in that only one of six mountain maple clumps perished even after nine successive years of 100 per cent clipping. These experimental clippings produced a sustained supply of deer food of which 80 per cent was utilized. In both the Idaho and Minnesota studies cuttings provided an effective management tool for improving deer food supplies.

Regulation of the Deer Harvest. One of the primary objectives of deer management is to provide a shootable surplus for the hunter. Several decades ago, when deer were relatively scarce, state legislatures restricted hunting by closing or abbreviating the season, by timing the season so as to ensure an absence of tracking snow, by restricting firearms to shotguns, and by restricting the kill to one per hunter. The doe was afforded special status. The deer herd build-up was further implemented by winter feeding, introductions, predator control, and the establishment of refuges.

In response to these measures, as well as to the great abundance of edge and food available in the wake of extensive fires and logging, the herd increased rapidly—too rapidly. In only thirteen years the white-tail population credited to forty-five states increased from 3,181,675 in 1937 to 5,135,040 in 1949, a gain of 61 per cent. It soon exceeded the range's carrying capacity, browse lines appeared, winter starvation was common, and the range rapidly deteriorated.

Many state game departments advised legislators to reverse the trend by liberalizing hunting regulations. After much prodding from the professional game biologists herd reduction was implemented by opening and extending seasons, timing the season with the occurrence of tracking snow, legalizing the use of rifles, lifting the ban on does, establishing bow seasons, and removing bounties on predators. Access roads were built to facilitate hunter movement to back country.

As of 1975 the overpopulation problem is far from solved. Despite liberalized laws, hunters rarely harvest more than 10 per cent of the herds. One reason is the deer's secretive behavior; the animals rarely emerge from protective cover during daylight hours of the hunting season. Dasmann reports the inability of hunters to *see* a single deer in an area supporting a population density of 100 per square mile (15). A 10 per cent annual harvest is simply not enough to appreciably check herd increase. According to Taylor:

> annual removal of deer (by hunting, transfer, or otherwise) should be based on actual yearly increase in numbers as related to available deer foods. Usually at least one third of a fall population of deer can be taken, year after year, if both sexes are removed in equal numbers. Ordinarily, the game manager does not need to be concerned either with inbreeding or with an overwide buck-doe ratio (60).

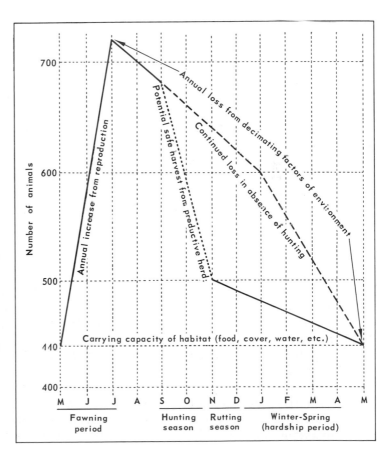

Figure 9-36. *Annual population fluctuation in a deer herd occupying a range with a carrying capacity of 440 head. Note that even during a closed season the various agents of ER (starvation, parasites, predation, disease, accidents, and so on) will reduce the herd to the carrying capacity of the range. It is apparent that a considerable surplus may be safely harvested by hunters. With or without an open season, the population of the herd by the end of the winter-spring hardship period will be virtually the same.* [After Raymond F. Dasmann, Environmental Conservation (*New York: John Wiley & Sons, Inc.,* 1968).]

Deer populations frequently vary from region to region within a single state, being high perhaps in semiwooded agricultural regions and low in climax forests and near urban centers. Therefore, a state may be divided into a number of zones, each with its own set of regulations. (One state has had sixty zones.) In zones where herds are at low levels, the season may be closed completely or may be open to bow hunters only. In overpopulated zones, the season may be opened on bucks, does, and even fawns. In some states game managers are not permitted to practice what they preach, because their technical knowledge in game management is far in advance of a receptive public or political climate. Too often the framers of our hunting laws yield to pressures exerted by hunters, misguided nature lovers, and resort owners, to whom the essence of game management is "more deer." Only when regulations are formulated in accordance with the advice of professionally staffed conservation departments will hunting regulations serve as an effective management tool.

Some Methods of Waterfowl Management

The various aspects of waterfowl management that shall be described include habitat development, banding studies, administrative use of the migratory flyways, population surveys, and the establishment of hunting regulations.

Habitat Development. Waterfowl habitat may be improved by retarding aquatic succession, creating openings in dense marsh vegetation, constructing artificial ponds, developing artificial nests and nest sites, and establishing waterfowl refuges.

RETARDING AQUATIC SUCCESSION. Ecological succession, which was described in an earlier chapter, may proceed in an aquatic as well as terrestrial habitat. Thus, the basin of a lake or pond, once providing excellent food, cover, and nest sites for waterfowl, may with the passage of time become filled with the bodies of decaying plants and animals, as well as with sediment washed in from surrounding hillsides. Eventually the aquatic community will be succeeded by a terrestrial community, which will proceed toward the climax typical of the region, whether it be coniferous forest, deciduous forest, or grassland.

It is apparent that were it allowed to proceed unchecked, ecological succession would slowly but surely impair and eventually completely destroy the carrying capacity of the site for waterfowl. This insidious trend of succession is retarded in many shallow ponds and potholes on the Great Plains by periodic droughts. In the more humid regions of the deciduous and coniferous forest biomes, drought may be "simulated" by draining the pond at regular intervals of about six years. When water milfoil (a rooted aquatic) begins to dominate the submergent vegetation at the Red Lake Wildlife Refuge in northern Minnesota, it serves as an indicator to the refuge manager that it is time to drain the pond. The exposed pond bottom is then broken up with a disc to eradicate any invading plants such as cattail, phragmites, or willow, which otherwise might secure a roothold. The pond is permitted to remain dry for one year. As a result of the increased aeration and the accelerated bacterial decomposition of organic materials that occurs at this time, a number of essential minerals such as calcium, magnesium, potassium, and nitrates are released in a form that can be absorbed and used by duck food plants. After one year in the

Figure 9-37.
Waterfowl habitat improvement. The area to the left of the fence was protected from grazing by cattle. Note that food and cover are abundant compared to the grazed area to right of the fence. [U.S. Fish and Wildlife Service]

bare bottom stage, the pond is reflooded; the mineralized nutrients dissolve to form high concentrations and greatly enhance the pond's nutritional value. Moreover, invading weeds such as golden dock and smartweed may become established on the exposed pond bottom, and when the pond is reflooded they may be available to hungry ducks.

CREATING OPENINGS. Although waterfowl require cover for protection from both weather and predators, they also require channels and openings through which they can paddle or waddle (between nest site and feeding area, between feeding and loafing area) or that may serve as areas where the birds may secure aquatic food supplies. Such essential openings may be established by the natural agencies of hurricane-and lightning-triggered fires or they may be developed by man-directed agencies such as controlled burning and the use of explosives.

Controlled Burning. Fire may be highly destructive to waterfowl habitat when it consumes a drought-parched marsh. However, when carefully controlled by trained personnel, it may serve as an important agent in habitat improvement. For example, in North Carolina at the Mattamuskeet National Wildlife Refuge, marshes are regularly burned each winter. Not only can openings be created in this way, but in a brief time over-wintering geese, hard-pressed for food, will move into the burn to feed on the green shoots that burgeon in the mineral-enriched earth. In Louisiana alone biologists burn nearly a million marsh acres yearly (66).

Use of Explosives. In marshland with a fairly high water table, explosives may be used to good advantage in blasting out potholes. This technique has been used successfully in recent years in South Dakota, Minnesota, Wisconsin, and Michigan. Although dynamite was originally employed, it proved to be rather expensive and has been widely replaced with ammonium nitrate (AN), which is soaked in fuel oil and then detonated with the aid of a dynamite primer. In Minnesota as of 1974, a pothole 35 feet long, 25 feet wide, and 7 feet deep could be blasted out of heavy clay soil at a cost of only $18 (6). Such dynamited potholes retain their usefulness as a waterfowl habitat for decades. In 1962 Strohmeyer evaluated potholes in northwestern Iowa that had been dynamited twenty-one to twenty-two years previously (57). Although on the average they retained only 29 per cent of their original depth, they were nevertheless effective in restricting the development of emergent vegetation. Moreover, waterfowl nests were situated near the potholes.

CONSTRUCTING ARTIFICIAL PONDS.   Where sloughs and potholes are scarce, waterfowl habitat can be created by the construction of artificial ponds. Between 1936 and 1962, the U.S. Department of Agriculture assisted Soil Conservation District farmers in building 2.2 million ponds; it is estimated that almost 3.5 million will have been completed by 1980. Roughly two thirds of these ponds will be usable by waterfowl, either as nesting, feeding, and loafing areas by resident birds or as rest areas where migrating waterfowl may touch down for a brief respite, before resuming their strenuous journeys. The farmer can increase the carrying capacity of his pond by erecting artificial nest boxes for mallards and wood ducks; by dumping piles of rocks or anchoring logs and bales of hay in the open water to serve as preening and sunning areas; by periodically draining the pond to promote the mineralization of organic matter and the release of nutrient elements, which can then be recycled into the waterfowl food chain; and by seeding the pond with

Figure 9-38.   *Taylor County, West Virginia. The waterfowl productivity of this farm pond could be increased by fencing portions of it from livestock, by providing anchored logs and gravel piles for sunning and preening sites, and by seeding the pond with choice food plants. [U.S. Department of Agriculture]*

choice duck food plants. With the extensive employment of such pond management procedures, the 3.5 million farm ponds of 1980 will provide at least partial use for an estimated 10 million birds (17).

DEVELOPING ARTIFICIAL NESTS AND NEST SITES.   Through eons of time and natural selection, each species of waterfowl has evolved its own unique instinct for nest site selection and nest construction. It would appear almost impertinent, therefore, for man to attempt to improve upon nature by constructing artificial nests and sites for waterfowl. However, game biologists have done precisely this—and with encouraging success. Moreover, not only do these man-made nests serve the reproductive function as well as natural nests, but they may be even more effective in minimizing the environmental resistance represented by mowing machines, predators, and nest site competitors.

Wood ducks have nested in tree cavities for millennia. Within the past two decades, however, it has been found that this species will readily accept a substitute in the form of a nest box constructed of roofing paper or wood. Two vexing problems, however, attend the use of such boxes. First, the eggs, nestlings, and incubating females are often destroyed by climbing predators. Thus, a seventeen-year study in Illinois of 820 wood duck nesting failures revealed that 51 per cent of the

Figure 9-39. *Natural nest site of the Canada goose. Note downy young emerging from egg.* [Wisconsin Natural Resources Department, Madison, Wis.]

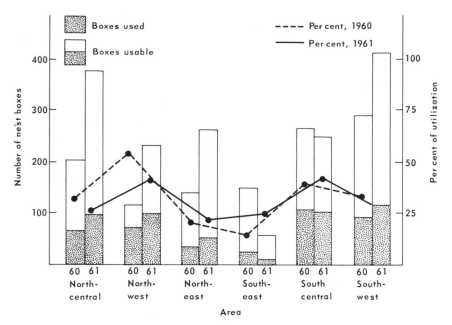

Figure 9-40. *Wood duck nest box utilization in Ohio, 1960 and 1961. The Ohio Department of Natural Resources erected nest boxes in an attempt to augment wood duck production. In 1960, 373 of 1,176 (31.7 per cent) were utilized, and 461 of 1,569 (29.4 per cent) were occupied in 1961. [Adapted from R. Kahler Martinson, "Wood Duck Nest Box Utilization, 1961," in Kenneth W. Laub (ed.),* Game Research in Ohio, Vol. 2 (August 1963).]

nests were destroyed by fox squirrels, 37 per cent by raccoons, 10 per cent by snakes, and 2 per cent by opossums (2). Such predation can be minimized by affixing a metal collar to the base of the next box to serve as a predator barrier. The second problem concerns nest box competition from the aggressive and ubiquitous starling. This has been resolved by the use of large entrance holes, the resultant increase of light within the box apparently serving as a deterrent to the starlings, which prefer relatively dark cavities (6).

At the Patuxent Research Center (Maryland), straw-filled wire baskets have proved particularly successful as nest sites for Canada geese. To reduce predation they are supported at least 1 foot above the water by stakes. At the Blackwater National Wildlife Refuge (Maryland), compound houses have been readily taken over by mallards. These houses have two side-by-side compartments within a single boxlike unit.

One of the most serious mortality factors for ground-nesting ducks in the southwestern Lake Erie region is the haymower, because mowing of the initial alfalfa crop here coincides with the duck nesting peak. Thus, only 3.3 per cent of 317 waterfowl nests in an alfalfa habitat in 1963 were successful in producing young, mowing machines being responsible for almost 75 per cent of the nest destruction. To offset such losses, biologists constructed a number of cylindrical, open-ended nesting units made of chicken wire and marsh grass. The program was initially set up in 1961; use by ducks gradually increased from 2 per cent (2 of 100) in 1962 to

25.9 per cent (28 of 108) by 1965, when 26 mallards, 1 black duck, and 1 wood duck raised clutches in the artificial nests. Nesting success in these artificial nests was remarkably high, for example, 71.6 per cent (9 of 11 nests) in 1963.

Establishing Waterfowl Refuges.   Our system of national refuges was launched in 1903 when Theodore Roosevelt established the Pelican Island refuge in Florida's Indian River to protect the rapidly depleting population of brown pelican. From this modest beginning the federal refuge system has grown to 304 refuges covering about 29 million acres. Of these, 229 (77.4 per cent) were primarily established to provide a suitable habitat for waterfowl, either for nesting purposes, as wintering grounds, or as stopover areas for migrants. In 1934 Congress passed the Migratory Bird Hunting Stamp Act, which authorized that funds for the acquisition, maintenance, and development of waterfowl refuges be derived from the sale of "duck stamps." These stamps must be purchased by each waterfowl gunner at the start of the hunting season. From 1937 to 1968 close to 90 million stamps were sold. Our national waterfowl refuges annually provide over 1.25 billion waterfowl-use days. (One waterfowl-use day is one day's use by one duck, coot, swan, or goose.) Our refuges produce over 500,000 ducklings each year. The Tule Lake (California) and Agassiz (Minnesota) refuges each produce 30,000 ducks yearly, and the Malheur (Oregon) refuge produces 40,000 annually (35). Huge concentrations of ducks and geese utilize some of the refuges during the fall migration. For example, in the Klamath Basin Refuge on the California-Oregon border, where considerable acreages of wheat and barley are grown exclusively as waterfowl food, a peak of 3.4 million ducks and geese were recorded in 1964. Similarly, during the fall of 1966, up to 147,000 Canada geese stopped over at the Horicon National Wildlife Refuge in southern Wisconsin—the greatest concentration of this species ever recorded in the United States (65).

Banding Studies.   Waterfowl may be captured for banding purposes by a variety of baited traps. Canada geese are effectively taken with nets that are shot over the baited birds with miniature cannons. (Fig. 9-42) During the late summer molting period, when ducks are temporarily flightless, thousands of adults and juveniles may be corralled in huge drives. Recently, tranquilizers have been employed. During the winter of 1965–1966, Crider et al. captured 573 Canada geese and five blue geese in Florida with the oral hypnotic alpha chloralose (12). At dosages of 0.25 gram per cup of bait mortality was only 2.6 per cent.

Scientific bird banding had its inception with the work of a Danish schoolmaster, Christian Mortensen, who marked storks, hawks, and starlings as well as waterfowl. The American Bird Banding Association, which was organized in 1909 in New York City, conducted pioneering banding studies in the United States (38). Since 1920, when bird banding became an official project of the old Biological Survey of the Department of Agriculture, over 11 million birds (of all species in addition to waterfowl) have been leg-banded with serially numbered metal bands. (On June 30, 1940, the Biological Survey was transferred to the Department of Interior and has been consolidated along with the old Bureau of Fisheries into the Fish and Wildlife Service.) Records of the species, age, sex, weight, date, and banding locality are filed in the Bird Banding Laboratory at the Patuxent Wildlife Research Center at Laurel, Maryland. About 7 million waterfowl had been banded by 1974. Each year, primarily in refuge areas, roughly 300,000 ducks, geese, and swans are banded. About

Figure 9-41. *Close-up of cannon showing firing mechanism on right and three ropes attached to a heavy metal piston, which, when fired, carries the net out over the waterfowl.* [*U.S. Fish and Wildlife Service*]

32,000 waterfowl bands are recovered annually. Although most recoveries are made by hunters, a considerable number are also recovered by biologists, bird watchers, and interested amateur naturalists who retrieve bands from birds killed by storms, pollution, predators, and disease.

Analysis of recovery data provides waterfowl biologists with information concerning growth rate, longevity, and hunting pressure, as well as the length, speed, and route of migration. From banding studies we know that some snow geese may travel 2,000 miles nonstop from James Bay, Canada, to the Texas coast in two days. Several years ago the Patuxent Wildlife Research Center received a letter from Rodolfo Marino, a pharmacist, who shot a blue-winged teal in a marsh 2 miles from his home in Peru. The serial number on the enclosed band revealed the bird had been banded only six months previously in Saskatchewan, fully 7,000 miles distant. Even more remarkable was the record of a pintail recovered in England only

Figure 9-42. *Waterfowl biologists removing Canada geese trapped under cannon net. Note corn used to bait the geese.* [*New York State Conservation Department, Photo by David G. Allen*]

eighteen days after being banded in Labrador. Another pintail, banded in northwestern California, was taken at Baykal Lake, Russia (67). Still another pintail banded in California turned up three months later in New Zealand after a transoceanic flight of over 2,000 miles.

From the practical standpoint of waterfowl management, however, the most significant information accruing from waterfowl banding studies is that most migratory waterfowl breeding in the northern states and Canada funnel into four rather well-defined flyways on their way to their southern breeding grounds. Known as the Atlantic, Mississippi, Central, and Pacific flyways, they have served as operational units in the formulation and administration of hunting laws by state and federal governments. It should be emphasized, however, that these flyways are not mutually exclusive. Thus, many mallards that nest in the prairie provinces of Canada begin their fall migration by moving southward along the central flyway into South

Figure 9-43. *Banding Canada goose at the Blackwater National Wildlife Refuge, Cambridge, Maryland. Note band dispenser. Cannon net is in background.* [Bureau of Sport Fisheries and Wildlife, U.S. Department of the Interior]

Dakota; eventually, however, they swerve southeastward, switching to the Mississippi flyway in Minnesota and continuing along the flyway to their wintering ground. Apparently, these birds do not consult the flyway maps. (Fig. 9-44)

Hunting Regulations and Population Fluctuations. North American waterfowl populations fluctuate from year to year, a population low being only 50 to 75 per cent that of a peak year (23). The waterfowl gunner too often expects a peak year every year, and if hunting falls short of his expectations he is apt to complain about how the state and federal waterfowl biologists have botched their management jobs.

As we have learned, the population of any game animal, including waterfowl, during a given year, is a result of the interaction of both positive and negative factors relating to reproduction, climate, food availability, competitors, parasites, disease organisms, nesting habitat, predation, and other phenomena. Now, if all these

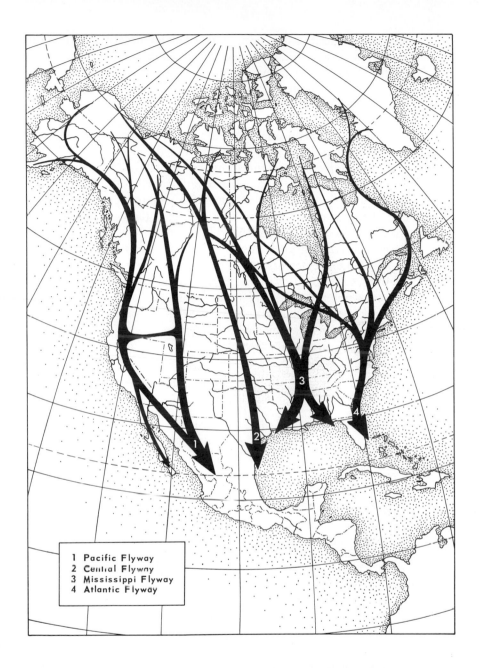

Figure 9-44. *Major waterfowl flyways. Recovery data on many thousands of waterfowl have revealed that four major flyways are followed during migration: (1) Pacific, (2) Central, (3) Mississippi, and (4) Atlantic. Note that flyways are not mutually exclusive. For example, ducks reared in Alberta and Saskatchewan might initially move down the Central Flyway and later switch over to the Pacific Flyway to complete their fall migration to wintering grounds in California or Mexico. Species like mallard, baldpate, and scaup might use all four flyways. [Adapted from Robert T. Orr,* Vertebrate Biology, *2nd ed. (Philadelphia: W. B. Saunders Company, 1961).]*

The legend in the figure reads:

1 Pacific Flyway
2 Central Flyway
3 Mississippi Flyway
4 Atlantic Flyway

factors, both positive (favoring survival) and negative (hampering or preventing survival) were constant, we would expect waterfowl populations to remain constant as well. However, the influences of these environmental factors are highly variable and the waterfowl harvest annually available to the hunter fluctuates accordingly.

Although hunting regulations such as closed seasons, length of season, and bag limits are adjusted according to shifting waterfowl population levels, hunting mortality represents only a small percentage of the total ER. Ludlow Griscom presents some interesting data (here slightly modified) in support of this thesis (23). Suppose, for example, that in the spring of 1975 the North American duck population numbered 125 million. Because each adult female can lay a clutch of ten to sixteen eggs, the biotic potential for 1975 would be 600 million to 1 billion young. However, because only about 125 million birds will again return to the breeding grounds in the spring of 1976, it is apparent that 475 to 875 million birds will have perished in the interim because of ER. Of this ER, the estimated 1975 hunting kill of an estimated 20 million birds represents only about *4 per cent* of the total annual mortality. This is not to say that hunting pressure regulation is not significant. It becomes extremely important, for example, when nesting success is poor (as from drought). The preceding data do illustrate, however, that despite the most intensive efforts of professional waterfowl biologists, waterfowl populations are bound to fluctuate. Consequently, the hunter should be prepared to accept the occasional low populations along with the occasional high.

Figure 9-45. *End of a good day's hunting.* [*Bureau of Sport Fisheries and Wildlife, U.S. Department of the Interior*]

BIBLIOGRAPHY

1. Adams, L. "An Analysis of a Population of Snowshoe Hares in Northwestern Montana," *Ecol. Mono.*, 29 (1959), 141–170.
2. Bellrose, F. C. "Housing for Wood Ducks," *Illinois Natural History Survey, Circular 45.* Urbana, Ill.: Illinois Natural History Survey, 1953.
3. ———. "Spent Shot and Lead Poisoning," *Waterfowl Tomorrow.* Washington, D.C.: U.S. Fish and Wildlife Service, 1964.
4. Bersing, Otis S. *A Century of Wisconsin Deer,* Madison, Wis.: Wisconsin Conservation Department, 1956.
5. Bourlière, François. *The Natural History of Mammals.* New York: Knopf, 1956.
6. Broley, Charles L. "Migration and Nesting of Florida Bald Eagles," *Wilson Bull.*, 59 (1947), 3–20.
7. Burger, George V., and Clark G. Webster. "Instant Nesting Habitat," *Waterfowl Tomorrow.* Washington, D.C.: U.S. Fish and Wildlife Service, 1964.
8. Burt, William Henry. *Mammals of the Great Lakes Region.* Ann Arbor: University of Michigan, 1957.
9. Burwell, Robert W., and Lawson G. Sugden. "Potholes—Going, Going . . . ," *Waterfowl Tomorrow.* Washington, D.C.: U.S. Fish and Wildlife Service, 1964.
10. Cahoon, W. G. "Commercial Carp Removal at Lake Mattamuskeet, North Carolina," *Jour. Wild. Mgt.*, 17 (1953), 312–317.
11. Chambers, R. E., and W. M. Sharpe. "Movement and Dispersal Within a Population of Ruffed Grouse," *Jour. Wild. Mgt.*, 22 (1958), 231–239.
12. Clarke, George L. *Elements of Ecology.* New York: Wiley, 1954.
13. Dahlberg, Burton L., and Ralph C. Guettinger. "The White-tailed Deer in Wisconsin," *Tech. Wild. Bull.*, No. 14. Madison, Wis.: Wisconsin Conservation Department, 1956.
14. Dale, F. M. "The Role of Calcium in Reproduction of the Ring-necked Pheasant," *Jour. Wild. Mgt.*, 19 (1955), 325–331.
15. Dasmann, Raymond F. *Wildlife Biology.* New York: Wiley, 1964.
16. Davis, David S., and Frank B. Golley. *Principles in Mammalogy.* New York: Reinhold, 1963.
17. Edminster, Frank C. "Farm Ponds and Waterfowl," *Waterfowl Tomorrow.* Washington, D.C.: U.S. Fish and Wildlife Service, 1964.
18. Ehrenfeld, David W. *Biological Conservation.* New York: Holt, 1970.
19. Ellis, James E., and John B. Lewis. "Mobility and Annual Range of Wild Turkeys in Missouri," *Jour. Wild. Mgt.*, 31 (1967), 568–581.
20. Elton, Charles, and M. Nicholson. "The Ten Year Cycle in the Numbers of the Lynx in Canada," *Jour. Anim. Ecol.*, 11 (1942), 215–244.
21. Ferguson, Robert B., and Joseph V. Basile. "Topping Stimulates Bitterbrush Twig Growth," *Jour. Wild. Mgt.*, 30 (1966), 839–841.
22. Green, R. C., and C. A. Evans. "Studies on a Population Cycle of Snowshoe Hares in the Lake Alexander Area," *Jour. Wild. Mgt.*, 4 (1940), 220–238, 267–278, 347–358.
23. Griscom, Ludlow. "Waterfowl," in Eugene Connett, ed., *Duckshooting Along the Atlantic Tidewater.* New York: Morrow, 1947.
24. Gustafson, A. F., C. H. Guise, W. J. Hamilton, Jr., and H. Ries. *Conservation in the United States.* Ithaca, N.Y.: Comstock, 1949
25. Hamilton, William J., Jr. *The Mammals of Eastern United States.* Ithaca, N.Y.: Comstock, 1943.
26. Hansen, William R. "Aggressive Behavior of Mule Deer Toward Bobcat," *Jour. of Mamm.*, 37 (1956), 458.

27. Hartung, Rolf. "Energy Metabolism in Oil-Covered Ducks," *Jour. Wild. Mgt.*, 31 (1967), 769–777.
28. Hawkins, R. E., D. C. Autry, and W. D. Klimstra. "Comparison of Methods Used to Recapture White-tailed Deer," *Jour. Wild. Mgt.*, 30 (1967), 460–464.
29. Jensen, Wayne I., and Cecil S. Williams. "Botulism and Fowl Cholera," *Waterfowl Tomorrow*. Washington, D.C.: U.S. Fish and Wildlife Service, 1966.
30. Johnson, Raymond E. "We Are Warned," in Alfred Stefferud, ed., *Birds in Our Lives*. Washington, D.C.: U.S. Fish and Wildlife Service, 1966.
31. Kabat, C., N. E. Collias, and Ralph C. Guettinger. "Some Winter Habits of White-tailed Deer and the Development of Census Methods in the Flag Yard of Northern Wisconsin," *Tech. Wild. Bull.*, No. 7. Madison, Wis.: Wisconsin Conservation Department.
32. Kalmbach, E. R., and M. G. Gunderson. "Western Duck Sickness: A Form of Botulism," *Tech. Bull.*, No. 411. Washington, D.C.: U.S. Department of Agriculture, 1934.
33. Kendeigh, S. Charles. *Animal Ecology*. Englewood Cliffs, N.J.: Prentice-Hall, 1961.
34. King, David G. "A Black Bear Kills a Fawn," *Can. Field Nat.*, 81, No. 2 (1967), 149–150.
35. Kolenosky, George B., and David H. Johnston. "Radio-Tracking Timber Wolves in Ontario," *Ecology and Behavior of the Wolf*. College Park, Md.: Animal Behavior Society, 1966.
36. Krefting, L. W., M. H. Stenlund, and R. K. Seemel. "Effect of Simulated and Natural Deer Browsing on Mountain Maple," *Jour. Wild. Mgt.*, 30 (1966), 481–488.
37. Lack, David. *The Natural Regulation of Animal Numbers*. New York: Oxford U.P., 1967.
38. Laskey, Amelia R. "A Study of Nesting Eastern Bluebirds," *Bird Banding*, 10 (1939), 23–32.
39. Lee, Forrest B., et al. "Waterfowl in Minnesota," *Tech. Bull.*, No. 7. St. Paul: Minnesota Department of Conservation, 1964.
40. Leopold, A. S., T. Riney, R. McCain, and L. Tevis, Jr. "The Jawbone Deer Herd," *Game Bull.*, No. 4, California Division of Fish and Game (1951), pp. 1–139.
41. Leopold, Aldo. *Game Management*. New York: Scribners, 1933.
42. Lincoln, Frederick C. "The Future of American Waterfowl," in Eugene Connett, ed., *Duckshooting Along the Atlantic Tidewater*. New York: Morrow, 1947.
43. McCallum, Gordon E. "Clean Water and Enough of It," *Waterfowl Tomorrow*. Washington, D.C.: U.S. Fish and Wildlife Service, 1964.
44. Milne, Lorus J., and Margery Milne. *The Balance of Nature*. New York: Knopf, 1961.
45. Moffit, J., and C. Cottam. "The Eel-Grass Blight and Its Effect on Brant," *U.S. Fish and Wildlife Service Leaflet*, 204 (1941), 1–26.
46. Moyle, John B., and Jerome H. Kuehn. "Carp, a Sometimes Villain," *Waterfowl Tomorrow*. Washington, D.C.: U.S. Fish and Wildlife Service, 1964.
47. Murie, Olaus J. *The Elk of North America*. Harrisburg, Pa.: Stackpole, 1951.
48. Nice, Margaret M. "The Role of Territory in Bird Life," *Amer. Mid. Natur.*, 26 (1941), 441–487.
49. Odum, Eugene P. *Fundamentals of Ecology*, 3rd ed. Philadelphia: Saunders, 1971.
50. Orr, Robert T. *Vertebrate Biology*. Philadelphia: Saunders, 1961.
51. Pitelka, F. A. "Population Studies of Lemmings and Lemming Predators in Northern Alaska," *15th Int. Cong. Zool.*, Sect. X, Paper 5 (1959).
52. Robinette, W. Leslie, J. S. Gashweiler, Dale A. Jones, and Harold S. Crane. "Fertility of Mule Deer in Utah," *Jour. Wild. Mgt.*, 19 (1955), 115–136.

53. Salyer, J. Clark, and Francis G. Gillett. "Federal Refuges," *Waterfowl Tomorrow*. Washington, D.C.: U.S. Fish and Wildlife Service, 1964.

54. Smith, Robert L. *Ecology and Field Biology*. New York: Harper, 1964.

55. Soil Conservation Service. "More Wildlife Through Soil and Water Conservation," *Bull.* No. 175. Washington, D.C.: U.S. Department of Agriculture, 1958.

56. Streseman, E., in W. Kuekenthal and T. Krumbach. *Handbuch der Zoologie*. Berlin and Leipzig: 1927–1934.

57. Strohmeyer, David L., and Leigh H. Frederickson. "An Evaluation of Dynamited Potholes in Northwest Iowa," *Jour. Wild. Mgt.*, 31 (1967), 525–532.

58. Studholme, Allan T., and Thomas Sterling. "Dredges and Ditches," *Waterfowl Tomorrow*. Washington, D.C.: U.S. Fish and Wildlife Service, 1964.

59. Taber, R. D., and Raymond F. Dasmann. "The Black-tailed Deer of the Chaparral," *Game Bull.* No. 8. Sacramento: California Department of Fish and Game, 1958.

60. Taylor, Walter P., ed. *The Deer of North America*. Harrisburg, Pa.: Stackpole, 1956.

61. Van Tyne, Josselyn, and Andrew J. Berger. *Fundamentals of Ornithology*. New York: Wiley, 1959.

62. Verme, Louis J. "Influence of Experimental Diets on White-tailed Deer Reproduction," *Trans. 32'nd North Amer. Wild. Nat. Res. Conf.* (1967), pp. 405–420.

63. Wagner, Richard H. *Environment and Man*. New York: Norton, 1971.

64. Welty, Joel Carl. *The Life of Birds*. Philadelphia: Saunders, 1962.

65. *Wisconsin State Journal* (April 22, 1969).

66. Yancey, Richard K. "Matches and Marshes," *Waterfowl Tomorrow*. Washington, D.C.: U.S. Fish and Wildlife Service, 1964.

67. Yocum, Charles F. "Pintail Banded in Northwestern California Taken at Baykal Lake, Russia (*Anas acuta*)," *Condor*, 69 (1967), 205–206.

10.

Freshwater Fisheries

In the fresh of the morning, when a hundred whitethroats had forgotten it would ever again be anything but sweet and cool, I climbed down the dewy bank and stepped into the Alder Fork. A trout was rising just upstream. I paid out some line—wishing it would always stay thus soft and dry —and, measuring the distance with a false cast or two, laid down a spent gnat exactly a foot above his last swirl. Forgotten now were the hot miles, the mosquitoes, the ignominious chub. He took it with one great gulp, and shortly I could hear him kicking in the bed of wet alder leaves at the bottom of the creel.

Aldo Leopold,
A Sand County Almanac,
New York, Oxford University Press, 1949.

In a typical year over 30 million anglers pit their luck and skill against the scaly denizens of our lakes, streams, farm ponds, mountain brooks, and impoundments.

Figure 10-1. *"Just fishin'." Copper Falls State Park, Wisconsin. [Wisconsin Natural Resources Department, Madison, Wis.]*

They spend over $3 billion, averaging about $100 per fisherman. Of this sum, 27 per cent is spent on bait and guides, 15 per cent on food and lodging, 14 per cent on transportation, 11 per cent on rods, reels, and other equipment, and 4.5 per cent on licenses and privilege fees. The average angler travels about 800 miles to and from his fishing haunts. Transportation media includes motor car, bus, train, airplane, helicopter, mule, and snowmobile. In aggregate, our nation's fishermen, whose numbers increased over 100 per cent from 1955 to 1975, travel about 25 billion passenger miles yearly.

The Lake Ecosystem

Fish occur in a great variety of freshwater habitats, from rushing mountain streams to sluggish rivers, from tiny farm ponds to large natural lakes. In order to develop an appreciation of the general features of aquatic habitat and to provide some background for our later discussions of fish conservation and management, we shall briefly describe the major features of a lake ecosystem. Ecologists usually recognize three major lake zones: the littoral, limnetic, and profundal.

Littoral Zone. The littoral zone may be defined as the "shallow, marginal region of a lake that is characterized by rooted vegetation." The rooted plants usually are arranged in a well-ordered sequence, from shore toward open water, as emergent, floating, and submergent. Representative emergent plants include cattail, bulrush, arrowhead, and sedge.

Characteristic floating plants include water lilies and duckweed. Among typical submergents are *Potamogeton, Chara Elodea,* and *Vallisneria.* Because sunlight penetrates to the lake bottom, this zone sustains a high level of photosynthetic activity. The swarming, floating micro-organisms known as *plankton* frequently impart a faint greenish-brown cast to the water. The term *plankton* means "the wanderers"; it is quite appropriate because these organisms are largely incapable of independent movements through the littoral zone and are passively transported by water currents and wave action. Plankton are divisible into plants (chiefly algae), known as *phytoplankton,* and animals (primarily crustaceans and protozoa), known as *zooplankton.* The littoral zone provides suitable food, cover, and/or breeding sites for an abundance and variety of aquatic life including both invertebrates (diving beetles, dragonflies, damsel flies, rotifers, protozoans, crayfish, mussels, snails) and vertebrates (pickerel, sunfish, yellow perch, frogs, salamanders, turtles, rails, grebes, ducks, herons, water shrews, muskrats). Per unit volume of water the littoral zone produces more biomass than either the limnetic or profundal zones. A small pond may consist entirely of littoral zone; however, a deep lake with an abruptly sloping basin may possess an extremely restricted littoral zone (36).

Limnetic Zone. The limnetic zone may be defined as the region of open water beyond the littoral down to the maximal depth of which there is sufficient sunlight for photosynthesis. This is the depth at which photosynthesis balances respiration—known as the *compensation depth.* The light intensity here is about 100 foot-candles, or 1 per cent of full sunlight. Although rooted plants are absent, this zone is frequently characterized by a great abundance of phytoplankton, dominated by filamentous algae and diatoms. In large lakes these phytoplankton may play a much more important role as producers than the more conspicuous rooted plants of the littoral zone. In spring, when nutrients and light are optimal, phytoplankton increase rapidly to form *blooms.* The limnetic zone derives its oxygen content from the photosynthetic activity of phytoplankton and from the atmosphere immediately over the lake surface. The atmospheric source of oxygen becomes significant primarily when there is some surface disturbance of water caused by wind action, a canoe paddle, or the propeller of a speedboat. Fish are the most characteristic vertebrates. Suspended among the phytoplankton are the zooplankton, primarily minute crustaceans (copepods) that form a trophic link between the phytoplankton food base and the higher aquatic animals (36).

Profundal Zone. The profundal zone embraces the area immediately beneath the limnetic zone. It extends downward to the lake bottom. Because of limited penetration of sunlight, green plant life is absent. In north temperate latitudes where winters are severe, this zone has the warmest water (4° C) in the lake in winter and the coldest water in summer. Large numbers of bacteria and fungi occur in the bottom ooze, sometimes up to 1 billion bacteria per gram. These bacteria are constantly bringing about decomposition of organic matter (plant debris, animal remains, and excreta) that accumulates on the bottom. Eventually these organic

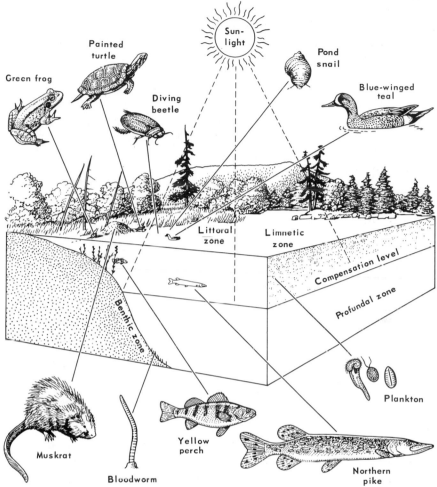

Figure 10-2. *Stereo view of a lake ecosystem in midsummer showing littoral, limnetic, and profundal zones. Observe rooted vegetation in the littoral. The level at which there is insufficient sunlight penetration to sustain photosynthesis is known as the compensation level.* [Adapted from Robert L. Smith, Ecology and Field Biology (New York: Harper & Row, Publishers, 1966). Used by permission of the publishers.]

sediments are mineralized and nitrogen and phosphorus is put back into circulation in the form of soluble salts. In winter, because of the reduced metabolism of aquatic life and the greater oxygen-dissolving capacity of colder water, oxygen ordinarily is not an important limiting factor for fish if the ice cover remains clear of snow. In midsummer, however, when the metabolic rates of aquatic organisms are high, the oxygen-dissolving capability of the warm water is relatively low, and the oxygen-demanding processes of bacterial decay are proceeding at high levels, oxygen depletion or *stagnation* of the profundal waters may result in extensive fish mortality, frequently involving desirable game species (36).

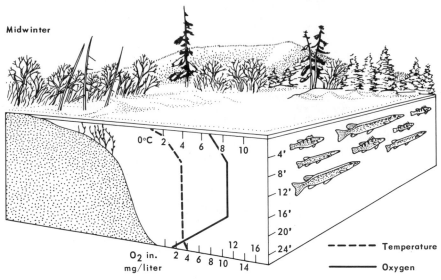

Figure 10-3. *Midwinter distribution of oxygen and temperature in a lake ecosystem. Note influence on fish distribution.* [*Adapted from Robert L. Smith, Ecology and Field Biology (New York: Harper & Row, Publishers, 1966). Used by permission of the publishers.*]

Thermal Stratification. In temperate latitudes lakes show marked seasonal temperature changes. In winter the coldest water forms ice at 0° C and floats at the surface. The water at increasing depth below the ice is progressively warmer and more dense. The heaviest water at the bottom of the lake has a winter temperature of 4° C. All winter the water remains relatively stable. In spring following the ice melt, the surface water gradually warms up to 4° C. At this point all the water is of uniform temperature and density. Hence the strong spring winds cause considerable stirring, which results in a complete mixing of water, dissolved oxygen, and nutrients from lake surface to lake bottom, a phenomenon known as the *spring overturn*. As spring progresses, however, the surface waters become warmer and lighter than the water at lower levels. As a result the lake becomes *thermally stratified*. The upper stratum, which usually has the highest oxygen concentration and is characterized by a temperature gradient of less than 1° C per meter of depth, is called the *epilimnion* ("upper lake"). The middle layer of the lake, typified by a temperature gradient of more than 1° C per meter, is known as the *thermocline*. The bottom layer of water, like the epilimnion, shows a temperature gradient of less than 1° C per meter and is known as the *hypolimnion* ("bottom lake"). Unless the lake is exceptionally clear so as to permit phytoplanktonic photosynthesis, the hypolimnion in late summer frequently becomes depleted of oxygen because of the *biological oxygen demand* (BOD) of bacterial decomposers, the reduced or nonexistent photosynthetic activity, and the minimal mixing with upper waters as a result of density differences (36).

In autumn the surface waters gradually cool, as a result of conduction, evaporation, and convection. Eventually a point is reached where the lake attains temperature uniformity from top to bottom. Because the water is now also of uniform

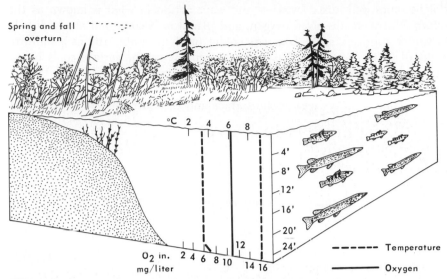

Figure 10-4. *Spring and fall overturn in a lake ecosystem. Note that uniformity of temperature and oxygen distribution is expressed in dispersal of fish through much of the lake from surface to bottom.* [Adapted from Robert L. Smith, Ecology and Field Biology (New York: Harper & Row, Publishers, 1966). Used by permission of the publishers.]

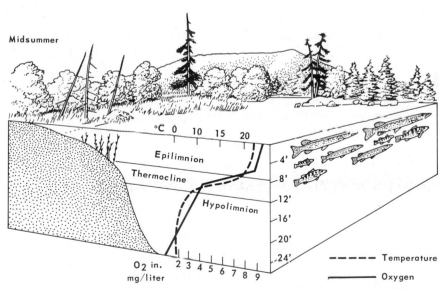

Figure 10-5. *Midsummer distribution of oxygen and temperature in a lake ecosystem. Note the stratification.* [Adapted from Robert L. Smith, Ecology and Field Biology (New York: Harper & Row, Publishers, 1966). Used by permission of the publishers.]

density, it becomes well mixed by wind and wave action in what is known as the *fall overturn*. Nutrients, dissolved oxygen, and plankton become uniformly distributed. As winter approaches, the lake gets colder until the water attains a uniform temperature of 4° C, at which it has maximal density. As the surface cools below 4° C it becomes lighter. Eventually the surface water may freeze at 0° C. During the winter season in icebound lakes there exists an inverted temperature stratification, with the coldest water (ice) at the surface and the warmest water (4° C) on the bottom (36).

The Stream Ecosystem

Although lakes and streams are both aquatic habitats, and, of course, have many characteristics in common, they are, nevertheless, quite distinctive in many aspects. Therefore, the problems facing the fisheries biologist in a lake may be quite different from those demanding his attention in a stream. Let us examine a few of the basic characteristics of a stream.[1]

Current. Water flow is the most important factor determining the kinds of organisms present. Current velocity is determined by stream gradient. Fish distribution is frequently correlated with gradient flow. For example, George Trautman, of Ohio State University, found that black bass were virtually absent from Ohio streams where the gradient is below 3 or above 25 feet per mile. On the other hand, the highest bass populations occurred in stream stretches where the gradient was from 7 to 20 feet per mile (31).

Land-Water Interchange. The amount of land-water interface is much greater in a stream than a lake per unit volume of water. Therefore, the stream is a rather "open" ecosystem in which materials are constantly being received from the terrestrial ecosystems that border it. For example, a stream receives a considerable portion of its basic energy supply from materials originating on land, such as leaves that fall into the water in autumn, or organic debris (stems, nuts, twigs, seeds, dead weeds, cow manure, and the bodies of insects, worms, and mice) that is washed into the stream during the spring run-off. In fact, many of the primary consumers living in a stream feed on such detritus (decomposing organic material) rather than on living green aquatic vegetation. This is not to say that a stream does not have its own distinctive population of producer plants. It does—in the form of fixed filamentous algae (*Cladophora*), specialized diatoms that form a "crust" on rocks and plants, and "water moss," which sometimes forms a bright green slipper covering to a stream bottom (to the distress of the wading trout and trout fisherman). However, the characteristic producer population of a stream can supply only a fraction of the energy required by the stream's animal population.

Oxygen. Streams are usually very well aerated. The reasons for this are multiple: flowing water, relative shallowness of the stream, and the large surface area exposed to the atmosphere. All things being equal, the waters of shallow, fast-moving streams

[1] Much of the material in this section was derived from *Fundamentals of Ecology*, by Eugene P. Odum, of the University of Georgia.

Figure 10-6. *A stream ecosystem. Note that the water is usually well aerated because of the large air-water interface per unit volume of water, and also because of the turbulence of the stream. Leaf fall from the overhanging branches provides an important source of organic material and energy. This stream has been improved for fish production by the establishment of three straight log dams. Water accumulates behind the logs and forms "cover" for game fish.* [*New York State Conservation Department, Photo by Nick Drahos*]

would have much higher oxygen levels than a deep, sluggish stream. The photosynthetic production of oxygen is not nearly as important as it is in a pond or lake. Because of the thorough mixing of stream water, the oxygen-starvation problems such as occur in the hypolimnion of deep lakes is less frequent, at least in unpolluted waters. However, stream fishes are very *sensitive* to even slight reductions of oxygen levels. Therefore, if a stream becomes polluted with oxygen-demanding organic material, such as human sewage, or the waste from slaughter houses, pulp mills, and canneries, the oxygen reduction that results may trigger a massive fish kill.

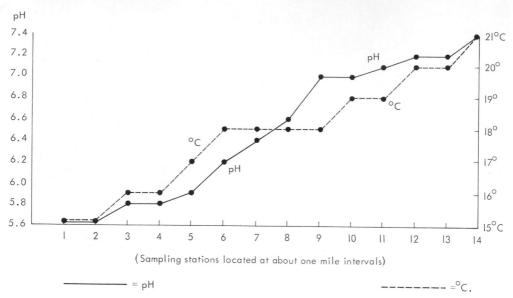

Figure 10-7. *Longitudinal differences in temperature and pH along a 14 mile stretch of Little Stony Creek, Virginia.* [*Data from G. W. Burton and E. P. Odum, "The Distribution of Stream Fish in the Vicinity of Mountain Lake, Virginia,"* Ecology, 26:182–193.]

Longitudinal Zonation. Odum describes the linear differentiation of the stream ecosystem as follows:

> In lakes and ponds the prominent zonation is *horizontal*, whereas in streams it is *longitudinal*. Thus, in lakes, successive zones from the middle to the shore represent, as it were, successively older geological stages in the lake-filling process. Likewise in streams we find increasingly older stages from source to mouth. Changes are more pronounced in the upper part of streams because the gradient, volume of flow and chemical composition change rapidly. The change in composition of communities is likely to be more pronounced in the first mile than in the last fifty (31).

Fish populations frequently reflect the changing physical (chemical, thermal, and so on) character of the stream. A study conducted by Burton and Odum of the fish distribution in Little Stony Creek near Mountain Lake, Virginia, revealed that a species distribution was correlated with changes in *p*H, water temperature, and velocity of the current. Thus, the colder (15° C), more acid (*p*H 5.6) upper stretches of the creek were populated only by brook trout. However, in the warmer (21° C), more alkaline (*p*H 7.4) lower stretches, the brook trout was missing, but seven other species were represented, including the rainbow trout, several species of minnows, and the common sucker (7).

Biotic Potential of Fish

As with most organisms, freshwater fish have an extremely high reproductive capacity. Thus Dreyer and Biel report an average of 6,357 eggs from Lake Superior ciscos (11). Thirteen thousand eggs were found in the ovaries of a brown bullhead only 1 foot long. Lake Michigan alewives produce 11,000 to 22,000 eggs per female.

The large-mouthed bass produces up to 7,000 eggs per pound of fish. Some bass nests in Michigan have had up to 4,000 fry per nest. A 10-pound female northern pike may deposit 100,000 eggs at spawning time. Up to 67,000 eggs have been found in one bluegill. A 35-pound female muskellunge may bear 225,000 eggs in her ovaries. Over 1.25 pounds of eggs were taken from a 12.50-pound Columbia River sturgeon. It is apparent that were it not for the negative effects of the ER, these species would soon choke river channels and lake basins with their aggregate biomass.

Environmental Resistance Encountered by Fish

Tagging studies have revealed that the environmental resistance operating on fish population is fully as impressive as their reproductive capacities, for roughly 70 per cent of a given fish population dies each year. Thus, theoretically, if a million young hatch, 300,000 will survive by the end of the first year, 90,000 by the end of the second, and only *six* by the end of the tenth. Some years ago an analysis was made in Minnesota of 15,000 perch caught in Ottertail Lake. Few were more than one year old. Age class analysis indicated that only 2.8 per cent survived to the second year, and only 1 per cent reached the age of four (12). A similar study on brook trout showed a survival of only 0.6 fish out of every 182,000 eggs laid at the end of five years.

Figure 10-8.   *Looking down on a male large-mouthed black bass guarding its nest.* [*Wisconsin Natural Resources Department, Madison, Wis.*]

Figure 10-9. *"A tight squeeze"—a symbol of the impact of technology on fish life. This 5½ inch brook trout was taken from the Au Sable River in Michigan. Note the metal ring from a beer can around the middle of the trout. The fish is permanently deformed. [Michigan Department of Natural Resources]*

Among the many types of ER encountered by fish, we shall briefly consider siltation, thermal pollution, industrial pollution, pesticidal pollution, oxygen depletion, rough fish, parasites, predators, and fishing pressure.

Siltation. Many tons of sediment may be discharged into lakes and streams by run-off waters as a result of abusive land practices, whether it be on a farm or at some urban construction site. If siltation continues unchecked for several decades, a shallow lake may gradually become filled with sediment and be converted into a marsh—a form of aquatic succession. Obviously, such a radical habitat conversion would eliminate all fish life. However, even from a short-term standpoint, siltation may adversely affect fish. Although fish may tolerate turbidities of up to 100,000 parts per million for brief periods, concentrations of 100–200 parts per million may be directly harmful under conditions of chronic exposure. Silt may clog up the gills of fish under extreme situations and cause death by asphyxiation, as has occurred in the Pecos River of New Mexico. Sand and gravel spawning beds may be detroyed. Fertilized eggs may be smothered with mud. A study of trout reproduction in Bluewater Creek, Montana, revealed that egg hatching rates were highest, up to 97 per cent, where sedimentation was minimal. The larvae of aquatic insects such as stoneflies and mayflies, which are favored fish foods, may be eradicated by a blanket of silt. Photosynthetic rates may be depressed by the reduced sunlight penetration resulting from water turbidity, causing diminished concentrations of dissolved oxygen. Here we see yet another example of how proper management of one resource (soil) indirectly enhances another (fish).

Thermal Pollution. Cold-water habitats that for many years had supported brook and rainbow trout have been desecrated by the removal of bordering thickets and overarching trees. Once such sunlight-intercepting vegetation has been removed,

Figure 10-10. *Dead fish in a bay across Arrowwood Lake, Arrowwood Refuge, Kensal, North Dakota.* [U.S. Fish and Wildlife Service]

Figure 10-11. *Fish kill caused by sediment. These fish were choked to death when sediment clogged their gills during a flooding of the Iowa River in New Mexico.* [U.S. Department of Agriculture]

average water temperatures increase and the trout, which generally cannot tolerate water temperatures above 70° F for any lengthy period, either succumb or emigrate. For most warm-weather species, temperatures of 93° F to 96° F are critical. Increased water temperatures make fish need *more* oxygen at the same time that the water's capacity to dissolve oxygen has been *reduced*. Such thermal pollution may result from *natural* causes. Thus excessive warming of the Anacostia River near Washington, D.C., in late summer has caused massive fish mortality. Modern steam-generating power plants are also important sources of heat pollution. They draw large volumes of water from rivers as coolant for their condensers. One Georgia plant utilizes over 400 million gallons *daily*. Later the warmed-up water is discharged back into the stream. Cold-water fish may incur severe mortality as a result. Moreover, heated water may destroy their phytoplankton and invertebrate foods. Spawning runs may be blocked by such temperature barriers. Warmed-up water may make fish more susceptible to the toxic effects of heavy metals such as copper and zinc. Heated water has certain redeeming influences, however. In the northern states it keeps streams ice-free; in the South it permits the threadfin shad, a valuable forage fish, to extend its winter range northward.

Oxygen-demanding Waste.   Pulp and paper mills, distilleries, vegetable canneries, breweries, creameries, and tanneries discharge considerable quantities of organic wastes into fish habitats. Massive fish kills have been triggered by the discharge of oxygen-demanding wastes from Wisconsin cheese factories. Domestic sewage is also a serious problem. Several years ago at Lake Tahoe, for example, sewage discharged into the lake after only minimal treatment resulted in such an increase in dissolved nutrient salts that phytoplankton blooms were triggered. As a consequence of the decomposition of this plant growth in late summer, game fish were adversely affected. In order to alleviate this problem a 6-million-gallon tertiary sewage disposal plant was constructed. The filtered effluents are piped over the mountains to provide irrigation water for nearby arid regions. Eutrophication has been checked, and scrappy trout are once again testing the angler.

Smith, Kramer, and MacLeod report significant mortality in fathead minnows at concentrations above 272 parts per million of ground wood and 738 parts per million of sulfite pulp; and walleye fingerlings succumb at concentrations of only 74 parts per million of both pollutants (35). Because these pollutants commonly occur in the effluent discharged by pulp mills, it is apparent walleye survival is in jeopardy adjacent to such plants.

Toxic Industrial Waste.   Some industrial chemicals may exert an indirect ER on fish populations by destroying preferred fish foods. Spawning beds may be defiled and fish reproduction curtailed. Other chemicals may affect fish more directly. For example, a large discharge of heavy metal salts may be immediately lethal. Crude oil derivatives and ammonium compounds may be absorbed by fish with disastrous results. Strong acids can kill fish by eroding their vital gill membranes. Heavy metal salts may stimulate excessive mucous secretions, which eventually interfere with gill function and cause suffocation. Other chemicals may serve as irritants to the skin, facilitating fatal invasion by bacteria and fungi.

Winter Kill Resulting from Oxygen Depletion.   During the long winter of the northern states lakes an icy barrier may effectively seal them off from their

Figure 10-12. *Trout kill. The death of these fish may have been caused by reduced oxygen levels resulting from the decomposition of large populations of algae. The nutrients responsible for the algae build-up probably had their source in septic tank discharge.* [*Soil Conservation Service, U.S. Department of Agriculture, Photo by E. W. Mustard*]

summer source of atmospheric oxygen by an icy barrier. However, as long as the ice remains clear of snow, sufficient sunlight may filter down through the ice to sustain photosynthesis. As a result, oxygen levels remain adequate. Snow, however, forms an opaque barrier that prevents sunlight penetration. The resultant cessation of photosynthesis and reduction in oxygen levels often result in heavy fish kills, especially if the lake is fertile and shallow. The decay of dead vegetation with its high BOD accentuates the problem. As winter progresses, oxygen levels may drop to 5 parts per million, at which point many of the more sensitive game species succumb; the more resistant rough fish, such as carp and bullheads, capitulate somewhat later when levels drop to about 2 to 3 parts per million. (Fig. 10-14.)

In a lake supporting a mixed population of game and rough fish, a *complete* winterkill is more desirable than a *partial* kill. A partial kill is selective, eliminating only the preferred game fish, and necessitates costly and time-consuming rough-fish removal operations (poisoning and seining) before game fish restocking can be initiated. On the other hand if all the fish die, fishery biologists can begin stocking immediately. In their excellent book *Northern Fishes*, Eddy and Surber describe a

Figure 10-13. *Massive winter kill of fish, Lake Odessa, Iowa. Snow cover reduced photosynthetic rates of aquatic vegetation and levels of dissolved oxygen dropped below the minimum required for survival.* [*Federal Water Quality Administration, U.S. Department of the Interior*]

classic example of winterkill in a shallow southern Minnesota lake that had a dense population of bullheads. Although the ice cover that formed in November ultimately became 20 inches thick, oxygen levels initially were adequate. However, during the second week of January, a storm covered the ice with a 6-inch layer of snow. Only two days later tests revealed that oxygen was severely depleted. After the spring ice melt thousands of dead bullheads littered the shore. Not one fish survived (12).

Summer Kill Resulting from Oxygen Depletion. Beasley reports that dense growth of *Microcystis,* a scum-forming algae, contributed to thermal stratification by heat absorption and promoted oxygen depletion at the lower levels of five experimental fertilized ponds in Alabama by blocking the incident sunlight. Oxygen depletion frequently may occur in the hypolimnion of thermally stratified lakes in late summer regardless of the development of such dense algal mats. A Kansas study showed that growth of channel catfish in 0.1 acre earthen ponds was retarded as a result of stress caused by critically low oxygen levels of less than 3 parts per million (34). However, when ponds were aerated, the affected fish resumed rapid

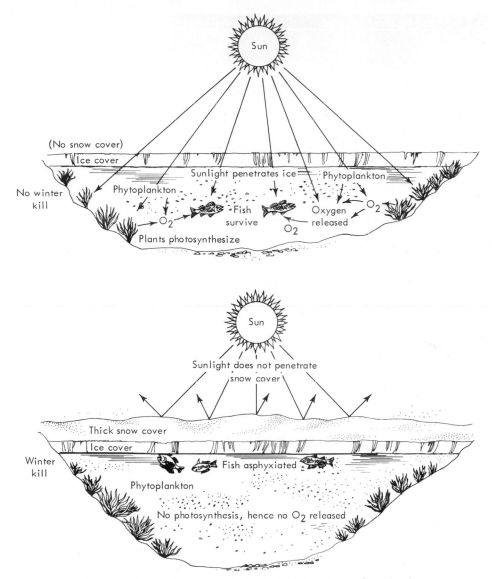

Figure 10-14. *Winter kill of fish. (See text for explanation.)*

growth. Fish mortality from oxygen depletion may be caused inadvertently by the use of formalin in the control of heavy plankton blooms. The sudden death and decay of the plants results in a sharply increased BOD and extensive fish kills. Oxygen depletion is usually less common in streams than in lakes and ponds because the rapid movement of the water promotes aeration. However, in a study of the effects of the spawning bed environment on the reproductive success of the pink salmon in three southeastern Alaska streams, McNeil recorded 60 to 90 per cent mortality associated with low dissolved oxygen levels in late summer during and after the spawning period.

Figure 10-15. *These white bass died from suffocation after algae clogged their gills. The dense algal population was caused by eutrophication. High Cliff State Park (Calumet County), Wisconsin.* [*Wisconsin Natural Resources Department, Madison, Wis.*]

Rough Fish. The most destructive of all *rough fish* (fish undesirable as game or food) is the carp. It was introduced to California from Germany in 1872, the Great Lakes in 1873, and Washington, D.C., in 1877. As has been the case with many introduced exotics, the carp population increased rapidly, following the characteristic sigmoid growth curve. Although they were not brought to Lake Erie until 1873, only twenty years later fishermen were able to remove 3.6 million pounds from that lake. Carp prefer sluggish waters rich in organic matter. Frequently this organic material is derived from sewage. In other cases it may have its origin in the biological growth stimulated by fertilizer-rich run-off from agricultural lands. Carp may uproot extensive quantities of vegetation during their foraging activities. King and Hunt report that carp consume the common aquatic plant *Chara* but merely uproot pondweeds (*Potamogeton*), most damage occurring in the growing season when the plants are young and delicate (19). Such activity may result in the destruction of game-fish spawning grounds, the eradication of fish foods, and the reduction of photosynthetic activity because of muddied waters.

The bowfin and long-nosed gar, which may attain weights of 10 and 50 pounds, respectively, are also extremely destructive. Both species are active carnivores, not only killing large quantities of game fish directly but also reducing forage populations on which game species such as black bass, walleyes, and northern pike depend for sustenance.

Parasites and Disease Organisms. Even if disease organisms and parasites do not cause mortality directly, they may depress growth rates and impair the reproductive function. Certain waters are rendered worthless to anglers as a result of parasitic infestations. Hatchery production may be severely limited by disease; production cost per fish may become excessive. The fisheries departments of several southeastern states are currently engaged in a cooperative research project, centered at Auburn University, Alabama, to develop control methods for warm-water fish diseases and parasites. The possibility of employing ultraviolet radiation in disinfecting hatchery water is being investigated by biologists in New Hampshire. New York state fisheries geneticists have conducted a fifteen-year selective breeding program to develop strains of brook and brown trout that are resistant to a serious bacterial disease known as *furunculosis.*

Fish are frequently plagued with intestinal tapeworms that slowly absorb partially digested food. Although tapeworms do not ordinarily kill their host, they may severely weaken fish, making them vulnerable to predation and disease organisms. Larval tapeworm infections studied by Becker and Brunson in Goodwin Lake, Washington, reached an epidemic stage when an average of 38 larvae were recorded per fish in spring-plant coho salmon, 78 per fish in spring-plant rainbows, and 140 per fish in fall-plant rainbows (1). The bass tapeworm that parasitizes black bass, rock bass, and sunfish may cause sterility by destroying ovaries. A recent survey conducted on 12 species of fish from Itasca State Park, Minnesota, showed that *every fish was parasitized!* Parasites included 31 species of trematodes, tapeworms, and roundworms; the most susceptible species were the yellow perch and the rock bass.

Predation. Fish are subjected to intense predatory pressure from members of all vertebrate classes, including other fish, amphibians, reptiles, birds, and mammals. Predation has the greatest impact when fish populations are high.

PREDATION BY FISH. Bluegill and large-mouthed bass show increased vulnerability to predation from the bowfin when starving, parasitized, diseased, or physiologically impaired as a result of stress from seining operations (17). A 6-inch muskellunge will consume 15 minnows daily. A walleye may consume up to 3,000 fish by the time it is three years old. When other food is scarce, many fish will resort to cannibalism. Smaller species may prey on the eggs of larger species that as adults regularly feed on the smaller forms. Thus one study revealed that the eggs of larger species occurred in the guts of 23 per cent of 146 herring examined from Lake Superior (11).

PREDATION BY REPTILES. An examination of the diet of thirty water snakes from Virginia showed that 60.9 per cent was composed of fish. Unusually low water levels may render fish expecially vulnerable to predation from osprey, terns, and mink. Brous reports garter snakes "devouring great numbers of smaller fish" stranded in shallow pools during a period of summer drought (4). Stomach analyses of 186 Michigan snapping turtles, according to Karl Lagler, revealed that game fishes made up one third of their food (20).

PREDATION BY BIRDS. Grebes, loons, and cormorants are superbly adapted for underwater fish pursuit. Kingfishers may pose serious problems at hatchery rearing ponds. Egrets, herons, and mergansers consume large numbers of fish. Kortwright has estimated that a single merganser may consume over 35,000 fish annually. The famous ornithologist John Audubon found over 9.5 pounds of fish in the stomach of one American merganser. New Brunswick salmon production increased 500 per cent when American mergansers and kingfishers were restricted to a population density of one per 50 acres of water or 15 miles of stream. Among mammals, the bear, otter, fisher, and mink have exerted considerable ER on fish populations, especially during periods of drought when unusually low water levels make the fish vulnerable. Of course, the most destructive of all fish predators is man himself.

Salmon Mortality During Migration. The salmon is an *anadromous* fish—one that spends most of its growing years in the ocean, and, after attaining sexual maturity, ascends freshwater streams in order to spawn. The chinook, or king, salmon is a handsome Pacific salmon that may attain a weight up to 100 pounds. On the breeding grounds the female excavates a shallow trough, the *redd*, in the sandy or gravelly bed of some swiftly flowing stream emptying into the Pacific Ocean, such as the Sacramento in California, the Fraser in British Columbia, or the Columbia River bordering Oregon and Washington. The female may deposit several thousand eggs in the redd. After the male has fertilized them they are covered with a protective layer of sand. Following a two-month incubation period the eggs hatch and the young gradually move downstream, eventually entering the open ocean. The average downstream travel rate for coho salmon in the Wallowa River, Oregon, is 48.1 miles per day for a distance of 433 miles (42). Only 10 per cent of the salmon fry ultimately reach the ocean. They incur heavy losses from predation. For example, it has been found that shortly after hatching, an estimated population of 30,000 sculpins in Big Kitoi Creek, Alaska, would, on the basis of stomach analyses, consume 135,000 (12 per cent) of the estimated 847,500 pink salmon fry in the creek (26). In some streams, such as the Columbia, many young salmon are killed by *nitrogen intoxication*, resulting from the high levels of nitrogen occurring in the turbulent waters below dams.

The salmon remain in the Pacific Ocean four to seven years, feeding ravenously on small fishes such as herring and anchovies, many moving hundreds of miles from the mouth of their native stream. Thus, adult salmon tagged off Baranof Island, Alaska, were recovered in the Columbia River of Washington. Upon attaining sexual maturity, the salmon ascend the mouths of their native streams, apparently recognizing them by their distinctive smell, and gradually make their way up to the shallow headwaters near the site of their hatching. This may be accomplished only after they have negotiated all sorts of obstacles, including rushing cataracts, a variety of predators (gulls, ospreys, bears), fishermen, pollution (silt, heated waters, radioactive materials, chemicals), the nets of research biologists, and big dams. Once arriving at the headwater, they immediately spawn and die, thus completing their life cycle.

In 1913, railroad builders inadvertently set off an avalanche of rock and rubble that clogged up the narrow channel of the Fraser River at Hell's Gate. As a result, the sockeye salmon run was hopelessly blocked, and countless thousands of fish, loaded with eggs and sperm, died below the rock slide, unable to press on to their spawning grounds.

Figure 10-16. *Salmon jumping Brooks Falls (Alaska) during migration to spawning grounds.* [Bureau of Commercial Fisheries, U.S. Department of the Interior]

The erection of dozens of power dams such as the 550-foot-tall Grand Coulee on the Columbia across the migration path of the Pacific salmon has effectively cut off considerable numbers from their spawning grounds. High water temperatures may be just as effective as a high dam. Thus, water temperatures of 70° F or above barred movement of sockeye salmon (*Oncorhynchus nerka*) from the Columbia River into the tributary Okanogan River (23). However, when temperatures drop below 70° F, the migration resumes. There has been a marked decline in the once-abundant Columbia River salmon harvest, the 1963 yield of 82,000 cases being only 13 per cent of the peak 629,000 case harvest back in 1883. Certainly such thermal and concrete barriers to migration have been important factors in this decline.

Fishing Pressure. Overfishing undoubtedly has been a major factor in the decline of many of our freshwater commercial and game fishes. The classic example of extreme fishing pressure is afforded by trout fishermen on the opening weekend of the trout season. During their enthusiastic quest for the king of American game fishes, they frequently become crowded shoulder to shoulder along stream margins. Fishing pressure is increasing. The number of licensed anglers has increased from 10 to 30 million within the last three decades. One of every eight Americans is a fisherman or fisherwoman. And with the nation's increasing population, the increase in leisure hours and mobility, and the desperate need for the release from urban pressures afforded by the wilderness, the pressure of the human predator on fish populations is bound to intensify.

Figure 10-17. *Spawning king salmon at the Nimbus hatchery on the American River near Sacramento, California.* [*California Department of Fish and Game*]

Fisheries Management

Fisheries management may be defined as "the manipulation of fish populations and their environment to increase sport and commercial fish harvests." In its broadest sense fisheries management embraces all the laws, policies, research, and techniques having as their ultimate objective all the enhanced value of the fisheries resource for the greatest number of people over the longest period of time. The sustained-yield concept is implicit in all sound fish management activities.

To manage a fish population effectively the fisheries biologist must understand the dynamics of the fish population. He must be able to predict the overall effect of a specific level of fishing pressure. He must be prepared to cope with the adverse environmental factors of disease, competition, parasites, pollution, drought, and oxygen depletion. Ordinarily the fisheries biologist draws on knowledge derived from life history studies of the species. From such studies data are secured on food habits, longevity, mortality factors, growth rates, sex and age ratios, breeding behavior, spawning habitat, and so on. We shall briefly discuss the following fish management procedures: restrictive laws, artificial propagation, introductions, habitat improvement, natural and artificial selection, and management of endangered species.

Restrictive Laws. As in the case of wild game, an early step taken in fisheries restoration was the establishment of protective laws. Closed seasons were established during the breeding period of a species. It was apparent that when a female bass or walleye was taken when swollen with eggs, the angler was removing much more than a single adult fish—he was also removing thousands of future young fish as well. Creel limits were imposed. Certain fishing techniques were outlawed, such as seining, poisoning, dynamiting, spearing, and using multiple-hook lines for taking game fish. It was felt that if the activities of the human predator were effectively controlled, fish populations inevitably would assume their original abundance.

In certain cases restrictive laws have been successful. A case in point is the sturgeon population of California's Sacramento River. In the late nineteenth century the sturgeon were heavily exploited, up to 5,000 being taken monthly in 1872. However, because the catch was reduced to virtually nothing by 1917, the sturgeon was placed on the protected list. The remnant population thereafter gradually increased to a level that was sufficient in 1954 to permit a limited game-fishing season (29).

In recent years fisheries biologists have been experimenting with more liberalized regulations on many species of warm-water fish. In many states size limits on pan-fish (sunfish, bluegills, rock bass, crappies) have been lifted, permitting fish of any size, from "runts" to "giants," to be taken! On the other hand, some predatory species, such as the black bass and northern pike, must attain a considerable length before they can be legally taken. The twin objectives of these regulations are to reduce overpopulation and stuntedness of the panfish and to provide more opportunity for anglers to land a "lunker" bass or pike. The effects of creel limits, varying fishing methods and gear, open and closed seasons, and winter fishing on fish populations are continuously being evaluated (6).

Figure 10-18. *Wisconsin angler poses with huge sturgeon which he has just speared through the ice.* [*Wisconsin Natural Resources Department, Madison, Wis.*]

Legislation in relation to fish management is discussed by Lagler in his excellent book *Freshwater Fishery Biology* (21). In his view there is a cause for both pessimism and optimism. The negative features of fisheries legislation include: (1) the multiplicity of restrictions, which make it difficult for even the well-informed angler to refrain from committing occasional violations; (2) the setting up of different regulations for two closely related species that are extremely difficult to distinguish in the field, such as the whitefish and cisco, the northern pike and grass pickerel, and the bluegill and green sunfish; (3) the establishment of different regulations for the two margins of the same river serving as a common boundary of two states, for example, the Mississippi River between Wisconsin and Minnesota.

According to Lagler, however, when properly conceived and administered, laws are effective management tools. Examples of legislation that has had a beneficial effect on our fisheries resources are the following:

1. In 1950 the Dingell-Johnson law was passed by Congress. It has raised money for federally approved fisheries research and habitat acquisition projects by placing an excise tax on fishing tackle. These funds are distributed to the states on the basis of fishing license sales and area.
2. Many states in recent years have learned that effective management of their common water resource demands an integrated effort. For example, in 1955 the Great Lakes Basin Compact was set up by the states bordering the Great Lakes, in which cooperation is pledged with regard to both fisheries research and use.
3. The United States has entered into agreements with Canada, which have established the Great Lakes Fishery Commission, to implement and coordinate sea lamprey control, and the International Pacific Salmon Commission, for the protection and restoration of salmon occurring in international waters (21).

Artificial Propagation. In the early history of fish management it seemed logical to biologists and anglers alike that if man could supplement natural reproduction of a given fish species by artificial methods, and introduce these artificially propagated fish into a given habitat, the fish population of that area would be augmented and the angling success of fishermen virtually assured. Since about 1935, however, on the basis of intensive studies of population dynamics, it has become apparent that this technique frequently results in dismal failure, especially if the objective is to increase the numbers of an already well-established species. Moreover, the cost of artificial propagation in terms of facilities, maintenance, staff, rearing, and eventual distribution of the young fish is almost prohibitive. For these reasons, artificial propagation is regarded critically by some fisheries biologists (except in the special cases described below). Fish stocking, other than introductions, may have various objectives: It may re-establish a fish population that had been destroyed by predators, drought, pollution, an epizootic disease, or some other environmental factor. A fisheries biologist may wish to stock a southern farm pond with *Tilapia* in order to get rid of excess aquatic vegetation. He may wish to stock a reservoir with a predatory species in order to reduce an overpopulation of stunted bluegill. Impoundments may be stocked with rainbow, brook, or brown trout if the water temperature does not exceed 65° F. Large-mouthed bass or spotted bass may be stocked in reservoirs and farm ponds where water gets too warm for trout. Frequently bass ponds are stocked with food fishes such as bluegills, crappies, rock bass, catfish, or even golden shiners and fathead minnows (21).

Stocking is mandatory if salmon and trout populations are to be maintained at

Figure 10-19. *U.S. Fish and Wildlife Service biologist delivers channel catfish to stock flood water retarding structure near Coolidge, Texas. [Soil Conservation Service, U.S. Department of Agriculture]*

reasonable high levels. The U.S. Fish and Wildlife Service maintains a number of salmon hatcheries along the Columbia and Sacramento rivers. Without the artificial propagation of trout, the thrill of snaring one of these scrappy fish would soon be nothing but a memory for most anglers, despite the most ingeniously tied fly and the most sophisticated arch of bamboo rod. Currently both federal and state fish hatcheries rear brook, brown, cutthroat, rainbow, and lake trout. In mountainous areas of Wyoming and Colorado trout fingerlings may be stocked by means of aerial drops (6). The official policy of the federal hatcheries is to propagate trout to fill the following needs: (1) To stock trout in suitable waters in which they do not occur. Such waters may be newly created reservoirs or may be waters from which competitive rough fish have been eradicated. (2) To stock trout in waters where conditions for growth are good, but where natural spawning sites are inadequate. Growth usually is rapid. Nevertheless, such streams must be restocked at intervals of one to three years. (3) To stock trout in waters where fishing pressure is too great to be sustained by natural reproduction. This is sometimes known as "put-and-take" stocking. The trout planted are of catchable size. Most of them are caught the same season they are planted. Several of our nation's sportsmen presidents, such as Dwight Eisenhower and Lyndon Johnson, have waxed eloquent about the fishing potential of a particular trout stream, on the basis of the "lunkers" they hooked only minutes after strategic stocking by publicity-sensitive conservation officials!

Figure 10-20. *Aerial view of Platte River (Michigan) Hatchery. Note the outdoor rearing ponds. [Michigan Department of Natural Resources]*

Figure 10-21. *Superintendent checks salmon eggs at the Platte River (Michigan) hatchery. Note the light-colored eggs in the egg tray in the foreground. The embryos in these eggs have died; these eggs will be removed from the tray to prevent contamination of the water supply.* [Michigan Department of Natural Resources]

Figure 10-22. *Fisheries biologists handling salmon at the Lake Oroville Fish Hatchery, California.* [California Department of Water Resources]

Figure 10-23. *Fingerling rainbow trout are planted by air in Lake Powell behind Glen Canyon Dam on the Colorado River.* [*Bureau of Sport Fisheries and Wildlife, U.S. Department of the Interior*]

Figure 10-24. *Stocking young trout in a Wisconsin lake.* [*Wisconsin Natural Resources Department, Madison, Wis.*]

According to a recent annual report of the Fish and Wildlife Service, our federal hatcheries distributed 227.5 million (eggs, fry, and fingerlings, and fish 6 inches or longer) individuals with an aggregate biomass of 4 million pounds. The most abundantly propagated species were the chinook, or king, salmon (69.4 million individuals), the bluegill (32.6 million), the rainbow trout (28.2 million), the large-mouthed bass (21.5 million), and the northern pike (13.7 million).

Introductions.   An *introduction* may be defined as "the stocking of an animal in a new geographical region." The introduced species may be native to the United States, or it may be an exotic.

NATIVE INTRODUCTIONS.   In 1966 the Conservation Department of Michigan introduced about 800,000 coho salmon from the Pacific coast into streams tributary to Lake Michigan and Lake Superior. It is hoped that these salmon will not only provide excellent sport and commercial fishing, but also serve as an effective agent of biological control in curbing the exploding populations of the alewife, a weed species whose activities severely compete with more desirable Great Lakes fishes. Because the coho has a short life span, an abundant food supply is essential for

Figure 10-25. *Opening day of the New Jersey trout season on the Musconetcong River near Hackettstown. These anglers hope to catch trout stocked on a "put-and-take" basis.* [*Soil Conservation Service, U.S. Department of Agriculture*]

Figure 10-26.
Wisconsin angler with good-sized coho salmon recently stocked in Lake Michigan. The coho grow rapidly because of the super-abundance of alewives on which they feed. [*Wisconsin Natural Resources Department, Madison, Wis.*]

appreciable growth. The Michigan conservation department has also successfully introduced the chinook salmon into Lake Michigan.

The Minnesota Conservation Department has enjoyed a great deal of success with walleye introductions. For example, only three years after walleye fry were introduced to 4,000-acre Brule Lake (Cook County, Minnesota), it was possible to catch legal limits of walleyes in any part of the lake. Hawaiian fishermen are catching 40-pound channel catfish that were introduced from the contiguous states. American smelt were successfully introduced to the Great Lakes region from the Atlantic and Pacific coasts. During the spawning run of the smelt in early April, fishermen come from all over Michigan and Minnesota to net or sein the silvery little fish as they ascend tributary streams. During a good run it is not uncommon for smelt fishermen to catch a tubful of fish in half an hour. During 1957–1962, smelt were introduced into six new environments in Maine. A notable fish introduction that met with failure or at least extremely limited success was that of the American eel to Michigan from the Atlantic coast. The ranges of many native minnows have been accidentally extended by fishermen who dump their surplus bait at the end of a day's fishing.

EXOTIC INTRODUCTIONS. The introduction of the European brown trout to the United States has been eminently successful. It has been able to establish itself

Figure 10-27.
Fisherman nets haul of smelt in river north of Algoma, Wisconsin. The smelt, which were introduced to the Great Lakes from the Atlantic coast, ascend streams to spawn and are netted in great numbers. [*Wisconsin Natural Resources Department, Madison, Wis.*]

in waters too warm or too badly polluted for survival of native brook trout. The infamous European carp is a celebrated example of an introduction that has been embarrassingly successful. Although this highly adaptable fish has delighted many a modern Tom Sawyer with canepole and worms, it has been the bane of the sophisticated adult fisherman, as well as most fisheries biologists. Recently the federal Fish Farming Experimental Station at Stuttgart, Arkansas, imported a number of Israeli carp for experimental purposes and found them effective control agents of undesirable pond weeds. At this same station, remarkable growth rates were observed in the grass carp (a species brought over from Malaysia); during their first year, 3-inch fish weighing 4 grams attained a length of 20 inches and a weight of 1,816 grams—a 454-fold increase in biomass.

Habitat Improvement. In recent years many fisheries biologists have come to the conclusion that the most effective long-range measure for improving sport and commercial fishing is *improving the carrying capacity of fish habitat*. Students of fish management have seen fishing in a particular lake and stream deteriorate despite the most stringently enforced restrictive laws (closed seasons, creel limits, and so on) and despite the most intensive and carefully supervised programs of propagation and stocking. A feeling persists in many professional circles that if the carrying capacity of the lake or stream is good (in terms of food supply, cover,

Figure 10-28. *Although considered a rough fish, the European carp, which was introduced, has some redeeming qualities. Here it provides sport for Wisconsin spear fishermen. [Wisconsin Natural Resources Department, Madison, Wis.]*

Figure 10-29. *Improving fish habitat. Personnel for the New York State Conservation Department are constructing a dam across a trout stream. Fish will use the deep water behind the dam as a refuge from predators or as a relatively cool loafing site. [New York State Conservation Department, Photo by Nick Drahos]*

unpolluted water, abundance of breeding sites, proper oxygen levels, suitable water temperatures, and so on), some of the other fish management measures may be de-emphasized or, in some situations, abandoned completely.

SHELTER AND COVER. Artificial shelters enhance fish survival in a number of ways. They provide cover enabling a forage fish to escape predators. They increase the substratum on which the green plant food base of many fish food chains can become established. They provide shaded areas where fish may retreat during the heat of midday.

A series of brush shelters may be anchored along the inner margin of a lake's littoral zone with great effectiveness. In the winter season brushpiles can be set up on the ice cover in strategic areas and weighted with bags of stones; they will gradually sink to their proper place on the lake bottom as soon as the ice melts in spring (21).

WEED CONTROL. A certain amount of aquatic vegetation is useful to fish populations as cover, refuge sites, spawning sites, food, and as a source of the oxygen released during photosynthesis. Nevertheless, when vegetation becomes too profuse, it may be more destructive than beneficial, by competing for nutrients with phytoplankton, by utilizing too much water space, and by permitting escape from predators to such an extent that overpopulation and stunting results. Moreover, in late summer the decomposition of the accumulated vegetation on the lake bottom exerts a high BOD, which may result in serious oxygen depletion. Under such conditions the weeds must be removed, either by weed-cutting machines, by biological methods, or by species-specific herbicides.

Among the more serious water-weed pests in the United States are the lotus (Texas, Tennessee), water chestnut (New York), and water hyacinth (Texas, Florida, Louisiana). At least twenty-seven major weed control programs have been conducted in fifteen states and Puerto Rico, with the aid of $400,000 in federal funds. The experimental control of algae and submerged plants has been achieved with copper sulfate. However, great caution must be exercised in the selection of such chemicals, for they may affect both fish food organisms and fish adversely. Considerable research is currently being conducted to determine the total impact of herbicides on the entire aquatic ecosystem, whether stream, lake, or reservoir.

Much interest has been generated in recent years in the possibility of controlling weeds with the fish *Tilapia mossambica*, introduced from abroad. In an experimental study it was found that a population density of 1,000 tilapias per acre will eliminate rooted submergent vegetation and algae (9). *Tilapia* might be useful as a weed control agent in artificial lakes and ponds and where aesthetic values are of consideration. Its use would be restricted to southern lakes, because the subtropical tilapias cannot tolerate water temperatures below 55° F for extended periods.

ARTIFICIAL SPAWNING SITES. The fish production of a body of water may be increased by providing artificial spawning substrates where suitable natural ones are lacking. Thus, sand or gravel might be introduced on the otherwise muddy bottom of a lake or stream to enhance bass or trout production. The use of commercially available nylon was tested by Chastain et al. as an artificial spawning substratum for large-mouthed bass in five ponds. Spawns were observed on 68 of 90 (75.5 per cent) mats over a 2-year period. Of 80 spawns observed in 1965, 71 per

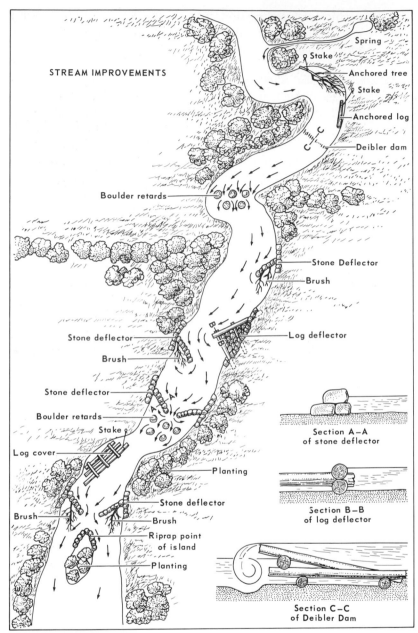

Figure 10-30. *Methods of improving stream habitat for fish. On hard
bottom streams spawning and refuge pools may be established by erecting
low dams constructed of either logs or boulders. In sand-bottom streams
use of properly situated deflectors will result in the build-up of a silt bank
and weed bed (essential substrates for many fish food organisms) on the
downstream side. In shallow streams the shelter area can be enlarged by
the introduction of streamside shrubs and trees. Note riprap at point of
island to prevent erosion. Shrubs may be planted to intercept sunlight and
prevent critical warming of water during midsummer. Note plunge basin
and shelter formed by Diebler dam. [Adapted from Karl F. Lagler,
Freshwater Fishery Biology (Dubuque, Iowa: William C. Brown Company,
Publishers, 1956).]*

Figure 10-31. *Stream improvement on the Plover River in Wisconsin. The deflector will provide a deep pool where game fish can find cover.* [*Wisconsin Natural Resources Department, Madison, Wis.*]

cent were located on nylon mats. Transfer of these spawn-laden mats to rearing ponds for incubation and growth was moderately successful, one trial resulting in a per-acre production of 54.3 pounds of biomass made up of 37,600 2-inch fingerlings.

Spawning habitat may be increased or decreased by manipulating water levels of reservoirs. Intensive study of the breeding behavior of the northern pike has revealed that shallow marshy fringes of the littoral zone are the preferred spawning habitat. Flooding of marshes with the aid of low dikes may enhance spawning conditions for this species (21). In recent years suitable spawning sites for the northern pike have been greatly reduced as a result of real estate developments, marina construction, and industrial expansion. State fish and game departments are attempting to rectify the situation. With the aid of $250,000 in federal funds (derived from a tax on tackle), Wisconsin, Iowa, and Minnesota recently acquired an aggregate 3,927 acres of marshes for the development of northern pike breeding and spawning habitat (6).

When overpopulation problems result in stunted fish, the situation may be rectified by destroying nests and spawning grounds, either by water manipulation at impoundments or by depositing unsuitable materials on the substratum.

FERTILIZATION. Just as the abundance of a farmer's corn crop depends largely on the fertility of his soil, so the black bass or pike crop of a lake or stream depends on the fertility of the water. Water fertility (that is, the concentration of dissolved salts such as carbonates, nitrates, sulfates, and phosphates) in turn ultimately depends on the soil fertility of the watershed. Water fertility determines the abundance of phytoplankton, which in turn forms the base of fish food chains.

Many lakes in central Minnesota, occupying a region of fertile soil, produce up to 80 pounds of animal food (dry weight) per acre; this is 400 times the 0.2 pound of animal food (dry weight) produced per acre by rockbound lakes in the infertile watersheds of northeastern Minnesota. It is apparent, therefore, that the use of artificial fertilizers can increase fish production in a lake or farm pond just as it can on a farmer's fields. It would, of course, be prohibitively expensive in a lake of any considerable area. Moreover, most lakes and streams in the United States are already *too rich* in nutrients (eutrophied), as was discussed earlier. Russian researchers have found that pond fertilization with superphosphate, ammonium nitrate, and manure increased production of both phytoplankton and zooplankton, and natural production of fish was increased two to three times (29).

Wild birds, of course, may assist man in fertilizing lakes. Immense quantities of droppings are voided by birds in the vicinity of their nesting areas. Some of this nitrate- and phosphate-rich material falls into the water, heightening its fertility. This may result in increased phytoplankton production, which, in turn, permits higher densities of the small aquatic invertebrates utilized as food by fish. Recently, fish and duck farms have been established in Russia, in which the ducks not only increase fish productivity by fertilizing the water but serve to control excessive aquatic weeds as well (29).

PREDATOR CONTROL. Just as many deer hunters feel that any deer-eating wolf should be shot on sight, so the angler becomes equally incensed over the depredations of fish-eating herons, egrets, mergansers, pelicans, grebes, loons, eagles, ospreys, kingfishers, mink, otter, and bear. It is true that egrets, kingfishers and herons may occasionally become destructive at hatchery holding ponds. However, most fish-eaters may be performing a beneficial population-control function that may minimize stuntedness caused by food shortages, as well as reduce the occurrence of epizootic diseases. The absence of this predatory pressure might leave more fish for the angler, but many would be so small as to be hardly worth catching. In any case, when food analysis studies are made, the accusations of sportsmen frequently appear unfounded. Thus a study of digestive tracts and scat contents of otters from Wisconsin, Michigan, and Minnesota revealed that although fish were indeed the otter's main prey, game fish were seldom taken.

SEA LAMPREY AND ITS CONTROL. Although most predators and parasites do not affect the fish population appreciably, on occasion a specific predator may cause a drastic population reduction. A classic example is the havoc wrought in the Great Lakes by the sea lamprey on the lake trout population. The lamprey is a primitive jawless vertebrate with a slender eellike body. The muscular suctorial funnel around its circular mouth enables it to attach tenaciously to its prey. Its pistonlike tongue, which is armed with numerous horny, rasping teeth, is moved back and forth through the lake trout's tissues, tearing both flesh and blood vessels and opening up profusely bleeding wounds. After gorging itself on a blood and body-fluid meal, the predator may drop off its host and permit it to swim weakly away. However, if the trout does not eventually die from the direct predatory attack, it may succumb secondarily to bacterial and fungal parasites that can freely invade the body through

Figure 10-32. *An adult lamprey tenaciously attached to a boulder by means of its suctorial funnel. The eye and seven openings to the gill pouches are clearly visible. [Courtesy of Carolina Biological Supply Company]*

the open wound. Even when a lake trout survives, the ugly scar left on its body would scarcely be admired by the grocery-buying housewife.

Originally, the lamprey was exclusively an anadromous fish, spending its adult life in marine habitats but ascending freshwater streams to spawn. Today, the lampreys along our Atlantic coast retain this anadromous behavior. However, the Great Lakes lampreys spend their entire life cycle in fresh water. The fasting adults migrate up tributary streams to mate, spawn, and die. The adults usually build a shallow nest on a gravel or sand bottom into which eggs are deposited. (A 15 inch female may produce 60,000 eggs.) The larval lampreys, known as *ammocetes*, hatch from the eggs and drift downstream until they come to a muddy substratum. They then burrow tail first into the mud, allowing only their heads to remain exposed to the swiftly moving current. Larvae employ a ciliary feeding method, sweeping minute insects, crustaceans, worms, and algae into their digestive tract. After several years, they acquire the suctorial funnel and rasping tongue of the adult, emerge from their burrows, swim into the open waters of the lake, and assume the predatory behavior of their parents.

The lamprey originally occurred in the shallow waters off the Atlantic seaboard from Florida to Labrador, in the waters of the St. Lawrence River, and also in Lake Ontario at the eastern end of the Great Lakes chain. For many centuries, the westward extension of the lamprey's range into Lake Erie was blocked by Niagara Falls. However, in 1833 man unwittingly provided an invasion pathway by constructing

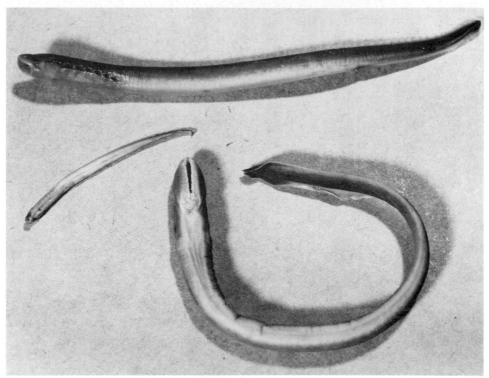

Figure 10-33. *Stages in the development of the sea lamprey. (Center) About one year old and still nonparasitic. Early eyeless state, about 2 inches long. (Upper) Three-year-old larva, still nonparasitic. About 4½ inches long. (Lower) Recently transformed larva almost ready to assume parasitic life. Ventral view showing untransformed mouthparts.* [U.S. Fish and Wildlife Service]

the Welland Canal to benefit commercial shipping. The spread of the lamprey through Lake Erie was relatively slow. (It was not taken in the Detroit River until the 1930's, possibly because of a lack of suitable spawning streams.) However, once it invaded Lake Huron it spread rapidly through the remainder of the Great Lakes chain and by the 1950's it had reached western Lake Superior. Its predatory activity soon threatened the multimillion dollar Great Lakes trout fishing industry with total collapse. The total annual catch declined from 10 million pounds in 1940 to one-third million pounds in 1961, *a 97 per cent reduction in twenty-one years.* Idle nets rotted along the waterfront. Veteran fishermen, too old to acquire new skills, went on relief. Many of the younger men emigrated to Minneapolis, Milwaukee, Chicago, and Detroit to seek employment.

Confronted with this economic and biological dilemma, research teams of the Lakes States fisheries departments and the U.S. Fish and Wildlife Service collaborated in an intensive effort to eradicate the predator. Various stratagems were employed. Adults were netted, seined, and taken in "electric fences" as they attempted to ascend their spawning streams. These methods, however, met with only partial success. From 1951 to 1959 over 6,000 chemicals were tested by biochemists to determine their suitability as agents of lamprey control. Finally, a selective poison (3,4,6-trichloro-2-nitrophenol) was developed, known by its trademark *Dowlap*. A concentration of 12 parts per million destroyed all lamprey larvae within 16 hours. A 24-hour exposure of 36 parts per million had no adverse effect on trout, sunfish, and rock bass. Moreover, it is harmless to fish food organisms such as creek chubs and aquatic insect larvae (28).

As a result of the encouraging findings, the Great Lakes Fishery Commission employed Dowlap and related nitrophenols on all lamprey-spawning streams tributary to the Great Lakes. By 1962 the lamprey had been reduced to 20 per cent of its peak numbers. In 1960 almost a million lake trout were stocked in Lake Superior; later stockings were made in Lake Huron and Lake Michigan. The combination of restocking and the continued chemical treatment of lamprey-spawning streams may restore the lake trout fishery (28).

ROUGH FISH REMOVAL. Because of their destructiveness to game fish, rough fish such as carp, bowfins, and gar are frequently the focus of intensive eradication projects. Even gizzard shad and panfish, ordinarily valuable as forage for game fish, may require control if they become abundant. However, eradication of any of these species from a given body of water would be enormously difficult to accomplish. Various control methods under study currently are chemicals, seining, commercial fishing, manipulation of water levels, and fish-spawning control. Carp, for example, probably could not be completely eliminated unless dynamite or a chemical were employed. The gizzard shad, a forage fish that has become excessive in certain

Figure 10-34. *Chemical being sprayed on lake surface in order to control rough (trash) fish populations. [New York State Conservation Department, Photo by Chuck McNulty]*

Texas reservoirs, can be eliminated by the precise application of selective chemicals released from low-flying helicopters (6). Rotenone, derived from the roots of an Asiatic legume, will kill fish at a concentration of only 1 part per million within minutes at water temperatures of 70° F. Unfortunately, both dynamiting and massive poisoning with rotenone would be unselective, resulting in the indiscriminate death of many species. Before state or federal biologists may employ a specific chemical, it must first be registered with the U.S. Department of Agriculture and approved not only by state health and pollution agencies, but also by the Federal Committee on Pest Control (6).

A recently developed toxicant, *antimycin*, was found to kill carp more readily than it does most other fish and does not appear deleterious to invertebrates. In 1972–1973 the Wisconsin Department of Natural Resources made extensive use of antimycin in an attempt to drastically reduce the carp population in the Rock River drainage system of southeastern Wisconsin. The project triggered a storm of controversy. Opponents of the program believed that irreparable damage would be inflicted on the ecosystem and that certain rare species of fish might be eliminated along with the carp. Moreover, if some fishermen came along some time later and dumped their surplus carp bait minnows into a stream that had just been "de-carped," with the aid of its tremendous reproductive capacities carp would soon be just as numerous as before the eradication project was launched. According to the opponents of the project, more acceptable methods would be to keep the carp population down to reasonable levels either by trapping them on their spawning grounds or by periodic seining. Thousands of pounds of carp have been removed

Figure 10-35. *Fisheries biologists removing many pounds of carp from New York lake by seining. The fish may be sold as food for eastern markets or may be converted into fertilizer.* [*New York State Conservation Department*]

from certain shallow lakes in southern Minnesota and Wisconsin in a single day by using these methods.

CONTROL OF OXYGEN DEPLETION IN WINTER. There are various methods of alleviating winterkill of fish from oxygen depletion. If the lake is small, the opaque snow blanket may be removed with snowplows to permit sunlight to penetrate to the aquatic vegetation. Parts of the frozen lake may be blasted with dynamite to expose surface waters to atmospheric oxygen. Oxygen may be introduced through ice borings by means of motorized aerators, a technique that has proven effective in Lake Upsilon, North Dakota. However, such an operation would require several dozen aerators and would be prohibitively expensive except on a small lake or under special situations where the improved fishing justified the investment. Finally, because winter depletion of oxygen is aggravated by the aerobic decomposition of aquatic vegetation on the lake bottom, removal of excess weedy growth in the littoral zone before the freeze-up might lessen the winterkill. It is apparent that lake fertilization to increase fish productivity can be self-defeating if the ensuing explosive growth of aquatic plants accentuates the oxygen depletion problem the following winter.

CONTROL OF OXYGEN DEPLETION IN SUMMER. As previously mentioned, mid-summer oxygen depletion frequently occurs in the hypolimnion of thermally stratified lakes. Water mixing and hence circulation of dissolved oxygen may be promoted by mechanical pumping. Irwin et al. reports success in reducing thermal stratification of four lakes in southern Ohio (which range in volume from 98 to 1,260 acre-feet) by pumping the bottom water to the surface. Oxygen depletion may limit fish distribution. For example, only 15 per cent of the volume of a certain western lake was habitable by coho salmon during certain periods as a result of the combination of high surface temperatures and oxygen depletion in the hypolimnion. The introduction of compressed air into the hypolimnion not only served to aerate the water but also mixed it, bringing nutrients from the hypolimnion up into the epilimnion. As a result, phytoplankton, and ultimately crustaceans and insect larvae, increased in numbers. With greater quantities of food available the salmon biomass production of the lake was increased 300 per cent.

CONSTRUCTION OF FARM PONDS AND RESERVOIRS. The construction of farm ponds, artificial lakes, and reservoirs is the most effective means of providing adequate fishing opportunities for the burgeoning recreational needs of our nation's growing population. As of 1974 the United States had over 1,000 reservoirs of over 500 acres, embracing more than 9,200,000 acres (6). The physical, chemical, and biological characteristics of many new impoundments are being scrutinized with respect to their potential as suitable fish habitat. During the period from 1950 to 1965 under the Dingell-Johnson program of federal aid to states for fish habitat acquisition and development, 246 lakes representing 3,000 water acres were constructed or modified in thirty-nine states at a total construction cost of $21 million. They have provided over 2 million fishing days annually. In 1974 farm ponds and reservoirs supported over 40 per cent of all fisherman days. By the year 2000 10 million more acres of reservoirs larger than 10 acres will be required to meet the demand. Between 1960 and 2000, according to the Senate Select Committee on Water Resources, an estimated 1,462 million acres of ranch and farm pond are to be constructed, pro-

Figure 10-36. *Fishing on a 20-acre Georgia farm pond. A good program of pond management has provided excellent fishing. Watershed above pond is fully protected with cover. [Soil Conservation Service, U.S. Department of Agriculture]*

viding 707,000 acres of fishing waters. By the year 2000 it is expected that a total of 2.9 million farm ponds embracing an area of 2.2 million acres will be contributing 157 million pounds of fish annually (6).

Natural and Artificial Selection of Superior Fish. For several years the Mississippi River has been heavily contaminated with pesticides borne in agricultural run-off waters. (This is reminiscent of the DDT resistance genetically acquired by house flies and mosquitos.) It is supposed that the selection for resistance-contributing genes probably operates at the highly sensitive embryonic or larval stage. Possibly fisheries biologists will be able to accelerate this process. Thus, scientists at the Federal Fish Genetics Laboratory at Beulah, Wyoming, are exploring the possibility of developing pesticide-resistant strains of trout by selective breeding experiments.

Larger and higher-quality fish for stocking southern fish ponds are being developed at the Federal Fish Farming Station at Stuttgart, Arkansas. A rapidly growing hybrid catfish has been produced by crossing a channel catfish with a blue catfish (15). Measurements taken in August after the second season of growth showed the hybrids to have a weight increment 32 per cent greater than that of the blue catfish and 41 per cent larger than the channel catfish. Even more promising, a seven-month-old hybrid buffalo-fish, resulting from crossing a black buffalo-fish female with a bigmouth buffalo-fish male, showed *twice the length and fourfold the weight of the nonhybrids*. This should be exciting news to our growing legion of farm pond fishermen.

Management of Endangered Species.   A few years ago the U.S. Fish and Wildlife Service reported that twenty-four species and subspecies of fish in the United States were *endangered*. This classification indicated that their reproduction and survival was in immediate jeopardy, because of one or a combination of factors, such as loss or defilement of suitable habitat, predation, competition, disease, and heavy fishing pressure. Among the endangered species listed were the following: shortnose sturgeon, longjaw cisco, Lahontan cutthroat trout, Piute cutthroat trout, Montana westslope trout, Gila trout, blue pike, and the Big Bend gambusia.

SHORTNOSE STURGEON.   This short-snouted sturgeon, which attains a length of 3 feet, is on the brink of extinction. Formerly widely distributed along the Atlantic coastal rivers from New Brunswick to Florida, its numbers have been drastically reduced in recent years. The most recent records have come from the Hudson River. According to the New York State Conservation Department, the most important reasons for its decline are domestic and industrial pollution combined with overfishing. Large numbers of this edible fish have been taken in shad gill nets. The only protective measure legislated to date apparently is the 20-inch size limit. Location of its spawning grounds and an intensive study of its breeding behavior would appear to be fundamental to perpetuating the species. Fertilized eggs removed from wild specimens may make propagation in captivity possible in the future (5).

ATLANTIC SALMON.   Because this species is still widely distributed in Canada, it is only the population occupying United States waters that is actually endangered. Here the fish is restricted to remnant populations in eight coastal streams in Maine. In the 1880's up to 200,000 pounds of this brown-backed, silver-sided salmon were taken yearly. From this original abundance the American population has become drastically depleted within the past 75 years, because of pollution and man-made barriers to its spawning runs. The total annual catch in recent years has been only about 450 fish with an aggregate weight of under 1,000 pounds. Although the reproductive potential is high, females averaging 6,000 eggs, only one salmon of every 1,000 eggs produced eventually reaches the sea, because of the intense ER. Survival in American waters currently depends primarily on propagation by state and federal hatcheries. Over 200,000 fish were hatchery-reared in 1962 (5). Commercial fishing of Atlantic salmon will be phased out in 1976.

BIG BEND GAMBUSIA.   The total world population of this brightly colored, orange-and-yellow-finned sprite is under 1,000 and is restricted to a small area in Texas. The extinction of this tiny fish would be most unfortunate, but its perpetuation presents a stern challenge to fisheries biologists. The Texas spring in which the species was originally discovered, known as Boquillas Spring, dried up in 1928. Hearteningly, however, in 1954 a second population was discovered in Graham Ranch Warm Springs. Currently the total world population of this species is represented by two pools in Big Bend National Park, Texas. Attempts at transplantation to other ponds within the park have been unsuccessful. Protective measures presently being practiced include the removal of the mosquito fish (*Gambusia affinis*), an aggressive competitor, and repeated habitat surveillance to ensure a constant water supply (5).

BIBLIOGRAPHY

1. Becker, C. Dale, and Wayne D. Brunson. "*Diphylobothrium* (Cestoda) Infections in Salmonids from Three Washington Lakes," *Jour. Wild. Mgt.*, 31 (1967), 813–824.
2. Behmer, David J. "Movement and Angler Harvest in the Des Moines River, Boone County, Iowa," *Proc. Iowa Acad. Sci.*, 71 (1965), 259–263.
3. Bowen, J. T., and R. E. Putz. "Parasites of Freshwater Fish. IV. Miscellaneous. 3. Parasitic Copepod *Argulus*," *Fish Disease Leaflet* 3. Leetown, W. Va.: Bureau of Sport Fisheries and Wildlife, Eastern Fish Disease Laboratory, 1966.
4. Brous, Henry. "Observations on Garter Snakes," *Amer. Natur.*, 16 (1882), 564.
5. Bureau of Sports Fisheries and Wildlife. "Rare and Endangered Fish and Wildlife of the United States," *Resource Publications*, No. 34. Washington, D.C.: U.S. Fish and Wildlife Service, 1966.
6. ———. *Fifteen Years of Better Fishing.* Washington, D.C.: U.S. Fish and Wildlife Service, 1967.
7. Burton, G. W., and Odum, Eugene P. "The Distribution of Stream Fish in the Vicinity of Mountain Lake, Virginia," *Ecol.*, 26 (1945), 182–193.
8. Cairns, John, Jr., Arthur Scheier, and Nancy E. Hess. "The Effects of Alkyl-Benzene-Sulfonate on Aquatic Organisms," *Ind. Water Wastes*, 9 (1964), 22–28.
9. Childers, William F., and George W. Bennett. "Experimental Vegetation Control by Largemouth Bass-*Tilapia* Combinations," *Jour. Wild. Mgt.*, 31 (1967), 401–407.
10. Colby, Peter J., and Lloyd L. Smith, Jr. "Survival of Walleye Eggs and Fry on Paper Fiber Sludge Deposits in Rainy River, Minnesota," *Trans. Amer. Fish. Soc.*, 96 (1967), 278–296.
11. Dreyer, William R., and Joseph Biel. "Life History of Lake Herring in Lake Superior," *Fish. Bull.*, 63 (1964), 493–536.
12. Eddy, Samuel, and Thaddeus Surber. *Northern Fishes.* Minneapolis, Minn.: University of Minnesota, 1947.
13. Edmondson, W. T. "The Relation of Photosynthesis by Phytoplankton to Light in Lakes," *Ecol.*, 37 (1956), 161–174.
14. Frantz, Ted C., and Almo J. Cordone. "Final Introductions of the Bonneville Cisco (*Prosopium gemmiferum* Snyder) into Lake Tahoe, California and Nevada," *Calif. Fish and Game*, 53 (1967), 209–210.
15. Giudice, John J. "Growth of a Blue X Channel Catfish Hybrid as Compared to Its Parent Species," *Prog. Fish-Culturist*, 28 (1966), 142–145.
16. Hessler, Thomas J., John M. Neuhold, and William F. Sigler. "Effects of Alkyl-Benzene-Sulfonate on Rainbow Trout," *Bureau of Sport Fisheries and Wildlife Technical Paper*. Washington, D.C.: U.S. Fish and Wildlife Service, 1967.
17. Herting, Gerald E., and Arthur Witt, Jr. "The Role of Physical Fitness of Forage Fishes in Relation to Their Vulnerability to Predation by Bowfin (*Amia calva*)," *Trans. Amer. Fish Soc.*, 96 (1967), 427–430.
18. "Keeping Tahoe Alive," *Time*, 88 (1966), 46 47.
19. King, Dennis R., and George S. Hunt, "Effect of Carp on Vegetation in a Lake Erie Marsh," *Jour. Wild. Mgt.*, 31 (1967), 18.
20. Lagler, Karl. "Food Habits and Economic Relations of the Turtles of Michigan with Special Reference to Fish Management," *Amer. Mid. Nat.*, 29 (1943), 257–312.
21. ———. *Freshwater Fishery Biology.* Dubuque, Iowa: Brown, 1956.
22. Lauer, Gerald J., J. Page Nicholson, William S. Cox, and John I. Teasley. "Pesticide Contamination of Surface Waters by Sugar Cane Farming in Louisiana," *Trans. Amer. Fish. Soc.*, 95 (1966), 310–316.

23. Major, Richard L., and James L. Mighell. "Influence of Rocky Reach Dam and the Temperature of the Okanogen River on the Upstream Migration of Sockeye Salmon," *U.S. Fish and Wildlife Service Bull.* 66 (1947), 131–147.

24. McClane, A. J. "Where East Meets West," *Field and Stream*, 71 (1967), 78–80, 89–90, 92.

25. McFadden, James T., Gaylord R. Alexander, and David S. Shetter. "Numerical Changes and Population Regulation in Brook Trout *Salvelinus fontinalis*," *Fish. Res. Board Can. Jour.*, 24 (1967), 1425–1429.

26. Meehan, William R., and William L. Sheridan. "Investigations in Fish Control, 8: Effects of Toxaphene of Fishes and Bottom Fauna of Big Kitoi Creek, Afognak Island, Alaska," *Resource Publication 12*. La Crosse, Wis.: Bureau of Sport Fisheries and Wildlife, Fish Control Laboratory, 1966.

27. Meyer, Fred P. "Parasites of Fresh Water Fish. II. Protozoa. 3. *Ichthyopthirius multifilis*," *Fish Diseases Leaflet 2*. Leetown, W. Va.: Bureau of Sport Fisheries and Wildlife, Eastern Fish Disease Laboratory, 1966.

28. Milne, Lorus J., and Margery Milne. *The Balance of Nature*. New York: Knopf, 1961.

29. Nikolsky, G. V. *The Ecology of Fishes*. New York: Academic, 1963.

30. Norden, Carroll R. "Age, Growth and Fecundity of the Alewife, *Alosa pseudoharengus* (Wilson) in Lake Michigan," *Trans. Amer. Fish. Soc.*, 96 (1967), 387–393.

31. Odum, Eugene P. *Fundamentals of Ecology*, 3rd ed. Philadelphia: Saunders, 1971.

32. Peters, John C. "Effects on a Trout Stream of Sediment from Agricultural Practices," *Jour. Wild. Mgt.*, 31 (1967), 805–812.

33. Schmittou, H. R. "Sex Ratios of Bluegills in Four Populations," *Trans. Amer. Fish. Soc.*, 96 (1967), 420–421.

34. Simco, Bill A., and Frank B. Cross. "Factors Affecting Growth and Production of Channel Catfish, *Ictalurus punctatus*," *Univ. Kansas Publ. Natur. Hist.*, 17 (1966), 191–256.

35. Smith, L. L., Jr., R. H. Kramer, and J. C. MacLeod. "Effects of Pulpwood Fibers on Fathead Minnows and Walleye Fingerlings," *Jour. Water Poll. Cont. Fed.*, 37 (1965), 130–140.

36. Smith, Robert L. *Ecology and Field Biology*. New York: Harper, 1966.

37. Surber, Eugene W. "Water Quality Criteria for Freshwater Fishes," *Proc. 16th Ann. Conf. Southeast. Assoc. Game and Fish Comm.*, 1962 (1965), pp. 435–436.

38. Trautman, Milton B. "Fish Distribution and Abundance Correlated with Stream Gradients as a Consideration in Stocking Programs," *Trans. 7th N. Amer. Wild. Conf.*, 7 (1942), 221–223.

39. Uhler, F. M., Cottam, C., and T. E. Clark, "Food of the Snakes of the George Washington National Forest, Virginia," *Trans. 4th N. Amer. Wild. Conf.* (1939), pp. 605–622.

40. U.S. Fish and Wildlife Service. "The Effects of Pesticides on Fish and Wildlife," *U.S. Fish and Wildlife Service Circular 226*. Washington, D.C.: 1965.

41. Werner, Robert G. "Intralacustrine Movements of Bluegill Fry in Crane Lake, Indiana," *Trans. Amer. Fish. Soc.*, 96 (1967), 416–420.

42. Witty, Kenneth. "Travel Rate of Downstream-Migrant Coho Salmon," *Prog. Fish-Culturist*, 28, (1967), 174.

43. Yeo, R. R. "Silver Dollar Fish for Biological Control of Submersed Aquatic Weeds," *Weeds*, 15 (1967), 27–31.

11.

Man and the Ocean

The ocean has its tolerances and stresses, and our technical ingenuity can break the ocean's back in a remarkable variety of ways. For all its imposing size, the ocean promises to be more vulnerable than redwood forests, wilderness streams, and buffalo herds. Its vital processes extend deep into our continental land masses, where dams can subvert beaches as well as egg-bearing salmon. Without even living within the ocean, we can exhaust it as easily as we exhaust the land. Desecration has seemingly been computerized and placed under remote control.

Wesley Marx, "How Not to Kill the Ocean,"
Audubon, July 1969

"Prepare to abandon ship!"—the captain's command still rings in my ears. It was during World War II. We were in mid-Pacific, aboard a troop transport. A Japanese submarine had been sighted near our prow. As I stood

Figure 11-1. *Menhaden fishermen hauling in seine, June, 1968, off Sealevel, North Carolina. (Bureau of Commercial Fisheries, U. S. Department of the Interior)*

by the deck rail, looking out over the churning, blue-gray vastness, I suddenly developed a fearsome respect and feeling of awe for the sea.

In the broader context of human ecology, however, the ocean deserves our appreciation and gratitude as well as our respect. From Stone Age to Space Age it has served man's needs:

1. By way of the hydrologic cycle its 31.7 million cubic mile volume represents a virtually limitless *water supply* for both man and all other organisms, from bacteria to the whale.
2. For eons the teeming trillions of tiny algae in its sunlit waters have aided in replenishing the *oxygen supply* of the earth's atmosphere.
3. For millennia it has served as a highway for international *transport*.
4. Ever since primitive man scooped fish from its tidal pools with his bare hands, it has provided abundant supplies of *essential protein*.

In a very real sense, the ocean is man's last frontier—*the last reasonably uncontaminated environment remaining on planet earth*. However, despite the multiple benefits derived from the ocean, it would almost seem as though man is indeed ready to "abandon" *it*—to write it off as expendable. For in recent years he has been using it more and more extensively as the world's largest "sewer," into which he dumps the assorted garbage that unfortunately accumulates as a by-product of his technological and cultural "progress." Into this last frontier man has discharged a bewildering variety of contaminants from raw human sewage to toxic industrial poisons, from household detergents to pesticides, from agricultural fertilizers to radioactive materials. Our chemical industry is developing thousands of new compounds yearly, many of which eventually find their way to the sea. Some of the effects are predictable; there are many others, however, that marine ecologists do not even pretend to understand.

While sailing through the Sargasso Sea some years ago, Thor Heyerdahl, of Kon Tiki fame, was dismayed to find a melange of man-generated litter floating on the surface of the placid sea, hundreds of miles from land. As reported in *Time* magazine:

> Almost every day, plastic bottles, squeeze tubes and other signs of industrial civilization floated by the expedition's leaky boat. What most appalled Heyerdahl were sheets of "pelagic particles." At first he assumed that his craft was in the wake of an oil tanker that had just cleaned its tanks. But on five occasions he ran into the same substances covering the water so thickly . . . that it was "unpleasant to dip our toothbrushes into the sea." . . . Oily and sometimes encrusted with barnacles, they smell like a combination of putrefying fish and raw sewage (30).

Let us now examine this unique ecosystem, so that we can develop some insight as to the nature and interactions of its physical and organismal components, the source, possible effect and control of its pollutants, and, finally, its significance as a food source in a malnourished world.

Major Features of the Marine Ecosystem

Eugene P. Odum lists some of the major ecological features of the oceanic environment (25):

1. It covers 70 per cent of the earth's surface.
2. It extends to depths of up to 6.5 miles (Mariana Trench) and hence has a much greater vertical dimension, or "thickness," than the terrestrial or freshwater environment.
3. The ocean is continuously circulating. Oceanic currents such as the Aleutian current, which brings cold water down the Pacific coast, and the Gulf Stream, which brings warm water upward along the Atlantic coast, move water masses horizontally and affect temperatures of adjacent coastal regions. As a result, New York City has a relatively moderate climate even in winter, whereas summer evenings in San Francisco may be quite chilly. There are also vertically moving currents; *upwelling*, for example, brings nutrient-rich cold water from the ocean bottom to surface level.
4. The ocean is salty. It has an average salinity of 35 parts salts (by weight) per 1,000 parts water; in contrast, fresh water usually has a salinity of less than 0.5 part per 1,000 parts water. In other words, the ocean is about 70 times as salty as a lake or stream.
5. The sea is relatively infertile compared to fresh water; nitrates and phosphates are extremely scarce. Two exceptions to this statement are the coastal areas where tributary streams discharge massive loads of sediment and the areas of upwelling just mentioned.

Zonation of the Ocean

The oceanic environment can be divided into five basic ecological regions, as indicated in Figure 11-2. In the context of this book it will be necessary to describe only the neritic, euphotic, and abyssal zones.

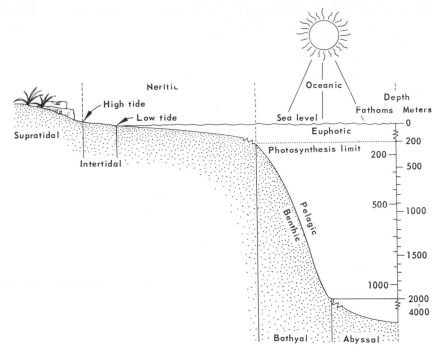

Figure 11-2. *Zonation of the marine ecosystem. The neritic, euphotic, and bathyal zones roughly correspond to the littoral, limnetic, and profundal zones of the lake ecosystem. Because of the high levels of dissolved nutrients and solar radiation, gross production, and hence plant and animal abundance and diversity, is greatest in the neritic zone. (Adapted from Eugene P. Odum, Fundamentals of Ecology (Philadelphia: W. B. Saunders Company, 1959). After Joel W. Hedgepeth, "The Classification of Estuarine and Brackish Waters and the Hydrographic Climate" in Report No. 11 of National Research Council Committee on a Treatise on Marine Ecology and Paleoecology. National Research Council, Washington, 1951, 49-56).*

Neritic Zone. The neritic zone is the marine counterpart of the littoral zone of a lake. It is a relatively warm, nutrient-rich shallow-water zone overlying the continental shelf. Occurring along our Atlantic, Pacific, and Gulf coasts, it has an average width of 10 to 200 miles and extends to depths of 200 to 600 feet. The neritic zone ends where the continental shelf abruptly terminates and the ocean bottom plunges to great depths. The fertility of the neritic zone is supplied primarily by upwelling and the sedimentary discharge of tributary streams. (The Mississippi River washes almost 2 million tons of nutrient-rich mud into the Gulf of Mexico daily.) Sunlight normally penetrates to the ocean bottom, thus permitting considerable photosynthetic activity and the presence of a vast population of anchored and floating plants. Animal populations are rich and varied. Oxygen depletion is not a problem because of photosynthetic activity and wave action. The *total amount of biomass supported by the neritic zone is greater per unit volume of water than in any other part of the ocean.*

There has recently been a sharp increase in the use of the neritic zone as a *dumping ground* for a great variety of wastes generated by industries, municipalities, and even federal agencies. Without the establishment of restrictions at the state and federal levels, and without the development of adequate alternative disposal methods, the waste volume might well become so great as to seriously impair the productivity of our coastal fisheries. Space for land disposal of these wastes is rapidly diminishing at the same time that the establishment of higher water quality standards for our nation's lakes and streams have forced many industries and municipalities to view the nearby ocean as an attractive sewer.

By 1968 the neritic zone along our coastline served as a receptacle for the following wastes (8):

1. Large quantities of explosives and agents of chemical warfare.
2. Twenty-six thousand tons of solid waste.
3. Two hundred thousand tons of dried sewage sludge.
4. Thirty-eight million tons of dredge spoils (one third of which was highly polluted with industrial and municipal waste).
5. Millions of tons of industrial wastes such as toxic metals and nutrients.
6. Vast quantities of construction and demolition debris.

Although only a negligible quantity of radioactive wastes have been discharged into the ocean since 1962, it is inevitable that such dumping will increase substantially in the future, since the Atomic Energy Commission estimates there will be a sixty-fold increase in radioactive wastes between 1970 and 2000.

In general the effects of the above waste loads on marine plant and animal life are similar to their effects on freshwater organisms. They increase the BOD, destroy spawning beds, increase turbidity, reduce photosynthetic rates, and defile the natural beauty of the oceanic environment. Toxic metals may directly destroy shrimp and oyster fisheries. The crucial point to be made is that this ocean dumping is defiling the neritic zone of the ocean, a zone that is the source of over 50 per cent of the annual marine fish harvest, even though it represents only 1 per cent of the ocean area.

Euphotic Zone. The euphotic zone is the open-water zone of the ocean, which corresponds to the limnetic zone of a lake. The term *euphotic*, which literally means "abundance of light," is appropriate to this zone, for it has sufficient sunlight to support photosynthesis and a considerable population of phytoplankton. In turn, the phytoplankton support a host of tiny "grazing" herbivores, such as the small crustaceans. The total energy made available to animal food chains by euphotic phytoplankton is much greater than that made available by plants of the neritic zone; this is largely because of the vast area of the euphotic zone, which extends for thousands of miles across the open sea. The degree to which light penetrates of course is dependent upon the transparency of the surface waters. Since sunlight cannot penetrate deeper than 200 meters in most marine habitats, this is frequently considered the lower limit of the euphotic zone.

Abyssal Zone. The abyssal zone is the cold, dark-water zone of the ocean depths that roughly corresponds to the profundal zone of the lake habitat. It lies immediately above the ocean floor. Animal life is extremely sparse. Any animal living in the abyssal zone must be highly specialized to adapt to the extreme conditions. It must adapt to darkness, to intense cold (because the abyssal water frequently approaches the freezing point), to greatly depleted levels of dissolved oxygen (because no photosynthesis can occur here), to water pressures over thousands of pounds per square inch, and to scarcity of food. There may be an abundance of nutrient-rich sediments on the ocean floor that may have come from the decaying bodies of marine organisms drifting down from the sunlit waters far above or that may have been derived from the excretions of animals living at upper oceanic levels. For example, in certain areas of the west Atlantic the concentration of phosphates at a depth of 1,000 meters may be ten times the concentration at 100 meters. Because both phytoplankton and herbivorous animals cannot exist in the abyssal zone, most consumers are either predators or scavengers. A number of the deep-sea fishes of the abyss have evolved luminescent organs that may aid them in securing food and mates.

The Estuarine Ecosystem

Estuaries are transitional zones between coastal rivers and the sea. In one sense they represent a river-ocean "hybrid" in that they posess some of the characteristics of each ecosystem. Nevertheless, the estuary has some distinctive properties in its own right and therefore must be considered a unique ecosystem. Let us examine some of its characteristics.

1. It contains *brackish* water, a mixture of "fresh" water flow from the stream and "salt" water from the ocean. The salinity of estuarine water is highly variable, changing by a factor of *ten*, within a twenty-four-hour period, the salinity being higher when the tide comes in, lower when the tide moves out.
2. The water density is intermediate between that of fresh (1.00) and salt (1.03) water. The actual density, however, depends upon the incoming and outgoing tides.

Figure 11-3. *Estuary of the San Joaquin River, California. (California Department of Water Resources)*

3. The water level rises and recedes in synchrony with the tides.
4. The concentration of dissolved oxygen is relatively high because of the shallow basin and the turbulence of the water.
5. The turbidity is characteristically high because of the stirring action of the tides. Phytoplankton populations, therefore are limited because of the restricted penetration of sunlight.
6. The estuary is extremely rich in nutrients because the tides tend to concentrate those nutrients carried "down" to the estuary by stream flow and carried "up" from the ocean by the incoming tides.

   As W. B. Clapham states, "The mechanism of concentration is quite simple: particulate nutrient material enters the estuary at its upper end, is carried seaward by the falling tide, and so on for several cycles. The length of time it takes for a nutrient particle to traverse the estuary is substantially longer than it would be for it to traverse a similar length of even the most slowly flowing river. Thus, the estuary acts as a *nutrient trap*, with an average nutrient level significantly higher than either the river or the sea that it connects. In a like manner the concentration of nutrient- and energy-rich organic material is very high" (6).

   The accumulating load of nutrients may be channeled into the biomass of organisms in two ways: first, by nutrient absorption on the part of both phytoplankton and rooted vegetation, after the nutrients have been released from organic material by bacterial decomposition; second, and much more important, the inert organic material (decayed bodies of marsh grasses, crustaceans, worms, fishes, bacteria, algae, and so on), known as *detritus*, may be consumed directly by *detritus* feeders, such as clams, oysters, lobsters, and crabs.
7. Because of the extremely abundant supply of nutrients and the high oxygen levels (among other factors), the estuarine habitat is *more productive than any other ecosystem known except the coral reef.*
8. Sixty per cent of the marine fish harvested by American fishermen spend part of their life cycle in the estuarine environment. Many marine species use the estuary as a "nursery" in which they spend the larval period immediately after hatching from the egg. Other species, such as the Pacific salmon, pass through estuaries twice during their stream-ocean-stream migration.

In the past twenty years many of the original estuarine habitats along the California, Oregon, Washington, Texas, Louisiana, Mississippi, Florida, Georgia, South Carolina, North Carolina, Virginia, Maryland, and New York coasts have either been destroyed outright or have been adversely effected by such human activities as ocean dumping or real estate development. Regneat M. Darnell of Texas A and M, has described the dilemma facing an estuarine fish, the Atlantic croaker, a valuable game and food species, in "attempting" to complete its life cycle.

Through millions of years of evolution, the larval croaker has become exquisitely adapted to precise environmental cues of water temperature, salinity gradients, water currents and estuarine "odors" that trigger, direct, and regulate behavioral patterns; these patterns enable it to move from the shallow coastal waters where it was hatched, into the estuary where it will feed and undergo its early development, and then finally back to the ocean where it eventually will grow to sexual maturity. Of the many thousands of eggs hatched, under even the most favorable conditions probably *less than 1 per cent* would finally develop into mature fish. Over 99 per cent of the hatch would have been destroyed as a result of some sort of ER, including disease, predation, toxic pollutants, and so on. However, in recent years, mortality has been even greater as a result of a whole constellation of factors. Darnell writes:

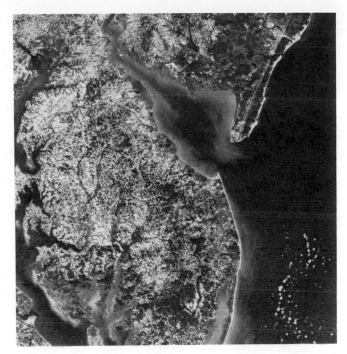

Figure 11-4. *Earth satellite photo of Delaware Bay and the adjacent Atlantic coast. The light gray areas indicate silt-polluted waters. The turbid waters of varying silt content of the Delaware River (center top) interact with clearer ocean water as the river enters the Bay (center). A significant amount of silt is maintained in suspension for several miles off-shore along the Maryland/Delaware coast. Note also the great amount of silt pollution in Chesapeake Bay (left). Satellite photos such as this can help assess top soil erosion and changes in water quality caused by processes such as heavy rainfall, urbanization, and construction activities in coastal areas. Photo released June 7, 1973. (NASA)*

Engineers, trained in hydraulics, construction, and cost-benefit ratios, have built dams which retain the fresh water in the up-stream reaches of the river. Bottom currents are not like they have been before. The subtle odors of the natural estuarine water are now masked by a thousand exotic chemicals which have entered the stream through the activities of streamside farmers and manufacturers and by city sewage disposal plants. The tiny crustaceans upon which the fish normally feeds have been greatly reduced by pesticides, aimed at insects, but also lethal for crabs, shrimp, and other insect relatives. Food is . . . charged with exotic chemicals which . . . reduce the vitality of the little fish. With the journey thus slowed . . . vulnerability to predation is correspondingly increased. If the fish does eventually make it into the estuary, he may encounter abnormally high salinity conditions. The normal river flow has been checked by a dam, its fresh water being diverted for irrigation, industrial and municipal use. As a result of the higher salinity, marine predators are in greater evidence, even in the former haven of the estuary. Food is scarcer than usual because the dam which impounds the water also holds back the silt and organic matter which formerly fertilized the estuary. Furthermore, many of the marshes and mud flats no longer support the luxurious plant and bacterial growths upon which the fish used to feed; instead they are now surrounded by concrete walls and filled in for housing developments and boat marinas. From time to time the local power plant . . . releases "slugs" of hot water into the estuary because the estuarine water must be used to cool the condenser coils. If not killed outright by the heated water, the fish is placed under great stress . . . [the heat] increases the fish's food and energy requirements at a time when it is killing the food supply. . . . If, by chance, the fish does survive the natural and artificial hazards of the estuary and is able to arrive successfully at the spawning grounds, the dangers are still not past. The eggs produced may be so loaded with toxic chemicals that many are unable to develop into normal young. Those which do complete their embryonic development begin life with a heavy chemical burden which further reduces their chances of fulfilling the normal life history pattern. Year after year, generation after generation, civilization adds burden upon load, stress upon strain, which in total, poses a many-horned dilemma in the fish's struggle to survive (10).

Marine Food Chains and Energy Conversions

Because the ocean covers 70 per cent of the earth's surface it obviously also receives 70 per cent of the earth's solar energy. Except for the anchored green plants of the neritic zone, this solar energy is trapped primarily by the phytoplankton producers swarming in the open waters of the sea. It has been estimated that 19 billion tons of living plant matter (mostly phytoplankton) are produced annually, which in turn support 5 billion tons of zooplankton biomass. The average number of plankton taken from the upper 50 meters of water in the south Atlantic (away from the continental shelves) at 55° C was about 100,000 per liter. The zooplankton may be consumed by a variety of filter feeders, including shrimp, herring, anchovy, and blue whale. The terminal link of the marine food chain is frequently represented by predators such as the shark, barracuda, moray eel, bonito, cod, salmon, and killer whale. As in the case of terrestrial food chains, the shorter the chain, the more efficient the production of terminal link biomass. Thus the three-link food chain of phytoplankton-zooplankton-herring that occurs off the California coast is much more efficient in the production of human food than the six-link food chain of phytoplankton-zooplankton-shrimp-lance-small fish-cod that occurs off the Grand Banks of Newfoundland. In the shallow waters of the neritic zone anchored green plants convert much more solar energy into chemical energy than the phytoplankton. However, the efficiency of energy conversion for food chains based on the anchored type of vegetation is not very great. Thus, it has been estimated that 24 million tons of eelgrass (*Zostera*) off the Danish coast is the primary food source of *5 million tons of animals of absolutely no food value to man*. It is also the primary food source of 1 million tons of animals, which in turn would be eventually consumed by 10,000 tons of food fishes (plaice and cod), which in turn would be eaten by man. Here, the ratio of *Zostera* crop to the ultimate food crop of plaice and cod usable by man is 2,400 to 1. Obviously this represents a high degree of wasted energy. In contrast, about 0.06 per cent of the annual phytoplankton crop in the English Channel is ultimately harvested as fish fit for human consumption— a somewhat more efficient biomass ratio of 1,666 to 1.

Marine Fish

We shall consider the natural history, ecology, and economics of three major marine resource categories: *marine fish, shellfish* (shrimp and oysters), and *marine mammals* (seals and whales). Our discussion will begin with marine fishes, not only because their ecology to some degree parallels that of freshwater fishes, but also because they are by far the most abundant source of protein food for mankind.

Fecundity. (The term *fecundity* may be defined as "the total number of fertilized eggs produced by an adult female.") Marine fishes on the average are more fecund than freshwater species, possibly because chances of survival are poorer in the oceanic environment. Among marine fishes fecundity is directly proportional to the species' vulnerability to predation and inversely proportional to the protection given by the parent (36). In the soup-fin shark (*Galeorhinus zyoptarus*), which has relatively few predators and which is ovoviviparous (the embryo developing within the female's body and being "born"), litters range in size from 6 to 52, with an average of 35. In decided contrast are the fishes which lay buoyant eggs and whose eggs and larvae become part of the plankton, transported by seadrift, tide, and current (24). Thus the moonfish (*Mola mola*) produces 3 billion eggs, the Atlantic cod (*Gadus callarius*) 9 million, the haddock (*Melanogrammus aeglefinus*) 3 million, the Pacific halibut (*Hippoglossus stenolephis*) 2.7 million, the winter flounder (*Pseudopleuronectes americanus*) 1.5 million, the hake (*Merluccius*) 1 million, and the mackerel (*Scomber scombrus*) 0.5 million (18, 22).

Fecundity appears to be *inversely proportional to population size*. Perhaps the greater productivity of a small population is related to the better breeding condition resulting from more abundant food supplies (24). Fish stocks that have been severely depleted by overfishing often show increased fecundity.

Migrations. According to Nikolsky, fishes conduct three basic types of migration —*spawning, feeding,* and *overwintering* (24). A few species, such as gobies and many coral fishes, are essentially nonmigratory. In some species, such as the white fish, the overwintering migration is lacking but feeding and spawning migrations are completed.

SPAWNING MIGRATION. The spawning migration ensures favorable physical and biotic conditions for developing eggs and larvae with regard to oxygen, temperature, salinity, currents, food, competitors, and predators. Fishes that live in the ocean for most of their life cycle but ascend freshwater streams to spawn are called *anadromous*. We have described the anadromous migration of the Pacific salmon. Other anadromous species are the American shad (*Alosa sapidissima*) and Atlantic smelt (*Osmerus mordax*), which migrate from the Atlantic into freshwater streams to spawn, and the Pacific herring (*Clupea pallasi*), which moves into shallow bays to deposit its eggs (18). On the other hand, a *catadromous* fish spends most of its life cycle in fresh water but descends to the ocean to spawn. The catadromous American eel (*Anguilla bostoniensis*) descends New England streams when sexually mature, swims hundreds of miles to a site in the Sargasso Sea east of Bermuda, spawns at great depths, and dies. The larvae float to the surface and migrate northward, transported in part by the Gulf Stream, and eventually ascend a freshwater stream, where most of their life cycle is spent.

Figure 11-5. *Pleasure craft and fishing boats at Newport Harbor, Oregon. (Rollin R. Geppert)*

Figure 11-6. *Sport fishermen have landed a record catch of 1122 yellowfin tuna taken from waters off the coast of southern California. (Southern California Visitors Council)*

Many north Atlantic fishes—such as mackerel, silver hake, scup, weakfish, and winter flounder (*Pseudopleuronectes americanus*)—migrate from deeper water to shallow coastal areas to spawn. The north Pacific albacore (*Thunnus alalunga*) moves southward from temperate waters to spawn (16).

FEEDING MIGRATION. Updrafts or convection currents bring nutrients to the upper layers of temperate seas in winter. When light intensities increase in spring, phytoplankton become highly productive. Zooplankton, in turn, increase in response to the superabundant food supply only to be consumed by small fish such as anchovy and herring. As waters warm in summer, bluefin tuna, albacore, mako sharks, blue sharks, basking sharks, swordfish, ocean sunfish, and opah migrate into this area of nutritional abundance from considerable distances.

Many fishes perform feeding migrations as eggs or larvae. Thus the Atlantic currents transport herring larvae and the eggs and larvae of cod from the Norwegian coast to their Barents Sea feeding grounds.

Some feeding migrations are *vertical* rather than *horizontal*. For example the mackerel ascends and descends in rhythm with the movements of the plankton upon which it feeds. Similarly, the swordfish shifts its vertical position in synchrony with that of its sardine prey. Some vertical migrations are concerned with escape from predation rather than feeding. Thus anchovies in the Black Sea remain at deep levels during the day, where they are unavailable to fish-eating birds; then at night they rise to the surface, after the birds have finished feeding (22).

OVERWINTERING MIGRATION. Nikolsky states that the purpose of the overwintering migrations, conducted by some species, is to provide the most favorable wintering conditions for a fish that will have a reduced metabolism and will therefore be relatively inactive. Presumably such a wintering area will be relatively free of predators. Marine fish do not begin an overwintering migration until they have accumulated sufficient body fat to sustain them during the winter period of minimal feeding activity. Anchovies of the Black Sea pass the winter in an inactive state at depths of 100 to 150 meters (24).

Water Temperature and Fish Distribution. Conditioning experiments have shown that both marine and freshwater species are capable of detecting extremely minute changes in the temperature, salinity, and hydrostatic pressure of their environment. Although the salinity-detecting receptors have not as yet been identified, the thermosensors apparently are modified cutaneous nerve endings. Some fishes can detect water temperature changes of only 0.03° C. It is not surprising, therefore, that distribution of certain marine fishes may show a high correlation with water temperature patterns. A few examples follow.

1. Although a great abundance of forage organisms exists all along the coast of Baja California, commercial quantities of yellowfin tuna (*Thunnus albacares*) are limited to areas where the water temperature is at least 19° C; skipjack tuna (*Katsuwonus pelamis*) occur only where the water temperature is a minimum of 17° C (27).
2. In the oceanic waters of the northwestern Atlantic, the bluefin tuna (*Thunnus thynnus*), which prefers relatively cool water, is dominant in the vicinity of the Gulf Stream during winter and spring; however, as water warms, the bluefin are replaced by the warm-water-loving yellowfin in summer and fall. According to

Squire, the temperature factor in determining tuna distribution in this area is brought into sharp focus at the edge of the Gulf Stream, *where a sharp temperature gradient permits warm- and cold-water tuna to exist adjacent to each other and yet be distinctly separated* (32).

3. The spawning grounds of many marine species are located within a narrow temperature range, as indicated for several north Atlantic species: cod 0.4–7° C, herring (spring) 3.7–9.3° C, herring (fall) 9.1–13.3° C, pilchard 9–16.5° C, and mackerel 10–15° C (28).

4. The swordfish prefers to breed in tropical waters with a temperature from 25 to 29° C (22).

In cooperation with the U.S. Coast Guard, airborne surface temperature surveys of three important fishery areas on the continental shelf of the Pacific coast (in which infrared detection instruments were employed) were conducted by the Tiburon Marine Laboratory, Bureau of Sports Fisheries and Wildlife, Tiburon, California. It is possible to produce a computer-drawn isotherm chart within ten minutes after transmission of data by telephone circuits to Monterey (California) from any U.S. Navy Weather facility.

The Atlantic Marine Gamefish Research Program has recently published *The Atlas of the Marine Environment*, based on fifty years of temperature records. It shows the average monthly temperatures for the continental shelf from southern Florida to Cape Cod, ranging from ocean surface to bottom. Any pelagic or demersal species of fish, by making the appropriate movements, could remain on this stretch of continental shelf and keep within narrow species-preferred temperature bound-

Figure 11-7. *Tuna fishing on the trade wind in the South Pacific. (Bureau of Commercial Fisheries, U. S. Department of the Interior)*

aries. Although fish distribution, as in the bluefish, is based on other factors, such as light intensity and day length, the atlas will greatly facilitate the prediction of game and sport fish occurrence.

Environmental Resistance. Among the many destructive agencies that marine fishes encounter we shall briefly describe the biotic factors represented by predators, parasites, red-tide organisms, and competitors, as well as such physical factors as adverse winds and thermal pollution.

PREDATORS. Commercially valuable fish are consumed by a great variety and number of predators, including other fishes, sharks, birds, seals, sea otters, and whales. The following percentage of fish occurs in the diet of sea birds from the Barents Sea: guillemot (*Vria lomvia*), 95; razorbill (*Alca torda*), 92; puffin (*Fratercula arctica*), 67; tern (*Sterna paradisea*), 55; and great blackbacked gull (*Larus marinus*), 40 (4). In the Volga Delta cormorants kill 5,000 metric tons of fish annually, equal to *1.5 per cent of the catch in the North Caspian Sea* (24). Herring spawn is consumed by haddock in large quantities, and its larvae are eaten by planktonic predators (11). Menhaden (*Brevoortia tyrannus*), silvery little fish that occur along the Atlantic coast of North America, are consumed by whiting, codfish, pollack, dogfish, tuna, flounder, pompano, cavally, bonito, bayonet fish, striped bass, weakfish, sharks, dolphins, and whales. It is estimated that natural predators annually destroy 1 *million million million menhaden* or 1,000 times the commercial harvest of 1948, a year of record catch (12).

In some cases one valuable commercial fish may be the predator of another. Thus, the cod is an avid consumer of herring. Studies in Scandinavian waters have shown that a good catch of cod one year is frequently followed by a poor herring catch the next. Conversely, a poor cod harvest may be followed by a sizable herring catch the ensuing year.

PARASITES. In general, parasitic infestations do not contribute to acute fish mortality, but are usually taken in stride by host populations. Fish are parasitized by bacteria, molds, protozoans, tapeworms, flukes, roundworms, crustaceans, and many other organisms. During the summer of 1963 the *Pasteurella* bacterium contributed importantly to the deaths of many white perch (*Roccus americana*) and striped bass (*Roccus saxatilis*) in American waters. Sixty tapeworms have been found in the gut of a single turbot (14). Flukes infest kidneys, urinary bladder, cerebral fluid, gall bladder, and the circulatory system.

Roundworms are common internal parasites that invade the intestines, swim bladder, liver, peritoneum, skin, and muscle. Kabata reports 15 per cent of the North Sea haddock to be infested with growth-retarding copepods (crustaceans) (21). He estimated that if each parasitized haddock lost only 1 ounce in weight, the total loss to the Scottish haddock catch in 1954 would have been 1.96 million pounds.

RED-TIDE ORGANISMS. Under certain conditions of water temperature, salinity, and/or nutrient salts, populations of marine protozoans may rapidly increase. The accumulating metabolic wastes may cause massive fish mortality. Sometimes the ocean water assumes the red-brown color of the densely massed organisms, which is the foundation for such expressions as "red sea" or "red tide." Outbreaks of

Gymnodinium along the Florida coast and of *Gonyalaux* along the southern California coast have caused spectacular fish kills of such proportions that many tons of fish carcasses have littered the beaches. In 1964 a "bloom" of the reddish-brown dinoflagellate *Cochlodinium* in Barnegat Bay, New Jersey, caused the destruction of many marine organisms, including sticklebacks, silver perch, eels, and crabs. An investigation of the outbreak's cause was conducted by the Sandy Hook Marine Laboratory of Highlands, New Jersey. The predisposing conditions for the outbreak were the combination of the low flushing rate of the bay in August and the resultant accumulation of domestic and industrial pollutants. The localized abundance of nutrients that resulted in turn made possible a rapid increase in the food organisms of *Cochlodinium*. Apparently, *Cochlodinium* did not kill the fish directly by means of metabolic toxins, but indirectly, through its high biological oxygen demand.

COMPETITION FOR FOOD.   Marine fish compete not only with each other for food but also with a diverse assemblage of aquatic mammals, birds, and invertebrates. Among the invertebrates, sea stars and brittle stars are especially significant (24). In areas of high density the starfish, which feed primarily on mollusks, may exceed 15 per square meter, and brittle stars may exceed 400 per square meter of ocean floor (36). Fishes consume only one third to one fourth as much food per unit pound as their echinoderm competitors. Along the Danish coast only 2 to 5 per cent of the potential fish food is actually eaten by fish (34).

Figure 11-8.   *Heavy fish mortality in a red tide area off Sanibel Island, Florida. (Bureau of Commercial Fisheries, U. S. Department of the Interior)*

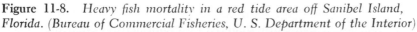

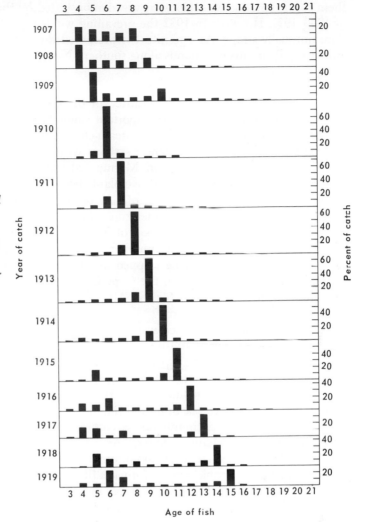

Figure 11-9. *Dominance of the 1904 age class in the commercial herring catch of the North Sea, 1907-1919. Optimal environmental conditions in 1904 must have prevailed for hatching success and early development. (Adapted from Eugene P. Odum,* Fundamentals of Ecology *(Philadelphia: W. B. Saunders Company, 1959). After John Hjort, "Fluctuations in the Year Classes of Important Food Fishes."* Jour du Conseil Permanent Internationale pour L'Exploration de la Mer, 1, 1-38 pp.)*

Off the California coast sardine and anchovy compete intensively for the same planktonic foods. As might be expected, therefore, when the sardine fishery severely declined in the early 1950's, there was a proportional increase in the anchovy population. It is currently estimated that there is an anchovy stock of 2 to 4 million tons off California and Baja California, partly as a result of the reduced food competition.

ADVERSE WINDS AS A MORTALITY FACTOR. The prevailing winds may have either a beneficial or adverse effect on the reproductive success of a species that produces buoyant eggs. A good example is the poor reproduction of the mackerel (*Scomber scombrus*) along our Atlantic coast during 1932, as reported by Sette (29). The estimated mortality was so severe among eggs and larvae that only one fish survived to an age of thirty-five days out of every 10 million eggs laid. The spawning grounds for this species extends from the coastal waters of Newfoundland south to Chesapeake Bay. Southwest winds are beneficial for young mackerel, for sea drift carries them to food-productive regions, as was demonstrated by the abundant year-classes of 1930–1931. However, in 1932 the prevailing winds were from the northeast and were unusually strong. As a result, it is presumed the larval mackerel were carried away from their nursery grounds along southern New England to the eastern end of Long Island (22).

THERMAL POLLUTION.   Gordon Gunter, of the Gulf Coast Research Laboratory, has called temperature "the most important single factor governing the occurrence and behavior of [aquatic] life." Most steam-electric generating plants situated near the coast cool their steam condenser systems with sea water. A water-temperature survey conducted by the Tiburon Marine Laboratory (U.S. Fish and Wildlife Service), on the California coast at five plants between Los Angeles and San Diego, showed that the total water output of 1.18 million gallons per minute was heated about 20° F above the intake temperature. Similar cases of thermal pollution occur along the Atlantic coast. A direct kill of fish by thermal pollution was recorded in the summer of 1968 when a large number of menhaden acclimated to temperatures in the 80's (degrees F) became trapped in effluent water at 93 to 95° during the testing of a new power plant on the Cape Cod Canal. (The upper lethal limit for the winter flounder is 77° F, for the Atlantic salmon 92° F, for the striped bass 94° F, and for the gizzard shad 97° F.) Fisheries biologists are concerned with the possible effect that this localized water-temperature increase may have not only on fish, but on their plankton and invertebrate food organisms.

Thermal pollution may be especially destructive in the estuaries. The unpolluted estuaries have great importance to human well-being— for over 50 per cent of our commercial food fishes, including the striped bass, herring, Atlantic and Pacific salmon, Atlantic croaker, sea trout and menhaden, spend at least a portion of their life cycles in estuarine environments. According to Warinner and Brehmer, of the Virginia Institute of Marine Science, "An estuary must be considered a *biological zone* and the establishment of subminimal conditions *across any point* in the estuary may affect valuable aquatic forms in the *entire* estuary" (38). Warinner and Brehmer studied the effects of warmed up power plant coolant water on the organisms in the York River estuary along the Virginia coast. They found that increased water temperatures in winter caused a reduction in the photosynthetic rates of phytoplankton. Moreover, localized elevated water temperatuers reduced the number of species of bottom-dwelling fish-food organisms such as worms, mollusks, and crustaceans, the greatest reduction occurring in summer within 300 meters of the point where the water was being discharged (38).

The Atlantic Marine Gamefish Research Program of the U.S. Fish and Wildlife Service is investigating the effects of thermal pollution by means of simulation studies. Researchers are concerned with the problem anticipated in the Cape Cod Canal as a result of operation of electrical generating plants (32). Warinner et al. report that increased winter water temperatures in the York River of Virginia (the result of the water passing through a power-plant condenser) caused depressed carbon assimilation by phytoplankton (38). Atomic-powered plants of the future may aggravate the already serious problem. Although warm discharges have been known to attract such game fishes as bonito and barracuda, the long-term effects may be highly deleterious. As Squire has suggested, it may be possible that warm-water discharges interfere with the normal migration of such species as the drums and surf perches.

In an era when America is in the throes of an energy crisis, the question arises of whether or not all this energy waste in power plant effluent could not be recycled, that is, put to some use rather than being discharged into estuaries and finally the ocean. Possibly it could be used to facilitate evaporation in desalination plants. According to John Clarke:

> Sea farming may offer the best hope of some day providing a needed outlet for discharges from coastal power plants; pilot studies now in progress in Boston and elsewhere in the United States are showing better growth of fish and shellfish in heated waters than in normal waters, but no economically feasible scheme has yet emerged. It appears, therefore, that for many years ahead we shall have to dispose of waste heat to the environment (7).

Oil and the Marine Environment. In a very real sense we are "pouring oil on troubled waters"—the waters being the oceans, already "troubled" with thermal pollution, sewage, industrial wastes, pesticides, and so on. The *oil* is coming from a number of sources: oil well blow-outs such as that at Santa Barbara (California) in 1969, tanker collisions, such as that of the Torrey Canyon, and coastal pipeline breaks. Much of this oil is also the result of deliberate discharges from tankers and

Figure 11-10. *Marine oil spill. A large volume of oil spreads over the water from the ruptured tanks of the stern half of the broken tanker OCEAN EAGLE lying aground on a shelf near San Juan Harbor, Puerto Rico. The 12,065 ton tanker, carrying 5.7 million gallons of crude oil from Venezuela to San Juan, grounded and split in half at the entrance to San Juan harbor in heavy seas March 3, 1968. More than two million gallons of oil spilled from the wreck forcing resort hotels to close their beaches. (Official U.S. Coast Guard Photograph)*

other vessels; some has its source in untreated industrial sewage. The Torrey Canyon break-up off the British coast was spectacular and made headlines, yet it released a mere 100,000 tons of crude oil—a veritable "drop" in the oil pollution "bucket" of roughly 8 *million* tons that enter our ecosystems yearly. According to the Massachusetts Division of Natural Resources, several tons of oil are spilled in Boston Harbor alone every third week (19).

ADVERSE EFFECTS OF OIL POLLUTION.　We shall consider the following effects of oil on the marine environment: animal mortality, food chain contamination with carcinogens, and the disruption of normal animal communication.

Mortality of Marine Animals.　The heaviest influx of oil occurs in the neritic zone, near the continental margins, the zone where virtually all of our shellfish (oysters, lobsters, shrimp, and so on) and over half of our commercial fish crop is produced. Max Blumer and associates at the Woods Hole Oceanographic Institution made a study of the effects of 700 tons of #2 fuel oil released from an oil barge that was grounded in Buzzards Bay, off West Falmouth, Massachusetts, in 1969. They report:

> Massive, immediate destruction of marine life occurred offshore during the first few days after the accident. Affected were a wide range of fish, shellfish, worms, crabs, other crustaceans, and invertebrates. Bottom-living fish and lobsters were killed and washed up on the shores. Trawls made in ten feet of water soon after the spill showed that 95 per cent of the animals recovered were dead and others were dying. The bottom sediments contained many dead snails, clams and crustaceans. Similarly severe destruction occurred in the tidal rivers and marshes into which the oil had moved under the combined influence of tide and wind. Here again fish, crabs, shellfish, and other invertebrates were killed; in the most heavily polluted regions of the tidal marshes almost no animals survived (3).

Figure 11-11.　*"Operation Pelican Wash." Coast guardsmen bathe one of some 500 pelicans which were coated with oil in the aftermath of the OCEAN EAGLE wreck off Puerto Rico. The pelicans were washed with an oil-dissolving solution. Unfortunately, the percentage of birds actually saved by these heroic measures is rather small. (Official U.S. Coast Guard Photograph)*

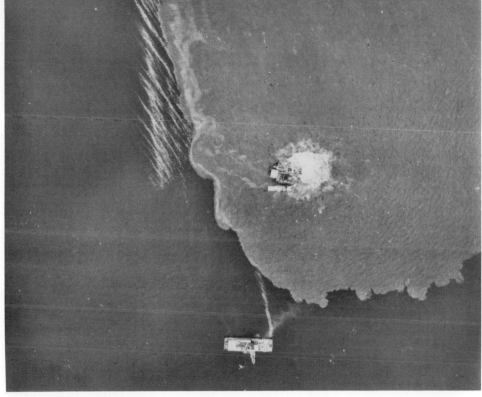

Figure 11-12. *Santa Barbara oil spill. A view from 1800 feet, showing the spreading oil leak from the well at the bottom of Santa Barbara Channel, as made in February, 1969. At bottom of photo is a barge which put down a pipe to the well in an effort to lessen the outpouring of oil from under the Union Oil Company rig (center). Thousands of gallons of oil covered the Channel and floated to and polluted nearby shores before the leakage stopped. (Environmental Protection Agency)*

Food Chain Contamination with Carcinogens. Crude oil is not just a single compound but a complex mixture of dozens of different hydrocarbons, including benzopyrene, an acknowledged cancer-inducing chemical (*carcinogen*). Body tissue analysis of sea cucumbers ("pickle"-like relatives of the starfish, which live on the ocean floor) indicates substantially higher concentrations than in the surrounding ocean waters. Although not as yet definitely established, it is possible that these carcinogens may also be concentrated in marine organisms consumed by man, such as shrimp, lobsters, or fish. The implications are not pleasant to contemplate.

Disruption of Chemical Communication in Marine Animals. Several of the hydrocarbons in crude oil mimic certain chemicals used by marine animals (oysters, starfish, lobsters, crabs, fish) as cues in guiding them during such activities as mating, feeding, homing, and migrating. For example, the males of some species may find a suitable female with which to mate by following a scent trail emitted from the female's body. Such chemical stimuli may also aid in food location. For example, certain chemicals in concentrations of only *a few parts per billion* may attract the predatory starfish to its oyster prey (19). It is apparent that the "flooding" of the oceanic environment with pseudo-signals as a result of oil spills might greatly derange the marine animal's behavior patterns, causing it to expend valuable energy

Figure 11-13. *Aerial view of a burning offshore oil platform in Gulf of Mexico just before fire was extinguished on March 10, 1970.*

The line of booms and barges across top center are ready to check anticipated oil spill. The oil, however, began to flow in opposite direction. Subsequent aerial views— including infrared color photography—by scientists of the U. S. Geological Survey, Department of the Interior, revealed the pattern of oil movement and helped in barricade and skimming operations. (Geological Survey, U. S. Department of the Interior)

in nonadaptive pursuits. The eventual decline in vitality and numbers of the species would seem assured.

Control of Oil Pollution. Let us examine some methods by which the oil pollution problem might be brought under reasonable control.

INTERNATIONAL REGULATIONS. Since the world's energy demands will increase sharply in the foreseeable future, and since much of this energy will be derived from oil that will be shipped via supertankers with up to 400,000-ton capacities, it would seem that oceanic oil pollution will become more "widely spread" than it has in the past. Since the routes of oil-bearing tankers belonging to several dozen different nations intersect in the global seas, it is unrealistic to assume that the individual nations involved will develop a strong sense of responsibility to prevent further oil spillage. The reasoning goes something like this: Since the ocean belongs to *all* nations, it belongs to no single nation in particular; therefore, no single nation has a

Figure 11-14. *A dead, oil-soaked bird—one of the many victims of the oil leak in Santa Barbara Channel in January-February, 1969. The leak started several miles offshore, at the site of the Union Oil Company's drilling rig. (Dick Smith, EPA)*

Figure 11-15. *This black and white print was made from a color infrared photo of the Gulf of Mexico oil spill of March 10, 1970. Firefighting boats are spraying water on hot platform metal (top). Oil can be seen flowing from underneath the platform (at top of photo). Note line of booms and barges attempting to check oil movement. (U.S. Geological Survey)*

399

well-defined responsibility to prevent marine pollution. It would seem that reasonable regulations would have to be formulated and enforced by an international body such as the United Nations. A nation whose tankers were guilty of flagrant violations would be subject to censure and possible economic sanctions.

POLLUTION ABATEMENT TECHNIQUES. Obviously such international regulatory authority would serve only to keep the number of spills down to a minimum. Once a spill actually occurred the volatile component would rapidly evaporate, causing a 25 per cent volume reduction within a few days. After several months bacterial decomposition would degrade the oil to a point where only 15 per cent of the original volume is left—most of it in the form of black balls of tar. Such processes of oil reduction, however, must be supplemented by man-contrived control methods. Techniques that were employed after the break-up of the 200,000 ton Torrey Canyon off the British coast in 1968 included (1) soaking up the oil with straw, (2) absorbing it with powdered chalk, (3) burning it, and (4) emulsifying it with the aid of detergents. The French were moderately successful in attempting to abate the oil problem with powdered chalk. Once absorbed by the chalk, some of the oil gradually

Figure 11-16. *Spreading chopped straw in order to contain oil spill at Santa Barbara, February 7, 1969. (California Department of Water Resources)*

sank to the ocean bottom. The British tried to burn the oil after applying aviation gasoline delivered by helicopter. When this proved ineffective, they scattered detergent in order to *emulsify* the oil, break the huge globules into smaller ones so that a larger surface area would be exposed to bacterial action and thus hasten decomposition. Although theoretically sound, the results were disappointing. Moreover, according to Wagner, the "cure was worse than the disease," in terms of the harmful effects on marine organisms (37).

In the spring of 1973 two Israeli scientists developed a technique whereby bacteria were used to break down the oil in the ballast water that is used to fill tankers after the oil has been removed at some port facility. This ballast water later is discharged when the tanker is ready to receive another load of oil. Theoretically, an oil slick could be "seeded" by helicopter with the bacterial powder, thus accelerating the rate of decomposition and ultimate oil slick break-up. In the process of breaking down the oil, the bacterial population multiplies rapidly to the point where it can be used as protein-rich food for livestock. The Israeli scientists estimate that 300 tons of animal food could be obtained by processing ballast water from a 200,000-ton tanker.

Figure 11-17. *Beach clean-up after Santa Barbara oil spill, February 7, 1969. (California Department of Water Resources)*

Marine Fisheries Management. We shall briefly describe the following phase of marine fisheries management: introductions, transplantations, habitat development projects such as the construction of artificial reefs, and the artificial induction of upwelling.

INTRODUCTIONS. One aspect of marine fisheries management is the introduction of food and game fishes into new suitable areas for the purpose of establishing or improving the commercial or sport fishing resource. Such introductions began in the late nineteenth century and are continuing today. The commercially profitable striped bass (*Roccus saxatilis*) industry that prevails along the Pacific coast (from Washington to southern California) and Atlantic coast is a notable result of introductions. This species was originally distributed along the Atlantic coast from northern Florida to the Gulf of St. Lawrence. However, in 1879 and 1882 a total of 432 individuals were planted off the California coast near San Francisco (18). Responding to a suitable physical and biotic environment, with abundant food and satisfactory breeding areas, the striped bass population increased so rapidly that commercial harvesting was possible in less than ten years. The striped bass has provided millions of pounds of food fish to commercial fisheries as well as splendid recreation for Pacific coast anglers (9).

Similarly, over 1.5 million young American shad (*Alosa sapidissima*), originally confined to our Atlantic coast and tributary streams, were taken from the Hudson River and stocked in the Sacramento River about 1880 (16). The shad catch increased forty-fold within sixty years, from 100,000 to 4 million pounds, and is well established along the Pacific coast from California to Alaska (5). The American smelt (*Osmerus mordax*) has become an important Great Lakes food fish since its introduction in 1912.

Occasionally, of course, a marine fish is transplanted by natural methods over which man has little control. Thus, fish spawn may be carried on the feet of migratory waterfowl for thousands of miles. In this way the southern stickleback (*Pungitius platygaster*) was probably introduced into enclosed west Siberian lakes from the Aral Sea basin.

TRANSPLANTATION OF PLAICE (*Pleuronectes platessa*). One of the pioneer experiments in fish transplanting was conducted by a British investigator, Garstang, about 1905, in an attempt to increase the plaice [1] harvest in the North Sea fisheries (14). From tag-recapture data it had been determined that growth in this species was correlated with food availability. Unfortunately, young plaice were numerous on the coast of Holland, where food supplies were scarce, but sparse on the food abundant Dogger Bank, with an area as large as Wales. Thousands of young 8-inch plaice taken from the Dutch coast were measured, weighed, and marked. Half were released immediately at the site of capture; the other half were transported in oxygenated tanks to the Dogger Bank for release. Recapture data indicated that the Dogger Bank transplants grew to nearly three times the length of the controls released off Holland. The International Council for the Exploration of the Sea conservatively estimated that the probable net profit in terms of increased fish yields resulting from a transfer of 1 million plaice from the Dutch coast to Dogger Bank would be about $15,000 (16). However, because a single nation is reluctant to finance a project

---

[1] Plaice = a flatfish similar to the flounder and sole.

whose fruits theoretically could be harvested by many countries, the operation has not as yet been undertaken on a commercial basis (18).

CONSTRUCTION OF ARTIFICIAL REEFS. Considerable interest has been shown recently by marine fisheries biologists in the potential of artificial reefs in providing food and cover for game and commercial species. Unger reports that artificial reefs are especially functional in raising the carrying capacity of otherwise flat, sandy coastal plains. As of 1965, nine artificial-reef projects had been launched in the United States; additional reefs had been completed in the Virgin Islands and Japan (35). Venice Pier in Los Angeles County is surrounded by artificial reefs constructed for the benefit of salt water anglers. In 1962 a reef composed of large boulders and building rubble was started in 70 feet of water off Fire Island, New York. When three years old, it was already frequented by large numbers of sea bass, squirrel hake, flounder, cunner, and ocean pout. The Sandy Hook Marine Laboratory constructed an artificial reef of sixteen junk automobile bodies sunk to a depth of 55 feet, two miles off Monmouth Beach, New Jersey. Monthly observations by scubadivers have revealed its attraction for tautog, cunner, black sea bass, scup, summer flounder, Atlantic mackerel, pollack, and others. The presence of a number of juvenile fishes generated speculation that such reefs may eventually function as nursery habitats. The laboratory plans to construct several more artificial reefs in the neritic zone along Long Island Sound with the cooperation of the New York State Department of Conservation. It may be that such reefs, much larger than the pilot types described, will not only diminish the municipal junkyard problem, but will provide increased sporting opportunities in an area of heavy recreational angling.

ARTIFICIAL INDUCTION OF UPWELLING. Upwelling and the resultant mineral enrichment of the important euphotic zone may be induced by artificial methods in the opinion of some authorities. It has been suggested, for example, that compressed air bubbling through perforated pipes laid on the ocean bottom may enhance the vertical movement of water sufficiently to fertilize relatively shallow regions of the ocean. According to Iselin, if the ocean bottom between Cuba and Florida could be adequately roughened (possibly by dumping gravel, rubble, or junk) the resultant turbulence generated by the Gulf Stream might bring cold, nutrient-rich bottom waters to the surface. Such nutrients might ultimately be carried into the Atlantic off the southeast Florida coast and increase fish harvests. Oceanographic experts from the National Academy of Science are of the opinion that nuclear reactors placed on the ocean bottom in areas of deep-lying stagnated waters might produce sufficient heat to cause bottom waters to rise and bring dissolved minerals to upper levels where they might be utilized by phytoplankton, and ultimately by fishes.

FISHING PRESSURE AS RELATED TO OPTIMAL YIELDS. In an attempt to appreciate the various positive and negative factors that determine the optimal yield of a fish stock during a given year, it would be helpful to express the pertinent relationships in the form of an equation discussed by Hardy (14):

$$S_2 = S_1 + (A + G) - (C + M)$$

S_1 is the harvestable stock at the beginning of the fishing year. In commercial fisheries it would represent the fish large enough to be taken by certain trawls and nets; they would be too large to slip through the meshes of the nets. In the context of

Figure 11-18. *A sport fisherman holds a big tuna which he caught off the California coast. (Southern California Visitors Council)*

sport fishing we might consider all legal-sized fish as S_1. S_2 signifies the weight of harvestable stock at the termination of the fishing year. A represents the addition of young fish to the harvestable stock as a result of the growth during the year. G represents the weight increment during the year as a result of the growth of A (after entering the harvestable stock) and S_1. C is the total weight of fish harvested during the year. M represents the weight of catchable stock that died as a result of all causes (both physical and biotic) except those associated with fishing. A obviously depends to some degree on food conditions, spawning success, and population density; G depends on the abundance of food and suitable temperatures; C, of course, is variable, depending on fishing pressure and the nature of fishing regulations; and M is based on such factors of the ER as parasites, competitors, disease organisms, predators, pollution, oxygen depletion, adverse winds, and thermal changes. An important point to remember in terms of optimal fishing pressure is that *young fish are more efficient in converting food to biomass than older fish.* Fishing pressure on an old-aged, slow-growing stock may be beneficial up to a critical point, beyond which the stock will be overfished, to permit younger age classes to become established.

In summary, for optimal sustained fishing harvests fisheries biologists must establish regulations that tend to ensure the most effective fishing pressure (or rates). To this end restrictions might be made on type of gear, seasons, regions, fish size, and even the number of fishermen.

Regulations. The formulation and enforcement of laws regulating the harvest of the marine fishery is essential to sound management. However, the establishment and enforcement of marine fishing regulations are infinitely more complex than are those for freshwater fish. The trout fisherman more or less expects to observe certain rules imposed by a state or federal agency so as not to undermine the delicate management of a sensitive and vulnerable resource. However, this is not the case for the fisherman of the high seas. As John Bardach, fisheries biologist at the University of Michigan (2), puts it, "The waters are international territory; they are not the property of a state, a club, or a landlord, and thus are the property of no one until they are captured. There are no international wardens; no fine is to be imposed for taking fish of sublegal size or in excessive numbers; no poachers are put into jail."

STATE REGULATIONS   The various coastal states have jurisdiction in establishing regulations governing fishing in territorial waters. A great number and variety of state laws have been enacted with respect to the restriction of season, locality, volume of catch, and type of gear. Although formulated with good intentions, both for the resource and the industry, it must be admitted that many of the laws are archaic and, in fact, prevent full realization of the marine fisheries potential. Consider the following examples:

1. Although abalone (a highly edible mollusk) is abundant along California's northern coast, state law forbids commercial harvest.
2. Trawl fishing is not permitted in southern California waters, although it is legal off central and northern California. Consequently, the 3 million tons of hake that are found seasonally off southern California cannot be effectively utilized, because they are taken almost exclusively by midwater trawl.
3. It is illegal to harvest anchovy off the coast of southern California despite an abundant stock that would easily yield 500,000 tons annually.
4. There exists a welter of state regulations associated with Atlantic coast fisheries, especially in the Chesapeake Bay area, which are as restrictive as those mentioned above (4).

This is not to say that all state regulations are poorly conceived. Many of them are certainly required and are effective. Nonetheless, many are still in the statute books because of pressure exerted on legislators by fishermen themselves. According to Wilbert Chapman, California Marine Fish Commission, our native fishermen are generally ultraconservative in their harvesting methods (5). They resist using newly developed devices for locating fish schools. They are against the replacement of their obsolescent boats with modern fishing vessels, so that they might favorably compete with more progressive, and aggressive, fishermen. Their resistance to change is based on an understandable effort to keep operating costs to a minimum, although in the long run the cost per ton of fish harvest would be less with the modern techniques and equipment. This attitude is deplorable from the standpoint of maximal sustained yield of a valuable marine resource.

INTERNATIONAL REGULATIONS.   It is simple for nations to adopt the philosophy that because the open sea belongs to all nations, the responsibility for their management belongs to no one in particular. Nevertheless, within the past few decades the phenomenon of decreased harvests of a particular species, such as halibut or tuna, despite intensified fishing effort, has caused concerned nations to form international

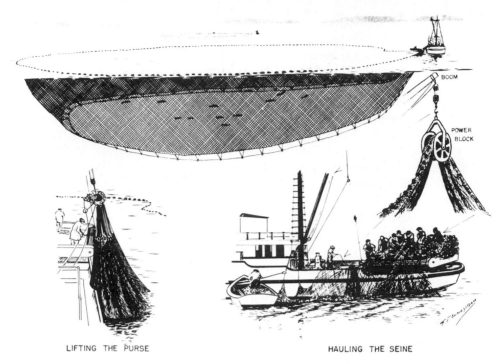

LIFTING THE PURSE   HAULING THE SEINE

Figure 11-19. *Salmon purse seining—equipment and techniques. (Bureau of Commercial Fisheries, U. S. Department of the Interior)*

Figure 11-20. *Chilean fisherman with big haul off the coast near Valparaiso. Many of these fish will be ground into fish meal. Just south of Valparaiso is the largest fish meal factory in South America. An average of 600,000 pounds of fish fillets are processed monthly and are mostly exported. (FAO photo)*

Figure 11-21. A large, yellowfin tuna about to be landed off St. Vincent Island, British West Indies. (Bureau of Commercial Fisheries, U. S. Department of the Interior)

conventions in which they agree to cooperate in halting further decline and in eventually restoring the fishery to a basis of maximum sustained yield.

Among the international marine fish commissions currently involving the United States are the following.

International Commission for the Northwest Atlantic Fisheries. Established in 1949, members of the International Commission for the Northwest Atlantic Fisheries include Canada, Denmark, France, Germany, Iceland, Italy, Norway, Poland, Spain, the USSR, the United Kingdom, and the United States. The commission coordinates research programs conducted by member nations. Haddock yields increased after mesh regulations were established by the commission in 1953 for two ocean regions (1, 23).

Inter-American Tropical Tuna Commission. Unlike most commissions, which are usually set up only after severe resource depletion, the Inter-American Tropical Tuna Commission was established during apparent tuna abundance. The IATTC with headquarters at La Jolla, California, operates laboratories and field stations in Puerto Rico, Peru, and Ecuador. In 1957, Milner Schaefer, the commission's first director (who is now director of the University of California's Institute of Marine Resources), predicted that the yellowfin tuna's maximum sustainable yield (MSY) would be 194 million pounds annually. This prediction has been borne out.

International North Pacific Fisheries Commission. The International North Pacific Fisheries Commission was established in 1952; its membership includes Canada, Japan, and the United States. The commission provides that a member nation would abstain from exploiting any stock being fully utilized and under conservation management by other nations. This regulation, in practice, is directed toward Japanese inroads on Pacific salmon stocks near the coasts of the United States and Canada (23). The precise definition of areas where salmon stocks of North American and Asiatic origin overlap has been determined only as a consequence of intensive commission-coordinated research (1).

Fish as a Future Food Source. Many authorities regard the ocean (our planet's last frontier) as a potential source of protein food that can be harvested in sufficient quantity to forestall the threat of global famine posed by the human population surge. Because the oceans cover 70 per cent of the earth's surface and receive the same percentage of the earth's incident solar energy, because marine phytoplankton are efficient photosynthesizers, and because the ocean is as yet relatively uncontaminated (although such pollutants as oil, pesticides, sewage, and industrial chemicals are of increasing concern in the neritic zones), there is some basis for this hope.

The Food and Agricultural Organization (FAO) of the United Nations has worked on an Indicative World Plan (IWP) so that accurate predictions could be made relative to world food supply and demand. S. J. Holt, director of FAO's

Figure 11-22. *International competition for the North Pacific fishery resource. The interest of the United States, Canada, Soviet Union, and Japan conflict in this region. The areas indicated in black include the best salmon rivers in the world. International fishing agreements must be formulated if the resources of the North Pacific are to be most effectively managed and harvested. (Adapted from Guy-Harold Smith,* Conservation of Natural Resources *(New York: John Wiley & Sons, Inc., 1965). After U. S. Fish and Wildlife Service.)*

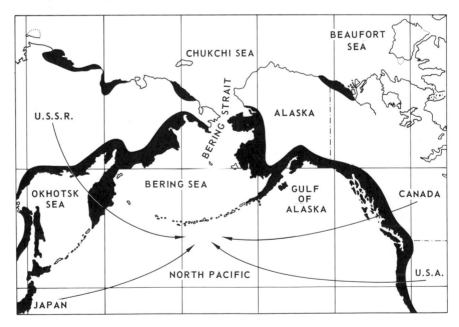

Division of Fishery Resources and Exploitation, believes that the estimated potential catch of 20 million tons in the coastal waters of the United States will easily meet our nation's demands of 10 million tons in 1975 and 20 million tons by 1985. He estimates that the potential *global* catch is roughly triple the 1969 harvest. His view for global production is equally optimistic: "It would be entirely reasonable to suppose that the maximum sustainable world catch of between 100 million and 200 million tons could be reached by the second IWP target date 1985, or at least by the end of the century." (27)

The realization of these goals, however, will demand much greater efficiency in utilizing the oceanic resources. First, it will require the development of new types of fishing equipment (especially for exploiting deep water stocks), the monitoring of equipment with TV cameras, and the study of behavioral responses of fish to the equipment.

Second, fish detection techniques must be improved. Survey planes of the U.S. Bureau of Commercial Fisheries research base at Pascagoula, Mississippi, flying at night over the Gulf of Mexico, have located schools of thread herring with the aid of an image intensifier. The faint bioluminescence caused by the school's movements is intensified 55,000 times before appearing on a TV screen. More developments of this type are needed.

Third, it will involve the breeding and rearing of marine animals and the upgrading of their food supplies. Some marine forms must be propagated and maintained on a semidomesticated basis, possibly in coastal bays. In Scottish coastal waters the growth rates of plaice, for example, have been greatly increased by adding fertilizer to the water.

Finally, the realization of a maximum sustainable world catch would involve our knowledge of the second law of thermodynamics. We will have to *shorten our food chains.* Instead of dining on halibut and snapper, we may have to move a link or two down the food chain, making greater direct use of crustaceans and perhaps marine algae.

Marine Shellfish

In addition to the true fishes our marine fisheries include a great variety of shellfish. Approximate value and poundage of the shellfish landings in a typical year are shrimp, $70 million, 240 million pounds; oysters, $25 million, 55 million pounds; crabs, $25 million, 245 million pounds; lobsters, $21 million, 35 million pounds (36). The economic importance of shellfish is apparent in the value ranking of America's ten most valuable fisheries: (1) shrimp, (2) salmon, (3) tuna, (4) oysters, (5) crabs, (6) menhaden, (7) lobsters, (8) flounders, (9) haddock, (10) scallops.

Shrimp Fishery. Although shrimp are our most valuable marine fishery, American stocks in 1965 supplied only about 40 per cent of the shrimp consumed by the American people; the remaining 60 per cent was imported. This resulted in a distressing dollar drain on the American economy. The annual American shrimp harvest has not been able to meet the enlarged market created by our burgeoning population and an annual per capita consumption that has increased from 0.8 to 1.4 pounds in recent years (4). The U.S. Bureau of Commercial Fisheries has employed several methods and approaches in an attempt to meet the nation's shrimp

Figure 11-23. *Shrimp trawler cleaning her nets off Sealevel, North Carolina. (Bureau of Commercial Fisheries, U. S. Department of the Interior)*

demands. For example, they have found dense populations of the large royal red shrimp (*Hymenopenaeus robustus*) off the Atlantic coast of Florida on the mud-and-ooze bottoms of the continental shelf, where water temperatures range from 46° to 52° F. Other populations of this valuable species have been discovered in the Gulf of Mexico 50 to 125 miles from shore at depths of 1,000 to 2,000 feet. Heavier gear, however, must be developed to make catches of these populations commercially feasible (9).

At the Federal Marine Biology Laboratory, Galveston, Texas, researchers are conducting intensive studies on various aspects of shrimp life history, including spawning behavior, feeding habits, migrations, response to temperature fluctuations, growth rates, sex ratios, pollution effects, burrowing and emergence behavior of young, predation, metabolism, longevity, and the relation of thermal influences on swimming activity (4). It has been found that most shrimp live only one to two years—indicating an extremely high mortality rate and a rapid population turnover. Special emphasis is being given to the destructive effects of hydraulic dredging for real estate development in the estuarine marshes used extensively by shrimp as nursery grounds. Because adult shrimp occur in deep water and young, rapidly growing shrimp are found inshore (after migrating from open-water spawning grounds), restrictions perhaps should be formulated that would prevent the harvesting (and depletion) of young inshore stocks. Finally, improved shrimp trawlers are being developed that operate electrically and enable shrimp fishermen to catch commercial quantities during daylight hours.

Oyster Fishery. Oysters thrive best in shallow bays or estuaries where temperature, currents, food abundance, salinity, and type of bottom are favorable. The American oyster (*Crassostrea virginica*) tolerates salinities ranging from 5 to 30 parts per thousand (13). Most oysters develop best on rocky or semihard mud bottoms. Occasionally oyster larvae will settle on the partially buried shells of previous generations.

Oyster colonies or reefs are frequently aligned at right angles to the prevailing water currents so that they can utilize them for the transport of dissolved oxygen and planktonic food organisms. The currents also remove metabolic wastes, sediment, and debris from the colonies (31). Oysters strain out plankton from large volumes of water swept into their gill cavities by ciliated tracts situated on the gill surface (9). Feeding activity is most intensive during the warm seasons.

Several biotic factors, including human activities, will be considered in relation to their effect on oyster mortality.

ADVERSE EFFECTS OF MARINE ORGANISMS. Oyster populations may be suddenly depleted as the result of a variety of biotic factors. Extensive oyster beds in the Chesapeake Bay region have been covered with dense blankets of Eurasian water milfoil (*Myriophyllum spicatum*), which has demonstrated explosive growth in the region since 1959 largely because of eutrophication. The milfoil's decomposing stems and leaves cause severe oxygen depletion; in addition, they cause mechanical interference with the oysters' filter-feeding mechanism. The fungus *Dermocystidium marinum*, which is the most destructive oyster disease organism in the South, has virtually eliminated seed oysters along the Louisiana coast during some summers

Figure 11-24. *Gigantic heap of shells of the highly edible and commercially valuable Pacific Oyster which was introduced to the West Coast from Japan. South Bend, Washington. (Rollin R. Geppert)*

and can be highly destructive along the coast from Delaware to Mexico. During recent years 77 per cent of the oyster populations off the New Jersey coast has been parasitized by the oyster crab, up to 161 parasites having been recorded on a single oyster host. The oyster crabs cause retarded growth and reduced vitality. The Japanese snail, which was accidentally introduced in 1907 along with infected Japanese oyster seed stock has been responsible for 15 to 22 per cent oyster mortality in some regions. Predatory starfish inflict several million dollars damage to the oyster fisheries annually.

ADVERSE EFFECTS OF HUMAN ACTIVITIES.   Man has destroyed oyster beds by establishing marinas, real estate projects, filling marshes for industrial development, and by using prime oyster habitats as dumping grounds for garbage and sewage. Oil spills may be deleterious not only to oyster vitality but to its commercial value. Thus, in September 16, 1969, 65,000 gallons of fuel oil spilled from a barge that had grounded off West Falmouth, Massachusetts. The high oil content of oysters harvested along the shoreline rendered them unfit for human consumption. The recent expansion of the paper and pulp industry along the Atlantic and Pacific coasts has resulted in toxic discharges that have proven highly deleterious to oyster growth and reproduction. Accelerated erosion due to poor agricultural practices, deforestation, and soil denudation at construction sites has caused the destruction of many once-profitable oyster fisheries along the Atlantic and Gulf coasts by smothering extensive oyster beds with sediment. For example, the neritic zone of Matagorda Bay, Texas, has received an accumulation of up to 14 feet of sediment, causing the obliteration of 6,000 acres of once highly productive oyster reefs.

Intricate chain reactions may be triggered by the excessive release of nutrients into marine waters, which may have deleterious effects on oysters. For example, several years ago a number of large duck farms on Long Island, New York, discharged large quantities of duck manure into streams tributary to Great South Bay. The sudden build-up of urea, uric acid, and ammonia, in combination with an adverse nitrogen-phosphorus ratio, resulted in a rapid population increase of several minute flagellates that ordinarily are quite uncommon. Eventually, they replaced the more common phytoplankton (green flagellates, dinoflagellates, and diatoms) that had been the principal oyster food. Unable to digest and assimilate the new type of phytoplankton, many oysters starved even though their digestive tracts were filled.

As in the case of other natural resources, the most serious threat to the perpetuation of America's oyster beds is exploitation by man. For example, overharvesting along with the gross discharge of a variety of pollutants reduced the public oyster fisheries of the Delaware and Chesapeake Bay regions to only 25 per cent of their yield in the early 1900's. Such population decrements could be more serious to oyster survival than that of most other organisms. Despite their great fecundity, oysters seem unable to recover their original abundance when reduced below a critical minimal level, even though afforded maximal protection from exploitation. Gross has attributed this phenomenon to the genetic inflexibility of small, isolated oyster populations.

OYSTER CULTURE.   The public abuse of the oyster resource, which continued unabated for much of this century, has largely been replaced by the far-sighted responsible programs of private interests. The commercial fishermen, who lease barren, unused areas of the ocean floor, have developed a type of oyster culture in which they provide a suitable substratum upon which the motile oyster larvae can attach themselves and grow into adults. This surface may be in the form of old mollusk shells, gravel, or even slag from blast furnaces. Once the larvae ("spat") have become affixed to the substrate, they may be transported by the fishermen to food-rich waters that permit a faster growth rate than the nursery grounds. The emphasis is on maximum production per unit of cost, time, and area. These culture methods are practiced primarily in the Chesapeake and Delaware bays and along the Louisiana coast. Oyster fishermen may harvest a "crop" of 100 bushels per acre under satisfactory conditions.

Because the adult oyster is immobile, and therefore has an extremely limited home range, it is more readily domesticated than forms, such as fish, that are highly motile. Researchers of the U.S. Bureau of Commercial Fisheries have been experimenting with a mode of oyster culture adapted from the Japanese. The bureau has established a series of artificial, brackish water ponds. Racks placed in the ponds bear thousands of clam shells strung on submerged wires. In this way the researchers utilize the *vertical dimension* of the habitat as well as merely the two-dimensional ocean floor in providing suitable substratum on which oyster larvae can become established. This technique substantially increases the carrying capacity of a given volume of oyster habitat. In Japan oyster culturists suspend shells from mobile rafts that can be towed to "plankton pastures" of suitable density for maximal oyster growth. Much of the ER that normally confronts oyster populations under natural conditions is reduced by this type of culture. For example, the ravages of bottom-feeding predators, such as starfish, are minimized. By such methods Japanese culturists have been able to secure an annual yield of 13,000 *pounds of oyster meat per*

Figure 11-25. *Experimental oyster ponds at the Bureau of Commercial Fisheries Biological Laboratory at Oxford, Maryland. (Bureau of Commercial Fisheries, U. S. Department of the Interior)*

Figure 11-26. *Experimental oyster raft. Mollusc shells are attached to the submerged ropes, thus providing an optimal substratum for oyster larvae establishment. Bureau of Commercial Fisheries Biological Laboratory, Oxford, Maryland. (Bureau of Commercial Fisheries, U. S. Department of the Interior)*

acre. Such a high meat yield cannot even be matched by livestock ranchers on land except under the most optimal conditions.

Marine Mammals

The marine fisheries resource includes whales, porpoises, walruses, sea otters, dugongs, manatees, and fur seals. Through the centuries these sea-going mammals have provided man with a variety of valuable materials—food and furs, bones and tusks for the fashioning of tools, ornaments, and illuminating oil. Here we shall consider the conservation and ecology of two marine mammals, the fur seals and whales.

Alaskan Fur Seal (Callorhinus ursinus). Fur seals may be observed during the winter season about 10 to 50 miles off the California coast, feeding primarily on squids and small fish, frequently diving up to 180 feet. After feeding they may float leisurely on the surface of the sea, making "parasols" out of their flippers in order to get some protection from the bright sun. The fur seal annually migrates between its breeding grounds in the Pribilof (300 miles west of Alaska) and Commander Islands in the Bering Sea and its wintering areas along the Japanese and California coasts. These journeys may be several thousand miles long.

BREEDING. This species shows marked sexual dimorphism; the ponderous bulls attain a weight of 500 to 700 pounds; the relatively puny cows weigh only 50 to 100 pounds. Many bulls may be fully ten times the weight of their cows. The sexually mature bulls (which usually overwinter near the Gulf of Alaska) arrive on the breeding grounds in late May or early June, before the snow has melted (26). They immediately stake out territories up to 40 feet in diameter close to the ocean shore. These territories are vigorously defended throughout the two-month breeding season. During this time the bulls take no nourishment and gradually slim down; some of them lose one third of their original weight. Territorial defense is a vicious business and occasionally results in the death of a badly gored rival. The younger bachelor bulls move somewhat farther inland and generally assume "bachelor societies" sometimes numbering many hundreds of individuals. The cows give birth to a single pup immediately after returning from their wintering grounds off the California coast and are bred by the harem master within one to two weeks. Each territorial harem master may have from 10 to 60 females. Periodically the cow will leave her pup to feed ravenously in the open ocean up to 100 miles from her home territory. Eventually returning, she instinctively seeks out and locates her own pup (from the hundreds of similar pups) and nurses it with her rich milk.

ENVIRONMENTAL RESISTANCE. The fur seal is plagued by a number of large predators such as the sharks and killer whales. A large killer whale may swallow a baby seal whole. Up to 24 have been found in the stomach of a single killer whale. A minute parasitic roundworm causes the death of almost one in every five pups on the breeding grounds. In 1964 roughly 22,000 pups died from one cause or another on St. Paul Island alone.

However, the greatest seal killer is man himself. In 1786, when the Russians discovered the Pribilof Island seal herd, seals on the island numbered at least 2.5 million (26). Nevertheless early in this century the Pribilof Island fur seal was almost extinct. Much of the decline was due to the environmental resistance exerted by the combined commercial sealeries of Japan, Russia, Canada, and the United States. The technique of pelagic sealing was especially destructive, for the animals were hunted during their migrations through the waters of the open ocean. Sealers would stealthily sneak up on the unsuspecting animals in canoes, a trick learned from the Indians of British Columbia. In the late nineteenth century, pelagic sealing rapidly expanded, and by 1879, 70-ton schooners were transporting hunters and canoes to sealing areas. About half of the kill from pelagic sealing was made up of pregnant cows. Almost 1 million skins were taken in the open ocean between 1868, when Alaska was annexed by the United States, and 1909. Under intense hunting pressure of this type, by 1910 the Pribilof herd decreased from an original 2.5 million to a mere 130,000.

PROTECTION AND MANAGEMENT. The situation was so serious that in 1911 it prompted the formation of the North Pacific Fur Seal Convention, composed of Japan, Russia, Canada, and the United States. This convention prohibited pelagic sealing (except by aborigines using primitive weapons) and instituted other badly needed restrictions on the seal harvest. Studies of the life history and ecology of the fur seal have been pursued by biologists of the U.S. Fish and Wildlife Service and have provided a "shore" of facts upon which a remarkably successful management program has been based. It was learned, for example, that the newborn have a 1-to-1 sex ratio; hence, because these seals are a polygynous species, a number of bulls could be harvested annually with no adverse effect on the herd. Currently, the United States has sole responsibility for the administration and harvest of the Pribilof herd. According to international agreement, the United States gives 15 per cent of the annual harvest each to Canada and Japan. Although normally only the three-year-old bachelor bulls are taken (at the end of the breeding season), in 1964, in order to reduce slightly the burgeoning herd, all bachelors were taken regardless of age, as well as 16,000 cows. As a result of sound international management of the herd, the Alaskan fur seal herd now represents about 80 per cent of the world's fur seal population.

In a typical year the United States sells 65,000 skins that have an aggregate value of about $4.6 million; the average value of a dressed, dyed, and finished bull skin is about $125. After the valuable skins have been removed by a highly skilled crew of Pribilof and Aleutian island natives, the stripped carcasses are processed into frozen ground meat, over 1.6 million pounds of which are sold as mink food to fur farmers. Since 1939 the Pribilof herd has sustained an average annual harvest of 69,000 skins (26).

Whales. Whales range in size from the 3-foot porpoise to the blue whale (*Balaenoptera musculus*), which attains a length of 93 feet and is the largest known animal, including those of prehistory. In 1926 an 89-foot female blue, 10 feet in diameter, was killed in the Antarctic. It was butchered, dismembered, and weighed piece by piece by the Japanese whaling crew and found to have a total weight of 300,707 pounds, or over 150 tons. It yielded over 56 tons of steak!

Whales may be divided into two major groups on the basis of feeding methods—the toothed whales and the baleen whales. The toothed whales include the porpoises, killer whales, and sperm whales, which feed primarily on octopi, squid, fish, and marine mammals. The killer whales (*Grampus sp.*) hunt in packs and may pursue a large baleen whale very much as a pack of timber wolves follow a deer. Aquatic birds and small seals may be swallowed whole. Whales frequently dive to considerable depths in their search for prey; a sperm whale (*Physeter catodon*) was found tangled up in a submarine cable off the northern coast of South America at a depth exceeding 3,700 feet. At least fourteen cases of such sperm whale-submarine cable entanglements have been reported (17). (Some recorded dive durations for several whales are sperm whale, 75 minutes; blue whale, 50 minutes; bottle-nosed whale, 120 minutes (20)). Occasionally sperm whales will void a compacted mass of feces known as ambergris, long valued as a perfume base. In 1953 a 926-pound lump washed up on an Australian beach and was sold for $120,000 (9).

The baleen whales include the gray whale (*Eschrichtius gibbosus*), right whale (*Eubalaena sp.*), humpback whale (*Megaptera novae angliae*), and finback (*Balaenoptera physalus*), among others. The baleen whales bear a series of 200 to 300 horny plates that extend downward from the upper jaw and serve as a mechanism for filtering plankton. Investigations over the last thirty-five years have shown that many baleen whales, including the fin and blue whales, feed almost exclusively on *Euphausia superba*, a minute crustacean. Almost a ton of these minute creatures have been found in a blue whale's stomach. Hardy and Gunther have shown a close correlation between *Euphausia* concentrations and whale abundance as indicated by catches (15). Sverdrup, Johnson, and Fleming have shown similar correlations west of Greenland involving sperm, blue, fin, sei, and humpback whales (33).

On the basis of the annually formed laminations in the waxy sound-conducting plug superimposed on the eardrum of whalebone whales, a life span of at least fifty years has been recorded for some individuals. Whale age may also be determined on the basis of seasonal growth variations of the baleen plates, as well as by the number of corpora albicantia [2] in the ovary.

CALIFORNIA GRAY WHALE (*Eschrichtius gibbosus*). The one species that one might have a fairly good chance of observing is the far-sojourning California gray whale. At Point Loma, California, where the National Park Service conducts a Public Whale Watch, hundreds are observed during their annual migration. The gray is 30 to 50 feet long, weighs about 20 tons, and is perhaps the best-known whale along the Pacific coast. Its 10,000-mile round-trip migrations are the longest of any mammal in the world. After spending the summer in the north Pacific, Arctic Ocean, and Bering Sea, the grays move southward to their wintering lagoons off the west coast of Baja California. There, in the shallow, warm, placid waters the cow gives birth to a single calf about 15 feet long and weighing half a ton. Mating occurs shortly thereafter and the impregnated cows, along with the bulls and calves, migrate to their Arctic summer home, traveling at an average speed of about 7 miles per hour and arriving at their northern destination in April.

Originally occurring all along the Atlantic coast in considerable numbers, the ill-fated gray whale apparently was eradicated in this region because of relentless persecution by the whaling industry in the nineteenth century. About 1850, observers in the San Diego, California, region could easily spot 1,000 of these magnificent mammals in a single day as they made their way to the wintering grounds. However, intensive slaughter by overzealous whalers who shamelessly harpooned pregnant female grays right on the calving grounds caused the apparent extinction of the Pacific coast population as well. Much to the delighted surprise and amazement of marine biologists and naturalists everywhere, the whales suddenly reappeared off the California coast early in the twentieth century. Carl Hubbs, eminent ichthyologist and marine biologist, estimated the population along our Pacific coast by 1949 to be in the neighborhood of 3,000 animals. Although the species is certainly no longer in danger of extinction, it is still on the protected list.

WHALING INDUSTRY. In 1846, when the American whaling industry was at its peak, a fleet of 746 ships, with an aggregate capacity of 233,000 tons and representing a capital investment of roughly $20 million, sailed the seas and netted the industry $7 million annually from the sale of whale oil and whale bone. Whale bone, which once commanded a price of $5,000 a ton, was originally used in the manufacture of everything from brushes to corset stays, from umbrella ribs to hoop skirts and buggy whips. These were the days when a whale had at least a fighting chance of survival, when the major weapon was the harpoon, hurled by the steady, muscular arm of the whaler. However, in the 1860's, when the Norwegians began to employ steamship, winch, and harpoon cannon, the industry soon made up in efficiency what it lost in color.

[2] Corpora albicantia = a mass of white connective tissue that eventually forms at the site where the egg was released.

The modern whaling industry employs two basic types of vessels, the factory ship and the catcher boat. The factory ship, or "mother" ship, hauls the dead whales aboard and butchers, dismembers and processes them with the aid of highly specialized machinery. The whale products are virtually packaged, frozen, or canned, ready for sale, even before the ship returns to port. The other vessel is the catcher, or "killer," boat. There are about twelve such boats for each mother ship; they are equipped with the harpoon cannon and do the actual pursuit and killing. Helicopters and special sonar facilitate their location. Once a whale is located the catcher ships move out for the kill, sometimes ranging as far as 100 miles from the mother vessel.

Today the whaling fleets of West Germany, USSR, Japan, Great Britain, and South Africa are composed of about 20 factory ships and 240 small 900-ton killer boats. Factory ship tonnage increased dramatically from 12,000 tons in 1935 to 586,000 tons in 1960, a 47-fold increase in only 25 years. The industry employs 15,000 men.

Currently the commercial whalers from Japan and Russia account for 85 per cent of a global whale catch that amounts to over one half million tons annually. The Japanese whaling industry, which alone employs more than 12,000 people, provides Japan with almost 7 per cent of its meat supplies. (The popularity of whale steaks in Japan is to some degree a matter of economics rather than flavor—a whale steak costs only $1.50 compared to $6.00 for a beef steak.)

In 1964 the American whaling industry operated only three shore stations, two at Point San Pablo, California, and one at Warrenton, Oregon. Operating from April to November, these stations took in a total of 274 whales of 7 species, including 147 fin whales, 64 sperm, 27 humpbacks, 20 grays, 13 sei, 2 blues, and 1 bottlenose. The fin whale harvest was the largest in 25 years, largely because of the great abundance of *krill*, composed principally of the minute crustacean *Euphausia pacifica*, which attracted the finbacks to the San Francisco area. Because of obviously depleted stocks, the humpback take in 1964 was only half that of 1963. The 20 grays were taken under a special permit for research purposes. In aggregate these whales were processed into 3.3 million pounds of meal, 3.2 million pounds of oil, and 4.5 million pounds of canned and frozen meat for use as animal food. The total value of these whale-derived products in 1964 was $734,000. Because of the severely depleted whale population all commercial whaling in the United States was banned in 1970.

The world's whale population has slowly but surely been depleted by man. For example, the blue whale population, which once numbered more than 200,000 animals prior to 1920, has been reduced to a mere 1,000 animals—a 99.5 per cent reduction! The blue whale has declined from 76 per cent of the catch in 1930–1931 (when 29,000 were harvested) to less than 5 per cent of the catch in 1959 when 1,200 were taken. In 1965–66 only *one* was caught. Each year since 1956, despite the most advanced techniques of locating and killing, there has been a steady decline in the whale harvest. This decline has continued despite the protective regulations formulated and accepted by the seventeen nations of the International Whaling Commission that was organized in 1946. The commission made it illegal for factory ships to operate in the calving grounds, and restrictions were put on total annual catch of each species. The commission employs the "whale unit" as the basis for regulating catch. Thus, one unit is equivalent to one blue whale, two finbacks, two and one-half humpbacks, or six sei whales. In addition to these restrictions, the whaling commission has zoned the ocean waters in such a way that the species most endangered secure at least partial sanctuary from the whalers.

Notwithstanding these regulations, the future is grim for these goliaths of the sea. There are several factors involved. First, whales have an extremely low reproductive potential. (This was not fully appreciated until an age determination method involving the examination of growth ridges on the baleen plates was discovered by the Norwegian scientist J. T. Rudd.) The female blue whale, for example, is not capable of giving birth until she is 4–7 years old. Moreover, because the gestation period of the blue whale lasts 12 months, and the nursing period 7 months, the average cow gives birth to a maximum of one calf every two years. Many ten-year-old cows probably have given birth to no more than two young (11). Second, many whales tend to concentrate in the summer waters of the Antarctic, apparently attracted by the swarming populations of crustaceans, their principal food supply. At this time, the whales become highly vulnerable to the explosive harpoon of the whaler. Third, and most important, the rules of the International Whaling Commission are not always respected. The whalers of signatory nations frequently pursued their short-term "quick buck" interests not only at the sacrifice of their future long-term gains (based on sustained yield harvesting), but also at the sacrifice of the largest and most fascinating mammals the human eye has ever seen. Thus, even though the commission recommended that the take in 1964–1965 be limited to 4,000 units, the fleets of USSR, Norway, and Japan brashly set up their own combined quota of 8,000 units—double the recommended catch.

In 1972 the United Nations Conference on the Human Environment recommended suspension of all whaling operations for ten years. Japanese and Russian whalers promptly rejected the recommendation and thereby incurred the heated antagonism of environmentalists and wildlife biologists, as well as large segments of the general public throughout the United States and Europe. At least 17 anti-whaling organizations in the United States have vowed to boycott all products made in Russia or Japan until they accept the United Nations moratorium. For example, Harvard University recently cancelled an order for an $85,000 Japanese electron microscope in protest against Japan's relentless persecution of remnant whale populations.

Ruthless exploitation by commercial whalers, however, is not the only threat to whale survival. Regrettably, even so called sportsmen are getting into the act. In his excellent book *Let Them Live*, Kai Curry-Lindahl, ecologist and conservationist for the United Nations Educational, Scientific and Cultural Organization, has described a lamentable example: "Recently . . . a new 'sport' has been introduced in Canada: killing white whales (*Delphinapterus leucas*) in Hudson Bay. The whale hunts are being promoted by the Canadian National Railways and supported by the Tourist Development Branch of Manitoba; according to a press release from the railroad, any sportsman who has $350 can kill a white whale. The limit is one beluga (white whale) a day and two per season. Native guides supply a motorboat, harpoon, and a high-powered rifle. The belugas, averaging about fourteen feet in length and weighing up to 1,300 pounds, are run down and harpooned at low tide in the Churchill River estuary and then shot."

Whales have been hunted for at least 1,000 years ever since the Basques pursued them in the Bay of Biscay. However, unless stringent conservation measures are both formulated and enforced several whale species may well go the way of the dinosaur and saber-toothed cat.

BIBLIOGRAPHY

1. Allen, Shirley W., and Justin W. Leonard. *Conserving Natural Resources*. New York: McGraw-Hill, 1966.
2. Bardach, John. *Harvest of the Sea*. New York: Harper, 1968.
3. Blumer, Max, Howard L. Sanders, J. Fred Grasole and George R. Hampson. "A Small Oil Spill," *Environ.*, 13, No. 2 (March 1971), 2–12.
4. Bureau of Commercial Fisheries. *Report of the Bureau of Commercial Fish Biological Laboratory, Galveston, Texas, Fiscal Year 1966*. Circular 268. Washington, D.C.: U.S. Fish and Wildlife Service, 1967.
5. Chapman, Wilbert McLeod. "Politics and the Marine Fisheries," *The Fisheries of North America*, Circular No. 250. Washington, D.C.: U.S. Bureau of Commercial Fisheries, 1966.
6. Clapham, W. B., Jr. *Natural Ecosystems*. New York: Macmillan, 1973.
7. Clark, John R. "Thermal Pollution and Aquatic Life," *Scientific American*, Vol. 220, No. 3 (March 1969), 18–27.
8. Council on Environmental Quality. *Ocean Dumping: A National Policy*. Washington, D.C.: U.S. Government Printing Office, 1970.
9. Cromie, William J. *The Living World of the Sea*. Englewood Cliffs, N.J.: Prentice-Hall, 1966.
10. Darnell, Rezneat M. *Ecology and Man*. Dubuque, Iowa: Brown, 1973.
11. Ehrenfeld, David W. *Biological Conservation*. New York: Holt, 1970.
12. Ellison, W. A. "The Menhaden," in H. F. Taylor, ed., *Survey of Marine Fisheries of North Carolina*. Chapel Hill, N.C.: University of North Carolina, 1951.
13. Galtsoff, Paul S. "The American Oyster," *Fishery Bulletin*, No. 64. Washington, D.C.: U.S. Fish and Wildlife Service, 1964.
14. Hardy, Alister C. *Fish and Fisheries*. Boston: Houghton, 1959.
15. ———, and E. R. Gunther. "Plankton of the South Georgia Whaling Grounds and Adjacent Waters, 1926–1927," *Discovery Reports*, 11 (1936), 1–456.
16. ———. *The Open Sea*. Boston: Houghton, 1964.
17. Heezen, B. C. "Whales Caught in Deep-Sea Cables," *Deep-Sea Rese.*, 4 (1957), 105–115.
18. Herald, Earl S. *Living Fishes of the World*. Garden City, N.Y.: Doubleday, 1961.
19. Holcomb, Robert. "Oil in the Ecosystem," *Science*, 166 (October 10, 1969), 204–206.
20. Irving, L. "Respiration in Diving Mammals," *Physiol. Rev.*, 19 (1939), 112–134.
21. Kabata, Z. "The Scientist, the Fisherman and the Parasite," *Scottish Fisheries Bull.*, 4 (1955).
22. Marshall, N. B. *The Life of Fishes*. Cleveland: World, 1966.
23. Marx, Wesley. *The Frail Ocean*. New York: Coward, 1967.
24. Nikolsky, G. V. *The Ecology of Fishes*. New York: Academic, 1963.
25. Odum, Eugene P. *Fundamentals of Ecology*, 3rd ed. Philadelphia: Saunders, 1971.
26. Riley, Francis. "Fur Seal Industry of the Pribilof Islands, 1786–1965," *Bureau of Commercial Fisheries*, Circular No. 275 (1967).
27. Schaefer, Milner B. "Oceanography and the Marine Fisheries," *The Fisheries of North America*. Washington, D.C.: Bureau of Commercial Fisheries, 1966.
28. ———. "Problems of Quality and Quantity in the Management of the Living Resources of the Sea," in S. V. Ciriacy-Wantrup and James J. Parsons, eds., *Natural Resources: Quality and Quantity*. Berkeley: University of California, 1967.
29. Sette, O. E. "Biology of the Atlantic Mackerel (*Scomber scombrus*) of North America," *Fishery*, Bulletin No. 50. Washington, D.C.: U.S. Fish and Wildlife Service, 1943.
30. "Shock at Sea," *Time*, 94 (August 15, 1969), 40.

31. Smith, Robert L. *Ecology and Field Biology*. New York: Harper, 1966.
32. Squire, James L., Jr. "Progress in Sport Fishery Research," *Resource Publication No. 39*. Washington, D.C.: Bureau of Sport Fisheries and Wildlife, 1967.
33. Sverdrup, H. U., M. W. Johnson, and R. H. Fleming. *The Oceans: Their Physics, Chemistry and General Biology*. New York: Prentice-Hall, 1942.
34. Thorson, G. "Marine Level-Bottom Communities of Recent Seas, Their Temperature Adaptation and Their 'Balance' Between Predators and Food Animals," *Trans. N.Y. Acad. Sci., Ser. 2*, 18 (1956), 8.
35. Unger, Iris. "Artificial Reefs," *Special Publication, Amer. Litt. Soc.*, No. 4. Highlands, N.J.: American Littoral Society, 1966.
36. U.S. Fish and Wildlife Service. *Fishery Statistics of the United States. Annual Report*. Washington, D.C.: Department of Commerce, 1968.
37. Wagner, Richard H. *Environment and Man*. New York: Norton, 1971.
38. Warinner, J. E., and M. L. Brehmer. "The Effects of Thermal Effluents on Marine Organisms," *Inter. Jour. Air and Water Pollution*, 10 (1966), 277–289.

12.

The Pesticide Problem

As crude a weapon as the cave man's club, the chemical barrage has been hurled against the fabric of life—a fabric on the one hand delicate and destructible, on the other miraculously tough and resilient, and capable of striking back in unexpected ways. These extraordinary capacities of life have been ignored by the practitioners of chemical control who have brought to their task no "high-minded orientation," no humility before the vast forces with which they tamper. . . . The "control of nature" is a phrase conceived in arrogance, born of the Neanderthal age of biology and philosophy, when it was supposed that nature exists for the convenience of man. The concepts and practices of applied entomology for the most part date from that Stone Age of science. It is our alarming misfortune that so primitive a science has armed itself with the most modern and terrible weapons, and that in turning them against the insects it has also turned them against the earth.

Rachel Carson, *Silent Spring,*
Boston, Houghton Mifflin Co., 1962

Causes of Pests

In undisturbed ecosystems there exist naturally occurring regulatory mechanisms (see Chapter 2) that keep population levels of a species at a point of equilibrium. However, whenever the original ecosystem becomes restructured by man, it tends to become simplified, with a resultant disruption of the stabilizing influences of density-dependent regulatory factors. The removal of forests to make way for freeways; the conversion of a swamp into a front lawn or a prairie into a golf course; the establishment of monotypic agriculture—that is, fields composed of a single species where originally there existed a natural ecosystem including several dozen plant species—all are examples of human intervention that tends to simplify the ecosystem. The net result is a man-made ecosystem characterized by high populations of a few species, in marked contrast to the original ecosystem, which was characterized by lesser populations of many species. In such biologically simplified ecosystems, a given organism may achieve "pest" status even though in the original diversified ecosystem it was never of economic concern. Let us give an exaggeratedly simple example. In the simplified ecosystem, organism X may be controlled by only one important predator (A). Any environmental change that would depress the population of predator A would, of course, result in a population surge of organism X. In the event that X attains a population level where it becomes detrimental to man—for example, as a transmitter of disease or as a destroyer of crops—it then may be classified as a pest. On the other hand, in the original biologically diversified ecosystem, relatively unaltered by man, organism X might well have been controlled, not only by predator A, but by predators B and C, and a number of parasites and competitors as well. In the more diversified ecosystem, it is readily apparent that a decrease in predator A might conceivably be countered by a concurrent increase in predator B, especially if they were competitors, so that regulatory pressure on species X would be maintained. As a result of the dynamic interaction of species populations, fluctuations within simplified (disturbed) ecosystems tend to be intensified, whereas those within a diversified ecosystem tend to be dampened.

Second, pests may become established in an ecosystem simply because they have been introduced from abroad. In so doing, man unwittingly releases them from their agents of control. Thus, of the 200 weed species regarded by the 1895 *Yearbook of Agriculture* as seriously detrimental to crops, 108 (54 per cent) were exotics (13).

Third, an organism may achieve pest status as a result of man's changing cultural patterns. For example, the lygus bug is considered a major pest to the lima bean industry because of the blotches it leaves on an occasional bean; nevertheless, before the era of frozen food processing, lygus bugs were considered of minor economic import (18).

Manufacture and Use of Pesticides

Before World War II most pesticides were unstable inorganic compounds (such as copper sulfate), which decomposed into their harmless components shortly after application. Organic pesticides were primarily derived from plant tissues. Thus, pyrethrium was obtained from chrysanthemums, nicotine from tobacco, and rotenone from the roots of tropical Asiatic legumes. Since World War II, however,

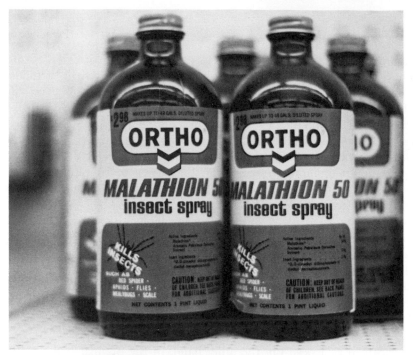

Figure 12-1. *A popular brand of insecticide which contains malathion as the active ingredient. According to the label it "kills insects such as red spider, aphids, flies, mealybugs, scale." (Michigan Department of Natural Resources)*

the great majority of pesticides have been organic compounds synthesized in chemical laboratories. Many of these, such as the chlorinated hydrocarbons, are *nonbiodegradable*; they may remain intact for many years in either water or soil (4).

The organic pesticide industry burgeoned at a fantastic rate in the immediate postwar years. Sales mushroomed from $40 million in 1939 to $300 million in 1959 and have now reached the $2 billion mark. By 1963 over 0.25 billion pounds of DDT were produced globally. In 1966 over 8,000 firms were making 60,000 different formulations from 900 basic pesticides. In addition to insecticides, other types such as herbicides, defoliants, fungicides, and miticides have been added. Escalating sales may be attributed to such factors as changing agricultural technology and farm ownership patterns (consolidations) but also to a multimillion-dollar advertising assault via all the communications media employed by big business. The use of pesticides will probably continue to expand because of the food requirements of a burgeoning world population and the implementation of insect vector control projects in underdeveloped countries.

George M. Woodwell, chief ecologist at the Atomic Energy Commission's Brookhaven National Laboratory on Long Island, brands pesticidal contamination as the world's most serious pollution problem. In the United States alone about 400 million acres are treated with pesticides annually. According to Robert L. Rudd, professor of zoology, University of California (Davis), in merely five control campaigns, against the spruce budworm (United States and Canada), gypsy moth

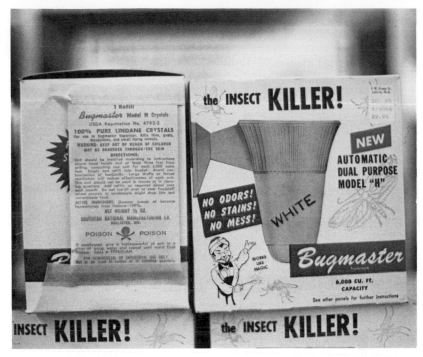

Figure 12-2. *A commercial insecticide employing lindane as the active ingredient. Note the warning on back of package: "Keep out of reach of children—may be absorbed through the skin." (Michigan Department of Natural Resources)*

(northeastern United States), Japanese beetle (mid-Atlantic, central United States), Dutch elm disease (northeastern and central United States), and the fire ant (southeastern United States), pesticides were applied to almost 5 *million acres* (16). In addition they are liberally applied to forests, rangeland, residential lawns and gardens, golf links, and parks. Local concentrations of these chemicals in the human environment sometimes approach alarming proportions. For example, a Tennessee farmer reported making 16 applications of 35 to 40 pounds of pesticides per acre, or an aggregate of 560 to 640 pounds per acre per season (4).

Classification of Pesticides

The following artificial classification of extensively used pesticides has been adapted from Rudd (16).

Insecticides.

ORGANIC PHOSPHATE COMPOUNDS. Examples of organic phosphate compounds are parathion and malathion. These chemicals inhibit the production of cholinesterase at the junctions between adjoining nerve cells. Because cholinesterase normally has the function of breaking down acetylcholine, a substance normally secreted by nerve cell axons when they are "fired," organic phosphate pesticides cause an excessive accumulation of acetylcholine, which tends to interfere with impulse transmission. Extreme muscular weakness, tremors, and dizziness are common symptoms in poisoned mammals. Fish and other aquatic organisms are apparently little affected.

CHLORINATED HYDROCARBONS. Examples of chlorinated hydrocarbons are DDT, dieldrin, and aldrin. The effects of these pesticides on animals are quite varied. However, DDT, the most extensively and abundantly employed worldwide, primarily affects the central nervous system. Symptoms in poisoned animals include increased excitability, muscular tremors, and convulsions. DDT residues frequently accumulate in fatty tissues (subcutaneous fat and fatty tissue of the mesenteries, heart, liver, thyroid gland, and gonads). With long-continued ingestion of contaminated foods, the DDT concentration in the fatty depots gradually increases. Residues may be released from these storage areas when stored fat is required as an energy source during periods of stress, as when the animal is engaged in strenuous physical activity (as a migration) or faced with food deprivation. Fish and other aquatic organisms are killed by chlorinated hydrocarbons because of impaired oxygen diffusion through gill membranes. Chlorinated hydrocarbons are quite resistant to biological disintegration by bacteria in either water or soil; in other words they are nonbiodegradable. It has been suggested by some authorities that DDT molecules may remain intact in ecosystems for twenty-five years. In clay-rich soils both DDT and dieldrin are less liable to contaminate food chains because they tend to be fixed by being bound to clay particles (12).

Rodenticides. *Sodium fluoroacetate* is an extremely hazardous rodent killer that results in hyperstimulation of the central nervous system (brain and spinal cord) and interferes with heart action. Because it is highly stable in protoplasm, it may be transferred in food chains. Rather safe to use, *warfarin* acts as an anticoagulant, depressing levels of prothrombin, a blood protein essential for blood clotting. Repeated intake of warfarin, therefore, eventually results in death from internal hemorrhaging.

Herbicides. The most extensively employed of the herbicides is 2,4–D, which causes plant death by accelerating growth rates. 2,4–D can be quite selective because it is much more effective on broad-leaved weeds (such as plantain) than on narrow-leaved crops (wheat, barley). 2,4,5–T has been used by the United States as a defoliant in Vietnam. The effects of its use on the environment have been highly adverse.

Fungicides. The fungicides are employed to destroy molds on seed grains, fruits, and vegetables. Many fungicides, especially those applied to seed grain, contain the element mercury. The accidental ingestion of this mercury (via food chains) may cause brain damage, kidney and liver malfunction, and death. During 1970 the U.S. Public Health Service became increasingly concerned with the relatively high concentrations found in the major rivers of at least twenty states. In some states, such as Wisconsin, anglers were warned against the excessive consumption of fish taken in mercury-contaminated waters.

Figure 12-3. *Aerial spraying of sulphur in order to check mildew on grapevines. Twenty miles south of Fresno, California. May, 1972. (EPA Documerica)*

Effect of Pests on Human Welfare

Pests cause irritation, mental anguish, pain, sickness, economic damage, and even death. Consider these items: The annual damage caused by rodents, insects, and weeds in the United States is $2, $4, and $11 billion, respectively (16). Ten per cent of the average annual cotton crop in the United States is destroyed by a single insect species—the cotton boll weevil. From 1940 to 1944 the codling moth caused a 15 per cent annual loss to American apple crops, equivalent to a $25 million set-back (8). The U.S. Forest Service reported in 1958 that insects inflicted mortality losses of 5 billion board feet annually as well as growth losses of 3.6 billion board feet. Among serious diseases transmitted to man by insect vectors are sleeping sickness, tularemia, dysentery, bubonic plague, typhus, Chaga's disease, Q fever, and Rocky Mountain spotted fever. According to E. F. Knipling, of the U.S. Department of Agriculture, mosquito-borne diseases alone are annually responsible for more than 100 million cases of illness throughout the world (13).

Figure 12-4. *Cotton boll weevil attacking cotton boll. Ten per cent of the average cotton crop in the United States is destroyed by this weevil. Pesticides have been employed to control its populations. (United States Department of Agriculture)*

Benefits Derived from Insecticides. It is no wonder, therefore, why mankind hailed the insecticidal properties of DDT during the years immediately after World War II. It is an excellent insect killer as are the numerous other insecticides that have been produced by the pesticide industry in the past two decades. There is no doubt that modern insecticides have been a boon to the agriculturist and have sharply decreased mortality caused by insect-transmitted diseases. Thus, Rudd reports that in Texas cotton bollworm control increased yields from 7,203 to 7,860 pounds and yielded a gain of $126.50 per acre. Weed control in a **North Dakota** barley field boosted yield from 45.5 to 49.5 bushels per acre and resulted in a per acre gain of $5 (16). According to A. W. A. Brown, writing in the *World Review of Pest Control,* DDT campaigns in Ceylon reduced human mortality by 34 per cent in a single year (24). They have been instrumental in controlling malaria, which at one time had such a high incidence that in 1938 Ralph Buchsbaum could state, "At least *half* the people who die, from all causes, are probably killed directly or indirectly by malaria" (3).

Negative Features of the Persistent Pesticides

1. MOBILITY OF PESTICIDES. DDT and other chlorinated hydrocarbon pesticides are highly mobile; that is, they can move rapidly and easily through a single ecosystem (corn field) or from one ecosystem (river) to another (ocean). DDT may

Figure 12-5. *Mosquito taking blood from a human arm. About 145 kinds of mosquitoes inhabit the United States. Their host preferences and life patterns vary so that a control method devised for one species may be futile against another. Entomologists therefore do not envision a single major defense against mosquitoes. United States Department of Agriculture scientists have pioneered in developing mosquito control methods including new repellents, better techniques for applying pesticides, and ways to enlist allies from among the natural enemies of mosquitoes,— parasites, predators and disease organisms. (United States Department of Agriculture photo by Robert Bjork)*

Figure 12-6. *Rice weevils in wheat. The United States Department of Agriculture is investigating the possibility of eradicating weevils and corn borers from stored grains by the process of irradiation. The point of an ordinary lead pencil is used here to show the actual size of the wheat grains and weevils. (United States Department of Agriculture photo by Fred S. Witte)*

be washed from a sprayed cotton field by run-off waters, and eventually be carried to a river and finally to the ocean. According to the U.S. Public Health Service, all major river basins in North America are polluted with dieldrin, endrin, and DDT. As the Health Service has warned, "these chemicals are undesirable additives to water and every effort should be made to keep their concentration not only below the threshold of any toxic effects but also as low as is reasonably possible." These pesticides may also gradually seep downward into ground water aquifers and eventually contaminate public drinking supplies. When water evaporates from an irrigated field, or from river or lake, the DDT molecules may *co-distill*—be carried into the atmosphere along with the evaporating molecules of water. Or DDT and the other chlorinated hydrocarbons may adhere to the soil particles of a sprayed field, be wafted aloft during a dust storm, and then eventually be washed to earth, lake, or ocean, many thousands of miles from the point of its original release. According to Paul Ehrlich, "four different chlorinated hydrocarbons have been detected in dust filtered from the air over Barbados" islands, hundreds of miles from the American coast (5). Various oceanic currents may carry the pesticide molecules to widespread regions of the world. The Gulf Stream, for example, might transport pesticide molecules that originated on a Georgia cotton field all the way

Figure 12-7. *Plane spraying DDT (one pound per acre) in a gypsy moth control project in the area of Lansing, Michigan. Spraying was done in 1954, prior to the banning of DDT. (Michigan Department of Natural Resources)*

Figure 12-8. *Sediment and soil samples are collected in the monitoring area here with a hand-operated corer to help scientists of the Agricultural Research Service, U. S. Department of Agriculture, study the impact of pesticides on the environment. Twenty-five cores are collected in a bucket and mixed together by a sifting process. One gallon of the mixture is then shipped to a laboratory at Gulfport, Mississippi, in a sealed can for analysis. (U. S. Department of Agriculture)*

to the west coast of Europe. The marine ecosystem has apparently been widely contaminated. For example, Food and Drug Administration chemists have found insecticide levels of more than 10 parts per million in 12 of 38 fish oils. Trace amounts (parts per billion) have even been found in the fatty tissues of seals and penguins from the Antarctic (12).

2. DESTRUCTION OF INSECT PREDATORS. Another deleterious aspect of broad spectrum pesticides, such as DDT, endrin, dieldrin, and many other chlorinated hydrocarbons, is that their use may kill not only the target insect, but also predatory species which may have been keeping the pest species at reasonably low levels.

The citrus industry in California was established on a large basis by the end of the nineteenth century. About the same time, a strange-looking flattish, snow-white insect, called the cottony-cushion scale, was accidentally introduced from Australia. The scale insects immediately began attacking the superabundant food source represented by the orange trees. These insects pierced the tender bark of the orange trees with their sharply pointed mouthparts and then rapidly sucked up the

Figure 12-9. *Two team members study a map of a pesticide-monitoring area where scientists of the Agricultural Research Service, U. S. Department of Agriculture, are studying the impact of pesticides on soil organisms, fish, birds, and mammals. In the background, members of a field team are bringing in a fish trap. (U. S. Department of Agriculture)*

tree's sap. Even if the scale insects did not kill the host trees, they could easily impair the tree's ability to produce marketable fruit. With its only natural predators 5,000 miles away back in Australia, the scale insect population surged upward. Many an orange rancher became threatened with economic collapse. Finally, after many attempts to control the pest met with failure, a natural predator, the *vedalia beetle*, (a type of ladybug) was introduced by C. M. Riley, an early advocate of biological control. With such an abundant supply of prey scale insects available (and flightless ones at that!) the vedalia beetle population soon flourished. Under this predatory curb, the scale insects were kept at relatively harmless levels for almost 70 years. However, shortly after World War II, the insect-destroying virtues of DDT were proclaimed across the land of America by aggressive, fast-talking pesticide salesmen. Citrus ranchers responded by making liberal and systematic applications of DDT to their orchards. In the excitement of using the new "wonder bug-killer," they pretty much forgot about the vedalia beetle and its 70-year record of scale beetle control. True, the DDT did kill some scale insects, but it also destroyed large numbers of vedalia beetles. In fact, they appeared much more vulnerable to DDT than the target insect itself. Predictably, the cushion scale population, released from predatory pressure, increased dramatically to levels reminiscent of the pre-vedalia years (14).

3. DEVELOPMENT OF RESISTANCE IN INSECTS. Another negative aspect of insecticide use is that repeated applications of a particular insecticide may result in the development of resistant or immune strains. It would almost appear as if the

insecticide were losing its potency. How is such resistance acquired? First of all we must appreciate that in all animal populations, whether mosquitos or men, there exists a great deal of *genetic variability*. In fact, even before a population of, say, house flies, is sprayed with insecticide X perhaps 1 per cent of the population may have genes that make them resistant to insecticide X, while the remaining 99 per cent do not have this special type of gene and hence are susceptible. How did the resistant flies acquire this resistance? Purely as a result of a chance change in the chemical structure of the sperm and/or egg cell from which the insect developed. Such a gene change is called a *mutation* and represents the "raw material" by which organisms, through eons of time, have been able to adapt to their particular environment—in other words, be biologically successful—in growing, feeding, escaping predators, mating, reproducing, and, in the present example, escaping the deleterious effects of insecticides. Let us suppose now that pesticide X is repeatedly sprayed on a given house fly population and that more and more of the susceptible population is destroyed while the resistant flies—those bearing the "resistant" mutation—survive. Eventually you may eliminate 99 per cent of the original fly population. You might think that such a 99 per cent reduction would be cause for jubilation. Not so. For remember, that the 1 per cent remaining are all resistant. Furthermore, since the house fly has an extremely high reproductive potential (producing ten generations yearly) within five years the resilient house fly population will have "bounced back" to its original population level before the use of pesticide X. (The reason for this rapid increase in numbers of resistant individuals is partly because of the fact that they have been released from competition with the nonresistant flies and partly because many of their insect predators were also destroyed by the same insecticide.)

The development of such resistance in pest populations is well documented. Since DDT-resistance in the house fly was first reported in Italy and California in 1947, resistance was also noted in malaria-transmitting mosquitos and disease-carrying lice (typhus) and fleas (plague). By 1943 12 species of insects had acquired resistance to pesticides, by 1954 25, by 1957 26, by 1960 137, by 1967 165, by 1971 220! Of great significance is the fact that this resistance is passed on from generation to generation. This means that progressively more toxic concentrations of the original pesticide must be employed or otherwise a new pesticide Y must be tried to replace X. However, the repeated use of Y will eventually result in a Y-resistant population, requiring still a third pesticide Z to keep it under (temporary) control. Moran et al. describe a classic example of such multiple-pesticide failure in the case of California's *pasture mosquito*:

> When DDT was first employed in 1945 the pasture mosquito population appeared to be under control. Within seven years, however, a DDT-resistant population developed, so a new chemical, *ethyl parathion*, was applied. By 1961, ethyl parathion was no longer effective, so *methyl parathion* was introduced; but it also became ineffective in 1963 as did *flenthion* in 1968. Presently there is no insecticide that can be used in safe dosages that will kill the pasture mosquito (14).

4. BIOLOGICAL MAGNIFICATION. Perhaps the most serious trait of the nonbiodegradable pesticides, such as DDT, aldrin, dieldrin, endrin, is that their concentrations are progressively increased as they move through the successive links of the food chain. Thus, even though the initial pesticide concentration, when released in the environment (cotton field, city park, lake, and so on) may appear relatively

harmless to wildlife (and man), by the time the pesticide has been channeled into the terminal link, the concentration may be *lethal*. A classic example of such biological magnification occurred in the marshlands of Long Island during twenty years of mosquito control involving the use of DDT. It had been assumed that the DDT would eventually be carried out to sea, be diluted, and be rendered perfectly harmless. After twenty years of control measures samples of marsh water showed a DDT concentration of only 0.00005 ppm. Unfortunately, however, the DDT was absorbed by algae, phytoplankton, and other marsh plants, stored in their cellular fat bodies, and then, by a series of ingestion-reingestion processes, eventually were so highly concentrated that the level in the terminal links such as fish-eating birds was 500,000 times the original concentration in the sea water (14).

Impact of Rachel Carson's "Silent Spring." During the years just before 1962 a number of scientists became apprehensive about the implications of continued massive release of the nonbiodegradable pesticides into ecosystems of which fish, birds, mammals, and man himself were integral components. They advanced the thesis that even though the short-term effects of pesticides were admittedly good, the long-term impact on the flow of nutrients and energy through the ecosystem's well-ordered but sensitive channels might be exceedingly adverse—for both wildlife and man. Most of these people were either ridiculed or ignored, not only by other scientists but by the prospering pesticide manufacturers. As a result, the average citizen was little aware that the wave of pesticide control might carry with it certain subtle effects deleterious to man. Then, in 1962, Rachel Carson, a distinguished marine biologist of the U.S. Fish and Wildlife Service, gave *Silent Spring* to the American public. Widely acclaimed throughout the nation, it precipitated a controversy that raged for years and even now has not completely abated. Miss Carson slashed through the arguments of the propesticide people. She described the pesticide industry as an industrial colossus inflicting environmental abuse on an unsuspecting society with little regard for future consequences and with primary interest in immediate monetary gains. This was disturbingly reminiscent of the "cut-out-and-get-out" tactics of the early lumber barons at the turn of the century or of the abuse wrought on our prairies by the wheat farmers of the 1930's.

Cycling of Pesticides in the Ecosystem

To elucidate the mechanisms by which pesticide residues may eventually have detrimental effects on other than target organisms, we cite two case histories.

Case History One: Dutch Elm Disease Control. The American elm is a stately tree, providing beauty and shade for countless urban dwellers, gracing parks, boulevards, and college campuses, and supplying cover, food, and nesting sites for many species of birds. Today, many elms throughout the Midwest and Northeast are either dead or dying because of an exotic fungus accidentally introduced from Europe about 1933. This parasite plugs the tree's phloem tubes, thus interfering with food transport from leaves to roots. The spores of the fungus are effectively dispersed by minute brownish bark beetles, also of European origin. The first indications that elms are afflicted are premature (midsummer) leaf yellowing and

Figure 12-10. *Washington, D. C., near the Jefferson Memorial. The branches of an American elm tree are cut off as the first step in destroying the tree which is infected with Dutch elm disease. The tree has witnessed the passing of twelve Presidents and several generations of Washingtonians. It will take eighty years to grow another tree of this size.* (U. S. Department of Agriculture)

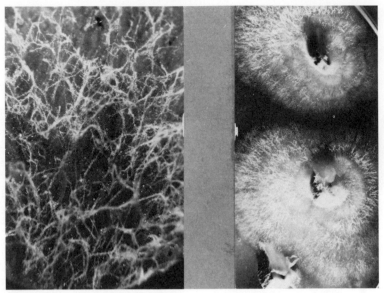

Figure 12-11. *(Left) Mycelium growing from spores of Dutch elm disease over surface of agar in a Petri plate. (Right) Chips of wood infected with Dutch elm disease in agar culture in a Petri plate, with fungus growing on them. (U. S. Department of Agriculture)*

defoliation. Although sanitary measures, such as the removal and burning of diseased trees, would be effective in controlling the disease, they are laborious and time consuming.

Under early recommendations from both federal and state agencies, thousands of municipalities initiated intensive DDT spray campaigns to control the elm disease. About 2 to 5 pounds of DDT were employed per tree, usually as a "slurry" (wettable DDT powder suspended in water), by means of spray trucks that projected streams of the insecticide into elm canopies. Because DDT is lethal to the elm bark beetles, this method would seem excellent for halting the spread of the disease across mid-America. On the contrary, however, although such control campaigns have been mounted vigorously, by 1974 the disease had spread from Massachusetts south to Virginia and west to Minnesota.

In the wake of Dutch elm disease control, communities throughout the elm's range are not only experiencing "silent springs" but silent summers, autumns, and winters as well. Although it is extremely difficult if not impossible to prove (dead animals were rarely observed in nature even before the advent of modern pesticide assaults), several authorities, including Rudd, are of the firm opinion that literally *millions* of birds in the United States have succumbed to DDT sprays intended for elm bark beetles.

In 1950 R. J. Barker and his colleagues initiated studies on the University of Illinois campus that revealed how DDT is concentrated as it is transferred from link to link of avian food chains (2). The data from his studies, and from those of George Wallace on the Michigan State University campus, provide insights into the events leading to avian mortality. First, the concentration of the DDT in the home range of a bird may be so high immediately after spraying (remember that 2

Figure 12-12. *European elm bark beetle many times enlarged. This insect may transmit the spores of the fungus that causes Dutch elm disease to healthy trees. (U. S. Department of Agriculture)*

to 5 pounds may be used per tree) that the bird dies shortly thereafter from ingesting contaminated foods, such as insects, worms, buds, and so on. Many bird watchers and biologists have observed the tremors and convulsions of dying birds in the wake of control programs.

Second, more subtly but perhaps more significantly, mortality results from the delayed expression of the pesticide. DDT remains on the elm leaf surface all summer long despite intermittent showers. After leaf fall in autumn the DDT, which is extremely stable, gradually becomes incorporated into the soil as the leaf fragments are decomposed by soil bacteria and fungi. Earthworms may subsequently become contaminated by ingesting leaf fragments. Tissue analysis of earthworms collected shortly after summer spraying revealed that *all* worms contained residues ranging from 4 parts per million in the nerve cord to 403 parts per million in the crop and gizzard. Of even greater interest, six earthworms secured six months *after* the last application averaged 86 parts per million of DDT and 33 parts per million of DDE (a metabolic derivative of DDT).

Shortly after migrant birds return in the spring from their wintering grounds, they begin consuming contaminated worms. It has been estimated that the ingestion of 11 contaminated worms might be fatal to an adult robin—a quantity easily consumed by a hungry bird in less than an hour. The ingested DDT becomes stored and eventually concentrated in the animal's fatty tissues. Up to 120, 252, and 744 parts per million of DDE have been found in the heart, brain, and liver, respectively, of dead robins. If stored in the gonads, DDE may interfere with gonadal development and function. The reproductive capacity of the bird may be depressed by impaired fecundity, fertility, hatching success, or vigor of the nestling.

Now that DDT has been banned, several alternative methods of Dutch elm disease control are being investigated. One involves the use of methoxychlor. Although a chlorinated hydrocarbon like DDT, it breaks down more rapidly, and appears to be much less destructive to wildlife. Another involves the interspersion of elms with other species such as sugar maple and ironwood. Other methods being studied included the development of resistant American-Siberian elm hybrids, the application of beetle-repellents to the elms and the use of parasitic wasps.

Figure 12-13. *Washington, D. C. The work of the elm bark beetle is visible (short dark veins) where the bark has been cut from this tree. (U.S. Department of Agriculture)*

Case History Two: Gnat Control in California. Clear Lake, located only 90 miles from San Francisco, has been a favored waterfowl nesting area for many years. In autumn, hunters would converge on the 19-mile-long lake. In 1949 a combined state and federal program was launched to eradicate the tiny gnat that formed dense cloudlike swarms and proved irritating to fishermen and other vacationists. Fourteen thousand gallons of TDE, a chlorinated hydrocarbon, were applied to the lake to destroy the insect's early aquatic stages. The concentration of the insecticide was only 0.02 part per million. By 1975 two additional applications of TDE were made. A few years after the campaign was launched the bodies of dead fish, gulls, ducks, geese, and grebes began to litter the beaches. In particular, the breeding population of the western grebe, a handsome diving bird, was drastically reduced from 800 to only 30 pairs, a decrement of over 96 per cent. Wildlife officials, bird watchers, and hunters became alarmed.

In the ensuing investigation by Eldridge G. Hunt and Arthur I. Bischoff of the California Department of Fish and Game, the bodies of dead grebes were dissected but revealed no internal parasites that might have caused the deaths (10). However, chemical analysis of the gonads revealed high concentrations of TDE. Chemical studies of other organisms in the lake indicated further that the grebes became poisoned by way of the algae-crustacean-fish links in the food chain of which they formed the terminal link. The TDE was originally absorbed by the algae and then transferred with its molecular structure intact to successive links, each functioning as a *biological magnifier* of the pesticide. Thus, although the original concentration of the pesticide was only 0.02 part per million, the crustaceans showed 5 parts per million, the tissues of crustacean-consuming fish revealed several hundred parts per million, and the gonads of fish-eating grebes showed an astounding 1,600 parts per million of TDE, an 80,000-fold increase over the original concentration (10). Apparently the insecticide severely impaired grebe reproduction. One grebe egg finally hatched successfully in 1962 after ten years (1951–1961) of complete nesting failure. The insecticide has shown great persistence, 808 parts per million being found in the fat of grebes in 1963, six years after the last application.

Sublethal Effects of Pesticides on Wildlife

The death of a fish, bird, or mammal is a forthright event, obviously resulting in a population decrement of one. However, of possibly more profound import to a

Figure 12-14. *Research biologist for the Minnesota Department of Natural Resources dissects rooster pheasant in order to determine cause of death. If no overt cause of death, such as internal hemorrhage, is discovered, tissues may be analysed for possible pesticide poisoning. (Walter H. Wettschreck, Minnesota Department of Natural Resources)*

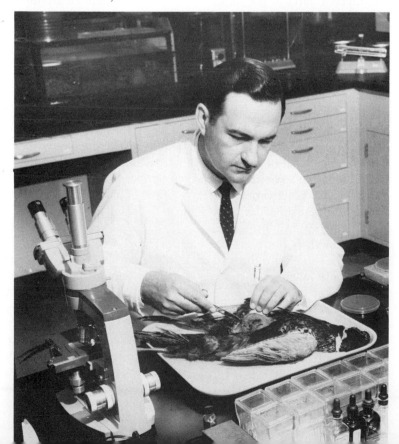

wild animal's population density are the subtle sublethal effects involving reduced vigor, modified behavior, retarded growth, and impaired reproductive function.

There is no evidence available from studies of natural populations that pesticide use has reduced their well-being or vigor. However, there is abundant presumptive evidence from laboratory tests. For example, many hydrocarbons (the chemical group to which DDT and dieldrin belong) are mutagenic in their action; that is, they are capable of inducing mutations in hereditary material. According to Rudd, geneticists employ such hydrocarbons to develop new crop strains. Experimental work by Dewitt has shown that when adult pheasants or quail are given long-sustained diets contaminated with sublethal amounts of chlorinated hydrocarbons, not only do they incur reduced vitality but they *pass this trait along to their progeny* (16).

Field observations reveal that even though wild animals may survive pesticidal exposure, their behavior patterns may be modified in such a way as to increase vulnerability to predators. This phenomenon has been recorded in insects, fish, birds, and meadow mice. Because of their need for increased oxygen, affected fish swim near the water's surface where they become easy prey for herons, egrets, and gulls. H. S. Shellhammer has shown a correlation between cholinesterase levels in the brain and learning ability in wild mice (17). By injecting the animals with parathion he was able to depress cholinesterase levels 25 to 50 per cent. Even though cholinesterase levels returned to normal three to four weeks later, the learning ability of the poisoned animals was impaired.

Surprisingly, DDT may actually have a *stimulating* effect on the reproductive processes of mites. Apparently certain nutrient elements in DDT such as nitrogen and phosphorus are first absorbed from the soil by the plant and metabolized. The mites then secure these nutrients from the plant. The ultimate effect is enhanced reproductive rates in the mites. Thus, despite expensive attempts at chemical control, the result is a population surge of the target organism (16).

DDT and Egg Shell Thinning in Birds. The peregrine falcon (duck hawk) is a magnificent animal, a supreme master of aerial maneuver. After pursuing a flock of teal for several miles and causing one or two birds to lag behind the main flock, the duck hawk will plunge precipitously toward its prey, attaining speeds up to 180 miles per hour. (This is the greatest speed attained by any animal in the world except for the Mesopotamian swift.) As the falcon's sharp talons rip through the helpless prey, the latter is killed instantaneously. (Certainly, the teal's fate is more desirable than that of many ducks that have been "crippled" by sportsmen and left to die slowly in some marsh. And, remember, the peregrine kills only in order to prevent its own starvation; we can't say as much for the duck hunter.) Without doubt, the peregrine has been a most "colorful" and exciting component of the North American wildlife scene.

In recent years, however, the peregrine, along with a few other flesh-eating species such as the osprey and the bald eagle, has seriously declined in numbers throughout much of its range, and, indeed, is on the verge of extinction in eastern United States. What has happened? Many scientists believe that most of the decline has been caused by the widespread dissemination of chlorinated hydrocarbon pesticides into the environment, especially since World War II. In recent years the number of young birds successfully reared per nest has sharply decreased. Ornithologists have not only noted that *fewer eggs* have been laid per nesting female, but also that

Figure 12-15. *Osprey at lookout post. The dramatic decline of this exciting fish hawk in the past two decades has been attributed to DDT-contamination of its prey. (Photo by Wisconsin Natural Resources Dept., Madison, Wis.)*

many of the eggs that *are* laid have abnormally thin shells. The weight of the incubating female frequently causes breakage of the thin-shelled eggs and the death of the embryo inside. Analyses of the thin-shelled eggs have revealed high levels of DDT, dieldrin, and other chlorinated hydrocarbons, up to 2,500 ppm being recorded for some eggs. Examination of eggs of known age in museums have shown that eggs laid prior to 1945 were relatively thick-walled, whereas those laid after 1945, when the wide scale use of DDT was initiated, had considerably thinner shells.

Controlled experiments in which DDT and dieldrin were fed in large quantities to mallards and sparrow hawks have confirmed the relationship between high chlorinated hydrocarbon levels and thin egg shells. A few experiments, however, have yielded conflicting results. George Moriber observes: "In 1971 it was reported that leghorn hens fed a diet of 100 and 200 ppm of DDT respectively, or diets containing 10–20 ppm dieldrin for a 12-week period produced *no decrease* in the thickness of the eggshells. In fact, those hens that were fed dieldrin laid eggs with thicker and heavier shells than those who received their regular feed. There was no effect on egg production or the weight of the eggs. It is entirely possible that some species are more sensitive than others to chlorinated hydrocarbon pesticides (15)."

Figure 12-16. *Newly hatched pheasant chicks. Experiments have shown that the ingestion of DDT-contaminated food greatly reduces the clutch size and hatching success in this species. (Wisconsin Natural Resources Department, Madison, Wis.)*

The precise mechanism involved in egg shell thinning is as yet unknown. However, available evidence suggests that the chlorinated hydrocarbons stimulate the liver to produce certain enzymes, which in turn reduce the levels of the hormone estrogen in the female bird. Apparently a certain minimum level of estrogen is essential for the production of normal-shelled eggs.

Pesticidal Effects on Fish. In recent years laboratory and field studies have been vigorously pursued to determine whether fish accumulate pesticide residues in their tissues, and, if so, whether these residues are harmful. Researchers of Wisconsin's Department of Natural Resources recently conducted a survey of 2,673 fish of thirty-five species taken from inland lakes and streams as well as from the Mississippi River and Lakes Michigan and Superior. *Every fish sample contained DDT or a chemically related pesticide.* Seventy per cent of the fish were contaminated with dieldrin, another nonbiodegradable chlorinated hydrocarbon (11).

Various researchers have found correlations between pesticide residues in fish tissues and impaired fecundity, fertility, and growth rate. Such sublethal effects obviously may have as great significance in depressing fish populations as direct mortality itself. Recently Anderson and Peterson have reported that although DDT did not result in locomotor or visual impairment of experimental brook trout, it reduced their learning ability, that is, their ability to form an association between a connecting doorway and escape from electric shock (1).

Effect of Ingested Pesticides on Human Health

There is no doubt that the persistent pesticides, such as DDT, dieldrin, and endrin, under some conditions, may cause considerable wildlife mortality, especially among fish, waterfowl, gallinaceous birds (pheasants, grouse, and quail), and songbirds (thrushes, warblers, and vireos). However, for many people who are not hunters, anglers, bird watchers, or nature lovers, such mortality does not cause great concern. But what about man himself? This is the most controversial aspect of the pesticide problem. We shall adopt no affirmative or negative position here but attempt to present both sides of the question.

In 1964 Mississippi's Congressman Jamie L. Whitten participated in a pesticide symposium sponsored by the prestigious National Academy of Sciences–National Research Council. As chairman of the House Appropriations Subcommittee on Agriculture, he asked his investigations staff to collect data relating to pesticide effects on public health. His staff interviewed twenty-three physicians, officials of the American Medical Association, professors at university medical schools, and 185 outstanding scientists, including specialists in the fields of biology, biochemistry, nutrition, pharmacology, toxicology, conservation, agriculture, and public health. We shall list some of the main points elucidated by Congressman Whitten (20):

1. In a test conducted by scientists of the U.S. Public Health Service and the Food and Drug Administration, a dose of 0.027 ounce of DDT was ingested by a human volunteer without adverse effect. However, other volunteers have felt ill after ingesting the equivalent of 0.024 ounce for a 150-pound man. Of course, ingestion of greater doses of DDT may prove fatal. Thus, 4 of 23 cases of DDT ingestion (15 of which involved attempted suicides) listed in the 1951 *Journal of the American Medical Association* had fatal results.

2. Wayland J. Hayes, Jr., toxicologist for the U.S. Public Health Service, stated at a congressional hearing that the death rate from insecticide poisoning in the United States remained at 1 per million people ever since 1939 despite the widespread use of organic phosphates and chlorinated hydrocarbons since 1946.

3. At the Congress on Environmental Health Problems held by the American Medical Association in 1964, Robert Blackwell Smith, Jr., president of the Medical College of Virginia, stated that he knew of "no evidence that the presence of pesticide residues in the human diet at or below tolerance levels, set by law on the basis of animal data, has had any adverse effect on the health of our citizens."

4. Although the ingestion of increased amounts of DDT results in a gradual increase in the amount stored in body tissues, an equilibrium is eventually reached at about 10 to 12 parts per million. Reported by Hayes, these findings would appear to allay the apprehension, so eloquently articulated by Rachel Carson, that pesticide residue might gradually build up to a threshold in human tissue that would result in some insidious malady with perhaps fatal consequences.

5. According to Frederick J. Stare, Harvard nutritionist, "there is not one medically documented instance of ill health in man, not to mention death, that can be attributed to the proper use of pesticides or even to their improper use as far as ill health from residues on foods."

6. Will DDT residues in the human body cause cancer? In an early study rats developed low-grade malignancies after eighteen months of DDT ingestion with food. However, because cancers have not subsequently been introduced in other test animals when purer forms of DDT were employed, it is assumed the cancers may have been induced by impurities taken along with the DDT. Moreover, similar tumors can be induced simply by *overfeeding* the animals. One pesticide, DDD, chemically allied to DDT, has actually been used to *reduce* tumors of the adrenal cortex. Although liver tumors can indeed be induced in mice with the chlorinated hydrocarbons aldrin and dieldrin, they are benign. Aminotriazole, the herbicide responsible for the cranberry scare in 1958, does cause thyroid growths in rats, considered to be cancerous by some; however, the Food and Drug Administration prohibits any residues of this chemical on foods.

It would appear from the preceding material that the threat of pesticides to human health is more imagined than real and that there is little basis for controversy. Nothing is farther from the truth. There are many highly regarded medical men, biologists, and ecologists who are definitely concerned despite assurances of the type just presented. Malcolm M. Hargraves, senior consultant of the Mayo Clinic, is of the belief that *more fatalities are caused by pesticides in the United States than by car accidents.* If he is correct, this means that pesticides are killing about 60,000 Americans yearly—about 18 times the mortality rate for American soldiers killed in action during the Vietnam war. Antipesticide crusaders are apprehensive about the increasing contamination of human diets. It is almost impossible not to ingest pesticide residues today. A recent study by the Food and Drug Administration showed that 50 per cent of many thousands of food samples contained pesticide residues; not only this, but 3 per cent contained residues above the legally accepted levels. It is ironic that the U.S. Department of Agriculture has had to reimburse farmers more than $1 million since 1964 for dumping milk with DDT residues above the legal limits, when this very same department vigorously recommended the use of DDT.

One would suppose that tolerance limits set by the federal government would unquestionably fulfill their objective: the prevention of pesticide poisoning in man. However, Paul Ehrlich, distinguished Stanford biologist, scoffs at such naiveté, "First of all most tolerances are set on the basis of short-term animal experiments and are set one poison at a time. Then, when it proves to be impossible to keep tolerances within limits, pressures are brought on the government, and the tolerances are conveniently raised."

Even though it has been suggested by American toxicologists that DDT residues in human tissues will stabilize at about 10 parts per million, up to 19.2 parts per million have been found in the fatty tissues of Israelis. The American public has been assured that pesticide residues in human tissues should be no cause for concern. Many knowledgeable people, however, are skeptical. Like Rachel Carson, their thoughts go something like this: "But do we really know? Perhaps no dire effects have been recorded to date. But the pesticide program is still in its infancy, and DDT residues have been present in human tissues for twenty-five years at most. How do we know that tissue storage of DDT for thirty or forty years will not ultimately result in serious affliction and death?" Such skepticism is often ridiculed by the propesticide forces as being the product of hysteria and emotionalism. But, as John Kormondy, of Oberlin College, recently stated:

> no self-respecting ecologist can fail to note the high frequency of food sample contamination . . . the accelerating use of DDT (and of other pesticides), and the concentration phenomenon of DDT and other pesticides in the food chain. Not only is continued surveillance of pesticide levels a must as a matter of human health and safety, but investigations are needed of the effects of pesticides in all kinds of populations, even the human one (12).

Biological Control of Pests

Although chemical control may indeed substantially reduce a pest population, it is frequently only a temporary success, followed by a resurgence of the pest to higher densities than before control was initiated. Moreover, the cost of this short-

Figure 12-17. *Biological control. The larva of the wasp* Drendrosoter protuberan *feeds on the larva of an elm bark beetle here. Though much smaller than its host, it will suck the body juices of the beetle larva and eventually kill it. (U. S. Department of Agriculture)*

term success (in addition to the price of the chemicals) frequently is ecosystem contamination, widespread wildlife mortality, and the development of resistance in the target pest. In the view of many ecologists, a preferred alternative would be *biological control*, which may be defined as the conscious intensification of the density-dependent mechanisms (predation, parasitization, and so on) that continuously operate in natural ecosystems. Such control agents may be used in combination. Thus, Gerberich and Laird report that researchers are increasingly exploring

> the potentialities of employing combinations of fish that occupy different niches in the same biotope and complement one another as mosquito control agents, e.g., fish that feed on algae and other aquatic vegetation facilitate the access of predaceous species to larvae. This type of biotic activity can be termed "bio-synergistic," the combined effects of different biotic agents greatly exceeding the effect which either is able to produce alone (7).

To elucidate the nature and function of biological control, we shall cite two case histories.

Case History One: Control of a Rangeland Weed. St. John's wort is an *exotic*, which apparently was accidentally introduced from Europe to Washington, Oregon, and California in 1900. Originally established as widely scattered plants, it spread rapidly to form dense stands embracing many millions of acres. Attaining a height of 3 feet, this hardy perennial bears numerous clusters of bright yellow flowers. Because it can reproduce by rhizomes, it is extremely difficult to eradicate from otherwise valuable ranges. Poisonous substances are produced by a series of tiny black glands on the undersurface of the leaves.

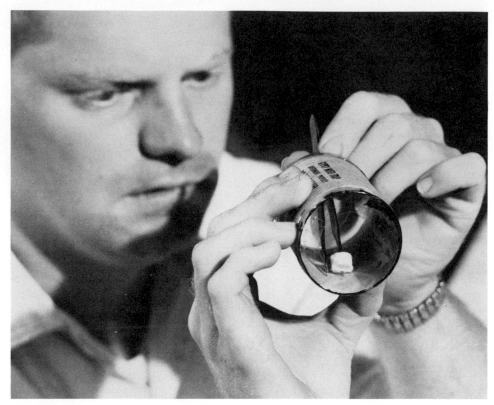

Figure 12-18. *Cape Cod, Massachusetts. A scientist at the Gypsy Moth Methods Improvement Laboratory places a small tuft of cotton moistened with gyplure inside a gypsy moth trap. This synthetic attractant is being used to lure male moths to traps and to chemosterilants. It is also being used in a study of a unique method called the* confusion *technique. An area is saturated with the synthetic attractant in the hope of confusing the male moths to the extent that they will not be able to find and mate with the females. (U. S. Department of Agriculture)*

The poison when ingested or touched results in sunburn and blistering. In severe cases open sores on the skin and head begin to swell, a condition known as "swell-head." Weight loss accompanied by diarrhea is common. Fatalities, although rare, may occur if the animal consumes 5 per cent of its body weight in plant tissue. Thus, a lethal meal for a 1,000-pound steer would be 50 pounds of St. John's wort.

Robert R. Humphrey, professor of range management at the University of Arizona, describes the fascinating method by which this range pest has been brought under control. Although various methods had been attempted since its appearance in the United States, such as grubbing, plowing, burning, and spraying with herbicides, none of these were successful. Finally, in 1944 researchers at the University of California imported a tiny beetle from Australia. The adult and larvae of this beetle were known to feed exclusively on the stem and leaves of St. John's wort. The beetles were released in the Klamath River Valley of California, where St. John's wort (here known as the Klamath weed) had become a serious pest. In a relatively short time the beetle reduced the population of this weed until only a small remnant remained, no longer of any consequence as a range problem. In the case of a flare-up of the pest, the beetle population, responding to the increased food source, would also increase, once more bringing the St. John's wort under control. Of course, were the beetles to move to valuable forage grasses for an alternate food supply, their usefulness as a control agent would terminate. Fortunately, this has not occurred (9).

Case History Two: Rabbit Control in Australia. The native Australian fauna is unique, being well represented by marsupials but almost completely lacking in placental mammals such as the wolf, fox, coyote, cougar, squirrel, and rabbit. Sheep were introduced to Australia in the nineteenth century. Today they form the basis of a multimillion-dollar wool and mutton industry. Many of the flocks graze on semiarid ranges in the continental interior. Early in the twentieth century the European rabbit was introduced to Australia, apparently at the instigation of European immigrants who longed to indulge once again in their favorite sport of hunting the elusive brushland "bounders." Unfortunately, once they were introduced, their numbers sharply increased. Apparently there were no natural predators to serve as limiting factors in controlling their population surge.

As their numbers increased, the rabbits invaded sheep range. In the semiarid grasslands of interior Australia, forage never had been lush. Now, under the combined grazing pressure of both sheep and rabbits, the rangelands rapidly deteriorated.

Figure 12-19. *The rabbit explosion in Australia. Rabbits gathering at a waterhole during a period of drought. Their population was estimated at one* billion *in 1950 about the time this picture was taken. Although the Myxomatosis virus, introduced in 1950, has reduced their numbers by 75 per cent, they still pose a problem for ranchers. (Australian News and Information Bureau)*

Figure 12-20. *The effect of a rabbit invasion. The range to the left was consumed by rabbits. The pasture to the right was protected from the rabbit hordes by the intervening fence. (Australian News and Information Bureau.)*

Grasses were clipped to ground level. The denuded earth became vulnerable. Dust clouds and sand dunes were the inevitable result. Faced with impending economic ruin, Australian ranchers banded together in an all-out effort to eradicate the rabbits. They tried all the conventional control methods. They poisoned. They trapped. They staged mammoth round-ups. They launched huge rabbit-hunting parties, the likes of which Europe had never seen. They even erected a fence several hundred miles long, from Queenland to North Wales, in an attempt to contain the dispersing rabbit hordes. These efforts were all to no avail. Finally, in 1950, government biologists introduced the myxomatosis virus, lethal to rabbits exclusively, into the target area. A healthy rabbit becomes infected by coming into contact with or by ingesting virus-contaminated forage. In a reasonably short time, the Australian rabbit problem was under control—at least temporarily. Whether the rabbits will ultimately develop immunity to the myxomatosis virus and again disrupt Australia's rangeland economy remains to be seen.

Synthetic Hormones and Insect Control. The normal development of insects, birds, mammals, and probably most forms of life is possible only because of the properly timed action of certain hormones. A *hormone* may be defined as a chemical produced by an organ in one part of the body, which is released into the blood stream, and transported to a target organ where it exerts its effect. In other words, the hormone acts like a "chemical messenger."

Now, almost all species of insects (perhaps all) produce a *juvenile hormone*, which has the function of regulating certain features of their development. The juvenile hormone in the case of a moth, for example, would regulate the transformation from the caterpillar to the pupa stage, and from the pupa to the adult winged stage. Scientists have discovered, however, that the juvenile hormone normally is *not* present in the egg, nor in the fully matured adult. In other words, a moth, for example, produces the juvenile hormone only at a precise stage in its life cycle—the caterpillar stage—and stops producing it once it has attained maturity. Recent experiments have shown that the injection of the juvenile hormone into the eggs or into the adult insect will have a highly destructive effect. Injected eggs, for example, will not develop normally, and injected adults will frequently become sterile because of the degenerative effects on the reproductive organs

It is apparent that the use of juvenile hormones, if capable of being synthesized and mass produced in the chemist's laboratory, might prove to be a valuable "biological" form of insect control. However, as George Moriber of Brooklyn College suggests, many unanswered questions remain. Would the synthetic hormones, if dispersed in the insect (and human) environment be sufficiently selective? Would they disrupt the normal development of only the *target* species, or would they interfere with the development and reproduction of beneficial insects as well? Would the hormones contaminate human food chains, and, if so, would they prove to be toxic to man? Moreover, even if the hormones were properly selective, and proved to be harmless to man, wouldn't the target species eventually develop resistance to the superimposed load of juvenile hormones, just as house flies eventually develop resistance to DDT? Certainly, such questions must be answered in a positive manner before the extensive dissemination of juvenile hormones into insect (and human) ecosystems may be initiated (14).

Integrated Control of Pests

Although biological control of pests holds much promise, and was highly successful in the St. John's wort and Australian rabbit problems, many experts believe that for most pest problems the most effective long-term method of control will be an *integrated* one that judiciously employs both biological and chemical control agents either concurrently or sequentially, depending on the problem. Chemicals would not be dispensed in a massive assault on the ecosystem, as was so commonly done in the 1940's and 1950's with disastrous results for wildlife. Instead of overwhelming the ecosystems, the chemicals will be *fitted into* them. A given pesticide would be employed in a highly selective manner, only after an intensive study had been conducted, not only of its immediate effects on target pests but also of its long-term influences on other biotic components of the ecosystem. In most cases, the pesticides would be employed only temporarily, to reduce the target population sufficiently to swing the balance in favor of the pest's predators and parasites. Both native and exotic biological control agents would play significant roles. In an official report of the California Agricultural Experiment Station, Stern et al. state that in the approach to integrated control

> we must realize that man has developed huge monocultures, he has eliminated forests and grasslands, selected special strains of plants and animals, moved them about, and in other ways altered the natural control that had developed over thousands upon thousands of years. We could not return to those original conditions if it were desirable. We may, however, utilize some of the mechanisms that existed before man's modifications to establish new balances in our favor (18).

There is mounting evidence, from agricultural regions in South Africa to the apple orchards of Nova Scotia and the citrus plots of California, that integrated control can be extremely effective. Integrated control has numerous advantages: (1) because it requires use of minimal amounts of chemicals, it is relatively inexpensive; (2) hazards stemming from food chain contamination are reduced; (3) the chance for a build-up of resistant insect strains is restricted; (4) it permits the gradual restoration of biotic components of the original ecosystem; and (5) it permits the introduction of exotic agents of control that prior study reveals to be effective against specific target pests (18).

In *Pesticides and the Living Landscape,* Rudd describes a fascinating example of the use of the integrated method in the control of the hornworm, a serious tobacco pest in the Southeast:

> Hornworms on tobacco are usually reduced in numbers by insecticides. Most states in which hornworms occur also recommend cultural control by burning or plowing-under the tobacco stalks that remain after harvest. Handpicking of larvae is sometimes recommended. Generally, there has been little effort to control them with natural antagonists, but any successful means of doing so would bring at once the advantages of lower cost of control and reduced residue problems (a particularly important aspect of insecticide use on tobacco). In recent years Rabb and his colleagues at North Carolina State College have successfully integrated a variety of control techniques against hornworms that are remarkable for their effective simplicity. Paper wasps, known to be effective predators of hornworms, were encouraged to multiply by providing easily constructed artificial shelters around tobacco fields. (Increases in the bird populations of forests in Germany, England and Russia have been achieved in a directly comparable way for similar purposes!) These shelters could be permanently stationed about fields or moved as needed, in the manner that beekeepers move hives for pollination. The predation of wasps alone accounted for a removal of about sixty percent of the total population of hornworms. Under some circumstances reduction was greater. Occasionally, for a variety of cultural and climatic reasons, predator populations were low and insecticides had to be used to effect control. In these instances the chlorinated hydrocarbon insecticides TDE and endrin were used to reduce numbers of hornworms to levels at which wasps could assume control. In contrast to previous insecticide applications, chemicals were applied only to crown portions of plants, and then in lesser amounts, and fewer applications were required. Costs and residue hazards were reduced by this integrated scheme of biological, cultural and insecticidal control (16).

Legal Restrictions on Insecticide Use

For many years, ever since abundant evidence of the devastating effect of pesticide cycling in ecosystems on wildlife populations (in some areas adjacent to massive spraying operations, 98 per cent bird mortality has been recorded), wildlife biologists, ornithologists, bird watchers, nature lovers, and sportsmen have joined forces in an attempt to convince legislative bodies that restrictive regulations must be adopted to prevent further decrements in wildlife populations, as well as mounting deterioration of the human environment. Until recently these antipesticide forces were frustrated in attaining their goals. Then, a series of events, centering around the introduction of coho salmon in the Great Lakes, finally enabled them to make a breakthrough.

As early as 1963 a group of distinguished scientists, forming the President's Science Advisory Committee, declared "elimination of use of persistent toxic pesticides should be the goal." However, despite this highly authoritative high-level prodding, legislators still dragged their feet. As George Laycock, well-known naturalist, so aptly has written in *Audubon* magazine, "the chemical companies and the agricultural establishment still call most of the shots six years later, arrogantly fighting every effort to halt contamination of the environment with their products."

In the spring of 1966 the Michigan Conservation Department initiated an intensive program of coho salmon propagation and stocking. Many thousands of 5-inch fish were released into Lake Michigan's tributaries. By the spring of 1967 some of these fish, having fed voraciously on the superabundant alewife population, had grown to 4 pounds; some time later salmon up to 22 pounds were recorded. It appeared as if the sports and commercial fishermen in that region were in great luck. Anglers flocked to the spawning streams when the coho salmon runs began, usually during later spring or early summer. Along the Manistee River (Michigan) anglers became so excited at seeing the huge silvery fish that a mob scene developed, anglers scooping the fish up in nets or dispatching them with clubs. The Wisconsin Department of Natural Resources also has become interested in the coho. It has started a similar program but on a lesser scale.

However, in the spring of 1969, the Food and Drug Administration found an average of 16 parts per million of DDT in commercially caught cohos that had been transported to Minnesota and Wisconsin markets. Considerably alarmed, the FDA confiscated 14 tons of the salmon. Moreover, the U.S. Bureau of Commercial Fisheries found up to 105 parts per million of DDT in the fatty tissues of Michigan cohos. On April 22, 1969, DDT tolerance levels for fish were set at 5 parts per million by the FDA. The ruling put a damper on the coho boom. Michigan conservation authorities were considerably embarrassed for they had spent several million dollars on facilities for coho propagation and research. The coho-based commercial fisheries in Michigan faced the prospect of an annual $2 million loss in sales.

However, unfortunate as it was, the coho episode probably served as a catalyst in accelerating legislative action on pesticide control. In the spring of 1969 a notable triumph was achieved by the proponents of environmental quality. The sale of DDT, America's most abundantly used pesticide, was banned in Michigan, and its use was prohibited by the Michigan Agricultural Commission. Soon afterward the use of DDT was either restricted or banned in Arizona, California, Florida, Washington, and Wisconsin. On November 12, 1969, Robert Finch, Secretary of Health, Education and Welfare, announced that the federal government, at long last, would phase out all except "essential uses" of DDT by 1971. Eventually, the Environmental Protection Agency, which assumed authority in such matters, officially banned DDT for virtually all except emergency situations, as of December 31, 1972. (In early 1974 the Environmental Protection Agency did permit the U.S. Forest Service to use DDT in the control of a highly destructive outbreak of the tussock moth in the valuable coniferous timber stands of the Northwest.) The most distressing feature of the whole problem is that even if not a single ounce more of DDT were released after the 1972 ban, which obviously is not the case, because of the "lag time" of DDT in moving to terminal food chain links, DDT levels will not reach their maximum in fish until 1982, and will not maximize in human tissues until much later. This means, therefore, that even with the present ban, the most serious effects of DDT on American citizens probably will not be observed for at least several decades. Moreover, it must be emphasized that there

Figure 12-21. *Down—out? Pesticides are responsible for the drastic decline of the peregrine falcon in the United States. This bird is being studied at the Patuxent Wildlife Research Center, Laurel, Maryland. (Bureau of Sport Fisheries and Wildlife, U.S. Department of the Interior)*

is currently no ban of DDT in South America, Asia, and Africa, where millions of pounds of DDT are employed annually. And where will *that* DDT eventually circulate? No one knows for certain. But we may be sure that a substantial amount of this DDT will be either air-borne, dust-borne or water (rain)-borne back to the United States, where it was produced, back to American streams, farms, and backyards. Or it may be transported in the form of exported foods (fish, rice, bananas, coffee, and so on) to the American dinner table.

In August, 1974, after two years of hearings, the Environmental Protection Agency finally banned the general use of two additional chlorinated hydrocarbons, aldrin and dieldrin, considered by some authorities as being even more toxic than DDT. When administered to mice on an experimental basis both aldrin and dieldrin have caused cancer and birth defects. The ban provoked the usual stereotyped response from the pesticide manufacturers: "Since there is no real proof of the harmful effects of aldrin and dieldrin on wildlife and man, this action by the Environmental Protection Agency is blatantly unfair."

Herbicides and the Ecosystem

If a weed may be defined as "a plant out of place," then an herbicide may be defined as a "weed killer." Before World War II, certain arsenical and nicotine-containing compounds were used to control agricultural weeds. However, much of the control was also done by mechanical means, by *cultivating* machinery. Crop growth of course, was promoted since competition for moisture, soil nutrients, and sunlight was reduced. Since about 1945, however, a great variety of organic herbicides have been developed in the chemical laboratories of such companies as DuPont, Dow, and Monsanto. The volume used (and hence dispersed into the environment) has risen even more dramatically than that of insecticides—about 0.5 million pounds currently being used, at a purchase price of about $1 billion yearly! These herbicides have been used in a variety of situations against an aggregate of about 30,000 weed species—to clear railroad, highway, and power line "rights-of-way"; to remove cropland weeds; to remove brush and undesirable trees from otherwise valuable timberland; and so on.

Mode of Herbicide Action. Weed killers may be divided into two major groups on the basis of their mode of action. 1. Photosynthesis blockers (fenuron, diuron, simazine, monuron, and so on). This group of herbicides kills weeds effectively because it interferes with the vital process of photosynthesis, ultimately causing plant death by starvation.

2. Growth hormone mimickers (2,4–D; 2,4,5–T). These herbicides mimic the role of the naturally occurring growth hormones in plants known as *auxins*. Auxins are commonly produced by the leaves as well as other plant organs. They are responsible not only for growth but also for flowering, leaf and fruit development, and fruit and leaf fall. Throughout the growing season the relatively high auxin levels cause the plant leaves and fruits to remain attached to the stem; however, in autumn, in response to diminishing quantities of auxins, leaves and fruits drop from the stem. It is possible to defoliate a plant at any time simply by applying a chemical that would cause a drop in auxin level. This technique has been employed on cotton plants at harvesting time to prevent the leaves from jamming up the harvesting machine. Conversely, by adding auxins premature fruit and leaf drop can be prevented—thus minimizing losses otherwise incurred by fruit ranchers by preharvest fruit fall (19).

Now the herbicide chemists have synthesized two herbicides (which were extensively used until restrictions were made by federal law in 1973) known as 2,4–D and 2,4,5–T. If a plant is sprayed with 2,4–D it absorbs this pseudogrowth hormone and "attempts" to grow at a more rapid rate than its supplies of nutrients and oxygen will sustain. As a result the plant literally *grows itself to death* (25). For some reason 2,4–D will destroy broad-leaved plants but will have no adverse effect on narrow-leaved plants. This characteristic makes it a highly desirable agricultural and horticultural tool—doing a good job of destroying (broad-leaved) bindweed in a crop of (narrow-leaved) corn, or a patch of (broad-leaved) dandelions in a suburban lawn of (narrow-leaved) grass.

Vietnam Defoliation Program.[1] In 1962 the U.S. Defense Department initiated a massive campaign to defoliate large sections of South Vietnam, with the aid of such herbicides as 2,4–D and 2,4,5–T. Picloram, an arsenic-containing herbicide that breaks down much more slowly than the biodegradable 2,4–D and 2,4,5–T, was also used for defoliation purposes. Moreover, a herbicide called cacodylic acid was employed to kill narrow-leaved rice crops. From a purely ecological viewpoint, this project was of extreme interest because of the use of herbicide concentrations almost ten times that permitted in the United States and because of the immense size of the treated area—5.4 million acres defoliated and 687,000 crop acres destroyed (6).

The purpose of this immense project was described in a letter from Assistant Secretary of State Dixon Donnelley to a group of concerned botanists, including Galston. According to Donnelley, the herbicides were employed to accomplish the following objectives:

1. To "clear jungle growth and to reduce the hazards of ambush by Viet Cong forces. . . ."
2. To enable "our military forces both on the ground and in the air, to spot the Viet Cong and to follow their movements. . . ."
3. "Destruction of food crops [was] undertaken only in remote and thinly populated areas under Viet Cong control and where significant denial of food supplies [could] be effected by such destruction . . ." (10).

The herbicides were applied by aerial spraying from planes equipped with 1000 gallon tanks—each plane being capable of covering 337 acres in only two minutes!

Effects on the Ecosystem. The defoliation program had multiple adverse effects. They included:

1. Entire mangrove communities (composed of up to 20 different species of plants and many animals) lining the estuaries in the Saigon and Mekong Delta regions were destroyed with a single application. A minimum of *twenty years* would be required for recovery—if indeed it does some day occur.
2. The destruction of the microhabitat formed by the maze of interwoven mangrove root systems, submerged in brackish water, may severely depress fish and shellfish production. As you recall, these organisms require the estuary for completing part of their life cycles. With the elimination of the mangrove root "nurseries," a valuable source of protein will be eliminated from the Vietnamese diets as well—diets that are already top-heavy with carbohydrate.
3. Removal of vegetative covering exposed the heretofore stabile estuarine margins to the erosive effects of torrential rains and vigorous tidal action.
4. The destruction of canopies in the hardwood forests permitted an extensive invasion of sun-tolerant thickets of bamboo. The invading bamboo may be eradicated only by bulldozing and burning. The destruction of 20 per cent (5 million acres) of South Vietnam's valuable deciduous forests has jeopardized a $150 million forest industry that has employed up to 80,000 people yearly.
5. The nutrient-rich organic material in the soils exposed by defoliation was rapidly broken down by the combined influences of sunlight and bacterial action. The

---

[1] Much of the following material was derived from the informative article "Warfare With Herbicides in Viet Nam," by Arthur W. Galston, director of Marsh Botanical Gardens, Yale University, which appeared in *Patient Earth*, by John Harte and Robert H. Socolow (6).

released minerals were then rapidly washed away during the rainy season by run-off waters. Many of these soils are lateritic, that is, characterized by a high iron content. Eventually these denuded, impoverished soils may compact into a hard bricklike, water-impervious mass, completely unsuited for growing either trees or crops.

6. Picloram, unlike 2,4–D and 2,4,5–T, has long soil persistence. The Dow chemical company, which manufactures it, has stated that in one particular American soil type only 3.3 per cent disappeared in 467 days (10). Since picloram is highly toxic to plants, soil containing a heavy residual of picloram may be reduced to a biological "desert" for many years.

7. Under anaerobic conditions, as may prevail in rice paddies, even 2,4–D and 2,4,5–T residues may accumulate in the soil, causing rice crops to absorb excessively high nitrate levels. Upon consumption of the nitrate-contaminated rice, both livestock and man might develop potentially lethal *methemoglobinemia*. (You recall in our discussion of the nitrogen cycle that nitrate is converted into nitrite in the human gut, and the nitrite in turn may cause a reduction in hemoglobin's ability to carry oxygen.)

8. Unfortunately, although many thousands of acres of rice crops were destroyed by cacodylic acid, many experts feel that the effectiveness of the Viet Cong military machine was only slightly blunted. In food-deprivation strategies such as this, unfortunately, the principal starvation victims are the civilians—the very young, the very old, the disease-ridden, and the pregnant women. Somehow, the fighting men usually manage to remain reasonably well fed.

9. The use of 2,4,5–T may have had serious direct effects on man himself. Experiments have shown that injections of 2,4,5–T into pregnant female mice may not only cause females to abort their offspring, but may induce birth defects such as cleft palate, abnormal kidneys, and deformed spinal cord and brain. It was of considerable interest, therefore, that in 1967, when the herbicide assault was at its peak, a relatively high incidence of unexplained birth defects appeared in South Vietnam. Galston has estimated that if the toxicity rate in human beings is similar to that in mice only 200 milligrams of 2,4,5–T could adversely effect a 100-pound Vietnamese woman. She could easily ingest that amount by drinking only *three quarts* of contaminated water (6).

Apparently the deformity-causing effects of 2,4,5–T are actually caused by an impurity called *dioxin*—an extremely toxic substance. Although the Dow chemical company, manufacturers of 2,4,5–T, believe they can produce 2,4,5–T with less than 1 ppm of dioxin, biochemists say *it may be possible for 2,4,5–T to be metabolized to dioxin in the plant tissues*. Galston therefore poses the questions, "Could this happen in the human body? In the soil? As the result of burning in a sprayed area?" (6). Because answers to these questions are not yet available, the herbicide 2,4,5–T has been banned for most agricultural uses, except for rangeland pest control. According to Wisconsin's Senator Gaylord Nelson, since dioxin is perhaps one of the "deadliest poisons synthesized by man," 2,4,5–T, which invariably bears some of this material, *should be banned for all purposes in the United States*.

BIBLIOGRAPHY

1. Anderson, John M., and Margaret R. Peterson. "DDT: Sublethal Effects on the Brook Trout's Nervous System," *Science*, 164(1969), 440–441.
2. Barker, R. J. "Notes on Some Ecological Effects of DDT Sprayed on Elms," *Jour. Wild. Mgt.*, 22:3(1958), 269–274.

3. Buchsbaum, Ralph. *Animals Without Backbones.* Chicago: The University of Chicago Press, 1948.
4. Carson, Rachel. *Silent Spring.* Boston: Houghton Mifflin, 1962.
5. Ehrlich, Paul R., and Anne H. Ehrlich. *Population, Resources, Environment.* San Francisco: Freeman, 1970.
6. Galston, Arthur W. "Warfare with Herbicides in Viet Nam," in *Patient Earth,* John Harte and Robert H. Socolow, eds., New York: Holt, 1971.
7. Gerberich, J. B. and M. Laird. "Bibliography of Papers Relating to the Control of Mosquitoes by the Use of Fish," *FAO Fisheries Technical Paper No. 75.* Rome: U. N. Food and Agricultural Organization, 1968.
8. Haeussler, G. J. "Losses Caused by Insects," *Insects: The Yearbook of Agriculture.* Washington, D.C.: U.S. Department of Agriculture, 1952, 141–146.
9. Humphrey, Robert R. *Range Ecology.* New York: Ronald, 1962.
10. Hunt, Eldridge G., and Arthur I. Bischoff. "Inimical Effects on Wildlife of Periodic DDD Applications to Clear Lake," *Calif. Fish and Game,* 46:1 (1960), 91–106.
11. Kleinert, Stanton, Paul Degurse, and Thomas Wirth, "Occurrence and Significance of DDT and Dieldrin Residues in Wisconsin Fish," Madison: Wisconsin Department of Natural Resources, 1969.
12. Kormondy, Edward J. *Concepts of Ecology,* Englewood Cliffs, N.J.: Prentice-Hall, 1969.
13. McMillen, Wheeler. *Bugs or People?* New York: Appleton, 1965.
14. Moran, Joseph M., Michael D. Morgan, and James H. Wiersma. *An Introduction to Environmental Sciences.* Boston: Little, Brown, 1973.
15. Moriber, George. *Environmental Science.* Boston: Allyn and Bacon, 1974.
16. Rudd, R. L. *Pesticides and the Living Landscape.* Madison: University of Wisconsin Press, 1964.
17. Shellhammer, H. S. "An Ethological and Neurochemical Analysis of Facilitation in Wild Mice." University of California, Davis. Doctoral Thesis.
18. Stern, Vernon M., Ray F. Smith, Robert Van den Bosch, and Kenneth S. Hagen. "The Integrated Control Concept," *Hilgardia,* 29: 2 (1959), 81–101. Calif. Agri. Exp. Sta., University of California, Berkeley, Cal.
19. Wagner, Richard H. *Environment and Man.* New York: Norton, 1971.
20. Whitten, Jamie L. *That We May Live.* Princeton, N.J.: Van Nostrand, 1966.

13.

Air Pollution

Today . . . it is not only the air over our cities that is polluted. The entire atmosphere of our planet is now afflicted to some degree. Meteorologists talk about a nebulous veil of air pollution encircling the entire Earth. Smog has been observed over oceans, over the North Pole, and in other unlikely places. Mankind is taxing the capacity of the atmosphere to absorb and to transport away from areas of high population density the enormous amounts of wastes exhausted into it. Air pollution is now recognized not only as an agent that rots nylon stockings and windshield wiper blades, that corrodes paint and steel, blackens skies and the wash on the clothesline, and damages $500 million worth of crops annually; it is recognized as a killer of people. A 1968 UNESCO conference concluded that man had only about 20 more years before the planet started to become uninhabitable because of air pollution alone.

Paul R. Ehrlich and Anne H. Ehrlich,
Population, Resources, Environment,
San Francisco, W. H. Freeman, 1970

Man breathes in and out about once every four seconds, sixteen times a minute, 960 times an hour, 23,040 times per day, 8,409,600 times each year. If one lives to be seventy years old, he will inhale about 75 million gallons of oxygen-containing air into the delicate recesses of his lungs.

In addition to providing a vital source of oxygen, the earth's atmosphere is of value to man in many other ways. Without the insulation and heat distribution provided by the atmosphere, man would be subjected to drastic day-night temperature changes completely incompatible with survival. Without an atmosphere, sound vibrations could not be transmitted; the earth would be silent. There would be no weather, no spring rains for crops and lawn, no snow, hail, or fog. Without its atmospheric shield, our planet would not only be more heavily bombarded with meteorites but would be exposed to potentially lethal radiations from the sun. In summary, without an atmosphere, life as we know it would be impossible, and the earth's surface would be as desertlike as the moon.

Evolution of the Atmosphere

The air man breathes today is vastly different from that which existed when our planet had its origin 5 billion years ago. According to Paul Weisz (24), the new-born earth probably had an atmosphere composed principally of water vapor (H_2O), ammonia (NH_3), and methane (CH_4). The energy required for the formation of these compounds (from the elements carbon, hydrogen, oxygen, and nitrogen) was probably derived from heat, light, and ultraviolet and X-radiation. Eons later, some of the earliest life forms, such as proto-viruses, possibly secured vital energy from the fermentation of the organic compounds that formed a rich broth in the ancient oceans. Releasing CO_2 as a by-product, such fermentation made possible photosynthesis—the all-important process by which green plants synthesize sugars from CO_2 and H_2O, with the aid of chlorophyll-trapped solar energy. As photosynthetic activity became more extensive, billions of tons of molecular oxygen (O_2) were released into the atmosphere. The stage was now set for the evolution of animals (and ultimately human beings), which utilized the precious gas in respiration. Moreover, with the release of copious quantities of oxygen, the atmosphere underwent an "oxygen revolution"; this extremely active gas combined with methane to form CO_2 and water, and with NH_2 to form N_2 and water. At higher altitudes oxygen molecules combined with other oxygen molecules to form ozone. By some such process of gradual change, operating over millennia of time, the present atmosphere, virtually devoid of NH_3 and CH_4, eventually developed (24).

Gases in the Unpolluted Atmosphere

Today, the dry unpolluted atmosphere has roughly the following composition:
1. *Nitrogen (79 per cent)*. Despite his inhalation of 11,000 quarts of nitrogen daily, this inert gas is unusuable by man. However, in the form of nitrates, it may enter biological food chains and eventually be utilized by man in the synthesis of vital proteins.
2. *Oxygen (20 per cent)*. Oxygen is a chemically active gas essential for the

respiratory processes of most organisms, including man, by means of which energy is released to power such biological functions as growth, reproduction, hormone synthesis, nerve impulse transmission, muscular contraction, perception of stimuli, and even (in man) thought itself. Fortunately, the world's green plants annually release 400 billion tons of oxygen to the atmosphere in a continuous process of renewal. It has been estimated that were it not for this replenishment, the oxygen supply of the world's atmosphere might become exhausted within 2,000 years.

3. *Carbon Dioxide (0.03 per cent).* Although not directly utilized by man, carbon dioxide, a colorless, odorless, tasteless gas, is an essential raw material for photosynthesis and hence a *sine qua non* for human survival. It has been estimated by Howard R. Lewis that an acre of deciduous forest removes 2,000 pounds of CO_2 from the atmosphere annually, and the world's green vegetation utilizes an impressive 550 billion tons yearly (8).

4. *Inactive Gases (1 per cent).* The air also contains negligible quantities of argon, neon, helium, krypton, and xenon, all of which are obviously inactive and of relatively little biological importance.

Pollution of the Atmosphere

Natural Pollution. Long before the first white man set foot on American soil, the atmosphere was to some degree polluted, not from man-made sources but from natural causes. Smoke from lightning-triggered forest fires billowed darkly across the land, presumably causing hardship to wildlife. Dust clouds occasionally obscured the sun then as now. In 1900 the Mt. Katmai volcano in Alaska erupted, sending countless tons of dust and ashes into the atmosphere where they circulated around the globe for two years and produced some strikingly beautiful sunsets! A given sample of today's atmosphere may contain a host of natural contaminants, from ragweed pollen to fungal spores, from disease-causing bacteria to minute particles of volcanic ash and salt. Ragweed pollen, which may be a real menace to human health, causes a variety of ills, from sniffles and headaches to hayfever and asthmatic problems. So extensive is the potential health hazard that city health departments make daily "pollen counts" during the ragweed season. The counts are published in the weather sections of newspapers to alert susceptible citizens.

Surprisingly, even extensive forests of spruce, fir, and pine (which otherwise are considered a valuable natural resource) may represent a source of natural air contamination. Thus, according to University of Nevada professor Frits Went, pine trees and plants such as sagebrush may emit terpenes and esters. These chemicals then react with sunlight to form the "smog" or bluish haze that veils many a mountain range and is familiar to every vacationer who has sojourned in the Smoky Mountains. Terpenes may be highly toxic and may actually inhibit the growth of other vegetation. Fortunately, they are washed from the air with rain or snow before attaining levels harmful to man (18).

Pollution Caused by Man. *Homo sapiens* has been fouling his atmosphere ever since Stone Age man first roasted a deer over an open fire, the smoke smudging some of his otherwise magnificent cave wall paintings in southern France—perhaps the first serious property damage caused by air pollution. Even before the Christian

Figure 13-1. *Natural air pollution. Satellite photo of brush fire raging out of control in Ventura County, California. Brush fires and forest fires generated massive quantities of atmospheric pollutants long before the white man appeared on the scene. Such fires may have been triggered by lightning strikes. (NASA)*

era a noted geographer censured the dye pits of Tyre as a source of offensive odors. The British queen fled to Nottingham in 1257 to seek haven from dense clouds of coal smoke. In 1306 Parliament passed a law making it illegal to burn coal in a furnace in London; at least one violator was actually tortured for his offense (8). However, it was not until the Industrial Revolution that air pollution reached such massive proportions that it seriously affected the health of large segments of society. In 1909 at least 1,063 deaths in Glasgow, Scotland, were directly attributed to polluted air. It was in conjunction with this incident that H. Des Voeux coined the word *smog* as a contraction of smoke-fog (8). Atmospheric contamination has progressively worsened over the last few decades. Let us examine the major pollutants that concern us today.

MAJOR POLLUTANTS. Major man-generated pollutants in our atmosphere include carbon monoxide, oxides of sulfur, hydrocarbons, particulate matter, and oxides of nitrogen.

Carbon Monoxide. When the author was in college, back in the 1940's, carbon monoxide poisoning was usually associated with suicides—the attendant conditions usually being a running motor and a closed garage. Since then, however, because of the rapidly mounting levels of carbon monoxide above our city streets and freeway systems, many hundreds of thousands of Americans are suffering from a subtle, unwanted type of carbon monoxide poisoning, not severe enough to cause death, but with markedly ill effects on human health. Each passing year, about 154 million tons of carbon monoxide (CO) are emitted into the atmosphere of the United States, 1.5 million tons into the skies above New York City alone. This single gas forms 52 per cent by weight of our principal atmospheric pollutants (12). Because it combines 210 times more readily with hemoglobin than does oxygen, it tends to replace oxygen in the blood stream. Exposure to 80 ppm of CO for eight hours has an equivalent effect in causing cellular oxygen starvation as the loss of one pint of blood! Policemen working in heavy urban traffic frequently work under these conditions in such cities as Tokyo, New York, and Los Angeles. When traffic policemen in Tokyo have a "yen" for oxygen, they place one or two in an oxygen-dispensing machine conveniently located near the intersection, take a few whiffs, and, when properly refreshed, resume their work. The California Department of Public Health indicated in 1960 that one hour's exposure to 120 parts per million of CO may be a serious health risk to sensitive people (21). At this concentration, CO inactivates about 5 per cent of the body's hemoglobin. Resultant symptoms include headache, dizziness, and lassitude. The presence of CO in the pregnant mother's blood stream has been suggested as a possible cause of stillbirths and deformed offspring. Certain conditions may render some people especially susceptible to CO poisoning. They include heart disease, circulatory impairment, asthma, diseased lungs, high altitudes, and high humidity. CO may be the indirect cause of many fatal traffic accidents in the United States yearly, because the effects of low-level CO poisoning may parallel those of alcohol or fatigue in impairing the motorist's ability to control his vehicle. Concentrations may frequently approach 100 parts per million in garages, tunnels, and even behind automobiles on the open road. Exposure to 200 parts per million for a lengthy period of time may cause fainting, coma, convulsions, and death. On rare occasions, levels as high as 500 *parts per million* have been recorded in heavy city traffic.

So CO concentrations are high at downtown intersections. But how about indoors? Certainly the urban office worker need not be concerned about CO while at his desk. Right? Wrong. A recent study conducted by the Environmental Protection Agency has shown that in old apartment and office buildings situated along heavily trafficked streets in New York City, CO levels *are not much lower inside than outside.* In fact, CO concentrations on the thirty-second floor of one apartment building exceeded the federal CO standards 19.7 per cent of the time (17).

Oxides of Sulfur. The 23 million tons of oxides of sulfur that are emitted into our atmosphere yearly form roughly 18 per cent (by weight) of our principal

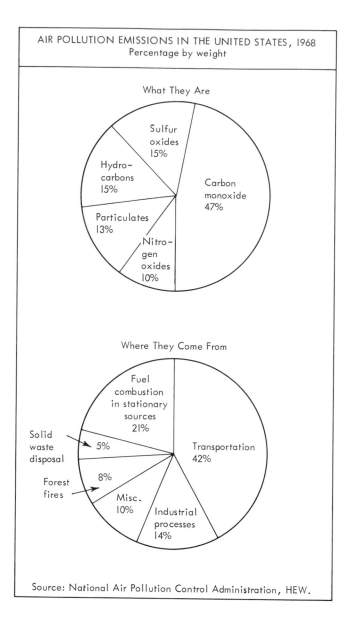

AIR POLLUTION EMISSIONS IN THE UNITED STATES, 1968
Percentage by weight

What They Are

Sulfur oxides 15%

Hydro-carbons 15%

Particulates 13%

Nitrogen oxides 10%

Carbon monoxide 47%

Where They Come From

Fuel combustion in stationary sources 21%

Solid waste disposal 5%

Forest fires 8%

Misc. 10%

Industrial processes 14%

Transportation 42%

Source: National Air Pollution Control Administration, HEW.

Figure 13-2. *Air pollution emissions in the United States. (From:* Environmental Quality. *The First Annual Report of the Council on Environmental Quality. August, 1970.)*

atmospheric contaminants (12). Oxides of sulfur form whenever sulfur-containing fuels, such as coal, oil, and gas, are burned. Coal burning yields 48,000 tons of sulfur dioxide (SO_2) in the United States daily and 1.5 million tons annually in New York City alone.

As every chemistry student knows colorless SO_2 stings the eyes and burns the throat. About 1 per cent of the population will develop chronic weariness, tortured breathing, sore throat, tonsillitis, coughing, and wheezing when exposed for lengthy periods to the concentrations of SO_2 normally occurring in smog (9). Since SO_2 may impede or even inactivate the ciliary cleansing mechanism of the lungs, it contributes importantly to such chronic diseases as bronchitis and emphysema. Sulfur dioxide will react with oxygen to form sulfur trioxide (SO_3), which in turn will combine with airborne moisture droplets to form lung-damaging sulfuric acid (H_2SO_4).

Hydrocarbons. The 35 million tons of hydrocarbons emitted yearly in the United States represent 12 per cent of all major atmospheric pollutants. The burning of gasoline in the automobile is by far the major source, 27,000 tons being emitted from auto exhaust daily (6). The hydrocarbons represent a large family of chemicals, most of which are not directly harmful to man at the low concentrations in which they normally occur. Unfortunately some of them may react with nitrogen dioxide (NO_2) in the formation of photochemical smog. Many hydrocarbons at high concentrations may irritate the eyes and respiratory tract. Benzopyrene and at least eight other hydrocarbons have been implicated as possible causes of cancer (8). Some of these also occur in cigarette smoke. In fact, in terms of these suspected carcinogens, the air breathed in one day by a man living in a badly polluted city would be equivalent to smoking an entire pack of cigarettes.

Particulate Matter. The soot or fly ash that issues from industrial smokestacks and blackens backyard laundry or sullies bright yellow sports cars is an example of *particulate matter.* The latter may be defined as "solid and liquid particles in the atmosphere, in contrast to gaseous matter." The kinds of contaminants in particulate matter may vary greatly from city to city depending upon the type of industrial source. Over 50 per cent of the particulates in the average air sample cannot be identified with currently available techniques. This is most unfortunate since many of these particulates might be injurious to health. It was estimated that, in November, 1954, a 1,000-foot-thick layer over a 1-square-mile area in downtown Los Angeles contained roughly 870 pounds of particulate matter. Included were at least twenty-one different substances, the most abundant of which were lead, iron, magnesium, sodium, potassium, sulfates, nitrates, organic matter, and hydrocarbons (5). Twenty-seven million tons of particulate matter are injected into our atmosphere yearly. According to a survey by the Robert Taft Sanitary Engineering Center of the U.S. Public Health Service, the following particulate matter *tonnage* occurs in an air sample 1 square mile in surface area extending from the ground to an elevation of 100 feet: Salt Lake City, 24; Pittsburgh, 45; San Francisco, 46; Houston, 57; Washington, D.C., 58; Atlanta, 61; Philadelphia, 83; New York, 108; Los Angeles, 118; Chicago, 124; Detroit, 153. A single electric power facility, the Four Corners Plant at the junction of New Mexico, Arizona, Utah, and Nevada at one time emitted over 400 tons of particulates per day. The federal standard for particulates is 75 micrograms (millionths of a gram) per cubic meter of air. However, this highest permissible level is greatly exceeded in many cities. For example, during a severe thermal inversion in 1969 Chicago had a maximum of 593 micrograms per cubic meter, more than *seven* times the acceptable level (3)!

Lead, in the form of antiknock fuels, is added to gasoline to enhance its octane rating. Man takes this lead into his system when inhaling air polluted with motor exhaust. A cumulative poison, it may also be ingested with food or water. It may have an injurious effect on the kidneys, blood, and liver. Moreover, it may damage the brains of youngsters, with ultimate lethal effect. On the basis of lead concentrations in snows at high elevations in the Rockies, Claire C. Patterson, a California Institute of Technology geochemist, suggested in 1965 that lead concentrations in man are 100 times the level of yesteryear. Although his statement has been criticized in some medical circles, the U.S. Public Health Service has been considering setting stiffer lead emission standards (6).

Less common particulates include arsenic, asbestos, beryllium, cadmium, and fluorides. Arsenic, emitted from copper smelters, is suspect as a possible carcinogen. Minute particles from asbestos fibers derived from the wearing away of roofing, shingles, insulations, and brake linings have been associated with lung cancer. Beryllium, used as rocket engine fuel, has induced the formation of cancers in experimental monkeys. Cadmium may adversely affect the heart and increase blood pressure.

Oxides of Nitrogen. The 8 million tons of oxides of nitrogen that are annually spewed into our nation's air form 6 per cent of all the atmospheric pollutants generated by man. New York City releases 298,000 tons of oxides of nitrogen yearly. Nitric oxide (NO) is relatively harmless at ordinary concentrations. It is formed when atmospheric nitrogen combines with oxygen at the temperatures generated during fuel combustion. At unusually high concentrations, nitric oxide may have lethal effects, causing death by asphyxiation, because it combines 300,000 times more readily with hemoglobin than does oxygen.

Nitric oxide readily combines with atmospheric oxygen to form nitrogen dioxide (NO_2), which may cause a variety of human ailments, from gum inflammation and internal bleeding to emphysema and increased susceptibility to pneumonia and lung cancer (8).

PHOTOCHEMICAL SMOG AND OZONE. The yellow-gray haze known as photochemical smog, which was first recognized in the Los Angeles area, is caused by reactions between precursor hydrocarbons, catalysts, and atmospheric oxygen. The precursors frequently exist in concentrations of less than 1 part per million. Nitrogen dioxide

Figure 13-3. *San Francisco under smog.* (San Francisco News-Cal Bulletin)

(NO₂) is the most common catalyst. The energy necessary for triggering these reactions is derived from sunlight; hence, on cloudy days the formation of photo-chemical smog is somewhat restricted, and at nightfall the process is halted. Various products are formed because of the oxidation of hydrocarbons, one important gas being *ozone*. These materials (known as *oxidants*) may be severely irritating to human eyes and mucous membranes, as any frequenter of downtown Los Angeles can well attest. Temperature changes can effect the rate at which ozone is pro duced. Ozone causes rubber to crack and decompose—but only during the day, not at night. It was this observation that provided a clue to the photochemical nature of smog formation (22). This explanation of the nature and origin of photochemical smog was first worked out in 1951 by Arie Haagen-Smit, of the California Institute of Technology.

Ozone occurs naturally in the ozonosphere at an altitude of twenty miles, where it is formed by the action of sunlight on oxygen. Here it provides a shield against potentially lethal ultraviolet rays from the sun and also screens infrared (heat) rays out of the earth's immediate atmospheric envelope, thus ensuring an earthly temperature amenable to life.

Ozone is the principal eye and mucous membrane irritant in photochemical smog. At concentrations frequently found in urban areas, ozone will cause nose and throat discomfort after an exposure of only ten minutes. Experimental subjects exposed for a few hours to 0.8 parts per million of ozone experienced impaired lung function and mental ability. People having prolonged occupational exposure to relatively high levels of ozone have experienced blurred vision, fatigue, recurrent headaches, breathing difficulty, and chest pains (21). It is possible that intermittent exposures over a period of twenty years to only 0.25 parts per million of ozone may induce pulmonary fibrosis (12).

Figure 13-4. *A volunteer is undergoing tests to determine the effects of auto exhaust irradiated by sunlight on the human eye. Pollution-free air is released through one set of tubes; irradiated, exhaust-mixed air through the other. The volunteer has no way of knowing which tube carries which type of air. Experiments like this are conducted at the Public Health Service Laboratory to test health effects of automotive air pollution. (National Air Pollution Control Administration)*

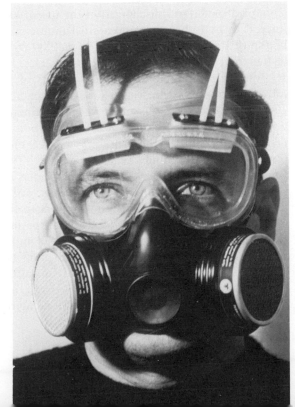

Figure 13-5. *Aerial view of smog above New York City. (U. S. Public Health Service)*

Sources of Pollution

Transportation. There are well over 100 million registered motor vehicles in the United States; by 1980 the number is expected to reach 150 million. Because the amount of pollutants discharged in the motor exhaust is related to mileage, it is of interest to note that the total annual motor mileage is expected to leap from 890 billion in 1965 to well over 1 trillion in 1980 (6). Something like 70 billion gallons of fuel are consumed yearly by motor vehicles. From each 1,000 gallons consumed, 1.5 tons of carbon monoxide, 300 pounds of hydrocarbons, and 100 pounds of nitrogen oxides are released into the atmosphere (2). If a combustion engine were 100 per cent efficient, the only exhaust components would be carbon dioxide and water vapor. However, because combustion is sometimes grossly inefficient (especially in some of the "rambling wrecks" chugging down our highways trailing plumes of smoke behind them), roughly 200 distinct compounds may be belched from motor exhaust pipes. When one considers all the chemicals added to gasoline, such as rust inhibitors, detergents, deicers, antiknocks, engine deposit inhibitors, and so on, the chemical "mix" emerging from the auto's exhaust must be complex indeed. It was estimated in 1966 that transportation activity (including planes) in the United States annually generates 59.6 million tons of carbon monoxide, 9.7 million tons of hydrocarbons, 3.1 million tons of nitrogen oxides, 1.8 million tons of particulate matter, 0.5 million tons of sulfur oxides, and 0.1 million tons of miscellaneous atmospheric pollutants (11). This represents a total of 74.8 million tons directly attributable to the combustion engine (12).

Figure 13-6. *Traffic congestion on the Southwest Freeway, Houston, Texas. (Blair Pittman, EPA-Documerica)*

Figure 13-7. *Jet plane pollutes the air over Washington, D.C. (U.S. Public Health Service)*

Industry. Foremost among the industries that pour out aerial garbage into the skies over the United States are the electrical power plants, which alone emit 15.7 million tons of pollutants yearly, largely from the use of coal. During its consumption, a single ton of coal releases 200 pounds of solids and 48 pounds of sulfur dioxide and nitrogen oxides. The refinery industry is also a prime source. With each passing day 12 million barrels of crude oil are processed by our nation's petroleum refineries, with a concomitant injection of particulates, sulfur oxides, hydrocarbons, ammonia, oxides of nitrogen, organic acids, and aldehydes into the air around us. Large ore smelters and metal industries release sulfur dioxide, carbon monoxide, metallic oxides, as well as lead and arsenic fumes. Ore smelters release 1.7 million tons of sulfur dioxide annually (12). The rubber industry releases vapors from solvents, and chemical industries pollute the air with sulfur dioxide, fluorides, ammonia, hydrogen sulfide, solvents, hydrocarbons, and carbon monoxide. Almost 500,000 tons of sulfur dioxide are released from sulfuric acid plants annually. Massive quantities of dust are produced by the glass, asbestos, and cement industries, as well as in the manufacture of stone products, concrete, and abrasives. In aggregate, all industries in the United States other than electrical power plants annually emit 8.7 million tons of sulfur dioxide, 6 million tons of particulates, 3.7 million tons of hydrocarbons, 1.8 million tons of carbon monoxide, 1.6 million tons of nitrogen oxides and 1.6 million tons of other miscellaneous air contaminants.

Several air pollution experts have suggested that the progressive deterioration of air quality that America has experienced might eventually render major cities such as New York, Chicago, Philadelphia, and Los Angeles unlivable by 1990. Such

Figure 13-8. *Air pollution from oil refineries in Baton Rouge, La., over 10 years ago. (National Air Pollution Control Administration)*

statements have been criticized as being "alarmist." However, air pollution, primarily from an industrial source, actually did cause the "death" of a European town, Knapsack, Germany, which was officially declared uninhabitable in early 1973. Once the mass exodus of the residents had been completed the homes of the townsfolk were systematically demolished. *Environment* magazine reports that

> the village was killed by air pollution from Knapsack AG, the world's second largest phosphate plant. The plant continues to emit tons of acids, sulfur dioxide, phosphate and coal dust into the atmosphere. Company officials claim that they have already spent $12 million on pollution abatement and that no further reduction of air pollution is possible (17).

Leaf-burning and Refuse Disposal. The burning of leaf piles in late autumn is for many a simple pleasure; moreover, it generates a pungent fragrance that delights thousands of gardeners everywhere. Surprisingly, however, leaf-burning may be a source of profound health problems, having caused allergic reactions in certain sensitive individuals that contribute to a variety of respiratory ills, including asthma, hay fever, and bronchitis. Inhaled leaf smoke has even been directly responsible for mortality in young children.

The great majority of American families burn paper, rags, and other refuse in crude backyard incinerators that frequently are highly inefficient and may be nothing more than converted oil drums. The emission from a single disposal unit is of little consequence, but the aggregate emissions from tens of thousands of such units in a major community can pose a serious health hazard. One ton of incinerated refuse, for example, releases 25 pounds of solids, 5 pounds of sulfur oxides, and 4 pounds of oxides of nitrogen. According to the Committee on Pollution, Waste Management and Control of the National Academy of Sciences, refuse disposal spews 3.3 million tons of contaminants into America's skies annually (12).

Culm and Gob Banks. Coal-processing plants dispose of inferior fuel of no commercial value by dumping it onto wasteland sites where it accumulates over the years into hills of culm (anthracite) and gob (bituminous). They blight extensive areas in Alabama, Alaska, Colorado, Illinois, Indiana, Kentucky, Montana, New Mexico, Ohio, Pennsylvania, Tennessee, Utah, Virginia, West Virginia, and Wyoming. A single bank may contain 20 million tons of coal waste. These banks are easily ignited by a carelessly dropped cigarette, by forest fires, or by the insidious process of spontaneous combustion. In 1965 the 450 culm and gob banks burning somewhere in the United States generated 183,000 tons of acrid sulfur dioxide fumes.

Influence of Air Circulation Patterns on Pollution

Thermal Inversion. The build-up of atmospheric contaminants to high levels is facilitated by a meterological condition known as a *thermal inversion.* Under normal daytime conditions, the air temperature gradually decreases with altitude, from ground level to a height of several miles above the earth's surface. With such a thermal pattern it is possible for fly ash, sulphur dioxide, and other contaminants from industrial smokestacks and other sources to disperse either vertically or horizontally, depending upon wind currents. However, in the case of a thermal inversion,

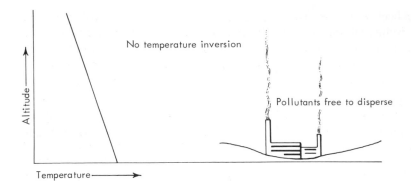

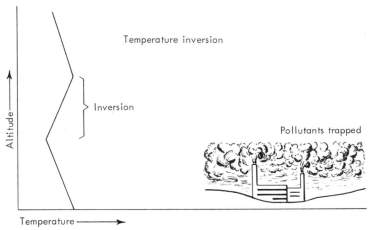

Figure 13-9. *Nature of a temperature inversion. (For explanation see text.)*

such dispersion is impossible. It is only because of engine exhausts and industrial smokestacks that the modern-day American need be concerned with thermal inversions. Were it not for our advanced technology, thermal inversions in August would be characterized as "lazy summer days, good for swimming, picnics, and looking at the stars" (3). Two basic types of inversions are recognized—*radiation* and *subsidence*.

RADIATION INVERSION.   At night the earth's surface cools off rapidly because of heat radiation into the atmosphere. As a result both the ground and the air layer next to it cool off rapidly. A condition therefore develops in which a warmer layer of air, perhaps 10 to 1,000 feet above the ground, forms a "lid" over the cooler layer beneath it. This effectively prevents any vertical mixing of air and air-borne contaminants. Pollution build-ups, however, need not necessarily occur unless there is little wind present to disperse the pollutants horizontally. Such *radiation inversions* are common but usually confined to a small area. The inversion usually dissipates by late morning when the earth's surface is warmed by the sun.

SUBSIDENCE INVERSION. While not as common as the radiation type, the subsidence inversion may be of greater duration and may be much more extensive, simetimes forming a canopy over a several-state area. It is formed when a high pressure air mass (one that is sinking and hence warming up) sinks toward the ground, possibly down to the 2,000-foot level. This type of inversion has caused many of the air pollution problems in California. During the summer months a high pressure air mass is constantly present above the Pacific Ocean off the California coast. This air mass occasionally moves inland over Los Angeles, Oakland, and other coastal cities and puts a "lid" on the pollutant-bearing air near the ground that has been cooled by oceanic currents moving along the coast (3). Coastal California experiences this type of inversion on nine of every ten days in summer (11). The frequency of a thermal inversion varies greatly, depending upon season and geographical area. During autumn the greatest number of inversions occur in Idaho, Nevada, California, and Arizona, while the least number occur in southern Florida and coastal Virginia and North Carolina (14).

Dust Dome. Any motorist speeding toward the outskirts of Los Angeles, Chicago, St. Louis, or any other large city has observed the haze of smoke and dust that frequently forms an "umbrella" over the town. This shroud of pollutants, which is known as a *dust dome,* is caused by a unique atmospheric circulation pattern, dependent upon the marked temperature differences between the city proper and outlying regions. Although the average annual temperature of a city such as St. Louis or Cleveland might be only 1.7° F higher than the surrounding rural areas, occasionally a city may actually be 27° F warmer.

Figure 13-10. *Downtown Los Angeles. Thermal inversions cause especially severe smog problems in Los Angeles because the city is located in a topographic "saucer" or receptacle, being hemmed in by mountains to the east. (Southern California Visitors Council)*

Figure 13-11. *Aerial view of Los Angeles on a clear day in 1956. (Los Angeles County Air Pollution Control District)*

Figure 13-12. *Aerial view of Los Angeles under smog in 1956. The smog is trapped by a temperature inversion at about 300 feet above the ground. The upper portion of the Los Angeles City Hall is visible above the base of the temperature inversion. The inversion is present over the Los Angeles Basin approximately 320 days of the year. (Los Angeles County Air Pollution Control District)*

Figure 13-13. *Heat "radiators" in mid-town Manhattan. The concrete, stone, brick, and steel used in the construction of the Empire State Buliding (foreground) and other skyscrapers radiate heat much more readily than the meadows and woodlands of rural areas. Because much of the heat radiated horizontally tends to be trapped in the skyscraper "canyons," Manhattan is a good example of a "heat island." (New York Convention and Visitor's Bureau)*

As described by Moran, Morgan, and Wiersma (11), several factors contribute to this "heat island" phenomenon:

1. There are many more heat-generating sources in the city than in the rural environment; they include people (with an average body temperature of 98.6° F), motor cars, space heaters, industrial furnaces, and so on.
2. Many of the materials of which streets, parking lots, office buildings and homes are constructed (brick, concrete, asphalt, steel) radiate heat much more readily than do, say, a field of alfalfa, an oak woods, or a mountain lake.
3. Because water bodies (streams, lakes, farm ponds, potholes, swamps) are much less numerous per unit area inside the city than in the surrounding countryside, less heat will be lost because of evaporation of water and more will be available for warming up the urban atmosphere.

In any event the urban-rural temperature differential is conducive to an atmospheric circulation pattern in which cool air from the countryside moves into the city to replace warm air rising from the urban center. As a result, smoke dust, nitrogen dioxide, and other aerial "garbage" tends to concentrate in a dust dome above the city. *One thousand times as much dust* may be present immediately over an urban industrial area as in the air of the nearby countryside (11).

When the air is calm the dust dome persists; however, when wind speeds get up to 8 miles per hour, the dome is pushed downward into an elongated *dust plume*. Those plumes emanating from Chicago may occasionally be visible from a distance of 150 miles (11).

Effects of Air Pollution on Climate

One disturbing aspect of air pollution is that it may directly modify such phenomena as the intensity of sunlight, cloud formation, rainfall, and temperature,

Figure 13-14. *The "greenhouse" effect. (For explanation see text.)*

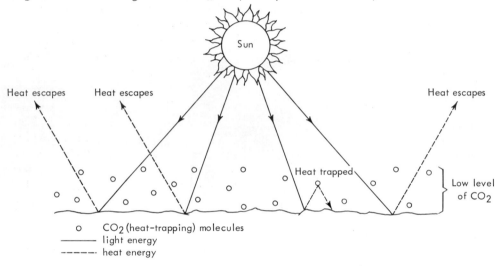

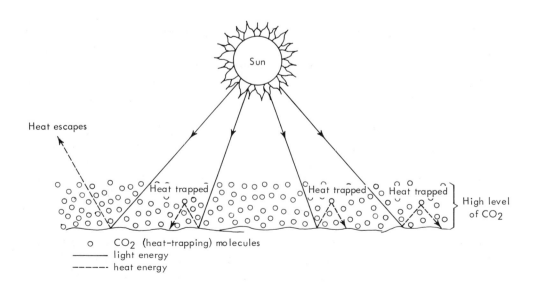

all of which are, of course, basic to the survival of all organisms from cabbages to kings. Moreover, relatively slight rainfall or temperature changes may disrupt the balance of ecosystems by eliminating "key" plant and animal species.

1. *Air pollution may increase the earth's average temperature.* As mentioned in our discussion of the carbon cycle, carbon dioxide molecules act as an atmospheric "trap" for heat radiating from the earth's surface. The heat is then radiated back to earth—the so-called greenhouse effect. Because of man's accelerating consumption of fossil fuels (coal, gasoline, and so on) the concentration of carbon dioxide has increased from the 290 ppm of 1900 to 330 ppm today. The average temperature in the Northern Hemisphere gradually increased during the period 1880–1940. It is of interest that during this period several species of birds and mammals native to the United States, such as the cardinal and the opossum, extended their ranges *northward* for considerable distances. Lamont Cole, of Cornell University, has suggested that an increase of the earth's average temperature of only a few degrees might be sufficient to cause melting of the polar icecaps and eventual inundation of coastal cities such as New York City, New Orleans, and Los Angeles.

2. *Air pollution may decrease the earth's average temperature.* Although an increase of carbon dioxide may have a *warming* influence, an increase in particulate matter may have a *cooling* effect. Not only may particulates (dust, soot, and so on) backscatter the incoming rays of the sun, but they may also absorb heat (infrared) rays radiating from the earth's surface into the atmosphere. The cooling effect of particulate matter was impressively demonstrated in 1883 when the island of Krakatoa in the Dutch East Indies partially disintegrated because of a gigantic volcanic eruption that injected countless tons of fine dust particles high into the atmosphere. Over a period of years these particles eventually circled the globe several times. A short time after the eruption the United States experienced a definite cooling trend—Bostonians, for example, had the rare privilege of throwing snowballs in June.

Now, the total annual load of particulates generated by the earth amounts to 800 million tons. This material has the cooling effect of one small volcanic eruption. Sources contributing to this particulate load include the combustion of fossil fuels; the razing of old buildings; agricultural activities such as plowing, cultivating, and harvesting; slash and-burn-farming in Asia, Africa, and South America; forest fires; debris burning by loggers; dust storms and strip-mine operations. The annual average temperatures in the United States have gradually declined. Does this signify that the cooling effects of particulate pollution is overriding the warming influence of carbon dioxide contamination? Just how these trends should be interpreted is not only uncertain but highly controversial. Much more research is needed in this area.

3. *Atmospheric pollution may reduce the amount of sunlight reaching the earth.* This effect is caused by the scattering of solar radiation by particulate matter. For example, according to the Smithsonian Institution, the streets, lawns, and gardens of Washington, D.C., are receiving 10 per cent less sunlight than they did during the beginning of this century when the air was relatively unpolluted. A few years ago smog in downtown Los Angeles reduced the sunlight reaching the city by 10 per cent. True, these are only two instances. It is probable, however, that air pollutants cause similar effects in almost every metropolitan area in the United States. And these effects are not limited to urban areas, since wind currents will widely disperse particulates. The smoke pall of a city, for example, may eventually shroud an area

Figure 13-15. *St. Louis, Missouri. The celebrated "gateway to the West" arch is almost engulfed in smog. November 14, 1966. (World Wide Photo—EPA)*

50 times the size of the urban source (3). Such reduction of solar energy, the power base of all ecological systems, could conceivably have profound and adverse effects, such as impaired growth in crop plants, for example. With an estimated 13,000 people starving to death somewhere in the world every day, any diminution in footstuffs would be tragic indeed.

4. *Air pollution induces precipitation.* We have previously described the conditions that transform cities into "heat islands." The warmed urban air combines with the moisture (a by-product of fuel combustion) emitted from industrial smokestacks and motor cars to form clouds above the city. Reinforcing this process are the particulates (soot, dust), omnipresent in the urban air, which serve as *condensation nuclei* in absorbing tiny moisture droplets. Now, if man-generated air pollution does indeed induce rainfall, then we would expect more rainy days from Monday to Friday when factories are operating, and pollutants are generated, than on weekends when the plants are closed. And this is precisely the case. For example, in Paris, France, the average daily rainfall during week days was 31 per cent higher than on weekends. The degree to which particulate dispersion occurs is revealed by their recovery over the Atlantic Ocean, hundreds of miles from the nearest urban area (3). According to Stanley A. Changnon, Jr., writing in the *American Meteorological*

Society Bulletin, industrial contaminants generated in Chicago are carried to the general region of La Porte, Indiana, thirty miles to the east, where they trigger considerable amounts of rainfall (3).

Effects of Air Pollution on Vegetation

Air-borne contaminants inflict a $325 million annual loss on our nation's agricultural industry (12). Pollutants damage at least thirty-six important commercial crops (21). Automotive pollution has caused vegetational damage in twenty-two states and, ironically, the District of Columbia. The exhaust emissions from the flood of vehicles rushing along our new interstate highway network seriously hamper commercial crop production on nearby farms. It has been estimated that in southern California automotive pollution causes $10 million worth of crop damage yearly (8), and damage recently has become equally serious along the Atlantic seaboard from Boston to Washington (21).

Flowers and ornamental plants of many varieties have also been injured. Backyard gardeners in the larger cities are noting increasing damage to such favorite flowers

Figure 13-16. *Effect of air pollution on potato growth. Plant pathologist Dr. H. E. Heggestad of the U. S. Dept. of Agriculture's Agricultural Research Service compares two Norland potato plants of the same age in research on air pollution injury to vegetation at Beltsville, Md. The sickly plant on the right was grown in polluted air; the healthy plant on the left was grown in filtered air. (Ag. Res. Mag., May 1970), United States Department of Agriculture photo)*

as petunias, snapdragons, chrysanthemums, larkspur, carnations, orchids, pansies, zinnias, and roses (21). Symbolically, even the potted plants in New York's City Hall, such as philodendron, pandanus, and podocarnus, in order to survive must be removed periodically from the contaminated Manhattan atmosphere for a "breather" in a greenhouse at the edge of town.

The specific chemicals inflicting plant injury have been identified to some degree. Among the more serious are ozone, sulfur dioxide, fluorides, ethylene, herbicides, and oxidized hydrocarbons. At least fifty-seven species are susceptible to ozone. Because plants are much more sensitive to this gas than is man himself, it frequently causes widespread destruction before man is even aware of the problem. Ozone diffuses through the stomata of plants and kills the palisade cells. The result is a reddish-brown spotting of the leaf. Ozone has severely curtailed the once prosperous flower-growing industry in the Los Angeles area (8). As little as 8 to 10 parts of ozone in 100 million will cause serious injury to tobacco plants after a brief four-hour exposure (12). Even trees are not immune to ozone. Thus, in West Virginia, large acreages of eastern white pine have succumbed to a disease known as postemergence chronic tip burn. Initially thought to be caused by a parasitic fungus, the Southeastern Forest Experiment Station of the U.S. Department of Agriculture has recently attributed the disease to ozone emanating from motor exhaust.

In the San Bernardino and San Jacinto Mountains of southern California, thousands of ponderosa pines have been killed by wind-borne ozone originating in Los Angeles 60 miles distant. Since the 1950's up to 60 per cent of San Bernardino

Figure 13-17. *The leaf of an ozone-sensitive tobacco variety (Beltsville W-3) shows white spots characteristic of air pollutant damage, called weather fleck. The leaf is shown at the U.S. Department of Agriculture's Research Center, Beltsville, Md. (Murray Lemmon— U. S. D. A.)*

National Forest's 160,000 pine acres has incurred moderate to severe damage. In early 1970 the smog was destroying about 3 per cent of the ponderosa pines annually. According to U.S. Forest Service pathologist Paul Miller, photosynthesis is inhibited almost immediately. Smog concentrations of 0.25 ppm will reduce photosynthesis 66 per cent. This in turn reduces the flow of resins under the bark. Since the resins protect the tree to some degree against the ravages of plant diseases and insect pests, the smog-triggered forest destruction may be extensive.

Sulfur dioxide (of which 300 million tons is annually emitted into the atmosphere of our nation) is also a threat to plants. Sulfur dioxide reacts with water inside the plant leaf cells to form a lethal sulfite. Some plants succumb to a concentration of 1 part of sulfur dioxide in 10 billion parts of air. Alfalfa is damaged by a 1 part per million concentration (12). In 1910–1911, sulfur fumes from an Anaconda (Montana) smelter killed all major tree species within a 5-to-8-mile radius (21). In the late 1920's a smelter near Trail, British Columbia, emitted 18,000 tons of sulfur pollution annually, causing plant injury 52 miles distant. During the early years of this century a mammoth copper smelter at Ducktown, Tennessee, daily belched 40 tons of SO_2 into the air. As a result over 7,000 acres were completely denuded of vegetation. Thousands of tons of valuable soil was washed from the exposed land, essentially converting the region to a man-made desert. However, in 1913 the smelter initiated a process that converted the waste SO_2 into a valuable product, sulfuric acid. Ironically, this by-product became more valuable than the original product—smelted copper. However, despite the fact that no additional SO_2 has been emitted since 1913, the immediate area around the plant is still desolate and barren fully six decades later (22). Attempts at artificial reforestation have largely failed. As ecologist Eugene P. Odum has stated, "No one can say how long it will take for natural processes to rebuild the soil and restore the forest, but it will not be within your lifetime, or that of your children" (13). Valuable stands of Douglas fir and ponderosa pine sustained 60 to 100 per cent injury. Even in 1936, two years after control devices had been installed, 80 per cent of the surviving pines were coneless (21).

Clarence H. Gordon, of the University of Montana, has made the surprising and disconcerting discovery that copious SO_2 emissions may indirectly cause extensive damage to timber stands hundreds of miles from the pollution source. What happens is that the SO_2 combines with oxygen to form sulfur trioxide (SO_3), which in turn combines with moisture droplets to form sulfuric acid (H_2SO_4). The latter actually causes rainfall to have a decidedly acid reaction, sometimes with a pH as low as 4.0. Extensive forest damage from acidic rain has occurred throughout the industrial regions of the United States. (Most plants thrive best in soil that is only slightly acid, with a pH of about 6.7.)

Hydrogen fluoride may damage plants at a concentration of only 1 part in 10 billion. Fluorides emitted from Florida phosphate plants have ruined 25,000 acres of citrus groves. In other regions, fluorides have damaged a number of shade and ornamental species including sycamore, silver maple, mountain ash, and mulberry (8).

Nitrogen dioxide has been found recently to restrict growth in certain plants without causing any diagnostic symptoms, thus posing an insidious curtailment of agricultural income the cause of which may not even be suspected (21).

Finally, one surprising note—air pollution does have some beneficial effects after all. Researchers have found that nitrogen dioxide, a characteristic component of automobile exhaust emissions, will be further oxidized to nitrogen pentoxide. The latter will then combine with moisture droplets to form nitrates that in turn are eventually washed to earth with snow or rainfall. In New Jersey an estimated 25 pounds of nitrogen per acre is added to the soil annually—tantamount to a mild sort of soil "fertilization." Thus the abundance of some New Jersey vegetable crops may be partially due to the exhaust gases emitted from speeding cars on freeways half a nation away.

Effects of Air Pollution on Animals

Cattle have been poisoned by eating vegetation contaminated with molybdenum from steel plants or foundry-emitted lead. Near Anaconda, Montana, arsenic from mammoth smelters settled on pasturage; when ingested it caused nose ulcers in horses and mortality among sheep that had been grazing up to fifteen miles from the pollution source (8).

In Norway the acidity of rainfall has increased 1 to 2 per cent each year. Rain-drop acidity is currently so high that fish populations of thousands of lakes and streams have been adversely affected. (River water with a pH below 5 will kill a salmon; a trout will die when the pH falls below 4.5 (3).) The increasing use of phosphate fertilizer by America's farmers has indirectly contributed to severe livestock losses caused by air pollution. Consider the following example from Montana as described by Prival and Fisher:

> When a rancher sold 54 acres of his Garrison, Montana, land to the Rocky Mountain Phosphate Company it was a matter of civic pride. The new factory promised jobs and tax revenues for the industry-hungry region. Four years later, the Ponderosa pine and Douglas fir were turning brown, and the cattle on Garrison's ranches were so crippled they could not stand up. It took six years of vigorous and frustrating campaigning before the residents of Garrison succeeded in forcing the Rocky Mountain Phosphate Company to close permanently in January 1970 (15).

What caused this extensive mortality in valuable timber and livestock? *Fluorides* —in the form of gases or solids that "belched" from the phosphate company's smokestacks. Fluoride emissions are generated by other types of industrial operations as well, such as aluminum processing plants, fossil-fueled power plants, steel mills, and brick and tile manufacturers. Prival and Fisher, research associates at the Center for Science in the Public Interest, based in Washington, D.C., have summarized the effects of fluorosis on livestock. The particulate fluorides settle upon the leaves of forage plants (alfalfa, clover, grasses), while the gaseous fluorides are absorbed through the "breathing pores" of the leaves. The plants act as "biological magnifiers," increasing the concentration of the fluoride many times above that of the surrounding atmosphere. When contaminated forage is consumed by livestock 90 per cent of the fluoride eventually becomes incorporated in the skeleton and teeth. High fluoride levels soften the teeth to such a degree that they may erode right down to the gums—an extremely painful condition, making it virtually impossible for the animal to feed. The limb bone structure becomes highly abnormal, the surface assuming a chalky-white appearance. Foot bones become so brittle that they may fracture when the animal walks over hard, stony ground. Ligaments and tendons become mineralized. Milk and beef production drops dramatically. Flu-

Figure 13-18. *Effects of fluorine on a cow. Note abnormal posture caused by bone damage in the forelegs. (U.S. Public Health Service)*

orosis has caused widespread economic losses to beef and dairy ranches in Montana, Ohio, New York, Washington, Utah, and Florida.

Effects of Air Pollution on Man

Pollution Disasters. It is estimated that the deaths of more than 10,000 Americans each year may be at least partly due to air pollutants. That is about ten times the number of American soldiers who were killed during each year of the Vietnam war! Let us examine a few pollution episodes of only a few days' duration.

MEUSE RIVER VALLEY IN BELGIUM. In December, 1930, a stagnant mass of air, accompanied by a dense fog, settled into the highly industrialized Meuse River Valley in Belgium. As glass factories, zinc smelters, blast furnaces, coke ovens, and sulfuric acid plants continued to belch poisonous chemicals into the air, residents along a 15-mile stretch of the valley soon found themselves enveloped in a thick industrial smog, which persisted for a full week. Factory workers stayed home, complaining of headaches and nausea, and school children fell unconscious onto classroom floors. Eventually, a violent rainstorm cleared the air, but only after the pollution episode had brought illness to 6,000 and death to 63 (8).

MONONGAHELA RIVER VALLEY, DONORA, PENNSYLVANIA. Thirty miles south of Pittsburgh, along a U-shaped bend of the Monongahela River, nestle the three industrial communities of Donora, Webster, and Carroll, with an aggregate population of 14,000. Major industrial plants in the area manufacture steel, wire, sulfuric acid, and zinc. On October 26, 1948, a fog closed in on the valley accompanied by a thermal inversion. In a short time the pungent odor of sulfuric dioxide permeated the air. A Donora high school football game was cancelled in mid-play when the players complained of chest pains and tortured breathing. Streets, sidewalks, and porches were covered with a film of soot so thick it recorded the footprints of pedestrians. The Donora fire department hauled oxygen tanks around the clock in an effort to provide emergency relief to people experiencing breathing difficulties. Six thousand people (43 per cent of the total population) became ill, the most prevalent symptoms being nausea; vomiting; headache; nose, eye, and throat irritation; and constriction of the chest. Although the smog persisted only five days, it left twenty deaths in its wake. Autopsies on three of the dead people showed marked changes in the lungs, such as edema, purulent bronchitis, capillary dilatation, and hemorrhage (8).

LONDON. From December 4 to December 9, 1952, the twin weather phenomena of fog and a thermal inversion blanketed a 700-square-mile area in London and triggered a major pollution disaster. The accumulating smog caused huge traffic jams, many motorists being forced to abandon their cars. The pea-soup smog "made visibility so low . . . that buses crept through the streets, led by conductors on foot, carrying flares, and people got lost only a few blocks from their homes . . ." (4). Outdoor shows and concerts had to be terminated because of poor visibility. Only twelve hours after the smog developed, people started to become ill. Hospitals were inundated with patients complaining of respiratory or heart problems. A characteristic symptom was labored breathing and cyanosis. The deaths of at least 4,000 people, primarily from heart disease, bronchitis, and bronchopneumonia, were directly attributed to the smog (8).

NEW YORK CITY. A stagnant mass of air persisted over our nation's largest city from November 12 to November 22, 1953. Soot, dust, and fly ash accumulated to an average concentration of 3.5 tons per cubic mile of air. Sulfur dioxide was five times the normal level. Airports were closed. One could not even take a ferry to the Statue of Liberty. Within a few days, untold thousands of inhabitants suffered from burning eyes and uncontrollable bouts of coughing. Although winds and rain finally dissipated the smog on November 22, during its 10-day persistence, it was directly responsible for the deaths of about 200 people (8). In 1956 the episode was repeated, but mortality was much higher, at least 1,000 people dying within an 18-hour period because of a heavy smog cover.

Factors Contributing to Pollution Episodes. When most of the air pollution disasters are studied, a common pattern is revealed: (1) they occur in densely populated areas; (2) they occur in heavily industrialized centers where pollution sources are abundant; (3) they occur in valleys, which might serve as topographical "receptacles" for receiving and retaining pollutants; (4) they are accompanied by fog; it appears that the minute droplets of moisture are adsorbed on the surfaces of the pollutants; (5) they are accompanied by a thermal inversion that effectively puts a meteorological lid on the air mass in the valley and contributes to its stagnation (8).

Body Defenses Against Inhaled Atmospheric Contaminants. What clearing mechanisms does the body have against inhaled atmospheric pollutants? Fortunately, they are numerous and highly efficient.

1. EXHALATION. Although numerous potentially dangerous gases, bacteria, and solid particles are inhaled and may penetrate the air stream passageways, they are quickly voided from the body along the reverse route with the next exhalation.

2. NOSE. The nose is lined with a veritable "jungle" of hairs that effectively filter out many solid particles. In addition the spongy, spiral-shaped bones in the nasal passages cause air turbulence, breaking up the air current into many smaller ones, eventually forcing the pollutants against the sticky mucus lining of the nasal chamber. The nasal membrane is lined with numerous *cilia* (tiny, protoplasmic "hairs") that beat 1,000 times per minute and direct a mucous stream toward the throat. As a result any air contaminants stuck to the film of moving mucous are eventually transported to the throat and swallowed. Of course, air pollutants would by-pass this clearing mechanism if a person were breathing through his mouth, as in the case of a child with enlarged adenoids.

3. WIND PIPE–BRONCHIAL TUBES. The filtering and cilia-trapping mechanism of the nose removes most of the large particles. Smaller contaminants are transported by the incurrent air stream to the trachea and bronchial tubes. Millions of tiny glandular cells lining these tubes continuously pour out a mucus stream that is propelled to the throat by cilia. Once in the throat any contaminants are promptly expectorated or swallowed.

4. WHITE BLOOD CELLS IN THE AIR SACS OF THE LUNG. The most minute particles, less than 1 micron (one 25,000th of an inch) in diameter, may evade all three of the above defense mechanisms and penetrate deep into the *alveoli*, the tiny bubblelike sacs at the end of the air passageways. (There are 300 million alveoli in the lungs.) Inside the alveoli there are numerous ameboid cells, known as *phagocytes* ("cell-eaters"), which normally feed on disease-causing bacteria. They are capable of "feeding" on tiny dust or soot particles as well, gradually engulfing, liquefying, and digesting them.

5. DIGESTIVE SYSTEM. It is apparent that even though the mucous-trapped contaminants have been swallowed and have been cleared from the respiratory system, they simply have been passed to another system, the digestive, where they could inflict possible damage. In most cases, however, the pollutants are simply passed through the throat, esophagus, stomach, intestines, and rectum and then are voided from the body with the feces.

Respiratory Diseases Caused by Air Pollution

LUNG CANCER. Several atmospheric contaminants have been strongly implicated as *carcinogens*—cancer-producing materials. Among them are benzopyrene, asbestos, nickel, and beryllium. For example, cancers have been induced in laboratory animals either by injecting benzopyrene or by implanting it under the skin (3). The hydrocarbon benzopyrene can get into the lungs from several sources—from the coal smoke issuing from industrial smokestacks or from the coal smoke issuing from "cancer sticks," known better as cigarettes. Apparently the benzopyrene particles are able to "knock out" the ciliary defense mechanism of the respiratory tract. Richard Wagner reports a little suspected source of benzopyrene—the smoke generated when fat drippings from a charcoal-broiled steak splutter on the hot coals. Just one "smoked" steak may contain as much benzopyrene as 600 cigarettes (22).

It has frequently been shown in laboratory experiments on rats, mice, and so on, that although two air pollutants (A and B) may not induce cancer independently, cancer, nevertheless, is induced when an animal is exposed to both of them *simultaneously*. (Such an effect is called *synergystic*, a phenomenon previously described in connection with water pollution and fish mortality.) For example, lung cancers resembling those in man have been induced in laboratory animals by exposing them first to *influenza virus* and then to *artificial smog*. Tumors have also been generated in laboratory animals by forcing them to inhale a combination of *benzopyrene* and *sulfur dioxide*. Radioactive uranium dust has been implicated as being carcinogenic.

Figure 13-19. *Lung taken from patient suffering from "black lung" disease. The lung is shriveled and hardened. (LeRoy Woodson—EPA Documerica)*

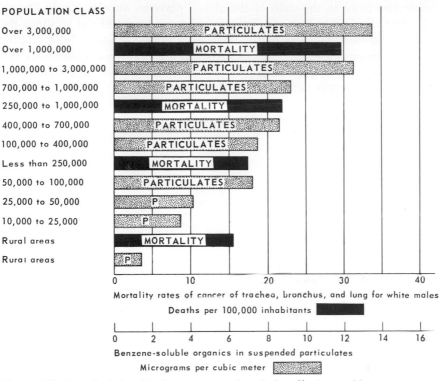

POPULATION CLASS

Over 3,000,000	PARTICULATES
Over 1,000,000	MORTALITY
1,000,000 to 3,000,000	PARTICULATES
700,000 to 1,000,000	PARTICULATES
250,000 to 1,000,000	MORTALITY
400,000 to 700,000	PARTICULATES
100,000 to 400,000	PARTICULATES
Less than 250,000	MORTALITY
50,000 to 100,000	PARTICULATES
25,000 to 50,000	P
10,000 to 25,000	P
Rural areas	MORTALITY
Rural areas	P

Mortality rates of cancer of trachea, bronchus, and lung for white males

Deaths per 100,000 inhabitants

Benzene-soluble organics in suspended particulates

Micrograms per cubic meter

Figure 13-20. *Relationship between severity of air pollution and human mortality rates from cancer in white males. (Adapted from Harold Wolozin (ed.), The Economics of Air Pollution. By permission of W. W. Norton & Company, Inc. Copyright © 1966 by W. W. Norton & Company, Inc.)*

However, it has been shown that the incidence of lung cancer is higher in uranium mine workers who are also smokers than in nonsmoking miners, or in smokers who are not uranium miners (3). Apparently the uranium dust–cigarette smoke combination is synergistic in its effect.

To show a cause-and-effect relationship between benzopyrene and cancer in laboratory animals, of course, does not mean that such a relationship also exists between benzopyrene and man. After all mice are not men. However, both mice and men are mammals and their physiological and cell growth patterns are very similar. Certainly an experiment involving man himself would be much more convincing. Fortunately, the results of such a fortuitous "experiment" are available. For example, researchers have found that the incidence of lung cancer in men over 45 living on Staten Island, New York, is 155 per 100,000 in the smoggiest area, as compared to only 40 per 100,000 in the less smoggy region (5). To research biologists such data strongly indicate a cause-and-effect relationship between atmospheric pollution and lung cancer in man.

EMPHYSEMA. As Figure 13-21 indicates, when air enters the air sacs, oxygen passes through the alveolar membrane into the blood capillaries, while CO_2 passes from the capillaries to the air sacs. The total respiratory membrane surface presented by the lung's 300 million alveoli is about the size of a tennis court. In exhalation, the elastic connective tissue in the walls of the alveoli plays an important role. It provides resiliency to the sacs so they can "recoil" and force air out of the sacs into the air passageway and eventually out of the body. In a person suffering from emphysema, the elastic tissue is progressively destroyed. As a result, the empyhsemiac can breath in easily, thus inflating the lungs. However, it is difficult for such a person to exhale, hence the sacs retain more air than they should after exhalation. With the next incoming breath the air becomes overinflated. This process is repeated many times until the alveolus "pops" like a burst balloon—resulting in the destruction of

Figure 13-21. *Healthy lung compared with a lung diseased by air pollution.*

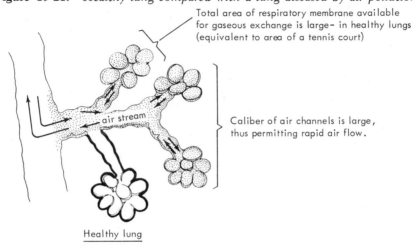

Total area of respiratory membrane available for gaseous exchange is large- in healthy lungs (equivalent to area of a tennis court)

air stream

Caliber of air channels is large, thus permitting rapid air flow.

Healthy lung

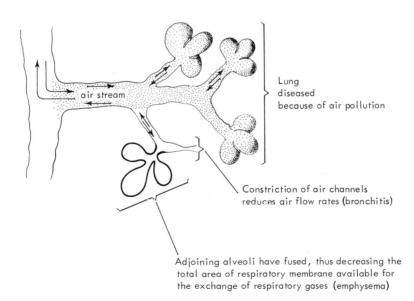

air stream

Lung diseased because of air pollution

Constriction of air channels reduces air flow rates (bronchitis)

Adjoining alveoli have fused, thus decreasing the total area of respiratory membrane available for the exchange of respiratory gases (emphysema)

Diseased lung (bronchitis, emphysema)

both respiratory membrane and blood capillaries. Eventually, therefore, the area available for the exchange of respiratory gases is greatly diminished. In a severe case of emphysema, therefore, the cells throughout the body tend to suffer from oxygen starvation. To counteract this the heart speeds up to dispel the blood more rapidly. The chest of the emphysemiac tends to become distended into a "pigeon chest."

At one time emphysema was a relatively rare disease. However, during the period 1951–1971 the emphysema death rate has doubled every five years—the rate being sixteen times as high during the period 1966–1971 as in the 1940's. A study of British mailmen has shown that emphysema death rates are much higher among those men who worked under conditions of severe air pollution than among those who distributed mail in relatively unpolluted areas (3). The death rate among smokers in highly polluted St. Louis, Missouri, is fully four times that of smokers in Winnipeg, Manitoba, where the air is relatively clean. Therefore, one can conclude that air contaminants may contribute to the development of emphysema. There is some evidence that a susceptibility to emphysema may be inherited (4).

CHRONIC BRONCHITIS. When a person has been long exposed to an atmospheric pollutant, such as sulfur dioxide, which has "knocked out" the ciliary cleansing mechanism, the contaminant usually simultaneously stimulates the production of excessive amounts of mucous, eventually causing the bronchial tubes to be plugged with the slimy material. Since there is no mechanism for voiding the excess mucous, such a person eventually develops a chronic dry cough. Moreover, since the mucous tends to fill the bronchial tubes, the air channels become severely constricted, resulting in shortness of breath and labored breathing. Wagner reports that one of every five British males forty to fifty-nine years of age have chronic bronchitis, and one of every ten deaths in England may be attributed to the disease (22).

Human Health and Air Pollution Control. Although great strides have been made in the last few years in showing definite association between various levels of atmospheric contamination and human health and disease, nevertheless the present state of our knowledge is quite fragmentary. As we have said, less than 50 *per cent of the particulates that occur in urban air samples can actually be identified* (3). Many questions of cause-and-effect relationships remain unanswered. The present state of expertise in this area and the rationale for more stringent pollution control has been nicely summarized by Virginia Brodine in her excellent book *Air Pollution:*

> On the basis of our present knowledge we are not likely to get firm answers to questions like: "How many additional cases of chronic bronchitis can be expected with every additional part per million of sulfur dioxide in the air?" "By what per cent will hypertension (high blood pressure) increase with an increase of a half a microgram of cadmium per cubic meter of air?" But if we ask whether it is likely that reducing sulfur oxides, nitrogen oxides, ozone and all the many forms of particles would result in improved health, the answer is an unequivocal "yes."
>
> The danger in such a generalization is that it may be so vague as to become meaningless. It can lead to the principle of reducing air pollution "as much as possible," and the art of the possible has many interpreters. The value in such a generalization is that it can force us to recognize that, if we wish to protect the health of those most vulnerable to the damage of air pollution, we cannot afford to wait for proof that X number of people exposed to Y amount of an ABC mix of pollutants will produce Z cases of asthma, emphysema, cancer, or birth defects. When there are so many unknowns, we

Figure 13-22. *One of 300 monkeys being exposed to normal, low levels of pollution of up to seven years duration in order to determine what harmful effects, if any, the pollutants will have on the animals' health. The $5.3 million project is being conducted by Hazleton Laboratories, Inc., Reston, Virginia.* (Washington (D.C.) Evening Star)

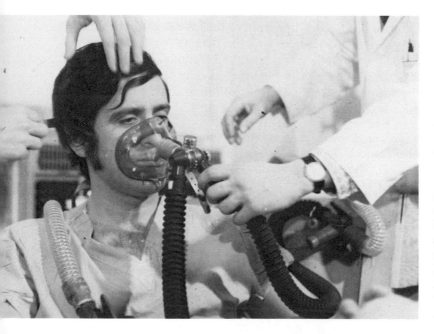

Figure 13-23. *At EPA's Research Triangle Park Laboratory in North Carolina tests designed specifically to determine the effects of carbon monoxide fumes from automobiles on humans are held, as shown here. The results of this and other tests will be the criteria on which EPA will set National Air Standards.* (Environmental Protection Agency)

Figure 13-24. *New York City's Central Park provides proof of the corrosive effect of air pollution. Here is evidence of wear on Cleopatra's Needle. What effect does the air pollution have on the delicate lungs of the two boys beneath the statue? (National Air Pollution Control Administration)*

are forced to gamble. Either we gamble with the lives and health of people, or we take a chance that we are paying more for control than we really need to in order to provide a genuine margin of safety, a truly healthy environment (3).

Cost of Air Pollution

According to federal estimates, air pollution may be costing each man, woman, and child in the United States a minimum of $100 annually. The average yearly loss sustained by farmers and ranchers alone may approach $0.5 billion. Air pollution costs the nation as a whole at least $20 billion (2). In a recent year the Civil Aeronautics Board cited air pollution as the direct cause of fifteen to twenty air crashes, involving multimillion-dollar plane damage and loss of human life. Air-borne contaminants tarnish, soil, abrade, corrode, weaken, discolor, and erode a variety of materials. Ozone causes textiles to fade. Sulfuric acid mist can reduce an expensive pair of nylon stockings to shreds in the time it takes a woman to walk to lunch and back. Store buildings, archways, and monuments are covered with grime and rendered unsightly. Grim testimony to the rapid rate at which we are degrading our atmospheric resource is demonstrated by the fate of Cleopatra's Needle in New York. Although the famed obelisk was not brought to this country until 1881, it has deteriorated more since its arrival here than during its entire 3,000-year history in

Egypt. Even the Acropolis, famed symbol of ancient Greece, is undergoing accelerated deterioration because of exposure to twentieth-century air. The "life expectancy" of priceless paintings by masters such as Rembrandt, Picasso, and Van Gogh are threatened by atmospheric contaminants that have penetrated the art galleries of Florence and Paris.

Electric light bills for many urban families are substantially higher simply because the available sunlight is reduced 15 to 20 per cent by smoke and dust. Corrosion of industrial equipment, raw materials, and facilities perhaps is the gravest economic blow dealt by air pollutants. Steel surfaces corrode two to four times faster in urban than in nearby agricultural areas because of sulfur pollution. Because palladium and silver are corroded by sulfur, electrical contacts must be made of costly gold by the manufacturers of electrical equipment, thus increasing the cost of the product to the consumer. Add to this the bills for medical treatment and hospitalization incurred by thousands victimized annually by pollution-triggered respiratory diseases, and the total air pollution cost to America becomes substantial indeed.

Air Pollution Abatement and Control

Several years ago, when our nation was just beginning to recognize the grave consequences of mounting atmospheric contamination, John W. Gardner, former Secretary of Health, Education and Welfare, summed up America's recourses, "Our choices are narrow. We can remain indoors and live like moles for an unspecified number of days each year. We can issue gas masks to a large segment of the population. We can live in domed cities. Or we can take action to stop fouling the air we breathe."

Industry (Other Than Automotive). Well over 50 per cent of all air and water pollution has its source in the operations of the 300,000 industrial organizations of our nation. Regrettably, however, certain segments of industry still resist any concerted attempt at pollution control. According to Stewart Udall, former Secretary of the Interior, one of the biggest roadblocks to atmospheric clean-up is the "attitude" of industry. Typical of this attitude is the statement of a Detroit industrialist, "People are hysterical about air pollution. There is no proof that it is injurious to public health." In light of published medical data, such a statement is completely ludicrous. However, pressure from an ever more enlightened and indignant public, acting through all levels of government, is mounting. Because the current air pollution crisis represents the cumulative end product of many years of environmental abuse, the Environmental Protection Agency feels that only a massive and sustained control effort will be of any avail.

In his Environmental Message to Congress, February 10, 1970, President Nixon advocated the use of court-imposed fines, up to $10,000 per day, as a deterrent to industrial pollution. There are indications that at least some industrial leaders are finally accepting the principle that pollution control costs are part of the cost of doing business. Indicative of this changing attitude is a statement made at a meeting of the American Marketing Association by Edward Gelsthorpe, Jr., president of Hunt-Wesson Foods, "Beginning right now you are going to see companies making substantial investments to clean up pollution. Companies will be saying to share holders: You don't need a dividend this quarter because we are going to use the money for a chimney in our Ohio plant that's putting sulfur in the air."

POLLUTION CONTROL DEVICES. Although many of the pollution control devices currently available are not 100 per cent efficient in removing industrial contaminants, they often do significantly reduce emission levels. Certainly industry cannot wait another few years for the "perfect" control device to be developed; that day may never come.

Four standard types of equipment for controlling particulates are available. In the *electrostatic precipitator*, dust particles, which have been negatively charged, are retained on positively charged plates. Although presently employed to only a limited degree, electrostatic precipitators can remove up to 99 per cent of the cinders, fly ash, and other particulates normally released during coal-burning operations. The *fabric filter bag house* operates like a giant vacuum cleaner that collects particles in huge cloth sacks. The *wet scrubber* removes dust from an incurrent air stream by spraying it with water. Frequently employed in conjunction with other devices, the *cyclone filter* removes heavy dust particles with the aid of gravity and a downward spiraling air stream. Sales of these four standard pollution control devices are expected to mushroom from $73 million in 1966 to $130 million by 1975.

Other types of control equipment, such as vapor conservators, afterburners, and condensation and absorption devices, are available for noxious gases. Research has recently been conducted on catalytic methods of control; calcium and magnesium oxides, for example, may be employed to convert foul-smelling sulfur dioxide into a harmless or even valuable product.

In many of the larger coal-using industries, the high sulfur content can be reduced before burning. About one third of the sulfur is present as tiny particles of iron disulfide. Much of this inorganic sulfur can be removed by physical methods after the coal has been pulverized. Some authorities feel that industry and government should spend $25 million to $50 million annually on research to develop better methods for desulfurizing coal and fuel oil (20). Recently New York City passed an ordinance making it illegal to consume coal or fuel oil with a sulfur content above 1 per cent. This could result in a substantial reduction of sulfur dioxide emissions, because coal sulfur levels have gone as high as 2.8 per cent (16).

The cost of control methods and equipment may add substantially to the overall cost of production, although such costs vary widely. It may cost a steel mill 5 per cent more to reduce emissions to acceptable levels; the cleanest cement plant may pay 10 per cent above its basic operational cost, and it may cost a foundry melt shop 15 to 20 per cent more to clean up its operation (9).

PROGRESS BY INDUSTRY. Although industry as a whole must be prodded repeatedly, an increasing number of concerned, responsible, far-sighted industrial leaders are showing not only that aerial contaminants can be markedly curtailed but that recovery of some commercially valuable wastes may help to absorb the cost of pollution control equipment. A few examples follow:

1. A major chemical company that installed control equipment for $85,000 is now recovering $50,000 worth of odious benzothiazole annually.
2. The massive St. Clair power plant of Detroit Edison has been experimentally employing a catalytic process that would reduce offensive sulfur dioxide fumes to

Figure 13-25. *Note how the installation of pollution control equipment at this industrial plant has reduced the emission of soot particles (smoke).*

Figure 13-26. *The mist eliminator for air pollution control. Cylinders are being lowered into position within the confines of a brick-walled tank. Under operating conditions the gas flow (carrying particles in mist), is directed into the tank and flows through the fiber bed of the cylinder, because no other exit is offered. At this point up to 99.99 per cent of the particles are trapped by the fiber bed. Clean gas then emerges through the top of the cylinder. There are about 1,400 such installations in the free world, with applications ranging from sulfuric acid plants to plastic operations and radioactive waste treatment facilities. (Monsanto Enviro-Chem Systems)*

easily disposable calcium sulfate (plaster of paris), a procedure that would increase utility costs a negligible 3 per cent.

3. American Cyanamid installed a dust-collecting apparatus that annually removes 4,000 tons of high carbon fly ash that is reusable as fuel.

4. Several large utility companies sell the fly ash recovered from their stack gases for use in the manufacture of cinder blocks, paving materials, abrasives, and portland cement.

5. Tennessee Corporation once decimated large stretches of the Tennessee hillsides with its sulfur gases; today these wastes are being converted into the company's major product, sulfuric acid. It is estimated that if other coal-consuming industries did likewise, the 23 million tons of annual sulfur dioxide emissions could be profitably converted into 15 million tons of sulfuric acid—almost equivalent to our country's total yearly consumption (7).

6. With only an $8,000 investment in control devices a mineral-processing firm is recovering high-quality particulates worth more on a tonnage basis than the original product.

The Control of Automotive Emissions. With the mandate given it by the Clean Air Act of 1970, the Environmental Protection Agency is waging the battle to form better air quality along two fronts: (1) the reduction of auto traffic volume in

Figure 13-27. *Before installation of special pollution control equipment, over 150 tons of smoke used to pour daily from these chimneys at U. S. Steel's Duquesne plant. Now, the new equipment wets down the smoke, washes it, and compresses it into disposable briquets. (U. S. Public Health Service)*

Figure 13-28. Detroit, Michigan. Crawling automobile traffic winding westward into the setting sun in Detroit, the automobile emissions contributing to the pollution of the air. (Tony Spina, Detroit (Mich.) Free Press—Environmental Protection Agency)

chronically congested urban areas, and (2) the modification of the conventional internal combustion engine and/or the development of alternative engine types.

REDUCTION OF TRAFFIC VOLUME.   Several specific proposals made by the EPA to reduce traffic flow include the following:

1. In Washington, D.C., the provision of free parking facilities by employers for their employees would be terminated.
2. A $5 daily tax would be added to parking fees in downtown Boston.
3. For one working day per week commuters would be prohibited from driving to their place of work in downtown Philadelphia and Pittsburgh, thus reducing commuter traffic by 20 per cent.

The overall pollution reduction strategy developed by New York City includes the following features:

1. All on-street parking in the main business section of Manhattan has been banned.
2. Cruising by Manhattan taxis has been restricted.
3. Several Manhattan bridges have been placed on the toll system.
4. All truck deliveries have been confined to evening hours.
5. Some lanes on busy streets have been set aside for the exclusive use of buses.

The EPA assumed that similar measures, instituted in all 31 of the "pollution problem" cities, would be required at least until 1985. It is hoped that at that time

Figure 13-29. *In Manhattan and some other major urban centers, certain lanes on busy thoroughfares have been reserved for the exclusive use of express buses. This strategem has proven effective in reducing the commuter traffic volume and hence the level of air pollution.*

sufficient emission reductions in car engines would have been made so that the restrictions could be relaxed (1).

REDUCTION OF POLLUTANT EMISSION.   The automobile industry once shrugged off its responsibilities in restricting exhaust emissions. For example, a standard Detroit joke in the early 1960's was, "What California needs is filter-tipped people!" That early mood of flippancy has changed to serious concern. The industry realizes that it has to make radical changes in motor design—mounting pressure from both consumers and pollution control agencies will demand nothing less. Car manufacturers now regard the pollution issue even more of a threat to car sales than the safety issue of the mid-1960's. Henry Ford II branded it "by far the most important problem" the industry will encounter in the 1970's.

Transportation vehicles emit 74.8 million tons of atmospheric pollutants yearly. This represents 59 per cent of our annual total air pollution tonnage (12). Certain advocates of strong air pollution control measures—such as John Gardner and Frank M. Stead, Chief of Environmental Sanitation for California—believe that the gasoline-powered vehicle sooner or later will have to be removed from the American scene in the interest of health (19). New York City's Task Force in Air Pollution has strenuously urged the development of a mammoth program to develop an efficient alternative to the internal combustion engine to keep America's greatest cities from becoming uninhabitable within a decade (6).

Figure 13-30(a).   *Ford's first Model T rolled from the company's Piquette Street plant in Detroit in 1908 and marked the beginning of an era during which it became known as the "car that put America on wheels." This milestone car lasted through 15 million basically similar vehicles produced until 1927. Unfortunately, the Model T also marked the beginning of an era of widespread atmospheric pollution. (Ford Motor Company)*

Figure 13-30(b). *The modern motor car provides speed, power, privacy, comfort, and "status" for the owner; but it also contributes importantly to current air pollution problems. (Ford Motor Company)*

Figure 13-31. *Traffic congestion in New York City. The exhaust fumes from these cars are contributing to the haze that shrouds the Empire State Building. (U. S. Public Health Service)*

The basis for such apprehension is underscored in a briefing document prepared in 1969 for Lee A. Du Bridge, President Nixon's science adviser:

There is strong evidence that the use of federal standards geared to controlling the internal combustion engine will not result in the drastic inroads on the problem needed to safeguard public health. At best the effect of present federal standards will be to postpone in time the upward growth of pollution levels rather than to reverse the trend. These controls [are] far less than adequate to cope with a problem already well out of hand. . . . There is no guarantee that the degree of control that is possible with the internal combustion engine will be adequate. *The problem is already beyond reasonable bounds.* . . .

In 1970 Senator Gaylord Nelson of Wisconsin introduced legislation (the Low Emission Vehicle Act) that would have phased out the internal combustion engine by 1978 unless it could meet national emission standards by that time.

ELECTRIC CARS.   The suitable alternative may be an electric car powered by a fuel cell, a special type of battery that is refuelable, like a gas engine, and that converts the fuel directly into electrical power, with air-contaminating emissions reduced to zero. Although several automobile manufacturers are working on the development

Figure 13-32. *The electric car— a possible solution to auto exhaust pollution. The car is displayed in front of the White House, and is examined by Rep. Richard Ottinger of New York City.* (The Washington Evening Star)

of an efficient fuel cell, it may well be 1980, if ever, before a reasonably good battery car (of short range and perhaps a top speed of 50 miles per hour) will appear on the highways of America. Some have suggested that private industry and the federal government mount a $100 million-a-year research program to this end, over a five-year period.

A more conventional type of electrical car, powered by a standard electrical battery, is already in limited production. Although the vehicle itself is relatively pollution-free eventually the battery has to be recharged, a process that utilizes electricity generated by centrally situated power plants. Thus, in one sense, instead of having numerous widely dispersed pollution sources (automobiles), the pollution problem is merely transferred to a few large sources (the power plants). It is true, however, that effective control of emissions in this case would be much easier. Several cities in the United States, including San Francisco and New York City, are already making limited use of electric buses and delivery vans.

STEAM CARS.   Another possible alternative to the internal combustion engine is the steam car. The propulsive steam is generated by burning kerosene. Since this fuel is virtually totally combusted, the only products emitted from the engine would be harmless carbon dioxide and water. Its performance, in terms of speed, safety, and reliability is quite acceptable. Why, then, hasn't the motor industry generated any enthusiasm about mass-producing the vehicle? The reasons are economic. As Virginia Brodine states:

> The established automobile industry has too much invested in the internal combustion engine to be interested in developing an alternative, and the costs for an independent manufacturer to enter the market are almost prohibitive. In addition to the enormous initial investment, there would be the difficulties of establishing dealerships and servicing facilities. The petroleum industry also presents an obstacle, since its refineries would have to be revamped to produce low-grade kerosene instead of the present high-octane fuels (3).

USE OF CATALYTIC CONVERTERS.   It now appears that the major automobile manufacturers, because of compelling economic reasons, will retain the gasoline engine, in one form or another. Under the provisions of the Clean Air Act of 1970, beginning with the 1976 models emissions of hydrocarbons, carbon monoxide, and nitrogen dioxide must be reduced by 97 per cent (compared to the 1967 emissions?). Detroit is exploring several approaches to accomplishing these objectives.

One method employs the *catalytic converter*, a muffler-resembling device that is attached to the exhaust. With the aid of platinum as a catalyst, the potentially harmful carbon monoxide and hydrocarbon gases are converted to harmless carbon dioxide and water. The older types of converters were criticized as being inefficient, unreliable, wasteful of gasoline, lacking in durability, and expensive—adding up to $300 to the cost of the car. (The converters will not work properly with leaded gasoline.) However, in mid-1973 General Motors apparently made a break-through, for they claimed development of a converter that would not only cut gas consumption by 20 per cent, but would operate properly for the life of the car (1).

THE STRATIFIED CHARGE ENGINE.   Detroit auto manufacturers have frequently been criticized by the EPA for their heavy reliance on the catalytic converter, which it regards as a costly, inefficient "patch-up" job tacked on to the conventional piston

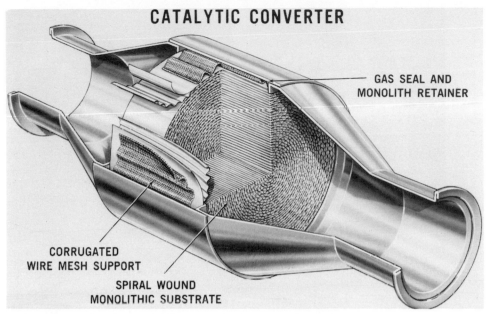

CATALYTIC CONVERTER

GAS SEAL AND
MONOLITH RETAINER

CORRUGATED
WIRE MESH SUPPORT

SPIRAL WOUND
MONOLITHIC SUBSTRATE

Figure 13-33. *Cutaway illustration shows a catalytic converter of the type the Ford Motor Company is considering for 1975–76 models. Resembling a small muffler, the emission-control device changes vehicle exhaust pollutants into harmless gases and vapors via contact with noble-metal catalysts. The noble metal (platinum, palladium, or a combination of the two) is deposited on the surface of the honeycomb-like substrate. (Ford Motor Company)*

engine. In the opinion of some automotive engineers much better pollution control would be possible with more basic modifications of the traditional piston engine. One such modified motor is the *stratified charge* engine currently used in the foreign-made Honda. It employs an extra combustion chamber that is situated above each cylinder of a conventional piston engine. Most of the pollutants are therefore consumed as a result of the prolonged combustion that results. The stratified charge engine has been under intensive development at both General Motors and Ford (1).

THE WANKEL ENGINE. The Mazda car, manufactured in Japan, employs the *Wankel engine*. A rotary type, the Wankel has a *thermal reactor* (something like a miniature oven), in which the exhaust gases emitted from the engine are burned with oxygen (1). One drawback is that it is 30 per cent less efficient in fuel consumption than the conventional piston type engine (10). In 1974 General Motors began offering the Wankel as an alternative engine in the Chevrolet Vega.

The Future

The increasing public awareness of the medical, ecological, and economic implications of our air pollution problem, as well as the upgrading of federal, state, and local pollution control programs, is encouraging. Nevertheless, within the remaining

Figure 13-34. *Ann Arbor, Michigan. After dedication of EPA's first federal laboratory designed specifically to control automobile air pollution, on October 27, 1971, in Ann Arbor, tests began and studies were made to formulate EPA's national air standards. The test shown here collects data on actual auto emissions, one of the criteria to be used in setting standards. (EPA)*

years of this century the major emission sources in this country will increase at an astounding rate as urbanization, industrialization, the consumption of fuels, and the use of motor vehicles all increase. Consider the following data: Our urban population is expected to mushroom from the 144 million of 1965 to 272 million by 2000; steel production will rise from the 220 million tons of 1960 to 460 million tons by 2000; chemical production will be 450 per cent greater in 2000 than it was in 1965; petroleum production will increase sharply from the 3 billion barrels of 1960 to almost 7 billion by 2000. By 2000 there will be 240 million privately owned motor cars on our highways, consuming an aggregate 160 billion gallons of gasoline yearly —roughly four times the figure for 1960. Moreover, it has been estimated that by the year 2000 the total annual production of combustible waste will zoom to a staggering 175 million tons, sufficient to bury all of Washington, D.C., in 30 feet of trash (20).

It is apparent that our recently strengthened pollution control programs will not even enable us to maintain our present position in the pollution crisis. *We must do much more than we are now doing, and we must do it quickly.*

We have a moral commitment, not only to fellow Americans, and to our children yet unborn, but also to Africans, Indians, Chinese—to all people crowded on this small planet earth. For air pollution recognizes no political, social, economic, or ethnic boundaries. As Bruce Wallace, of Cornell University, has stated, we Americans must constantly remind ourselves what we are unwilling to admit, even subconsciously, that we rely on the inability of other peoples of the world to match our industrial achievements. If the rate of pollution of the world's atmosphere were to be increased 20-fold (since the United States contains only 1/20th of the world's population) and then doubled (because our consumption of gasoline is expected to double by 1975), worldwide levels of pollution would be intolerable. This is the message that must be brought to the attention of all persons over and over and over again so that we in the United States can start rational corrective steps at once (23).

BIBLIOGRAPHY

1. "Ahead: New Headaches for Auto Drivers." *U.S. News and World Report* (July 9, 1973), pp. 29–31.
2. Bregman, J. I., and Sergei Lenormand. *The Pollution Paradox.* New York: Spartan, 1966.
3. Brodine, Virginia. *Air Pollution.* New York: Harcourt, 1973.
4. Ehrlich, Paul R. *Human Ecology: Problems and Solutions.* San Francisco: Freeman, 1973.
5. Faith, W. L. *Air Pollution Control.* New York: Wiley, 1959.
6. Lessing, Lawrence. "The Revolt Against the Internal Combustion Engine," *Fortune* (July 1967), pp. 79–83, 180–184.
7. "Let's Clear the Air!" *The American City* (August, 1967), p. 1324.
8. Lewis, Howard R. *With Every Breath You Take.* New York: Crown, 1965.
9. Lund, Herbert F. "Industrial Air Pollution," *Factory* (October 1965), p. 11.
10. McConagha, Al. "Car Emission Control: Environment vs. Economy," Minneapolis *Tribune* (June 3, 1973).
11. Moran, Joseph M., Michael D. Morgan, and James H. Wiersma. *An Introduction to Environmental Sciences.* Boston: Little, Brown, 1973.
12. National Academy of Sciences. *Waste Management and Control.* Publ. No. 1400. Washington, D.C.: National Research Council, 1966.
13. Odum, Eugene P. *Fundamentals of Ecology,* 3rd ed. Philadelphia: Saunders, 1971.
14. Pack, D. H. 1964. "Meteorology of Air Pollution," *Science,* 146 (November 1964), 1125.
15. Prival, Michael J. and Farley Fisher. "Fluorides in the Air," *Environ.,* 15, No. 3 (April 1973), 25–32.
16. Ridgeway, James. "Stench from New Jersey," *New Republic* (July 16, 1966), pp. 13–15.
17. "Spectrum," *Environ.,* 15, No. 3 (April 1973), 23.
18. "Trees as Source of Pollution," *Time,* 88, No. 11 (1966), 57.
19. U.S. Public Health Service. *The Federal Air Pollution Program.* Publ. No. 1560. Washington, D.C.: Division of Air Pollution, 1966.
20. ———. *Today and Tomorrow in Air Pollution.* Publ. No. 1555. Washington, D.C.: Division of Air Pollution, 1966.
21. ———. *The Effects of Air Pollution.* Publ. No. 1556. Washington, D.C.: 1967.
22. Wagner, Richard H. *Environment and Man.* New York: Norton, 1971.
23. Wallace, Bruce. *People, Their Needs, Environment, Ecology.* Englewood Cliffs, N.J.: Prentice-Hall, 1972.
24. Weisz, Paul B. *The Science of Biology.* New York: McGraw-Hill, 1959.

14.

Noise Pollution

Noise abatement and the need for it are virtually neglected issues in American life today. Unless the medical and public health professions become deeply involved in these problems, it is likely that apathy and inertia will defer any effective action for another decade or even longer. But we, the public, cannot wait that long. Air pollution kills us slowly but silently; noise makes each day a torment.

Robert Alex Baron,
"Noise and Urban Man,"
American Journal of Public Health, 58, November 1968.

In the Bronx borough of New York City one evening last spring, four boys were at play, shouting and racing in and out of an apartment building. Suddenly, from a second-floor window, came the crack of a pistol. One of the boys sprawled dead on the pavement. . . . The killer . . . confessed to police that he was a night worker who had lost control of himself because the noise from the boys prevented him from sleeping. . . .

John M. Mecklin,
"Its Time to Turn Down All That Noise,"
Fortune (October 1969).

Figure 14-1. *The snow-mobile—sleek, beautiful, fast—and noisy! As of 1975, manufacturers were being pressured by environmental agencies to develop quieter engines. The roar and whine of snowmoblies seem to permeate small northern Wisconsin towns on Friday and Saturday nights. (Milwaukee Chamber of Commerce)*

Nature of Sound

The gurgling chuckle of a trout stream; the first rustle of an evening breeze moving through a pine stand; the timid whistle of a spring bluebird—all these are sounds that have been part of the environment even before there were Americans. The staccato of a jackhammer ripping up concrete, the whine of a jet on take-off, the blatant babel of construction machinery—these too are part of the environment, but they followed the appearance of Americans and their technology.

Sound is a form of energy and as such can ultimately be traced to its original form—solar energy. It moves through the air in the form of "waves" at a speed of about 1,060 feet per second. One of its most interesting characteristics is its remarkable range in intensity. (Sound energy can be measured in terms of *watt*—electrical energy—equivalents.) For example, the loudness of a piano rendition of the *Moonlight Sonata* might measure about 0.1 watt, Tchaikovsky's *1812 Overture* about 1 watt, while that of a moon shot rocket at blast-off might be measured at 10 million watts (21). In fact, the sound intensities to which the twentieth-century human ear is exposed ranges from 1 billionth (0.000000001) watt to 10 million (10,000,000) watts. However, since watt measurements are very clumsy to work with, scientists use the *decibel* rather than the *watt* as the unit of sound measurement. (*Deci* means "ten"; *bel* is used in honor of Alexander Graham Bell, who

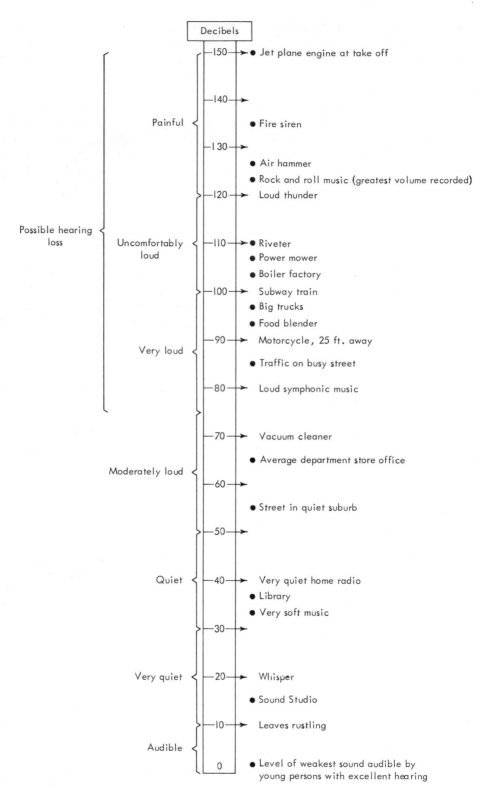

Figure 14-2. *Noise levels in the urban environment. (Data from several sources.)*

invented the telephone.) In the decibel system we employ logarithms of the ratios of loudness to compare sound intensities. Let us assume, for example, that the faintest sound audible to the human ear has an intensity of 1 decibel. Then a sound 10 times as loud would be given a rating of 10 decibels, and a sound 100 times as loud would be given a value of 20 decibels, and so on.

Figure 14-2, which includes data from several sources, is a decibel scale for a broad spectrum of sounds audible to the human ear. Note that industrial workers exposed to continuous levels of 80 decibels during eight-hour working days may suffer hearing loss, while sounds ranging from 85 to 180 decibels are considered "dangerous" in the sense that they can cause damage not only to the hearing mechanism but possibly also to the circulatory, nervous, endocrine, and reproductive systems as well.

Hearing Loss

There is mounting evidence that when a person is subjected to high sound intensities, day in and day out, as, for example, a traffic policeman or a jackhammer operator, some degree of hearing impairment inevitably results. Surprisingly, it has even been found that rock and roll music, a source of enjoyment for millions of American teenagers, may cause deafness. The "rock" sound generated at some discotheques may reach 125 decibels—a level just below that at which the ear perceives pain.

Several years ago David Lipscomb, of the University of Tennessee, conducted an intriguing experiment that shed light on the adverse effects of "rock" music. He dropped in at a Knoxville discotheque and tape recorded several numbers. Upon returning to his laboratory he played back the music to a pen full of guinea pigs, exposing them to ninety hours of intermittent "rock and roll." After sacrificing the animals he examined the *cochlear cells* of their inner ear. (These cells are concerned with converting sound energy to nerve impulses.) He was surprised to find that they "had collapsed and shriveled up like peas" (11, 4). (See Fig. 14-3.)

According to Clifford R. Bragdon, an environmental specialist with the U.S. Army Environmental Health Agency:

> Sound-induced motion of the fluid in the cochlea induces shearing and bending movements of the hair cells in the organ of Corti, which in turn result in electrical stimuli transmitted by the auditory nerve. Prolonged and excessive noise eventually produces deterioration and finally, destruction of *hair cells*, and this disrupts the sound transmission mechanism. The insidious nature of hearing loss is revealed by the fact that a person can suffer forty per cent bilateral hearing impairment without being aware of it in a subjective manner (5).

Several years ago Samuel Rosen, of New York City's Mt. Sinai Hospital, found that the hearing acuity of the Maabans, a primitive tribe in Egypt, was superior to that of Americans in all age groups. He discovered that even a seventy-year-old Maaban could hear as well as a young American boy! He attributed this to the relatively quiet Maaban environment compared to the technological hubbub that characterizes urban America (4, 19). He believed that high-intensity sound causes blood vessel constriction, which in turn results in auditory malfunction (4).

It is estimated that roughly 16 million workers in the United States are threatened with hearing loss because of the high intensity sound associated with their jobs.

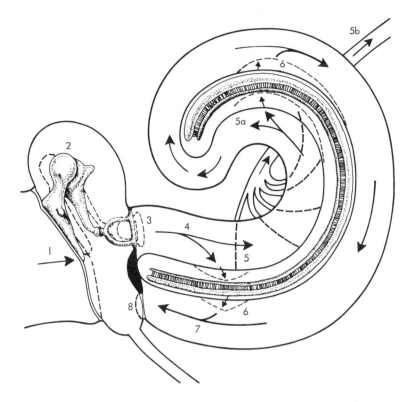

Figure 14-3. *Structure of the human ear. Sound waves are transmitted to the ear drum, then by means of three small bones, through the middle ear to the snail-like inner ear or cochlea. Pulsations of fluid in the inner ear eventually result in the stimulation of the hair cells. Nerve impulses generated in the hair cells are carried by the auditory nerve to the brain where they are interpreted as sound.*

Insurance companies are paying out over $1 billion annually to compensate workers for job-related hearing loss. However, because of the technological developments that characterize our affluent society, one can suffer hearing loss simply by being exposed for many years to the "ordinary" noises of the average American city. You don't have to be a "boiler maker"!

Other Harmful Physiological Effects

Since the pioneering work of Rosen, other researchers have shown that high intensity sound can cause health problems much more serious than deafness. For example, Alexander Cohen reports:

> intense noise of sudden onset will cause marked physiological changes including a rise in blood pressure, increase in sweating, changes in breathing, and sharp contractions of muscles in the body. These changes are generally regarded as an emergency reaction of the body, increasing the effectiveness of any muscular exertion which might be required. Although perhaps useful in emergencies (fire, car accident, boat mishap), these changes may be harmful for long periods since they would interfere with other necessary activities or produce undue amounts of fatigue (10).

Russian researchers have shown that the high-level sound occurring in ball-bearing plants will interfere with the normal functioning of the circulatory system, causing unstable arterial blood pressure and a slowed heart beat (10).

Heart and blood vessel diseases are among the leading "killer" diseases in the United States and other technologically advanced countries. They are frequently caused by the deposition of fatty substances, including *cholesterol*, in the blood vessel lining. This causes a narrowing of the arteries, including the coronary artery that supplies the contracting heart muscle with nutrients and oxygen. Eventually the coronary artery becomes so narrow that blood flow is insufficient to maintain healthy heart muscle, at which point a heart "attack," or *coronary*, occurs.

You say, what has this got to do with noise? This. Experiments conducted at the University of South Dakota, involving rats and rabbits, have indicated that noise intensities characteristic of the human acoustic environment may cause blood cholesterol levels to *rise* (3). It would seem, therefore, that high sound intensity might be an important factor contributing to coronaries in man, even though one cannot safely extrapolate rodent data to the human organism. In fact, Rosen, an expert in this area, is much concerned. He warns, "We now have millions with heart disease [and] high blood pressure . . . who need protection from the additional stress of noise. . . . If a disorder such as . . . coronary heart disease is present, [excessive] noise exposure would endanger human health . . . "(3).

Most people who work in a din-and-clamor world certainly would believe that once they're back home in bed "sound" asleep, noise would have a negligible effect, if any, on their body functions. Not so, Samuel Rosen reports:

> the reflex effect which causes contraction of the blood vessels occurs with equal intensity during sleep as during wakefulness. Not only do noise signals make the blood vessels contract, but the skin becomes pale, muscles constrict and adrenalin is shot out into the blood stream. This adrenalin output causes tension and nervousness. If chronic, it can elevate blood pressure . . . (4).

British studies have shown that noise definitely causes gastric upsets, resulting in diminished bowel action and reduced digestive juice flow (14). Other investigations have tentatively implicated high sound levels with a variety of malfunctions

Figure 14-4. *Decibels rise during rush hour traffic on the urban freeway.*

from simple headache and pupil dilation to stomach ulcers, intestinal spasms, and neurosis.

Surprisingly, noise may even have a harmful effect on the *unborn child*. At least such was the opinion of Lester W. Sontag, reporting recently to the American Association for the Advancement of Science (3). As Robert Baron suggests in his informative book *The Tyranny of Noise,* much more research should be conducted in this area (3). For example, quantitative studies should be made of the number of stillborn and defective offspring born to mothers living adjacent to noisy airports and highways and compared with the number born to mothers living in relatively quiet, rural environments.

After considering the well-documented evidence of the harmful effects of high level sound, we must assume that noise pollution may be fully as deleterious to human well-being as such air contaminants as sulfur dioxide and carbon monoxide. *Decibels may be deadly.* Does America need another "Donora episode" (in which twenty people were killed by air pollution)? Do we really need blood running from human ears before we appreciate this fact? This may sound alarmist. It is meant to be. Pertinent to this point is the following statement made by William H. Stewart, former Surgeon General of the United States:

> Donora incidents occur daily in communities across the United States. Not in terms of specific numbers of deaths attributable to excessive noise exposure, but in terms of many more than twenty cardiovascular (circulatory) problems . . . for which the noises of twentieth century living are a major contributory factor . . . (3).

It is apparent that noise pollution, yet another unwanted environmental side-effect of technological "progress," has adversely affected human health to a degree that the general public has been only dimly aware.

In this section we have emphasized the health effects of noise. It should be emphasized, however, that the spectrum of noise effects ranges much wider. The overall influences of unwanted sound have been nicely summarized by Bragdon:

> The environment can be evaluated with the aid of nine health indexes symptomatic of noise pollution: vascular constriction, hearing loss, mental stress, sleep interference, task interference, communication interference, property damage, friendship formation and/or maintenance, and annoyance. These indexes cover the potential range of effects of noise, from a threat to human survival and physical injury to reduced efficiency and decreased personal comfort and enjoyment . . . (5).

How Can Noise Be Reduced?

It is ironic that even while the collective American eardrum is being assaulted with a multi-source, multi-directional, multi-intensity noise barrage, the technology and methods for substantial abatement in some areas is *already available* but is not being exploited. In other areas, such as aircraft noise, technical problems are still formidable.

Automobiles. Much vehicle noise can be reduced considerably below the decibel levels now being tolerated by both the driver and the general public. A few car manufacturers are marshaling considerable expertise to justify their advertising claims of "silent ride" transportation. For example, Ford currently employs a highly

Figure 14-5. *High decibel noise generated by jet planes at takeoff has caused mass translocations of residents in the vicinity of some major airports.*

trained research team whose primary objective is to reduce the decibel levels being generated by more than 15,000 sound-producing components of a single Ford car.

Long before noise was ever conceived of as being a pollutant, the industry developed a dramatically successful "muffler" to prevent a noise assault on human ears. Right? Wrong—to prevent frightening horses and causing them to run "wild" (3).

The relatively silent electric motor could replace the internal combustion engine in many of our vehicles, thus reducing both air and sound pollution simultaneously. Surveys have shown, for example, that electric buses that have been operating in England for several years are considerably quieter at a distance of 7 meters (60 decibels), than their gasoline-powered counterparts (80 decibels) (3).

Possibly because it was the first in the United States, the New York City subway is certainly the noisiest. It is of interest, therefore, that the modern subways of Montreal and Mexico City, are astonishingly quiet by comparison, primarily because they run on *rubber* wheels (22).

Even the U.S. Army is developing an interest in silence. According to Hanson Baldwin, military editor of the New York *Times*, the Army is considering the substitution of silent planes for noisy helicopters in surveillance work. (Our helicopters were extremely vulnerable to enemy gunfire during such activity over the Vietnam jungles!) Certainly, if silent planes can be built for military purposes, they can be constructed for commercial aviation as well (3).

Airports. The noise pollution problem in the vicinity of major airports poses one of the most serious challenges to authorities entrusted with sound abatement. The enormity of the problem has been aptly described by Kenneth E. Maxwell, of California State University at Long Beach:

> Aircraft, due to their increase in size and enormous increase in numbers, have become one of the most troublesome sources of noise pollution. For example, O'Hare International Airport in Chicago, the busiest airport in the world, has more than a *thousand* operational jet flights on an average day. This means a flight in or out every 40 seconds. Within a 15-mile radius of the airport there are several hundred thousand people

clustered in homes, apartment houses, businesses, schools, hospitals, and nursing homes. The scream of jet engines is not conducive to tranquility and repose. In some locations, conversations cease every few seconds, television viewing and listening becomes impossible, and sleep and relaxation are interrupted . . . (12).

This problem is by no means restricted to O'Hare—there are about 100 million airplane flights in the United States daily, with more than 500 airports servicing jets (12).

Just what can be done about the airport noise "arsenals"? Regulations can be developed by the Federal Aviation Authority (FAA) that would *restructure flight patterns* during both approach and takeoff. Manufacturers of aircraft engines could reduce jet noise by a few relatively minor modifications of design. It is possible for residents living in the vicinity of airports to *sound-insulate* their homes. There are certain drawbacks. For example, even though the *interior* might be quite pleasant, the occupants probably wouldn't care to make much use of the front porch swing, where the sound assault would be as intense as ever. Moreover, insulation is expensive, ranging from $3,200 for a $20,000 home, to $12,550 for a residence originally costing $30,000 (5).

In extreme cases, *mass translocation* of affected residents may be the only realistic method of "solving" jet-craft noise. The community (or county) could purchase the sound-besieged homes. For example, a few years ago the city of Los Angeles agreed to purchase 1,994 homes adjacent to the Los Angeles International Airport. It was a rather expensive undertaking, costing the city nearly $300 million by the time the project was completed in 1973. In West Germany aircraft noise actually caused the "death" of one town and the "birth" of another. When the 225 residents of Oberbolheim complained about the noise problem, the West German government decided to construct a brand new town—homes, schools, stores, roadways, and all. When everything was ready the citizens of Oberbolheim moved "lock, stock, and barrel" to the new town, which was appropriately named New Oberbolheim (5). A similar phenomenon is developing in the vicinity of the immense new airport at Roissy, France, which by 1980 will be able to handle 60 million passengers yearly. Some villages that date back to the fifteenth century, such as Le Mensil Amelot, will probably be abandoned (1).

Use of Vegetational Sound Barriers. In earlier chapters, we have considered the multiple functions of vegetation with regard to the soil erosion control, flood abatement, timber production, wildlife habitat development, and environmental aesthetics. Here we may mention yet another function—that of sound pollution abatement. Vegetation is particularly effective in absorbing high frequency sounds. Eugene P. Odum describes the possibilities in this area:

> A dense evergreen hedge can reduce the noise of garbage collection by 10 decibels (i.e., a tenfold attenuation). Border planting along highways or streets can be effective if plantings are lower towards the noise source and higher towards the hearer, thus not only absorbing but also deflecting the noise upward. A fifty-foot wide band with an inner strip of dense shrubs and an outer band of trees can be quite effective (a sort of forest edge that is also good for small wildlife) . . . (15).

Value of City Planning. The USSR is somewhat farther advanced than the United States in noise control. When a new Russian town is on the planning boards, engineers will construct miniature models of it, with residential, industrial, and commercial buildings being represented by toy blocks. Traffic sounds are then simulated, and the *commercial* and *industrial* "buildings" are strategically placed *between* the main traffic arteries and the *residential* "buildings" in such a way that any traffic noise reaching the residential area will be substantially reduced. Highway traffic can also be reduced by the use of recessed roadbeds, like those extending from downtown Chicago to the O'Hare airport, and by the use of sound-absorbing plastic in surfacing materials (3).

Financial Costs of Noise Pollution Control

The general public seems to have developed an apathetic attitude toward the noise problem because it is under the impression that it is an unavoidable concomitant of America's high living standard. To the contrary, however, the technology is available to greatly diminish the current noise barrage, generated by many products with—out excessive expenditures. Consider a few items:

1. The screech of truck tires on concrete in most cases can be diminished by a simple redesign of tread. Added tire cost to consumer? None.

Figure 14-6. *A jack hammer ripping up concrete generates enough noise to cause deafness in construction workers exposed to it for long periods of time. The technology for making these jack hammers much less offensive to the human ear is available. The cost increase per unit would be negligible.* (EPA)

2. The back-lawn crescendoes issuing from the home power mower can be greatly reduced. Increased cost? A mere $15 per mower.
3. A small air compressor, noisy "villain" of construction projects, can be appreciably silenced. Cost? An extra $500 above the original $5,300 sale price (13).

As John M. Mecklin has so appropriately observed:

The expense becomes even less formidable when measured against the savings from noise suppression. The World Health Organization estimates that industrial noise alone costs the U.S. today more than $4 billion annually—in accidents, absenteeism, inefficiency, and compensation claims. The human costs in sleepless nights, family squabbles, and mental illness are beyond measure, but they surely must be enormous . . . (13).

Noise Control Regulations

The mounting volume of environmental noise is more than just a nuisance about which Americans can shrug their collective shoulders and can tolerate as an irritating by-product of an industrial society. To the contrary, it represents a serious environmental threat to human well-being that must be controlled and eventually reduced to an absolute minimum. Noise control will be no easy task. First, it will require a massive educational program directed to the general public—"the man on the street." Second, it will require a high level of public responsibility in the form of pressure on local, state, and federal lawmakers to ensure that more effective noise control legislation is enacted. And third, the laws must be properly enforced to ensure that manufacturers employ the latest sound-reducing technology available in the fabrication of machines and vehicles and to ensure that in the operations of all these machines, whether garbage grinders or jet planes, sound generation will be minimized.

Despite the well-documented evidence of the harmful effects of noise on human well-being, regulatory attempts have been strenuously opposed by certain groups that have a vested interest in noise production. For example, when the state of New York proposed a ban on the playing of transistor radios in public vehicles, a Buffalo radio-TV station had the incredible gall to brand such proposals as "insanities" (13). In a similar vein, at a conference of 125 industrial officials recently, 90 per cent opposed noise regulation on the basis of arguments that they were "unrealistic and impossible to comply with . . ." (13). Now the attitudes expressed above are to some degree explicable in the context of raw economics. Most inexplicable, and highly disheartening to noise control advocates, was an editorial that appeared in the distinguished *Journal of the American Medical Association* asserting that "some noise must be tolerated as an unavoidable concomitant of the blessings of civilization . . ." (13).

City Regulations. Very few American cities have objective ordinances that specify in quantitative terms the precise maximum decibel limits permitted for motorized vehicles. This seems almost incomprehensible in view of a recent report appearing in *Medical World News*: "Some psychiatrists and psychologists believe that in the unusually high noise levels—*traffic, sirens, police whistles, noisy children, blaring television sets* and *transistor radios*—in the slums, just one extra "startle sound" may often trigger violence . . ." (16). Cincinnati, Ohio, and Bloomington, Indiana, are exceptions in that they do have well defined noise codes, in each case specifying 95 dBA as the maximum noise level permitted by *any* vehicle. However, having the ordinance is one thing, and enforcing it is another. It is ironic, for example, that as late as 1972, fourteen years after Cincinnati had passed her ordinance, *only two citations had been issued.* Could one contributing factor be that this city of 1 million inhabitants owned only one sound level meter? (16).

State Regulations. Except for a few states such as California and New York, noise pollution control regulations at the state level with regard to transportation are almost nonexistent. True, most states have laws on the books that require motor vehicles to be equipped with properly working mufflers. However, no specific noise limits are set. California and New York, however, have enacted regulations with which they are effectively clamping down on truck noise. A California state trooper now may issue two tickets simultaneously, one for breaking the *speed* limit, and the second for exceeding the *noise* limit! The California code stipulates that vehicles with a gross weight of 3 tons (or more) must not exceed 88 dBA at speeds below 35 miles per hour and should not exceed 90 dBA above that speed. During the first year after California adopted her noise code in 1969, there were 2,861 violations out of 605,932 vehicles checked, with 2,425 of the violations being trucks. "The California code has caused truck manufacturers to make modifications in their equipment to conform to the noise limits. . . . Three makers obtained redesigned muffler systems to meet the California standards and one started a recall campaign on 1969 and 1970 models as a result of California's Highway Patrol noise enforcement reports . . ." (16).

Federal Noise Control Act of 1972

Responding to increased pressure from the general public, as well as prodding by environmental groups, and the opinions of medical researchers and public health authorities, the U.S. Congress finally passed the landmark Noise Control Act of 1972. The following major provisions are provided:

1. The Environmental Protection Agency is directed to administer research and disseminate information on the noise limits required to protect the public health and welfare; it is further directed to identify major noise sources (in industry, transportation, recreation, and so on) and to publish material on noise control techniques (9). (The law authorizes the expenditure of $21 million over a three-year period for noise pollution abatement (8).
2. The EPA will set noise emission standards for the major noise pollution sources involving "construction equipment, transportation equipment (except aircraft), all motors and engines, and electrical equipment" (9).
3. The EPA is given the authority to require all manufacturers to *label* their products with regard to the noise level generated. Nonconforming manufacturers *"are subject to fines up to $25,000 per day for each violation and to imprisonment for up to one year . . ."* (9).
4. The EPA was required to "make a comprehensive study of aircraft noise and cumulative noise exposure around airports. . . ."

This law is of considerable impact. It represents the first legal step to abate the

American noise pollution problem on a nation-wide basis. As the EPA states, "The comprehensive nature of the Noise Control Act of 1972 brings under Federal regulation for the first time, nearly all of the major new sources of noise. An incentive now exists for the full employment of noise control technology that is already available, and the day when quiet is restored appears closer. We know how to build quieter. Now the law is to give the Nation stimulation to do it . . ." (9).

BIBLIOGRAPHY

1. Antar, Elias. "Paris Air Travelers to Be Taxed to Protect Villagers from Noise" (Associated Press Dispatch), *Minneapolis Star* (April 25, 1973).
2. Armour, Claude A. "Noise Abatement—Memphis Style." *Proceedings of Fourth Annual Noise Abatement Symposium.* Chicago, Illinois, 1953, 32–38.
3. Baron, Robert Alex. *The Tyranny of Noise.* New York: St. Martin's, 1970.
4. Benarde, Melvin A. *Our Precarious Habitat.* New York: Norton, 1970.
5. Bragdon, Clifford R. *Noise Pollution: The Unquiet Crisis.* Philadelphia: University of Pennsylvania Press, 1971.
6. Christman, R. F., B. W. Mar, E. B. Welch, R. J. Charlson, and D. A. Carlson. *The Natural Environment: Wastes and Control,* Pacific Palisades, Calif.: Goodyear, 1973.
7. Domestic Council Executive Office of the President. *Emerging Problems,* The President's 1971 Environmental Program, Book 3, Washington, D. C.: Domestic Council Executive Office of the President, 1971.
8. Environmental Protection Agency. *EPA Citizen's Bulletin.* Washington, D.C.: U.S. Environmental Protection Agency (November, 1972).
9. Environmental Protection Agency. *The Noise Control Act of 1972.* Washington, D.C.: U.S. Environmental Protection Agency (December, 1972).
10. Hosey, Andrew D., and Charles H. Powell, eds. *Industrial Noise: A Guide to Its Evaluation and Control.* U.S. Public Health Service Publication No. 1572. Washington, D.C.: U.S. Government Printing Office, 1967.
11. Lipscomb, David M. "High Intensity Sounds in the Recreational Environment," *Clinical Pediatrics* 8:63 (1969).
12. Maxwell, Kenneth E. *Environment of Life.* Encino, Cal.: Dickenson Publishing Company, 1973.
13. Mecklin, John M. "It's Time to Turn Down All That Noise." *Fortune* (October 1969), 130–133, 188, 190, 195.
14. Murrel, K. F. H. *Ergonomics.* London: Chapman & Hall, 1965.
15. Odum, Eugene P. *Fundamentals of Ecology,* 3rd ed. Philadelphia: Saunders, 1971.
16. Price, Fred C., Robert L. Davidson, and Steven Ross, eds. *McGraw-Hill's 1972 Report on Business and the Environment.* New York: McGraw-Hill, 1972.
17. Rienow, Robert, and Leona Train Rienow. *Moment in the Sun.* New York: Dial, 1967.
18. Rooney, Angela. "Freeways: Urban Invaders." *National Parks and Conservation Magazine* (October 1971), 4–8.
19. Rosen, S., and P. Olin. "Hearing Loss and Coronary Heart Disease." *Archives of Otolaryngology* 82:236 (1965).
20. Svadlrouskaya, N. F. "Effect of Long-term Noise on Cerebral Oxidation Processes in Albino Rats." *Gigiena I. Sanitaria,* Vol. 7 (1967).
21. Turk, Amos, Jonathan Turk, and Janet T. Wittes. *Ecology, Pollution, Environment.* Philadelphia: Saunders, 1972.
22. Wagner, Richard H. *Environment and Man.* New York: Norton, 1971.

15.

The Solid Waste Problem

Solid wastes etch a trail of visible blight that leaves few corners of the country unspotted. Across the Nation the same scenes repeat—refuse in the streets, litter on beaches and along roadsides, abandoned autos on isolated curbsides and in weeded vacant lots, rusty refrigerators and stoves in back yards, thousands of dumps scarring the landscape. And the less visible aspects of the problem—solid wastes in the ocean, contamination of ground water, and wasted resources—are just as critical. America's well-known penchant for convenience has come face-to-face with major environmental problems.

Environmental Quality,
The First Annual Report of the Council on Environmental Quality. Transmitted to the Congress, August 1970.

When Stone Age man finished gnawing on a rabbit leg bone, in the semidarkness of his cave, he got rid of it by simply tossing it away. Likewise for other waste. Eventually, when the rubbish heap got too big, he simply forsook his old cave and found another. In

America today over 500,000 years after the Stone Age man has faded into history, the average housewife takes out the day's accumulation of junk and garbage—consisting in part of leg bones, but in addition of a twentieth-century jumble of tin cans, milk cartons, catsup and vinegar bottles, broken plastic toys, old newspapers, and hair spray cans. Now, if she could only throw this "crud" away, à la Stone Age man! The only problem is that the human population has increased several hundred times since 500,000 B.C. There is no longer any "away"—it has become the manicured lawn of the neighbor next door!

Volume of Solid Waste in America

America "the Beautiful" is the world's champion producer of solid waste! Although representing only 6 per cent of the global population, it generates a whopping 70 per cent of its rubbish and garbage. In 1920 the average American disposed of 2.75 pounds of waste per day, but by 2000 he will make a daily "throwaway" of 8 pounds. As Wesley Marx has observed:

> The uncontrolled growth of population, cities and industry creates an ugly anomaly . . . we exhibit an unrivalled concern with hygiene. We probably shampoo our hair, deodorize our armpits, and shave our faces with more regularity than any civilization to date. . . . Yet aboriginal hunters must rank as cleaner creatures than we, simply because they were unable to dirty their living space to the degree we can . . . (6).

In a message before Congress Senator Gaylord Nelson of Wisconsin recently observed, "It must be viewed with a bitter irony that the enduring pyramid for our affluent and productive age may prove to be a massive pile of indestructible bottles, cans and plastic containers paid for by the collective sweat of the public brow. . . ." That statement was well founded. Roughly 10 billion tons of solid waste will have been generated in the United States in just the thirty-five years from 1965 to 2000 (11). Were this to be compacted, it would fill a sanitary landfill the size of the entire state of Delaware (11). It would cost American taxpayers $0.5 *trillion* simply to properly bury the stuff (11). We litter our highways with 20 million cubic yards of trash annually and then pay out $100 million just to have it removed (9). Each year 20 million Californians alone produce enough trash to form a gigantic mound 100 feet wide and 30 feet high extending from Oregon to Mexico. Each year Americans junk 100 million tires, 20 million tons of paper, 48 billion cans, 28 billion bottles, and 7 million motor cars. American industrial plants generate 165 million tons of solid waste yearly. In 1970 America junked 360 million tons of solid waste; by the year 2000 she will dispose of 400 million tons.

Types of Solid Waste

Waste Paper.   Waste paper today forms over 50 per cent of municipal refuge. The average American disposes of 540 pounds of old newspapers annually. Each day over 10 million pounds of newspapers and magazines are discarded in Los Angeles County alone. The reuse of waste paper for processing into newsprint has been sharply decreasing in the United States. For example, by 1980 only 18 per cent of the waste paper will be reused, compared to the 35 per cent utilized in 1945. (Com-

Figure 15-1. *Dozens of cans tossed from a moving car at a highway intersection near Orange, North Carolina. Every litter-bit hurts. (U. S. Dept.of Agriculture)*

pare this to Japan where 46 per cent of the old paper is recycled!) One reason more waste paper is not recycled is because it is difficult to separate from other refuse. One solution to this dilemma, according to New York City Sanitation Commissioner Samuel Kearing, Jr., is to add the cost of disposal to the cost of the paper product. Kearing feels, for example, that if the incineration cost, which amounts to $8 per ton in New York City, were added, newsprint manufacturers would spend money in developing more efficient recycling techniques. Despite Kearing's pessimism, a few plants have produced fresh newsprint from old discarded paper with considerable success. In 1969, for example, the Garden State Paper Company, with plants in New Jersey, California, and Illinois, produced 320,000 tons of newsprint from 365,000 tons of old newspapers, with gross income from sales amounting to $45 million.

Recycling of paper cannot only be desirable from an economic standpoint, but also from the standpoint of forest conservation. In a recent year (1966), the recycling of 10 million tons of paper provided $45 million in salaries to 10,000 workers. Moreover, it saved the equivalent of 12.8 million cords of wood that did not have to be cut from 13 million forested acres.

Cans. The term *tin can* is a misnomer—its really a steel can in tin "clothing." Tin has been used because it presents an attractive shiny surface and does not react chemically with food contents. Suppose you opened up a can of tuna for supper

Figure 15-2. *Conversion of newspapers to beef steaks? A steer at the Agricultural Research Center, Beltsville, Md., is shown feeding on a mixture of one part ground newspaper and nine parts concentrates, such as molasses, soy bean meal, and cracked corn. The newsprint serves as roughage in the diet and does not appear to have any adverse effect on the animals. In the context of this research, old newspapers would have to be regarded as a "resource" rather than as waste. (United States Department of Agriculture photo by Murray Lemmon)*

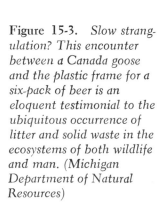

Figure 15-3. *Slow strangulation? This encounter between a Canada goose and the plastic frame for a six-pack of beer is an eloquent testimonial to the ubiquitous occurrence of litter and solid waste in the ecosystems of both wildlife and man. (Michigan Department of Natural Resources)*

Figure 15-4. *"Beauty and the waste." Human thoughtlessness has caused the desecration of this lovely woodland glade. (Michigan Department of Natural Resources)*

and then threw the empty can through your open kitchen window (à la Stone Age man) onto your front lawn. How long would that can remain there? Probably ten to twenty years, assuming some complaining neighbor did not remove it in the meantime! The can would eventually disintegrate because of the weathering of the tin and the rapid rusting of the steel. That is not too bad. Of course you would be putting up with an ugly eyesore, but eventually the can would disappear and the tin and iron components would have been incorporated into the soil.

However, since it is an energy-consuming process to make steel out of iron ore, wouldn't the steel industry save money by reclaiming the steel from the tin can, thus by-passing the smelter process? It would, except for one thing standing in the way—the tin alloy. It is a mixed metal contaminant that is not acceptable to the newer steel furnaces. Because of this steel scrap from tin cans is worth only $20 per ton. Not very much of this is currently reclaimed. United States manufacturers are producing *fewer tin cans and more aluminum cans.*

Now suppose, however, that you threw an aluminum can onto your front lawn. How long would it last? You might not live long enough to find out! If not removed

Figure 15-5(A). *Through publicity and advertising the Reynolds Metals Company urges individuals and organizations to collect all-aluminum beverage cans and bring them to one of more than 1,000 collection points. At the Reynolds Recycling Center in Los Angeles each can collector is assigned a bin for his scrap.*

Figure 15-5(B). *The cans are placed in a hopper and carried along a moving belt through a magnetic separator, which kicks out the steel cans. Payment for aluminum scrap is made at the rate of ten cents per pound. (Reynolds Metals Company)*

by some enterprising youth hoping to redeem it for a penny, or by a disgruntled neighbor, it probably would remain there virtually intact for a century. Fortunately, aluminum scrap is worth $200 per ton, and much of it is being collected by scrap dealers and sold to the aluminum industry.

We junk 55 billion cans per year—from the beer cans sullying the white shoulders of Mt. Rainier to the soup cans bobbing in Wisconsin's canoe waters. Even parts of the California desert sparkle in the sun, reflecting light from millions of cans flung by absent-minded tourists and mindless "hoods" on motorcycles. Robert Rienow and his wife once made a random stop in the middle of the desert and counted 120 cans amid the cacti within a 40-foot radius of where they stood (9). In order to reduce the littering problem, the Adolph Coors Brewing Company of Golden, California, recently offered 1¢ for every can collected. The results were gratifying. In a single year they retrieved 12,409,176 (9).

Bottles. The United States produces over 11 million tons of glass containers yearly and it junks 28 billion bottles a year. As a result glass forms a substantial 6 per cent of municipal solid waste. Part of the problem has been the tendency for industry to use *nonreturnable bottles.* A returnable bottle, on the other hand, makes about nineteen round trips between bottler and consumer before it is finally junked (2). It appears, however, that the deposits required on the bottles should be raised. For example, several years ago the Pepsi Cola company of New York distributed

Figure 15-5(C). *The scrap is reprocessed, cast into ingots, rolled into sheets, and eventually fashioned into new cans such as these. (Reynolds Metals Company)*

Figure 15-6. *"Scotch-on-the-rocks." Jumble of cans and bottles discarded by ice fishermen on a Michigan lake. (Michigan Department of Natural Resources)*

14.4 million bottles, which required a 5¢ deposit. Within only six months they had all disappeared—apparently ending up in trash buckets (2). Maybe a 25¢ deposit would work better.

Considerable research is being funded by the federal government to develop effective methods of recovering glass from municipal refuse, sort it by color, pulverize it, and utilize it in the production of new glass. Such grants have recently been awarded to Baltimore, San Diego County, and Lowell, Massachusetts. A highly advanced municipal waste reclamation unit at Franklin, Ohio, handles up to 1 ton of waste glass per hour (3). In an attempt to mitigate the problem, industry has experimented with two unique types of bottles. One is a bottle that when broken is reduced to many tiny granules, having a considerable smaller volume in aggregate than the large pieces of broken glass resulting from the breakage of a conventional bottle. The second type is a "dissolvable" bottle; both its lining and covering is waterproof. However, when the cover is broken the bottle dissolves in water and can be flushed down the sink. In this way, however, we avoid one problem and create another. As Wagner states, "Instead of getting rid of a pound of solid glass bottle, we would ask a sewage plant to get rid of a pound of synthetic material dissolved in the sewage effluent" (13).

In the past few years technology has been developed to make use of waste glass as a valuable raw material in the production of everything from road surfacing to floor tile. Consider a few examples:

1. The crushed glass fraction in incinerator residue has been used in the manufacture of the glass beads in the reflective paints used on highway signs.

Figure 15-7. *Recycling of glass. Empty glass containers are being collected and transported to a central location for weighing and sorting before being recycled. Flint glass went into the first trailer, amber into the second, and green into the third. (Owens-Illinois)*

2. Recently crushed glass has been used to replace sand in the manufacture of *glasphalt*, a surfacing material used on highways, runways, parking lots, and so on. It is much more durable than ordinary asphalt. Moreover, because of its heat-retaining properties glasphalt may permit road paving in weather that is too cold when ordinary asphalt is used (2).

3. Up to 50 per cent waste glass has been used by a Milwaukee concern in the fabrication of *mineral wool insulation*, which has been used in a number of construction projects, including an industrial building in Fullerton, California (3).

4. Scientists at the University of California at Los Angeles have developed a technique for making resistant, highly durable *floor tiles* from a half-and-half mixture of glass and sewage sludge—a nifty way to abate two serious waste problems simultaneously (3).

Junked Cars. As an environmental eyesore a rusty tin can is bad enough, but how about a whole car? How about 7 million cars—the number that affluent Americans junk yearly? Things weren't so bad in the 1950's. You could get $40 per car at any salvage yard. Whatever the make—Volks, Ford, Chevvie—it is a lot more than just steel. And in the 1950's enterprising junk dealers could recover almost 20 pounds of lead, 35 pounds of zinc, 37 pounds of copper, and 66 pounds of aluminum from one vehicle, while the steel that remained meant about $40 in his pocket. Although this steel contained copper impurities, it was nevertheless in demand by the steel industry, which would mix the scrap steel with iron ore in their furnaces. As a result of this auto carcass value, very few were left lying around to desecrate the landscape (13).

Figure 15-8. *An ingredient of "glasphalt." Ground up glass crystals that look like rock candy are the glass part of the new "glasphalt" (glass and asphalt) pavement laid at Owens-Illinois, Inc.'s Technical Center in Toledo in an experiment by O-I and the University of Missouri (at Rolla), which seeks to find a new use for discarded glass containers. (Owens-Illinois)*

Figure 15-9. *Workmen spreading "glasphalt" along a busy street in Toledo, Ohio. (Owens-Illinois)*

In the 1960's, however, things changed. The steel industry began to employ a different method of production, resulting in a more highly refined steel, with a minimum of impurities. Unfortunately the process could no longer utilize copper-contaminated steel of junked cars. (According to a recent report by the National Academy of Sciences, car manufacturers should reduce the copper content of cars from 1.4 per cent to 0.4 per cent or less in order to make it easier to recover the steel.) The value of a junked car went down to about $5, not worth having it towed to the salvage yard. Countless car owners, especially teenagers, left their car in the street or alley where it "conked out." About one in every seven cars is abandoned in this way in the United States. Roughly 60,000 cars are abandoned yearly on the streets of New York City alone, up to 200,000 for the nation as a whole (13). Rusting car hulks appeared everywhere—in backyards, on vacant lots, along rural side roads, even in cemeteries. True, a few of the junk cars have been put to good use. As mentioned previously in our discussion of marine fisheries management, the U.S. Bureau of Sports Fisheries and Wildlife has been using rusting cars in the construction of artificial reefs in areas where the ocean bottom is relatively flat. Initial indications suggest that the reefs are of considerable value in providing both breeding sites and cover for a variety of marine fish.

Finally, in the early 1970's a few technological advances made it economically feasible to recover the steel from junked cars. Thus, in Colorado, the National Metal Processing Company launched a "car-eating" operation that employed a gigantic hammer mill capable of "feeding" on 500 cars daily. This mill can convert a rusty old Chevvie into compact baseball-sized pellets within sixty seconds. This company first cleaned up a two-year accumulation of junked cars in the Denver area and then planned to move through the entire state, thus reducing the junked car problem to negligible proportions (6). A similar "car-eating" machine has operated in other urban areas including Minneapolis–St. Paul. As a result of this new technology, the steel makers can dispense with 0.5 ton of limestone, 1 ton of coke, and 1.5 tons of iron ore, simply by using 1 ton of the scrap pellets (6). Moreover, substantial energy savings will be made.

Perhaps the car manufacturers should bear some responsibility ensuring that the metals from their products can be more easily recycled. It has been suggested, for example, by Fred Singer, U.S. Department of Interior, that the federal government might even prod industry toward this end with the use of tax incentives (10).

Tires. One beautiful summer's day in 1972 I drove lazily through the picturesque hills of northern Wisconsin. Suddenly, as I came to the crest of one hill, a column of dense smoke appeared, black and hideous against the azure sky. Curious, I traced the smoky plume to its source—a pile of burning tires in a nearby village dump. What possible excuse could there be to generate such a volume of air contaminants, let alone violate countryside aesthetics? Yet in the early 1970's this was still a commonplace method of disposing of many of the 100 million tires annually discarded by American motorists. One reason for the mounting tire "mountain" has been the low rate of recapping—only 10 per cent in affluent America compared to 80 per cent in not-so-affluent Europe. Another reason is that tires tend to bob around in sanitary landfills—sometimes springing up even after they were seemingly firmly covered with dirt. This vexing problem, however, may now be solved. Norman R. Braton, of the University of Wisconsin, has developed a technique that would greatly reduce tire volume and facilitate their disposal. He freezes them with liquid

Figure 15-10. *Smoke from the Redding, Califronia, city dump, December 13, 1965. (National Air Pollution Control Administration)*

nitrogen at a temperature of $-80°$ F and then pulverizes them into gravel-sized pellets (8). Recently a technological breakthrough, resulting from research conducted jointly by the U.S. Bureau of Mines and the Firestone Rubber Company promises that junked tires may prove to be a valuable source of both chemicals and energy. The tires are first shredded into fine particles and then subjected to a process similar to that used in coking coal, being heated up to $500°$ C in a closed chamber from which oxygen has been excluded. Fifteen hundred cubic feet of natural gas (superior to ordinary natural gas as a fuel) and 140 gallons of oils may be derived from a single ton of scrap tire rubber (13).

Plastics. We are living in a "plastic world." Wherever you happen to be reading these words, why don't you raise your eyes and look around. It's a good bet that you would see at least half a dozen plastic items. Just looking around my office I can see the following: telephone, thermos bottle, cup, plastic book covers, plastic name plate, plastic barreled ballpoint pen, plastic picture frames, plastic bird skin cases, plastic magic marker, plastic electrical receptacle, and plastic binoculars! By 1980 the per capita disposal of plastic in America will amount to 0.25 pound per day.

The big problem with plastics, as with the chlorinated hydrocarbon pesticides, is that they resist breakdown by bacterial action. You could toss away a plastic spoon at a picnic in 1980 and the chances are good that the spoon would still be intact in the year 2080 long after you yourself had decomposed. Sheets of plastic have even been found floating far out at sea. True, plastic materials *can* be incinerated, but the result might be highly adverse—corrosive fumes of hydrochloric acid being emitted that may not only be destructive to vegetation, but might be extremely injurious if inhaled by man. Incineration of plastic is simply not feasible without the most stringent control of the gases thus generated.

The plastics industry, of course, is sensitive to the mounting public pressure that the problem has generated and is conducting intensive research to develop a type of plastic that would eventually break down. For example, Japanese chemists have produced a polystyrene foam plastic, (such as is used in meat trays and egg cartons) that will disintegrate after six months exposure to ultraviolet light from the sun (8). Sounds great! However, a dilemma might develop if the plastic breaks down too fast. For example, in 1971

Sweden's Tetra Pak Company, a big producer of polyvinyl chloride (PVC) beer bottles, said it was developing a paraffin additive to make plastics biodegradable. Such plastics would break down into constituents that microorganisms could consume. But the company found that the decay took place within *hours*, prompting fears of beer bottles slumping into reeking puddles because of a tavern's fluorescent lights (8).

It would indeed be frustrating for a thirsty patron to have his beer suddenly gush foamily onto the bar.

The plastic waste problem remains a severe challenge to human ingenuity and technological know-how.

Collection Methods

In most American cities garbage and trash is hauled by *packer trucks* that are capable of reducing volume by 60 per cent. This method, however, has certain distinct drawbacks. The 100 or more trucks required by a major city will add significantly not only to traffic congestion in already overburdened city streets, but also to noise and air pollution as well. Many an urban dweller has been rudely awakened by the predawn crescendos generated by the packer truck–garbage can combo.

But things are different in Sundbyberg, Sweden. There are no garbage cans, no rubbish trucks. For the town uses a *vacuum* collection method—the most important advance in collection technology since the invention of the wheel. The housewife simply drops her garbage bags or old newspapers, and so on, into chutes recessed into the walls of her apartment. The waste is then whisked at 60 miles an hour to a central collection point. In describing this novel process, Bertram B. Johansson writes:

The central refuse pile may contain such diverse items as Christmas trees, heavy steam irons, coat hangers, umbrellas, paint cans, bottles, paper, and cardboard—in fact any thing that can be pushed through the chute openings. . . . An automatic process sifts glass and metals out of the heap. Putrid odors are removed from the air before it is expelled. The refuse remaining in the pile is whisked on into an incinerator to provide heat for the 1100 apartments that now use the vacuum disposal system . . . (5).

Burning of the refuse generates sufficient heat to provide hot water for all apartments using the system. Wind velocities are so high in the suction pipes that it takes only twenty minutes to collect the waste from 1,000 apartments. Since only one man (with the help of an automatic electronic panel) can remove the waste from 2,200 apartments, labor costs are drastically reduced (5).

A similar system has been operating at Disney World outside Orlando, Florida. Each day 50 tons of waste—hot dog wrappers, popsickle sticks, paper cups, and so on, are whisked at high speed through an underground suction tube network to a collection center. After being baled the trash is hauled to an incinerator.

Disposal Methods

Dump.   In seventeenth-century Paris and London it was a common, though odious, procedure for the urban housewife simply to dump the accumulated day's domestic waste out the open window into the gutter below; the vile symphony of sights and smells must have been a delight for passers-by.

In the days of the ancient Greeks and Romans, about 500 B.C., the most widely used method of waste disposal was to haul the stuff outside the city walls and dump it downwind so as not to offend the sensitivities of the residents. Today, over 2,000 years later, there are a goodly number of cities in the United States, the most technologically advanced nation on earth, that still make use of the "dump." When the trash is burned, in order to reduce volume, a medley of gases and odors assualt the nostrils of downwind inhabitants. Until a relatively few years ago, the Kenilworth Dump in Washington, D.C., was burned in this manner—the black smoke issuing from it eventually drifting past the windows of the Capitol itself. Not only are these dumps eyesores, but they serve as fine breeding habitat for disease-disseminating flies and rodents. Moreover, if the soil underlying the dump is highly permeable, the town's water supplies may easily become contaminated with in-

Figure 15-11. *Moab, Utah. Burning dump creates haze and smoke visible throughout town. Such a dump attracts disease-spreading rats and flies. Note auto "carcass." (David Hiser, EPA Documerica)*

fectious viruses and bacteria. The Environmental Protection Agency and state regulatory bodies as well are insisting that communities phase out the dump and convert to a more favorable method such as sanitary landfill disposal or incineration.

Landfill. The most extensively employed disposal method today is the *sanitary landfill,* in which waste is deposited in a trough that has been excavated in a low-value area at the edge of town. Sometimes a borrow pit or abandoned gravel pit is selected as a site. At the end of each day's dumping, the accumulated trash is compacted and then covered with a layer of soil. Advantages to this method obviously is superior to the dump-and-burn system since it minimizes air and water pollution, restricts fly and rodent breeding, and reduces the possibilities for the dispersal of disease organisms. There are also "fringe benefits" that may accrue once the landfill sites use for solid waste disposal has ended. A few examples follow:

1. Some sites have been converted into *recreational facilities.* A prime example is Mile-High Stadium in Denver, Colorado, where the Denver Broncos football team now cavorts. Mount Trashmore, a recreational area in Evanston, Illinois, was also built up from solid wastes. Until 1965 it was used for disposal of incinerated residue, at which time it had grown to a height of 65 feet and embraced 48 acres (14). It was then made available as a recreational area replete with baseball fields, tennis courts, sled hills, and toboggan runs. During its first year of operation, 15,000 people made use of the facility (7). Since it is becoming progressively more difficult and expensive for municipalities to acquire suitable landfill sites perhaps more trash hills, or even whole "mountain ranges," may be built in the future.
2. Landfills have also had *landscaping value.* In England, for example, the "hills" formed by the soil-and-vegetation mantled waste have added interest to an otherwise flat, monotonous terrain.
3. Landfills have been useful in *spoil bank rehabilitation* in western Maryland where strip mining has left 2,000 ugly scars. According to Wilfred Shields, chief of Maryland's Division of Solid Wastes, a modified landfill operation will be used to efface these scars. Waste will be transported from 87 roadside and open burning dumps to an abandoned strip-mine site dissected by 50-foot gullies. The waste will then be covered with soil from spoil piles left after strip-mining operations. Not only will aesthetics be improved but acid mine drainage will be curbed because of soil compaction, proper grading, and the strategic placement of drainage canals (6).
4. Former landfill sites on the edge of major cities have been converted into "educational parks" where urban youngsters are afforded a first-hand opportunity to study wildlife and ecology.

DISADVANTAGES. One big drawback to the landfills is that they require large acreages of land. For example, a town of 10,000 people generates so much trash that a single year's production would cover a whole acre to a depth of 10 feet. Gravel pits, abandoned stone quarries, marshes, and "waste" areas are rapidly being filled up in major urban areas such as New York City, Philadelphia, and San Francisco. It was estimated that over 50 per cent of the cities operating municipal landfills in 1972 would be forced to acquire new sites by 1978 (8). Former landfill operations in San Francisco Bay has caused reduction of bay area and attendant disadvantages to shipping, aesthetics, and marine life.

Composting. Composting is a disposal process by which bacteria decompose garbage to produce a humuslike material rich in organic content. When I was a kid about ten years old my granddad assigned me the task of dumping the day's garbage (apple cores, bread crusts, soup bones, and so on) into a backyard pit. The debris was then covered with a light layer of soil—the process being repeated the next day. The end product was a humuslike material, which served as a valuable soil conditioner that resisted compaction, reduced erodability, and promoted aeration and drainage.

In view of the progressive deletion of nutrients from American soils, and the need to provide more and more food for a mushrooming population, one would suppose that composting would be a highly popular disposal method. However, since the final product is relatively low in nutrients, many farmers simply prefer to use commercial fertilizer. Another negative feature is the necessity of removing noncompostable materials such as plastic, metals, and glass—a rather costly and intricate process. Some composting is done nevertheless. For example, the Salvage and Conversion System of Shawnee, Oklahoma, is an ingenious disposal system that combines composting with recycling. In the first step all commercially valuable materials, such as rags, paper, rubber, plastics, tin, and glass are removed from the waste. The remaining material, largely garbage, is then ground up, liberally sprinkled with bacterial additives, and then quickly composted. The final product is packaged and marketed as a soil conditioner.

Composting has had much wider acceptance in Europe than in the United States. In Holland, for example, a single company produces 200,000 tons of compost annually from the waste generated by 1 million Dutchmen (6). Even then only about 10 percent of Holland's waste is composted. Rome has one of the largest plants in the world, capable of composting 600 tons daily. Other large composting units are located in Ghent, Belgium, Leicester, England, and Jerusalem, Israel (1).

Submarine Disposal. Some researchers are exploring the feasibility of dumping waste in the ocean. This method appears especially attractive because of the scarcity of landfill sites in our large coastal cities. Solid wastes accumulating in New York City, for example, might be hauled to harbor barges by special trains. Joint research conducted by scientists at Harvard and the University of Rhode Island indicates that disposal should be limited to *incinerated waste* and be buried at a minimum depth of 100 feet to prevent fouling of fish nets. Others have suggested the eventual construction of entire "archipelagos," which might serve as recreational sites (marine fishing, and so on), or even as jetports, where the whine of aircraft engines would not affend urban ears (6).

Solid waste from San Francisco, New York City, and other coastal cities has been used in the formation of *artificial reefs*. The rusting hulks in automobile graveyards as well as the rubble from razed buildings have been used in reef building. Not only does this help solve the waste problem, but it also provides shelter and breeding sites for valuable marine fish. Moreover, it has been suggested that when such reefs are strategically placed in the paths of ocean currents, they might intensify the upwelling phenomenon and thus increase the fishing potential of the region.

Incineration. Incineration may be defined as "the controlled burning of combustible waste." In contrast to the simple burning of refuse in an open dump, incineration involves several steps: (1) the burning of waste in a specially designed furnace at temperatures ranging up to 1,900° F; (2) the removal of ash residue to a sanitary landfill; (3) the removal of atmospheric contaminants; and (4) the recovery of waste heat. Gaseous emissions may be removed by consuming them in a secondary combustion chamber. Ninety per cent of the particulate contaminants may be removed by electrostatic precipitators (12). Before precipitators were installed in New York City's municipal incinerator, stack effluents formed an estimated 10 to 15 per cent of the city's air pollution (2).

Incineration has several distinct advantages: (1) it requires much less space than a sanitary landfill; (2) the cost of waste collection is less costly than landfilling because the incinerator may be located closer to town; (3) the steam generated from waste heat may be sold for industrial use; Chicago's municipal incinerator, which consumes 1,600 tons of refuse daily, generates 440,000 pounds of steam per hour (8); (4) it can dispose of both rubbish (furniture, tires, mattresses, and so on) and garbage without a costly separation process (12). One negative aspect of incineration is that many potentially valuable resources (paper, rags, glass, and so on) are consumed.

Pyrolysis. Remember how they used to make charcoal? By excluding air from wood or coal and then applying external heat. The old-fashioned name for this process was *destructive distillation*: the modern name is *pyrolysis*, which literally means "to break down with fire." Pyrolysis of solid waste has several advantages. For one thing, since the process is virtually a closed system, air pollution is minimized. Further, a considerable number of valuable products can be recovered. A ton of ordinary municipal refuse could yield up to 2 gallons of light oil, 5 gallons of pitch and tar, 133 gallons of liquor, 25 pounds of ammonium sulfate, 230 pounds of char, and 17,000 cubic feet of gas (12). The oil, char, and gas, of course, would be usable as fuel (of considerable value during the current energy crisis). Ten million British Thermal Units may be derived from a single ton of garbage. Acetic acid and methyl alcohol, familiar items in every college chemistry lab, may also be recovered. The first major pyrolysis plant in the United States, operated by Hercules Corporation,

Figure 15-12. *Modern solid waste disposal plant. Artist's rendition shows the Landgard solid waste disposal plant to be constructed on Staten Island for New York City. The plant will process one thousand tons of the city's trash daily. It requires only 3½ acres of land. Wastes will be unloaded from barges, shredded, and stored in a large silo (upper right). Material will be continuously fed to a horizontal, rotating kiln (center) where pyrolytic action will reduce the trash via "baking." Gases will be cleaned before discharge from the square exhaust structure (left of kiln). A minor amount of residue, such as recovered iron, will be hauled away. (Monsanto Enviro-Chem Systems)*

was constructed in Delaware at a cost of $10 million. After the bulk of the trash has been composted, and metal and glass have been recycled, the residual material is pyrolyzed. The plant disposes of 500 tons of waste daily (4).

BIBLIOGRAPHY

1. Benarde, Melvin A. *Our Precarious Habitat.* New York: Norton, 1970.
2. Cailliet, Greg, Paulette Setzer, and Milton Love. *Everyman's Guide to Ecological Living.* New York: Macmillan, 1971.
3. "Glass Recycling Makes Strides," *Environmental Science and Technology,* 6, No. 12 (November 1972), 988–990.
4. Grinstead, Robert R. "The New Resource," *Environ.,* 12, No. 10 (December 1970), 3–17.
5. Johansson, Bertram B. "Whisking the Garbage," *Saturday Review* (July 3, 1971), pp. 40–43.
6. Marx, Wesley. *Man and His Environment: Waste.* New York: Harper, 1971.
7. Moran, Joseph M., Michael D. Morgan, and James H. Wiersma. *An Introduction to Environmental Sciences.* Boston: Little, Brown, 1973.
8. Price, F., R. Davidson, and S. Ross, eds. *McGraw-Hill's 1972 Report on Business and the Environment.* New York: McGraw-Hill, 1972.
9. Rienow, Robert, and Leona Train Rienow. *Moment in the Sun.* New York: Dial, 1967.
10. Segerberg, Osborn, Jr. *Where Have All the Flowers, Fishes, Birds, Trees, Water and Air Gone?* New York: McKay, 1971.
11. Stanford, Neal. "Atomic Energy Commission Scientists Push Project to Eliminate All Wastes," *Christian Science Monitor* (1969).
12. Turk, Amos, Jonathan Turk, and Janet T. Wittes. *Ecology, Pollution, Environment.* Philadelphia: Saunders, 1972.
13. Wagner, Richard H. *Environment and Man.* New York: Norton, 1971.
14. Woods, Barbara, ed. *Eco-solutions: A Casebook for the Environmental Crisis.* Cambridge, Mass.: Schenkman, 1972.

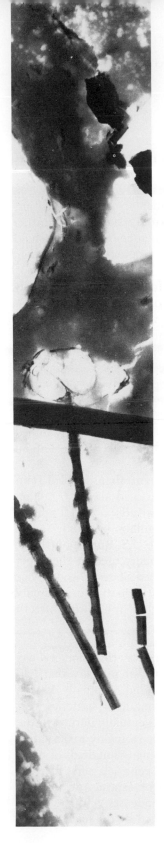

16.

Poisonous Substances in the Human Environment

[Among atmospheric pollutants, lead and mercury] constitute the greatest threat to our environment at the present
time because they accumulate in the system and produce
illnesses that develop slowly and insidiously.

George L. Waldbott, M. D.,
Health Effects of Environmental Pollutants,
Saint Louis, The C. V. Mosby Company, 1973.

Unfortunately, the potential toxicity of asbestos is not at
all widely recognized and it is handled quite casually by
people who assume it as harmless as cement or plaster.

Richard H. Wagner,
Environment and Man,
New York, W. W. Norton and Company, 1971.

Mercury, lead, and asbestos have at least two characteristics in common: First, their concentrations in

human tissues have greatly increased in recent years. Second, their effect on man may be severely debilitating and, in some cases, lethal.

Mercury in the Environment

Mercury is fascinating. Ever since I was introduced to it in freshman chemistry class, I have been intrigued by it. It was fun to play with—watching the silvery drops roll about in the bottom of a beaker. It must have held a similar attraction for the ill-fated school boy who took about 200 grams of mercury to his home—just for fun: "The metal spilled over the living room carpet, from which it was further dispersed by means of an electric vacuum cleaner. Every member of the household contracted mercury poisoning. . . . All had a generalized tremor, a skin eruption, and one member experienced hallucinations . . ." (21).

Although mercury is widely distributed in water, air, rocks, and soil, it usually occurs in only trace amounts forming only 30 billionths of the earth's crust (11). Soil concentrations may reach 0.8 ppm. Natural waters may contain only a few parts per billion. However, as a result of the technological and cultural developments of the industrialized world, man has accelerated and redistributed the cycling of mercury through the environment. Even worse, in a few localized areas, mercury build-ups have reached sufficiently high levels to cause serious outbreaks of mercury poisoning. About 3,000 tons of mercury, for example, are released into the global atmosphere yearly simply by the burning of coal. A single coal-fired power plant may emit 5,400 pounds of mercury vapor annually. Of the 10,000 tons of mercury mined each year, roughly 5,000 tons (50 per cent) are "lost" (dispersed) to the human environment.

During the period 1948–1966 industrial use of mercury more than doubled from 2.7 million pounds to 5.5 million pounds. In 1969 America used almost 6 million pounds, the greatest use being in the production of chloralkali (over 1.6 million pounds), in the manufacture of electrical equipment (1.4 million pounds), and in paint production (over 0.7 million pounds), according to the U.S. Bureau of Mines. Although there has been a decrease in the amount of mercury used in the paper industry and in agriculture during the past decade, the United States is using twice as much in drugs and three times as much in paints. Currently dentists use mercury in the preparation of fillings, 20 tons of mercury being "cycled" into Swedish teeth annually (21).

Movement Through the Ecosystem. Let us follow one pathway that mercury may take through the human ecosystem. A considerable amount of mercury that had been locked in the earth's crust for centuries may be mined and eventually used in the manufacture of dry cell batteries. When the mercury-containing batteries wear out they may be tossed into the refuse heap, collected, and eventually burned in the municipal incinerator. The liberated mercury then vaporizes (a highly toxic state), enters the atmosphere, and may be carried by wind currents many hundreds of miles from the incinerator site. (The Environmental Protection Agency classifies mercury as a "hazardous" air pollutant—signifying that even a slight exposure to it could cause serious illness and death.) Eventually the mercury condenses, and the atoms are "washed" from the atmosphere by rain or snow and carried by run-off into some lake or stream. Now, if it would only remain in this *elemental state* it would not pose too great a problem. However, it may now be converted into methyl mercury, a soluble organic compound formed by the activity of anaerobic bacteria, and then enter the algae-crustacean-fish-man food chain, with considerable potential for detrimental effect.

Poisonous Effect of Inorganic Mercury. Ever since medieval times mercury has been regarded as a somewhat sinister substance. As Leonard Goldwater, professor of community health at Duke University, states, "its toxic properties became so well known that some mercury compounds came to be used as agents of suicide and murder. There are indications that Napoleon, Ivan the Terrible and Charles II of England may have died of mercurial poisoning, either accidental or deliberate . . ." (11).

In the early nineteenth century the expression "mad as a hatter" was frequently used to describe a mentally deranged person. The Hatter, of *Alice in Wonderland* fame, as you recall, was a man of great emotional instability. Just how did this curious expression get started? During the early nineteenth century felt and beaver hats were highly fashionable, and in great demand. It was customary to treat the animal pelts from which the fur hats were fashioned with mercuric chloride. Of course, in the process of making the handmade top pieces the unfortunate hatters breathed in considerable amounts of mercury fumes. Apparently the mercury levels in the body caused sufficient malfunction of the brain to generate symptoms of "madness" (20). Repeated cases of inorganic mercury poisoning of this kind have been reported in the United States in recent years. In 1935, for example, a detailed study of 529 fur cutters revealed that 42 were afflicted with chronic mercurial poisoning (21).

The effects of inorganic mercury poisoning on the body are insidious, since most of the early symptoms are seemingly innocuous—loss of appetite, headache, ill temper, and fatigue—all of which the average person might easily attribute to one of a dozen different causes, from eating too much turkey to a poor grade in biology. This is extremely unfortunate, from the medical standpoint, because if the cause were identified at this stage, appropriate measures could be initiated to control the mercury intake.

The Episode at Minamata Bay. Between 1953 and 1960 a strange malady severely disabled 111 and killed 43 people, including adults and children, in a rather localized area along the coast of Minamata Bay, Japan. Even household pets became ill. The *Minamata disease*, as it came to be called, was characterized by muscular weakness, blindness, paralysis, and, in severe cases, coma and death. An investigation into the mysterious outbreak revealed that the symptoms varied from individual to individual, but the cumulative list of disorders closely matched the known effects of mercury poisoning. A bit of scientific sleuthing revealed that just before the outbreak a major plastics plant located in the city of Minamata at the head of the bay had suddenly increased the production of its major product—vinyl chloride. Mercuric chloride, which is employed as a catalyst in the manufacture of vinyl chloride, apparently was flushed in considerable amounts (60 grams for each ton of plastic produced) into the waters of the bay in the plant's waste effluent.

Further research has shown that this inorganic mercuric chloride, being insoluble, accumulated in the bottom sediments of the bay and was then converted by anaerobic bacteria to an organic form, such as methyl mercury, which is quite soluble in water, and therefore has much greater potential for gaining entry into the blood and tissues of living organisms. An interesting point here is that this bacterial conversion will occur most rapidly in oxygen-depleted waters. As we noted earlier, such depletion occurs when water becomes polluted with organic material having a high BOD, such as human waste, livestock manure, and wastes from pulp mills and vegetable canneries. In other words, relatively harmless inorganic mercury molecules may lie as inert residue on ocean, lake, and river bottoms for centuries; then, when man uses the water as a "septic tank" for his domestic and industrial wastes, he unknowingly facilitates the circulation of mercury through the aquatic ecosystem, this time in a form with possible serious implications for human well being. Eventually this organic mercury may enter human food chains such as algae-crustacean-fish-man, being progressively concentrated as it moves through the successive links.

By the time it enters the fish, its concentration may be 3,000 times greater than it was before entering the food chain. Since it takes at least 200 days for half of a given load of mercury in a fish to be excreted, the toxic metal tends to accumulate readily. According to Waldbott, fish may also absorb methyl mercury through their gills, the more rapid breathers and the fast swimming predators such as tuna and swordfish absorbing more than species with lower respiratory and feeding rates (21).

Figure 16-1. *Methyl mercury impairs brain functions. It attacks the cerebellum, visual cortex (gray matter), and to a lesser extent the frontal cortex (concerned with thought and voluntary responses). (From: George L. Waldbott,* Health Effects of Environmental Pollutants, *Saint Louis: C. V. Mosby Company, 1973)*

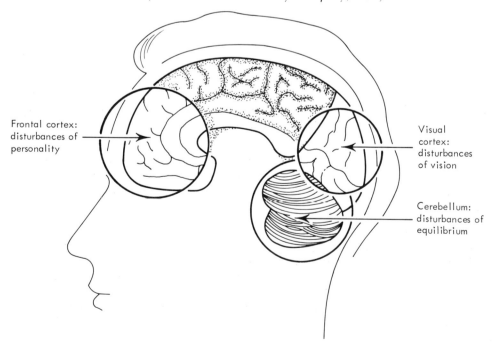

Methyl mercury concentrations in fish taken from Minamata Bay reached 50 ppm (wet weight), which is 100 times the level considered "safe" by authorities in the United States. Analysis of kidney tissues from Japanese who succumbed to Minamata disease revealed organic mercury concentrations ranging from 13 to 144 ppm (20).

Problems Arising From Mercury-treated Seed Grain

IN SWEDEN. One common problem vexing the farmer is the destruction of substantial amounts of seed grain by mold. In order to solve this problem both American and European farmers have made increasing use of methyl mercury fungicides, which control the growth of molds on seed grain not only during winter storage, but also in the fields after spring plantings. However, the solution of the mold problem resulted in another with serious implications for wildlife, livestock, and man. Scientists in Sweden, where mercurial fungicides had been intensively employed, became suspicious of the problem when analysis of chicken egg whites revealed surprisingly high concentrations of mercury—about four times the levels occurring in eggs from countries where seed grain fungicides were not used. Ensuing experiments revealed that crops grown from mercury-treated seeds had more than twice the amount occurring in crops grown from nontreated seeds (20).

Richard Wagner, in his excellent book *Environment and Man*, describes how the problem was brought under control by the Swedish health authorities:

> Changes in the formulation of the fungicide and in the rate of its application were recommended to Swedish farmers. A less toxic form of organic mercury, methoxymethyl mercury, replaced the highly toxic methyl mercury, and only seeds containing mold were treated before planting, reducing the percentage of treated seeds from 80 per cent to 12 per cent. It was found that the yield of grain was not reduced by these practices, and the mercury level in eggs decreased from 0.029 ppm in March, 1964 to 0.010 ppm in September, 1967 . . .(20).

Regrettably, however, the above policy was not launched soon enough to prevent the destruction of thousands of rooks and other seed-eating birds. In southern Sweden the yellow bunting was virtually exterminated (20).

IN NEW MEXICO. Wildlife destruction is bad enough, but human blindness and paralysis is infinitely worse. In the winter of 1970, Ernestine, Dorothy, and Amos Huckleby, of Alamogordo, New Mexico, became violently and mysteriously ill. After considerable sleuthing on the part of health and medical authorities, the outbreak was traced to methyl mercury-contaminated pork chops. Apparently the pork came from a pig that Mr. Huckleby fed with a mixture of garbage and mercury-treated seed grain. The insidious progress of the disease in the three youngsters, ranging in age from eight to eighteen, is vividly described by William H. Likosky, Epidemic Intelligence Service Officer, who was called on the case:

> Ernestine came home sick from school a little before noon on December 4th. She said she had fallen off the monkey bars at recess, and she had a pain in her left lower back . . . she had a temperature of 104. [The doctor] noticed that Ernestine wasn't walking right—that she was staggering. . . . She got steadily worse. Amos Charles took sick . . . on Christmas eve. He went to bed with an ear ache, and when he woke on Christmas morning, he said he couldn't see very well. The next day Dorothy took sick. It began as a generalized malaise. Then she began to feel "wobbly."

Then she couldn't walk at all, and her speech began to slur. Meanwhile, much the same thing was happening to Amos Charles—trouble walking, trouble talking, trouble seeing. Then he went into . . . a "rage." . . . He was wild, uncoordinated, thrashing around on the bed. He and Dorothy both got steadily worse. They sank into coma. . . . I saw [them]. It was terrible. I'll never forget them. It was shattering. Amos Charles was a big, husky, good-looking boy, and he lay there just a vegetable. His brain was gone. Ernestine was much the same. Dorothy was a little more alive. Her arms kept waving back and forth . . . (15).

Fetuses and newborns are much more sensitive to mercury poisoning than adults. Methyl mercury appears to have a greater affinity for placental and fetal tissue. Medical authorities were understandably apprehensive, therefore, when Mrs. Huckleby gave birth to a 7-pound boy, a scant six weeks after the family ate the contaminated pork. Although the infant seemed normal, it was seized by violent convulsions only a few hours after birth. Despite its recovery, the infant's health prospects are not good (15).

Industrial Source of Mercury Pollution. The manufacture of numerous products that make America's grandiose life style possible—detergents for making clothes "whiter than white," pesticides for eradicating crop-destroying insects, plastics for making slick, shiny car seat upholstery, rubber to cushion high speed highway jaunts; all require synthetic organic compounds as raw materials in their manufacture. Furthermore, the synthesis of many of these organic compounds is a chlorine-dependent process. And this is where mercury enters the picture, for the major chlorine-liberating process (its removal from brine by means of an electric current) requires mercury as an electric current conductor. In addition, a considerable number of industrial processes that employ mercury either as a catalyst or as a basic component of the finished product release substantial amounts of mercury in their waste effluent.

Let us examine just one such industry—the production of chlorine gas from brine —in some detail. The general chemical reaction involved follows:

sodium chloride + water → chlorine gas + sodium hydroxide (caustic soda) + hydrogen gas (passed into the air)

Although mercury does not appear in the actual chemical reaction, it serves as an electrode at the bottom of the chamber in which the chlorine is produced. When the salt water becomes too dilute it must be discharged along with a certain amount of mercury into some convenient body of water (18). Since the hydrogen emitted into the atmosphere is also mixed with mercury vapor, it is apparent that the chloralkali industry contributes to mercury contamination of both water and air. The increasing magnitude of the pollution problem originating in this source is eloquently expressed by the fact that mercury pollutant output from these plants has increased 2,100 percent during the period 1946–1971.

It has long been known that trace amounts of mercury occur in the air we breathe, the foods we eat, and the water we drink. However, for many years the concentration remained so low as to give no cause for alarm. However, in 1970 Norvald Fimreite, a young graduate student at the University of Western Ontario while making a routine tissue analysis of northern pike caught in Canadian waters was startled when he discovered mercury concentrations as high as 7 ppm, fully *fourteen times the mercury concentration considered "safe" for human consumption.* After reading

Fimreite's report, the Canadian Department of Fisheries and Forestry acted promptly and effectively. All commercial and sport fishing was prohibited in the waters from which fish with excessive mercury burdens were taken. The mercury was eventually traced to a number of chloralkali plants. They were requested to make substantial reductions in the level of their mercury emissions.

Following this episode, researchers in the United States found similarly high mercury concentrations in American waters. To cite one extreme example, downstream from the General Electric battery manufacturing plant in Michigan the mercury concentration was 1,000 ppm. This is 200,000 times the 5 ppb concentration considered "safe" for drinking water (12). Some of the mercury was traced to chloralkali plants. Much of it also originated in the waste effluent of pulp mills where mercurial fungicides were used to inhibit the growth of molds that tend to clog up machinery.

Tissue analysis of game fish in many states revealed that mercury levels were considerably higher than the 0.5 ppm considered "safe." As a result anglers were requested not to consume fish caught in the Niagara, Oswego, and St. Lawrence rivers, and Lakes Ontario, Erie, Champlain, and Onanadaga (19).

In the aftermath of the mercury "scare" a number of major American corporations, such as Olin, Allied Chemical, and Weyerhauser, found themselves facing federal lawsuits because of their excessive mercury emissions (12).

Eventually much methyl mercury is borne downstream into estuaries and to the shallow coastal waters of the ocean. Roughly 5,000 tons of mercury follows this route annually. It was most alarming a few years ago when the Food and Drug Administration discovered excessive mercury concentrations in millions of cans of tuna—a fish occupying a terminal (predator) link in the marine food chain. Even higher levels were found in another predator, the swordfish. As a result, 5 million pounds of swordfish were withdrawn from market in 1971.

Restrictions on the Use of Mercury. In summarizing the action that must be taken to minimize the possibility of mercurial poisoning episodes in the future, we can do no better than to quote from Goldwater's "Mercury in the Environment":

1. A system should be set up for frequent monitoring of the environment for the detection of significant increases in mercury contamination.
2. Research should be carried forward to establish measures for the levels and forms of mercurial pollution that signal a threat to health.
3. Techniques for mass screening of the population to detect mercurial poisoning should be developed.
4. Controls should be applied to stop the discharge of potentially harmful mercury wastes at the point of origin.
5. Toxic mercurials in industry and agriculture should be replaced by less toxic substitutes.
6. To implement such a program we shall need, of course, realistic education of the public and legislative action with adequate enforcement . . . (11).

Lead in the Environment

Episodes similar to the following, described by Dr. George Waldbott, have occurred in the United States:

On June 11, 1967, two sisters, age 2 and 3 were admitted to the Bradford [England] Children's Hospital. They died in convulsions within a few days. At the same time several domestic animals in the neighborhood where the two sisters lived had convulsions and died. . . . An initial survey . . . revealed . . . lead poisoning caused by inhaling fumes of lead-containing storage batteries that were being burned . . . (21).

Source. Some lead has always circulated in the human environment, for it is a natural and ubiquitous component of the earth's crust. Certainly, even the Stone Age man, living a million years ago, must have carried a small burden of lead in his blood stream, as a result of inhaling it from the atmosphere or by ingesting it along with lead-contaminated food and water. However, as in the case of mercury, industrial man's life style and technology has resulted in localized concentrations that have been the source of human lead poisoning episodes such as the one described above.

The Greek physician Nicander first described the symptoms of lead poisoning over 2,000 years ago. Some historians have attributed the decline and fall of the Roman Empire to toxic levels of lead in the Roman blood stream, which resulted in a high rate of stillbirths, deformities, and mental retardation, especially among members of the ruling class. This hypothesis has recently been supported by the discovery of unusually high lead concentrations in the skeletons of the Roman ruling class, who lived at the time of the empire's decline. Apparently the lead was used to line their bronze wine casks, wine cups, and cooking vessels, in order to replace the bad taste of copper with the pleasant taste of lead. The major Roman aqueducts, some of them over 100 miles long, apparently were also lined with lead, thus contributing further to the lead-poisoning phenomenon. Lead was also a characteristic component of cosmetics and medicines during the Roman era, luxuries that could be afforded only by the Roman aristocracy.

On the basis of dated snow sample analysis from the Greenland ice cap, lead concentrations have increased greatly in the last two centuries. The data indicate that during the 190-year period from 1750 to 1940 the weight of lead per ton of ice increased about 400 per cent from 20 micrograms (millionths of a gram) to 80 micrograms. On the other hand, during the relatively brief span of 25 years, from 1940 to 1965, the weight of lead per ton of ice increased from 80 to 210 micrograms —a 260 per cent gain (19). Furthermore, scientists have found 10 times as much lead in contemporary skeletons as in Peruvian Indian bones dating from the fourteenth century (5). Apparently this rapid increase in background lead in the past century has been largely due to the technological developments that have accompanied the Industrial Revolution. Especially the modern motor car, which requires leaded gasoline in its high compression engine and requires lead in the manufacture of its rubber tires, and more in the fabrication of its storage batteries. Other sources from which lead has been channeled into human tissues include old window putty, lead-based paints of pre-1958 vintage (lead was replaced with titanium in 1958), lead arsenate (formerly employed as an insecticide on a variety of crops including tobacco and other crops), solder used to seal cans, tiny particles eroded from lead-bearing glassware and pottery, as well as lead-lined water pipes. However, lead concentrations in human blood and urine cannot always be related to industrialization. Thus E. J. Underwood observes:

New Guinea natives, living under conditions completely divorced from industrialization and motorization revealed average levels comparable with those of highly industrialized communities. These findings illustrate the difficulty of defining "natural" levels in the manner proposed by Patterson, or at least in applying them with much confidence to particular geographical locations . . . (19).

It is possible, apparently, that lead concentrations in some human tissue may be high simply because of locally high concentrations in the earth's crust.

Lead Poisoning Among Ghetto Children. For many years physicians were puzzled by the high rate of lead poisoning occurring in children from the inner city slums of Chicago, Philadelphia, and New York. In June, 1970, forty cases of lead poisoning were found in a sample of 435 ghetto children from the East Bronx in a survey conducted by fifteen medical teams from New York City. Intensive investigations have revealed the surprising manner in which these youngsters got the lead into their systems. Apparently one of every five youngsters, aged one to five, "eat" non-food materials, such as tattered wallpaper, dirt, flower petals, grass, pencil erasers. In most cases this behavior is innocuous. However, in the "asphalt jungles" (where grass and flower petals are scarce) the kids frequently nibble on the sweet-tasting flakes of leaded paint peeling off old tenement walls, as well as on leaded window putty. Melvin A. Benarde, of Hahnemann Medical College, Philadelphia, has described the reason for the pronounced seasonal variation in the number of lead poisoning cases among the children. The cases "begin their annual rise in the spring, reaching peak proportions in July and August. Apparently, after ingestion of a quantity of chips of lead-based paint, the higher temperature, combined with the active (ultraviolet) rays of the sun stimulate increased intestinal absorption of the lead . . ." (3). Glenn Paulson, head of the New York Scientists Committee for Public Information, states, "There are 25,000 cases of lead poisoning a year in urban areas. This is a case of an earlier technology whose consequences were completely unknown. No one thought to test the paint for toxicity."

Leaded Gasoline. You should feel a little guilty as you roar down the freeway in your sleek, late model motor car. If you are powered by leaded gasoline you may be spewing (in addition to a host of other contaminants) countless molecules of potentially toxic lead bromide into the air. Although atmospheric lead is certainly derived in part from industrial sources, the greatest percentage undoubtedly has its origin in "antiknock" gasolines—that is, those which have had tetraethyl lead added to enhance engine performance. During the period from 1923 (when this treatment was first initiated) to 1971, at least 2.6 *trillion* grams of lead have been injected into the skies of the Northern Hemisphere, the United States alone generating about 750 million pounds yearly during the early 1970's. Today the North American atmosphere bears 1,000 times the "natural" amount (18). And the volume of motor traffic is increasing rapidly. It has been estimated that during the late 1970's at least 1.5 tons of lead will belch from motor car exhausts along each mile of roadway annually. Henry A. Schroeder, of the Dartmouth University Medical School, in testifying before a United States Senate Subcommittee, has emphasized the extremely high lead concentrations occurring along traffic arteries:

We have found enough lead in vegetation (up to 200 ppm, wet weight) growing beside a secondary highway to abort a cow subsisting on this vegetation; the concentration has trebled in six years. Fifteen of twenty samples of melted snow from the same place had more lead than the allowable limit for potable water, and seven samples had more than five times that limit . . . (16).

Wagner states that the 7 million gallons of gasoline consumed daily in Los Angeles alone generates 15 tons of lead (20). Not surprisingly, the average lead load in the Los Angeles atmosphere is 2.5 micrograms per cubic meter, compared to only 1.6 and 1.4 micrograms in Philadelphia and Cincinnati, respectively. And what is most disturbing, the problem is rapidly worsening—lead concentrations in Los Angeles increased 50 per cent during the 7-year period from 1963 to 1970, according to U.S. Public Health Service surveys. In fact the air over Los Angeles has 50 times that occurring over farmlands, and 5,000 times the natural concentration.

Recent studies have shown that garage mechanics, traffic policemen, and parking lot attendants have the highest lead concentrations (about 0.36 ppm) in their blood; people living along highways also have abnormally high lead concentrations (9). Among children 0.6 ppm of lead is considered the clinical level of blood poisoning; an industrial worker with a blood level of 0.6 ppm would be removed from his job to prevent continued exposure.

Toxic Effects of Lead on the Body. A significant question to ask is, "Just how much lead can the average person tolerate in his blood stream without incurring manifest symptoms of toxicity?" According to research conducted by Dr. Robert Kehoe, of the University of Cincinnati, a lead concentration of 80 micrograms per 100 grams of blood is the maximal concentration tolerated by adults without *apparent* ill effect. However, children are considerably more susceptible, some youngsters having shown symptoms of poisoning even though the lead concentration was only 60 micrograms (5). Above the 80-microgram level in adults, the blood, kidneys, and nervous tissue are adversely affected. Brain damage may be irreversible. Ordinarily the brain is protected from the toxic materials in the blood, but heavy metals such as lead appear to be an exception. Some of the early symptoms include headache, weakness, loss of appetite, and fatigue (20). Research on rats by Charles Xintaras, of the National Air Pollution Control Administration, has indicated that lead exposure may cause sleeplessness (2). Lead poisoning may cause anemia because of its interference with normal red blood cell reproduction in the bone marrow. A rise in blood pressure may occur. The microscopic tubules of the kidney, concerned with the vital function of filtering nitrogenous poisons from the blood stream, may be damaged to such an extent that the kidney may stop functioning—with inevitably fatal results. Choie and Richter, of the University of Rochester Medical Center, have observed cell abnormalities in rat kidney tubules only one to six days after the animals received a single injection of lead (0.05 milligram per gram body weight). This work indicates the rapidity with which lead toxicity occurs in the mammalion body (6). Swelling of the brain and convulsions may result from nervous tissue malfunction. High blood lead levels have been suspected by some researchers to cause hyperactivity in youngsters three to twelve years old. When lead poisoning occurs in a youngster between the ages of one and five, the period of rapid brain development, brain tissue may be irreversibly damaged, resulting in mental impairment, even though the child may make a complete *physical* recovery. According to Bernarde, people who have been severely poisoned with lead "suffer from convulsions, seizures, tremors, periods of manic behavior accompanied by auditory and visual hallucinations. Nightmares are not uncommon . . ." (3). Lead is taken into the body with food and drink. It must be rather unsettling for parents to know that evaporated skim milk, used in baby formula preparation, as late as 1973 has had lead concentrations of 1 ppm, according to Steven Lamm, of New York City's Bronx Municipal Hospital. Apparently the lead has its origin in the solder used in making the seams of the milk cans (1).

The source of some of this "dietary" lead may be most surprising. The medical sleuthing required to trace the toxic material to its source is well described in the following account of lead poisoning in a physician's family from Pocatello, Idaho, in November, 1969:

> Five of the six members of the family experienced fatigue, poor appetite, vague pains in the stomach, and vomiting. Unexplained changes in personality in three of the four children as well as in the parents took place. They left most of their meals unfinished. They became increasingly irritable to the point of quarreling with each other. Only the infant who was still on formula experienced no ill effect. Considerable detective work was required to identify the source of the lead poisoning: an earthenware pitcher had contaminated the orange juice that all members of the family, with the exception of the infant, had been drinking daily. Because the pitcher had not been fired long enough at a high temperature, lead had leached from the pitcher's glaze into the acid juice. The local health department determined that enough lead chromate came out of the juice pitcher in one washing with acid to kill two people. Lead in the orange juice, after 24 hours in the pitcher, was estimated at 15 mg in 100 ml of juice . . . (21).

Chronic Lead Poisoning and the Future.   It is indeed tragic that lead poisoning should kill 15 Americans annually and cause thousands more to suffer from kidney malfunction, convulsions, and mental retardation. However, these are only the cases that have actually been "pinned down" by the medical authorities. But what about the milder, earlier symptoms? Do we *really* know how many cases of headache, fatigue, and ill temper might *not* be due to the hustle-bustle of high-tension living, such as fighting the rush hour traffic, but *may actually be due to low level lead poisoning?* As a matter of fact, medical men don't really know *how* much lead the body can tolerate before it incurs severe damage. True, it has been stated that *overt* symptoms may appear when there is more than 80 micrograms of lead per 100 grams of blood. But at what level do *subtle* symptoms appear? As Cornell University's Bruce Wallace states, "The safe dose (80 micrograms) is one calculated for clinical purpose . . . a safe dose for the exposure of an entire population from birth to death has not been established . . ." (22). Is a chronic burden of 70 micrograms harmful? How about 60? Or 50? It is always possible, as in the case with pesticides, that relatively small amounts of lead might be involved in synergistic reactions with other body contaminants that might be highly harmful to human health. In the opinion of Clair C. Patterson of the California Institute of Technology, "There are definite indications that residents of the United States today are undergoing severe chronic insult!" He feels that we are much too complacent in this matter. Other authorities have expressed similar concern. Thus, Dr. David J. Clark and Dr. K. Voeller, writing in the British medical journal *Lancet*, state: ". . . the definition of what is a *toxic* (lead) level for blood levels needs re-evaluation . . ." (1).

Precise answers to these questions await future research. In the meantime it is obviously imperative to make the changes in life style and cultural patterns that will keep lead levels in food, water, and air as low as possible. Anti-knock qualities can be provided by tetra ethyl lead substitutes, which would increase gasoline costs by a paltry penny per gallon (19). Certainly, in any cost-benefit analysis, this would indeed be an extremely small price to pay.

We must make certain, however, that future substitutes for tetra ethyl lead are not equally or more injurious to human health than the lead itself. The federal Environmental Protection Agency has the authority to control new gasoline additives. In an article facetiously titled "And for Our Next Number . . . ," Sheldon Novick writes in *Environment* magazine:

". . . no one has any information about the effects of the new additive TAP on health; no one knows whether it is more or less dangerous than the . . . tetra ethyl lead which it will be replacing. . . . As things look now, it will be at least two years before the federal government is even in a position to ask questions about the health effects of TAP, which is meanwhile being added in considerable quantities to the environment . . ." (13).

Asbestos in the Environment

Industrial Use. *Asbestos* is a popular term for several types of fibrous mineral silicates that occur naturally in the earth's crust. The richest deposits are located in Canada, Russia, and South Africa. Because of its flexibility, great tensile strength, and resistance to heat, friction, and acid, it has found use in over 3,000 industrial products. The world's industries use at least 3 million tons yearly. Asbestos has been used for over 2,000 years, and it could well be that Christ himself ignited lamp wicks that were made from asbestos. In the asbestos mine regions of South Africa, waste asbestos rock has been commonly used for road surfacing. In the United States it is used in a multiplicity of products from pipe and boiler insulation to ironing board pads, from brake linings to clothing for firemen, from plasterboard to baby talcum. Fireproofing material having a 20 per cent asbestos component is sprayed on the steel "skeletons" of skyscrapers.

Dispersal Through the Environment. Wherever asbestos is mined or processed, or wherever asbestos products undergo wear, asbestos dust (composed of extremely minute particles) is released into the atmosphere from which it may eventually be channeled into the soft, moist, sensitive interior of the human lung. For example, a housewife sets a flat iron down on her ironing pad, inadvertently sending asbestos dust in the air; a carpenter's saw slices through plasterboard, again generating asbestos dust; a woman puts on an asbestos-containing coat, disseminating asbestos dust throughout her home in the process. Whatever happens to the material that has been worn from brake linings? They're still around, in pulverized form, as asbestos dust—possibly in the air, possibly on roadside meadows, or possibly in your lungs.

Asbestos Pathway to the Human Lung. Inhalation of asbestos fibers, even though of a transitory nature, may trigger a chain of events ultimately leading to cancer and death. It is true that the human respiratory system is equipped with a most efficient filtering mechanism that prevents most fibers from reaching the microscopic air sacs of the lungs. Particles that are more than ten microns [1] in diameter are almost completely filtered out by the hairs, sticky mucous, and twisting channels of the nasal chambers. On the other hand, asbestos particles ranging from .3 to 2 microns in diameter may penetrate to the windpipe and bronchial tubes. These materials may be expelled by coughing; if not, most of them will be trapped in a mucous stream that is kept in continuous motion by the synchronized beat of billions of microscopic hair-like cilia. The particles are then borne upward to the throat where they may be expelled by coughing or may be swallowed. (Nevertheless, despite this remarkable filtering process, some particles do pass through. Thus, before the widespread use of electronic precipitators, the lungs of residents in highly industrial areas would virtually turn black because of the billions of soot particles that had penetrated to the air sacs.)

Of greatest clinical interest are the fibers under one micron in diameter and about 35 microns long. Apparently they are the most effective in causing lung disease (3). With the aid of the electron miscroscope, which can magnify an object over 200,000 times, it has been demonstrated that for every fiber that can be detected with an ordinary microscope (which only magnifies about 1,000 times), there are probably at least 100 undetected fibers actually present in the lung tissue.

Furthermore, experiments with guinea pigs have shown that these ultra-small bits of asbestos can be just as deadly in causing lung disease as the larger, easily detected

[1] One micron equals one thousandth of a millimeter or one twenty-five thousandth of an inch.

Figure 16-2. *Asbestos fibers and asbestos bodies found in the lung of an individual worker occupationally exposed to amosite asbestos. Magnified 6,774 times. (Courtesy of Dr. I. J. Selikoff and Dr. William J. Nicholson, Mount Sinai School of Medicine, City University of New York)*

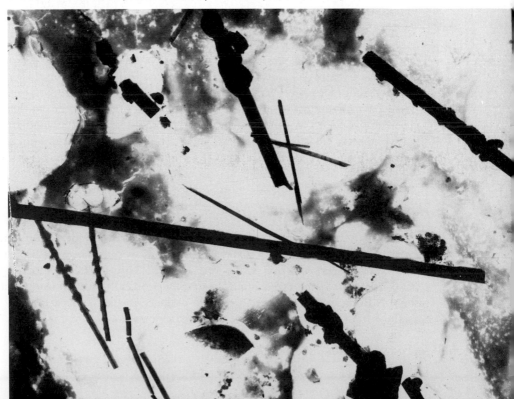

particles. Sometime after an asbestos fiber invades a delicate air sac, it in some way apparently triggers the development of a fibrous thickening of the lung wall and forms the core of a yellowish-red, rod-shaped *asbestos body*. Once such bodies form, an individual is said to suffer from *asbestosis*.

Asbestos and Disease. The symptoms of chronic asbestosis have been well described by George L. Waldbott:

> Like other cases of "dust lung" diseases, asbestosis develops slowly. It becomes manifest usually twenty to thirty years after the first exposure, often long after exposure to asbestos has completely ceased. . . . Unexplained breathlessness on exertion and cough often precede the disease by many years. The tightness in the chest is frequently associated with pain. In the advanced stage, the patients show *cyanosis* (a bluish discoloration of the skin), restricted chest expansion, and the barrel type of chest seen in emphysema. The tips of the fingers become enlarged and assume a bluish color, a condition called club fingers . . . (21).

British workers have found that over 50 per cent of the patients afflicted with asbestosis eventually die from lung cancer (20). Smoking raises the incidence of asbestos-associated lung cancer dramatically. It has been estimated that a cigarette-smoking asbestos worker has *ninety* times the chance of developing lung cancer than a nonsmoker not working with asbestos (21). I. J. Selikoff, a national authority on asbestos-related diseases, has reported a type of gastrointestinal cancer occurring among insulation workers in New York City. He has suggested that the malignancies may have been caused by asbestos particles that had been ingested with contaminated food or saliva (21).

As might be expected, surveys have revealed a relatively high incidence of asbestos-related lung cancers among the 120,000 people (miners, asbestos product processors, and so on) in the United States who work directly with asbestos. *Mesothelioma* (cancer of the chest cavity lining), formerly quite rare, has become much more common, especially among asbestos workers.

Asbestos contamination of water supplies has been an issue in a classic court battle that has been raging for months. The Reserve Mining Company, located at Silver Bay, Minnesota, has processed taconite, a low grade iron ore, since the mid-1950s. As a result of this operation, about 67,000 tons of residue (tailings) is dumped daily into the once-clear waters of Lake Superior. For years environmentalists have strenuously objected to this massive act of pollution and have appealed to Reserve Mining to shift to an on-land disposal system. The company has arrogantly rejected all such requests. Finally, in 1973, the Environmental Protection Agency, together with the states of Minnesota, Wisconsin, and Michigan, all of which border in part on Lake Superior, brought suit against Reserve Mining for contaminating Lake Superior. During the ensuing investigations, Dr. I. J. Selikoff made the surprising discovery that the levels of asbestos in the air and water in the vicinity of the plant were extraordinarily high. Apparently the asbestos had its source in the mine tailings. As a result of these findings, federal court judge Miles Lord ordered the plant to suspend operations because of the health threat to thousands of people living along the western shore of Lake Superior who were using the lake water for drinking purposes. Ironically, and most regrettably, Reserve Mining was permitted to resume operations after only a one-day shutdown as the result of a hurried appeal to a higher court.

One curious aspect of asbestos-associated diseases is that there is frequently a long time lag after initial exposure before the disease symptoms eventually appear. This means then that just because there is no case of asbestosis or lung cancer in an asbestos-exposed worker population in a given year, say 1975, this does not mean that their exposure is of no concern. A case in point is a study of the incidence of asbestosis among shipyard workers whose job it was to insulate pipes. Not a single case was found among workers exposed less than five years; however, among those exposed twenty years or more, almost 40 per cent were afflicted with asbestosis (4). Fortunately, the asbestos industry has been taking vigorous steps to eliminate the asbestos problem in the shops by the employment of vacuum devices, by the mandatory use of gas masks, and by automating many manufacturing processes.

However, according to the Environmental Protection Agency, perhaps the most disturbing feature of the asbestos problem is that "such prophylactic measures have not prevented the gradual long-term development of cancer in persons who come into occasional, slight, or temporary contact with asbestosis. This group certainly includes wives of asbsetos workers and all persons living within 1.5 kilometers of an asbestos plant. . . ."

The possible tragic outcome of a mere incidental, transistory exposure to asbestos is well demonstrated in a case involving a fifty-three-year-old woman, who suffered from scarred lungs, increasing breathlessness, and spontaneous lung collapse. As reported by Waldbott:

> [the attending physician] suspected asbestosis, but the patient denied occupational exposure. Subsequently she recalled that her husband had built two asbestos bungalows, one in 1947 and the other in 1948. She had held the asbestos sheets while her husband sawed them. They had resided in one of the bungalows for about two years before painting the sheets that lined the walls and ceilings. Subsequently, the diagnosis of asbestosis was confirmed in her case as well as in that of her husband, who had never been occupationally exposed to asbestos. Once asbestos particles reach the lungs, they are neither expelled nor dissolved . . . (21).

BIBLIOGRAPHY

1. Aaronson, Terri, and George Kohl. "Spectrum," *Environ.*, 14, No. 9 (1972), 23.
2. American Chemical Society. "Behavioral Toxicology Looks at Air Pollutants," in Maurice A. Strobbe, *Understanding Environmental Pollution*. St. Louis.. Mosby, 1971.
3. Benarde, Melvin A., *Our Precarious Habitat*. New York: Norton, 1970.
4. Brodine, Virginia. *Air Pollution*. New York: Harcourt, 1973.
5. Bromel, M. C. "Pollution and Disease," in Donald R. Scoby, ed., *Environmental Ethics*. Minneapolis: Burgess, 1971.
6. Choie, David D., and G. W. Richter, "Lead poisoning: Rapid Formation of Intranuclear Inclusions," *Science*, 177 (September 29, 1972), 1194–1195.
7. Commoner, Barry. *The Closing Circle*. New York: Knopf, 1971.
8. Curry-Lindahl, Kai. *Conservation for Survival*. New York: Morrow, 1972.
9. Ehrlich, Paul R., and Anne H. Ehrlich, *Population, Resources, Environment*. San Francisco: Freeman, 1970.
10. Environmental Protection Agency. *Asbestos and Air Pollution: An Annotated Bibliography*. Washington, D.C.: U.S. Government Printing Office, 1971.

11. Goldwater, Leonard J., "Mercury in the Environment," *Scient. Amer.*, 224, No. 5 (1971), 3–9.
12. Johnson, Oscar W. "The Impact of Industry Upon Our Environment," in Donald R. Scobie, ed., *Environmental Ethics*. Minneapolis: Burgess, 1971.
13. Novick, Sheldon. "And for Our Next Number . . . ," *Environm.*, 13, No. 5 (1971), 29.
14. Patterson, Clair C. "Contaminated and Natural Lead Environments of Man," *Archives of Environmental Health*, 11 (September 1965), 344–360.
15. Roueché, Berton. "Annals of Medicine: Insufficient Evidence," *New Yorker* (January 31, 1970).
16. Schroeder, Henry A. "Trace Elements in the Human Environment," in Ira Winn, *Basic Issues in Environment*. Columbus, Ohio: Merrill, 1972.
17. Segerberg, Osborn, Jr. *Where Have All the Flowers, Fishes, Birds, Trees, Water and Air Gone?* New York: McKay, 1971.
18. Turk, Amos, Jonathan Turk and Janet T. Wittes. *Ecology, Pollution, Environment*. Philadelphia: Saunders, 1972.
19. Underwood, E. J. "Trace Substances," in *Environmental Health IV*, D. D. Hemphill, ed., Columbia: University of Missouri, 1971.
20. Wagner, Richard H. *Environment and Man*. New York: Norton, 1971.
21. Waldbott, George L. *Health Effects of Environmental Pollutants*. St. Louis, Mo.: Mosby, 1973.
22. Wallace, Bruce. *People, Their Needs, Environment, Ecology*. Englewood Cliffs, N.J.: Prentice-Hall, 1972.
23. Weisberg, Barry. *Beyond Repair: The Ecology of Capitalism*. Boston: Beacon, 1971.

17.
The Energy Crisis

Consumption of the earth's stores of fossil fuels has barely started; yet already we can see the end. In a length of time which is extremely short when compared with the span of human history, and insignificant when compared with the length of time during which man has inhabited the earth; fossil fuels will have been discovered, utilized and completely consumed.

Harrison Brown,
The Challenge of Man's Future,
New York, Viking Press, 1954

It was symbolic. In early June, 1973, America's long-anticipated Skylab mission was in deep trouble. The spaceship had incurred a 6 per cent electrical power deficit because of the failure of two of its eighteen solar batteries. The implications were grave. In order to conserve energy lights aboard the spaceship were dimmed, fans were turned off, and a much-heralded long-distance mapping of the earth's mineral resources was canceled. Ironically, the crisis aboard the tiny spaceship, involving three astronauts, was a symbolic vignette of the *global* energy crisis on Spaceship Earth (a luminous sphere 300 miles far below), involving almost 4 billion people!

Power Shortages

Take Wisconsin as an example. On July 20, 1972, a stagnant mass of hot humid air blanketed densely populated southeastern Wisconsin, an area embracing the cities of Milwaukee, Racine, Kenosha, and Waukesha, with a combined population of well over a million people. During the day hundreds of thousands of electricity-demanding home and office air conditioners were turned on to relieve the muggy discomfort. By 2:00 P.M. a record demand for electrical power (2,311 million watts) strained the combined capacities of the Wisconsin Electric Company and the Wisconsin-Michigan Power Company to the limit. The next day was a repeat performance. Although Wisconsin Electric had access to a power pool formed by eleven midwestern utilities (the Mid-America Interpool Network, MAIN), the available power from this network had been sharply reduced because of ill-timed breakdowns in Illinois plants and because of a fire that knocked out a key generator in St. Louis. Wisconsin Electric eventually made an urgent radio and television appeal to its users to voluntarily curtail consumption. (Ironically at that very moment the Milwuakee *Journal* was carrying advertising promoting several dozen electricity-demanding gadgets, from power mowers to chain saws, from electric toothbrushes to stereo phonographs and self-cleaning ovens.) Further, the power company made ready a much more serious strategy—to black out whole sections of Milwaukee (population 800,000) on a rotation basis. As luck would have it, just before the blackout was to go into effect, the thermal inversion lifted and a cool breeze moved in from Lake Michigan to ease the crisis (15).

Milwaukee's power problem is not an isolated case. Near "blackouts" and "brownouts" have developed with increasing frequency in many other densely populated regions of the United States. During the hot July of 1972, New York City and sections of Massachusetts and Rhode Island were temporarily blacked out. In May, 1973, when San Antonio's natural gas supply was temporarily reduced by 66 per cent because of severe shortages, the city's utility experts predicted a "catastrophe" within ten days in the event that new sources of supply were not found. Moreover, a survey conducted by the Federal Power Commission disclosed that the southeastern and westcentral areas of our country did not possess a suitable generating capacity reserve to cope with equipment breakdowns or unforeseen demands. In December, 1972, Senator Walter Mondale of Minnesota alerted President Nixon to an oil-gas-electricity shortage in Minnesota of "severe magnitude" (21). Electrical power shortages have also been experienced recently in Virginia, the Carolinas, Florida, and Illinois.

The Great Gasoline Shortage

It was the autumn of 1973 when the man on the street finally realized that the United States was in deep gas and fuel trouble. Although college professors, indus-

Figure 17-1. *"Lit up like a Christmas tree." Seattle, Washington, at night—one reason for the nation's energy crisis.* [Rollin R. Geppert]

trial experts, and federal officials had been predicting shortages for months and even years, their pronouncements had always seemed a bit alarmist and unreal. Suddenly, however, the energy crisis was indeed very real. Consider the following developments.

1. Gasoline supplies became so scarce that thousands of independent dealers throughout the nation were forced to stop pumping gas. The personal distress experienced by these people was well expressed in a crudely scrawled sign placed between two meters at an abandoned Detroit service station: "Out of gas. Out of patience. Out of business. Bitter? H - - - yes!"
2. The price of gasoline suddenly zoomed from 40 cents to 55 cents and more per gallon. (By 1974 it was expected to climb to 75 cents.) A few unscrupulous operators in New York City briefly gouged their customers at the rate of $1.00 per gallon.
3. Motorists lined up in pre-dawn darkness for gas in New York and other major Eastern cities, sometimes for two hours, only to finally receive a half-tank of gas.

4. A federal regulation reduced maximum highway speed from 70 to a "crawling" 55 miles per hour—a stratagem that insured more efficient gas consumption (and probably will save 10,000 lives yearly as well).
5. The "Big Three" of the auto industry—Ford, Chrysler, and GMC—feverishly converted from the gas-profligate "big" cars to the gas-conserving "compacts."
6. Economic setbacks were severe. Overall, the nation edged closer to a major recession, the GNP growth rate the lowest since 1971. By early 1974 at least 100,000 workers had lost their jobs in the steel, automobile, auto sales, auto parts, tire, highway restaurant, camper-trailer, resort, and snowmobile industries—all largely dependent upon a bounteous supply of inexpensive gasoline for their vitality. Disgruntled auto workers, who had suddenly been released from their jobs, blamed fuel shortages on a government-industry conspiracy; they gave vent to their dismay with picket signs that read "Nixon—you closed the Watergate, now open the gas gate!"
7. In March 1974, the hurriedly established Federal Energy Office headed by William Simon estimated that Americans were using 2.9 million barrels per day less than they would under normal conditions of fuel supply.[1] Total gasoline supplies in March 1974 were 4.6 per cent lower than just a year before.

The very thought of this resource-blessed nation suffering from an energy shortage seems bizarre, indeed. But the crisis is very real and might persist for decades. The gravity of the situation is underscored by John A. Carver, member of the Federal Power Commission, who recently stated, "I think our energy shortage is not only endemic, its incurable. We're going to have to live with it the rest of our lives" (24). Is this being unduly pessimistic, or alarmist? We should be so lucky. Carver's is not a lone cry in the energy night. According to James R. Schlesinger, chairman of the Atomic Energy Commission, "We must shape our energy policies under a set of constraints hitherto *unimaginable*. I think I can see the day when the country might have to *ration* electricity . . ." (25).

What Has Caused the Energy Crisis?

So the crisis is upon us. One might well ask why a nation that once had energy sources so vast it could blithely squander them on the manufacture of such items as throw-away beer cans and electric toothbrushes could ever find itself in such straits. A complex of factors have contributed to our present plight. We shall comment on just a few of them.

Federal Restrictions on Fuel Imports. There are tremendous supplies of oil and natural gas in the Middle East. However, in order to ensure a continuing market for fuels produced by home-based industries here in the United States, for many years tight restrictions were placed on the volume of fuels imported from abroad. The restrictions have been relaxed by the Nixon administration.

The Embargo on Oil Exports to the United States. Imposed by the oil countries of the Middle East, the embargo extended from December 1973 to mid-March 1974.

---

[1] One barrel contains 42 gallons.

Inaccurate Estimates of Energy Needs. Some sources have suggested that the energy demand was grossly underestimated, not only by regulatory agencies such as the Federal Power Commission, but also by the fuel industry itself. Now, somewhat belatedly, the Federal Power Commission predicts that America's demand for electrical energy alone in 1980 will be roughly twice what it was in 1970 and then will double again by 1990. In 1980 production of electricity in the United States will be about 2 million megawatts or 2 billion kilowatts. In other words, during the 1975–1985 decade the United States will be compelled to set up *as much new generating capacity as it had established since the first kilowatt was generated way back in 1882.* The per capita use of energy in this country is growing five times as fast as the population increase. Within the next two decades America will require 340 additional electrical generating plants and 200,000 additional miles of transmission lines—a complex that will take up twice as much space as the entire state of Delaware! Can such exponential increase in the demand for electrical power actually be met without seriously adverse side effects on land, water, atmosphere, and plant and animal life? The answer of environmentalists is an emphatic no! Even the FPC in its 1970 National Power Survey suggests that such accelerating power production cannot long be sustained:

Figure 17-2. *High voltage transmission lines march across the land. The transmission lines required by the average-sized nuclear power plant will pre-empt 40 acres of land per mile of line, and present a visual blight as well.* [Northern States Power]

Some are concerned about the accumulative environmental effects; others about the strain such growth would place on raw energy and land resources; and still others about the nation's ability to finance it. . . . Sooner or later, the rate of growth of electrical demand must either decline of itself or be reduced by external factors. . . .

Lack of Economic Incentives for Gas and Oil Exploration.   For many years, until mid-1973, the federal government clamped a lid on gas and oil prices. This policy inevitably caused oil and gas exploration activities to stagnate; the cost of drilling new wells has risen appreciably because many of the remaining deposits occur at considerable depths. For example, back in 1931, "wild-catter" N. P. Powell made an oil strike in the fabulous east Texas field at a depth of only 3,600 feet involving a total cost of a mere $15,000. By 1973, however, costs were running as high as $4 *million* per well in western Oklahoma, with deposits being tapped at depths of over 22,000 feet. Between 1956 and 1971 drilling costs rose 85 per cent despite the fact that average prices for gas and oil increased a mere 37 per cent and 17 per cent, respectively (24).

Obstructionist Activity of the Environmentalists.   Environmentalists have been greatly concerned in the past few years over both the proposed and the actual

Figure 17-3.   *Some days a fisherman almost needs a reservation to find room at the newest "fishin' hole" in the St. Croix River valley on the Minnesota-Wisconsin border. These boys have been fishing in the cooling-water discharge canal at a coal-fired electrical power plant. Of course, only trash fish can survive in this warmed-up water. If the water nears the 86° maximum set by the Minnesota Pollution Control Agency, the operators of the plant cool the water by evaporation in the large cooling towers to the right. The tall smokestack at back left discharges some fly-ash, but 99 per cent of this pollutant is removed by electrostatic precipitators.* [Earl Chambers—Northern States Power Company]

sitings of numerous nuclear power plants. They are especially disturbed with plant construction in highly populous areas, such as Manhattan, because of the threat to human life and health from radioactive emissions. They have also strenuously objected to plant siting along lake shores because of resultant thermal pollution, destruction of aquatic life, and accelerated eutrophication. A good case in point was the attempt by environmentalists to delay the operation of the Consumers Power Company plant on the shores of Lake Michigan. Although the $125 million plant was almost completed, the environmentalists filed a suit to prevent the Atomic Energy Commission from granting the company an operating license. Various groups entered the controversy that ensued—the Michigan Water Resources Commission, the Federal Water Quality Administration, the environmentalists, and the Consumers Power Company. Scientists representing each of these groups could not come to a final agreement. The dilemma was finally resolved when the power company decided to construct a mammoth cooling tower at an initial expense of $15 million and an annual operating expense of $3 million. Now, the environmentalists may have had very sound ecological grounds for intervening. It is nevertheless true, from the simple-minded standpoint of energy production alone, that such intervention, repeated in conjunction with the sitings of numerous nuclear and fossil-fuel fired power plants scattered across the nation, undoubtedly has contributed to regional energy shortages. Speaking at a 1973 emergency meeting of the Wisconsin Petroleum Institute during the critical oil shortage attending a subzero cold spell, George Thaler, the association's president, accused environmentalists of blocking offshore drilling, fighting the development of the trans-Alaskan pipeline, and exerting pressure to decrease oil depletion allowances. In his words, "Hell, they're the ones who caused the problem, let them solve it . . ." (5). On the other hand, John Steinhart, of the Institute of Environmental Studies at the University of Wisconsin, believes that even if *all* environmental activism suddenly stopped, the long-range power crisis would still be with us (18).

Figure 17-4. *Offshore oil drilling platform. Standing on rigid steel legs high above the water off Louisiana's Gulf Coast, this barge-mounted rig drills for oil beneath the bottom of the sea. [Bureau of Mines, U.S. Department of the Interior and Humble Oil and Refining Company, Public Relations, Houston, Texas]*

Restrictions on the Use of High-Sulfur Fuels. At the present time the great bulk of electrical power is generated in plants fired by fossil fuels (coal, oil, and gas), and for almost a century, from 1882 until about 1970, these plants were able to burn any quality of fuel they desired. However, in the past few years, in such major cities as New York, Boston, Chicago, and Los Angeles, the electric utilities, along with other fuel-consuming industries have been required to use only low-sulfur fuels in order to keep sulfur dioxide emissions down to a minimum. Since such low-sulfur fuel is not nearly as abundant as high-sulfur fuel, power production may be hampered as a result.

Energy Consumption for Pollution Control. It is ironic that the energy crisis confronting America today is in part the result of our attempt to end another crisis —that of pollution. Twenty years ago "pollution abatement" was little more than an academic phrase. Today, however, our nation is committed to clean up the atmospheric, aquatic, and terrestrial "garbage" that inevitably accumulates as a by-product of our life style and affluence. And pollution clean-up requires huge amounts of energy. For example, the federal government is currently subsidizing the construction of thousands of modern sewage treatment plants across the nation; but to pump sewage water through these plants *requires energy*—0.5 million kilowatt hours annually for a secondary treatment plant accommodating a city of 90,000 people. We are beginning to control the noxious emissions generated by foundry operations, but it requires the employment of a new type of *energy-demanding* electric conduction furnace. We are beginning to reduce the solid waste problem posed by rusting old Fords and Chevvies. This is being done with the aid of a car-crushing machine that mashes the cars into compact blocks of scrap steel: regrettably, however, the machine is activated by an *energy-demanding* 5,000-horse-power electric motor.

America's High Standard of Living. Through the years the average American has exerted a progressively greater demand for energy-demanding creature comforts —high-powered motor cars, color television sets, air conditioning units, motor bikes, snowmobiles, self-cleaning ovens, power saws, even motorized golf carts, as well as a whole series of electrical gadgets for slicing meat, opening cans, brushing teeth, polishing shoes, and drying hair. Wisconsin's Senator Gaylord Nelson has observed that *the amount of energy required merely to run America's air conditioners is greater than that used by 700 million Chinese for purposes essential to survival itself.*

> In 1971 the United States consumed 5.6 billion barrels of oil and 22.1 trillion cubic feet of natural gas. The country's 109 million cars used 90 billion gallons of gasoline, its 2000 jetliners more than one billion gallons of jet fuel and its 3400 power plants one billion barrels of oil, four billion cubic feet of gas and 300 million tons of coal . . . (24).

Somehow it seems incongruous (or should we say immoral?) for the United States, with only 6 per cent of the world's population, to be consuming 30 per cent of the world's energy resources. In other words, you and I are using five times as much energy as the average human inhabitant, and fully thirty times as much as a native of India or Africa. The American housewife can cook (in some cases overcook) the family meal by using copious quantities of either electricity or natural gas simply by flicking a switch or turning a valve. Contrast this situation with the one in rural

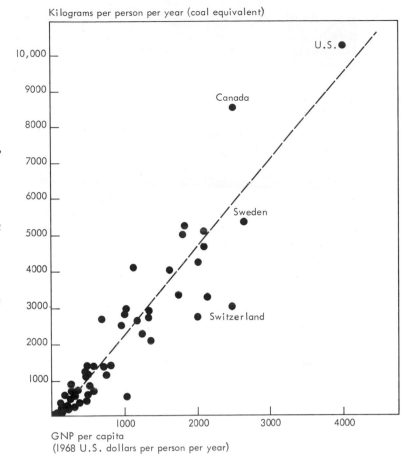

Kilograms per person per year (coal equivalent)

Figure 17-5.
Relationship between energy consumption and GNP. Although the nations of the world consume greatly varying amounts of energy per capita, energy consumption correlates fairly well with output per capita (GNP per capita). The relationship is generally linear. The scattering of points is largely due to climatic differences, local fuel prices, and emphasis on heavy industry. India, Pakistan, and other undeveloped countries would be represented by the clustering of dots in the extreme lower left corner of the graph.

GNP per capita
(1968 U.S. dollars per person per year)

India, where the commonest fuel is dried manure, of which 300 million tons are used yearly (6). According to James P. Lodge, Jr., in terms of energy consumption the average American has 500 *energy slaves* at his beck and call—the equivalent of 500 human slaves working for him. In this respect the average American is far better off than was the most powerful Roman emperor. The "true" population in America, therefore, is not merely 220 million, but 220 million *plus* 110 billion energy slaves. In contrast, how many energy slaves are available to the rice-paddy farmer in South Vietnam or the berry-and-egg gathering tribesman in South Africa?

These, then, are a few of the factors contributing to our energy crisis. However, even in the act of listing them, the cause of the crisis has probably been grossly oversimplified. According to the nonprofit research corporation, Resources for the Future, America's energy dilemma

> arises from an extraordinary coincidence of events involving each particular form of commercial energy—factors as diverse as problems with nuclear technology, Middle Eastern politics, the quest for a cleaner environment, the health and safety of mine workers, and the federal government's policies toward natural gas prices and oil imports. All of these strands are so interwoven that it is difficult to tag this or that factor as contributing this or that much to the overall problem. . . .

Figure 17-6. *The average American uses fully thirty times as much energy as these wretched houseboat-living Pakistani.* [WFP/FAO photo by E. Ragazzini]

Status of America's Traditional Energy Resources

Coal. It has been estimated that the geologic formation of coal required about 500 million years. Coal was formed as the result of the incomplete oxidation of plant and animal bodies that had been buried under sedimentary deposits of sand and mud. Your ability to read this very page under the electric lamp in your study room may well be possible only because of the sunlight that streamed to earth during the Carboniferous ("coal-bearing") period 250 million years ago! Some of this solar energy was trapped by green plants during the process of photosynthesis. The tremendous impact the use of coal has had on human culture is well described by M. King Hubbert, of the U.S. Geological Survey:

> Emancipation from this dependence on contemporary solar energy was not possible until some other and hitherto unknown source of energy should become available. This had its beginning about the 12th or 13th century when the inhabitants of the north-eastern coast of England discovered that certain black rocks found along the shore, and thereafter known as "sea coales," would burn. From this discovery, there followed in almost inevitable succession, the mining of coal and its use for domestic heating and for the smelting of metals, the development of the steam engine, the locomotive, steamships, and steam-electric power (18).

Since coal deposits usually occur in continuous seams that frequently lie just below the surface, it has been possible to make fairly accurate estimates of coal abundance by drilling a number of deep, widely spaced borings into the coal-bearing seams (6). By such techniques the coal fields of the North American continent have

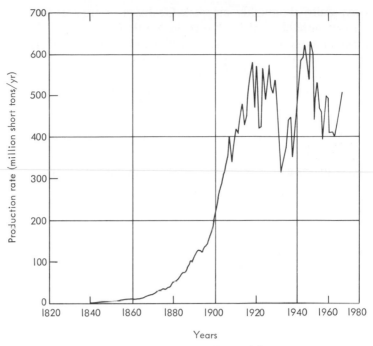

Figure 17-7. *Coal production in the United States.*

Figure 17-8. *Transporting coal by shuttle car deep below the earth's surface. [Joy Manufacturing Company and U.S. Bureau of Mines, U.S. Department of Interior]*

been quite thoroughly mapped. Geologists estimate, for example, that 2 trillion tons of minable coal lay buried in North America (8). It is also known that it is most unlikely that another coal "bonanza" like the Pittsburgh coal field will be discovered (18). Although man has mined coal for at least eight centuries, his use of this "black gold" has been accelerating at a phenomenal rate—one half of all the coal ever dug, for example, has been taken in just the last thirty-three years (4).

Although the United States actually has enough minable coal to last her for centuries, there are two very important environmental concerns attending its use. First, about 50 per cent of the coal America burns (254 million tons in 1970) is *stripmined*,—scooped from the earth by mighty earth-moving machines. This process converts a once-attractive, aesthetically satisfying site (such as the lovely rolling, wooded mountains of Kentucky and West Virginia) into a sterile, ugly wasteland (8). Acid mine drainage (see the chapter on water pollution), with its accompanying aquatic plant and fish kills, is a common strip-mining sequel. In the Four Corners area (near the junction of New Mexico, Arizona, Utah, and Colorado) massive machines have been scooping up 25,000 tons of coal daily to power the gigantic electrical plants that supply the city of Los Angeles 1,000 miles to the west (8). (Perhaps the good citizens of Los Angeles subconsciously are practicing an "out of sight, out of mind" philosophy toward ecosystem abuse?)

A second environmental concern is the high sulfur content in many of our remaining coal deposits. It is estimated, for example, that 60 per cent of the 14 million

Figure 17-9. *Strip mining for coal in West Virginia.* [*U.S. Department of Agriculture*]

Figure 17-10. *Use of lime permits lush growth of weeping lovegrass on strip mine spoil, White Oak Mountain, West Virginia. The highly acid soil had an original pH of 2.8. The bare spots were seeded but not limed. [U.S. Department of Agriculture]*

tons of sulfur dioxide belched from the American smokestacks in 1971 had its source in coal. In order to curb the emissions of sulfur dioxide, many municipalities, such as New York City, Boston, Chicago, and Los Angeles forbid utilities and other industries to burn coal with a sulfur content higher than 1 per cent (10). It is rather ironic, in this era of environmental enlightenment and concern, that a *federal agency*, the TVA, has strip mined some of the dirtiest coal (in terms of sulfur content) in the nation to power certain uranium processing plants operated by the Atomic Energy Commission in Paducah, Kentucky, Oak Ridge, Tennessee, and Portsmouth, Ohio (10).

There is hope that high sulfur coal may yet be used as fuel by *gasification*, a process by which the coal is converted into methane gas by steam-heating it under high pressure. The Office of Coal Research expects to have a demonstration gasification plant operating by 1976. The Bureau of Mines has recently been conducting tests near Hanna, Wyoming, to determine the economic feasibility of gasifying coal subterraneously. This would involve pumping air into a coal bed lying 600 feet below the ground surface. After igniting the bed, the resultant gases, including methane (the principal component of natural gas) would be pumped out as the fire smolders. Environmentalists would welcome the substitution of gasification for land-desecrating strip mining. However, Arnold Silverman, chairman of the Western Montana Committee for Environmental Information, has noted the possibility of "surface collapse" above the caverns formed by extensive gasification (1).

Figure 17-11. *This coal gasifier requires 40 atmospheres pressure. [Bureau of Mines, U.S. Department of the Interior]*

In the event that gasification proves to be economically feasible, a marked upsurge in the mining of high-sulfur coal is expected in the western states. To date only 4 per cent of the nation's coal mining occurs in the West even though this region holds 64 per cent of America's coal deposits (10).

Oil. Both oil and natural gas are highly desired fuels because when burned they emit relatively few atmospheric pollutants. However, both of these fuels are becoming more scarce, since America's consumption is exceeding her production (25). Although the United States is *producing* 1 of every 4 oil gallons in the world, it is *consuming* 900 gallons yearly for every man, woman, and child in this nation— *about eight times the average consumption rate for the nations of the "free" world* (6). In 1970 America burned 15 million barrels of oil daily, or an aggregate 710 million tons. However, by 1980 our consumption will rise to about 23 million barrels per day. Since our maximum daily production will be 11 million barrels per day, we will incur a 12 million barrel daily deficit that can be made up appreciably only by imports (8). According to S. David Freeman, who once counseled both

Figure 17-12. *America's first oil well at Titusville, Pa. Photo taken in 1864.* [*Bureau of Mines, U.S. Department of Interior*]

President Johnson and President Nixon on energy matters, "It doesn't matter that we may have found 30 billion barrels of oil and more than 20 trillion cubic feet of gas in Alaska. . . . Our rates of consumption are now so large that we can see the *bottom of the barrel* . . ." (25). Already in 1972 the United States was importing 27 per cent of its oil, largely from Canada and Venezuela. Roughly half of our oil and gas will be imported by 1985, representing a ten-fold increase since 1972, for which the American oil industry will pay $34 billion (22). Foreign relations and international diplomacy may, therefore, well be an important factor in determining the adequacy of our imports, for much of this fuel will be secured from Algeria, Libya, Nigeria, Saudi Arabia, and the Soviet Union (25). W. J. Levy, a New York oil consultant, along with other oil analysts are concerned that the oil producing Arab nations may decide to curb production of the oil upon which the Western industry and life style are so largely based. Prices would thus be artificially inflated—the oil eventually going to the highest bidder, the acceptable bid being in terms of a combination of money and financial, technical, political, and/or military assistance to the Arab nations in their chronic struggle with Israel (20). Wayne Aspinall, congressman from Colorado, long before the Arab embargo began, was quite apprehensive over the prospects, "I am truly frightened by the potential conflict between pro-Israel sentiment in this country and our increasing reliance on Arab oil. I believe the United States is about to be caught in a Middle Eastern power play . . ." (8). Aspinall proved to be prophetic. The attitude of the Saudi Arabian minister of petroleum affairs is not very reassuring. He has stated bluntly, "We are in a position to dictate prices and we are going to be very rich" (2).

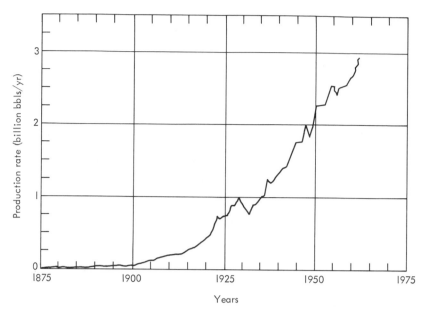

Figure 17-13. *Crude oil production in the United States.*

Figure 17-14. *Symbol of the energy crisis. Summer, 1973. "Service is our business" but "Sorry No Gas." Will this type of "service" plague American motorists repeatedly in the future?* [Rollin R. Geppert]

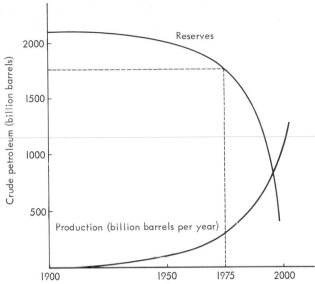

Figure 17-15. World reserves of crude petroleum will not last long at current consumption rates. Note that in 1975, with no more than fifteen years left before demand exceeds supply, the total global reserve will have been depleted by only 12½ per cent.

Figure 17-16. Employing dynamite charges in Arabian desert oil explorations. [Aramco-Texaco]

According to the National Petroleum Council, at least 360 new $37 million super-tankers will be required to convey the Middle East oil from the Persian Gulf. Oil companies are being frustrated in their attempts to satisfy the nation's growing oil needs. Although offshore drilling might prove productive, the industry has become quite sensitive to pressure being exerted by environmentalists because of the potential oil spill hazard. Several states along the Atlantic coast are proposing legislation to prevent construction of the deepwater terminals required to accommodate the supertanker fleet (25). Once the oil has been imported, it must be refined, and this poses yet another problem. According to Frank Ikard, president of the American Petroleum Institute, we will require five new refineries yearly from 1973 to 1985 (2). So how many were being constructed in 1973? None! The net result of these problems besetting the oil industry will be substantial price increases for the consumer, not only for oil itself, but for the electricity that is generated by oil consuming power plants. Thus one official from Consolidated Edison of New York has predicted a doubling of electrical rates during the 1972–1982 decade (25).

THE CONTROVERSIAL ALASKAN PIPELINE.   Exciting news came out of Alaska during the summer of 1968, for the richest oil deposit in the Western Hemisphere was discovered by the Atlantic Richfield Company, its value being estimated at $50 billion. In order to convey this oil to markets in the United States the Trans-Alaskan Pipeline System (TAPS) proposed to build a 789-mile pipeline extending from northern

Figure 17-17.   According to the National Petroleum Council, at least 360 new $37 million supertankers, such as the one in the picture, will be required to convey the Middle Eastern oil from the Persian Gulf to the United States. [Skyfotos-Texaco]

Figure 17-18. *The recently completed "Explorer" pipeline being sheathed with a protective coating before being buried in Illinois soil. Products flow through this 1,300 mile line to the Midwest from south-western refineries. [D. Guravich-Texaco]*

Figure 17-19. *A work crew manipulates drilling equipment on an offshore drilling and production platform. [Clark Oil and Refining Corporation]*

Figure 17-20. *Conductor pipes housing drill bits extend downward from an offshore drilling platform.* [*Clark Oil and Refining Corporation*]

Alaska's Prudhoe Bay to the ice-free port of Valdez on the Gulf of Alaska. However, the only "fuel" provided thus far has been for heated controversy. Environmental activists succeeded in blocking the pipeline's construction for several years. They have had good reason. Its potential for derangement of the delicate tundra ecosystem is considerable. Let us consider some of them:

1. Since the oil flowing through the line will be heated to 180° F (to ensure even flow despite winter temperatures of −50° F) that portion of the line which will be placed under ground might melt the permafrost. As a result the pipeline might

subside and eventually break, releasing millions of gallons of oil. A Canadian scientist has determined that even were the pipe heavily insulated it "would thaw a cylinder of soil 20 to 30 feet in diameter within a few years. . . ." The resultant spill would not only ruin the tundra's aesthetic appeal, but, more seriously, would destroy Arctic vegetation and wildlife.

2. Wildlife authorities are concerned that the pipeline will interfere with the migrations of caribou, since the proposed route crosses the migratory paths of several hundred thousand of these magnificent animals. Since many Alaskan natives depend upon caribou for food, clothing, and shelter, any major disruption of migratory patterns might force the natives to make drastic life style adjustments and even then might eventually become recipients of "handouts" from the state coffers.

3. The pipeline might jeopardize the $150 million Alaskan fishery, especially that portion occurring in the productive Gulf of Alaska. The heavy oil tanker traffic required to transport oil from Valdez to West Coast ports such as Seattle would inevitably result in collisions and fish-destroying oil spills. According to the Department of Interior, *at least three major collisions could be expected annually* (13).

4. Since two thirds of the pipeline route passes through regions where earthquakes are potentially active, a distinct threat of eventual damage during the 15 to 30 years of the pipeline's operation definitely exists. Since 0.5 million gallons of oil will be contained by each mile of pipeline, any break could result in an oil spill of considerable magnitude.

5. Valuable salmon-spawning beds will be destroyed, since the 10-foot-thick gravel bed on which the subterranean portion of the pipeline will rest will be scooped from them.

6. In the event of a war with Russia, the pipeline would be extremely vulnerable to attack, since it is located only a few hundred miles from the Russian border.

Despite these many objections to the construction of the pipeline, the federal courts, in late 1973, finally gave TAPS permission to go ahead. The severity of the energy crisis apparently swayed public opinion, and eventually congressional and court opinion in this direction, environmental objections to the contrary. Typical of this sentiment was the following opinion of James J. Kilpatrick, writer for the Washington *Star*:

> The trans-Alaskan pipeline must be built. That statement, it seems to me, has passed beyond opinion and become simple fact. Alaska's North Slope contains an estimated 10 billion barrels of proven reserves. Once the pipeline is built, some 600,000 barrels a day can be moved; after five years, production will rise to an estimated 2 million barrels a day. We have to have that oil—and the ecological price painful and distressing as it may be, will have to be paid.

Natural Gas. Natural gas, which is primarily methane, is a fossil fuel like coal and oil, having been formed through long periods of time by the incomplete decomposition of plant and animal remains that had been covered for millenia by sedimentary deposits. In 1971 America burned 49 per cent of the world's consumption of natural gas—22.1 trillion cubic feet. At this rate of use our nation's proven domestic reserve of 247 trillion cubic feet will be exhausted by 1982 (6). The number of producing natural gas wells drilled in the United States *diminished* by more than 50 per cent during the years from 1955 to 1968; yet it is estimated that within the period from 1970 to 1990 America's gas demand will be *one and a half times the total gas volume ever discovered in America since the first American oil gushed from the* *well at Titusville.* United States gas companies state that while there are probably substantial gas reserves, either inland or offshore, current exploration costs are almost prohibitive, new supplies of gas being reached only after drillers have gone to depths of two or three miles (8). Because of these increased costs incurred by industry, consumer prices are expected to double or even triple within the next few years. A mere doubling of prices would increase the industry's revenues by $4.4 billion annually. Gas heat was in such demand during the winter of 1972–1973 that even though the rate of gas flow from wells in Texas and Louisiana was at an all time high, distributors were rationing gas among old customers and rejecting orders from new ones. What can be done about the critical gas shortage? It is true that a considerable amount of gas could be obtained by the processing of such wastes as garbage, sewage sludge, and livestock manure, procedures that would not only alleviate the solid waste problem but would also ease the gas shortage. True, such procedures are commendable and should be attempted whenever feasible. Natural gas production could also be increased by expanding offshore drilling. To this end President Nixon called for a 300 per cent increase in the acreage leased on the outer continental shelf. It must be clear, however, that the production gains will have a proportionate ecological cost measured in oil spill defilement of the neritic zone— which is already highly productive—of shrimp, tuna, and red snapper, if not of natural gas and oil. However, in the final analysis, as in the case with oil, the only way the United States can meet the demand of gas in the long run is by importing increasingly large quantities from abroad.

It is estimated that about 2 trillion cubic feet will be imported annually as liquid natural gas (LNG) by tanker from South America, Africa, Alaska, and the North Sea (9). By 1980 America will be conveying LNG with a fleet of 130 tankers with an average capacity 125,000 cubic meters. (Each tanker would be carrying the equivalent of 2.7 billion cubic feet of gas.) The Federal Power Commission has already approved the plan of El Paso Algeria Corporation to import (by 1976) 1 *billion* cubic feet of gas daily from Algeria to supply customers along the densely populated East Coast. Costly terminals required for the transfer of LNG from tanker to storage facilities are being planned for Elba Island, off Savannah, Georgia, and for Cove Point on Chesapeake Bay in Maryland. The proposed Maryland site has triggered firm opposition from environmentalist groups who would prefer to have the area converted to a state park to preserve the unique beauty of the area (9).

James A. Fay, of the Massachusetts Institute of Technology, and James J. Mackenzie, of the National Audubon Society, have investigated the possible aftermath of the accidental release of LNG near a densely populated region, caused by either a tanker collision or a faulty transfer operation. They estimated:

> a 100,000 cubic meter spill . . . would form a vapor cloud more than a mile wide and twenty feet deep in less than fifteen minutes. The cloud could then blow ashore and be ignited in populated areas. Given the many possible sources of ignition on land, such as automobiles and home heating units, it is very likely that such a cloud would eventually ignite. A conflagration of that size . . . (equivalent to the burning of 100 Hindenburg zeppelins) . . . in a major city would be a disaster . . . (9).

True, there is an estimated 300 trillion cubic feet of natural gas imprisoned between layers of solid rock in Colorado and Wyoming (25). The question is how to release this captive gas.

The Atomic Energy Commission proposed a project in 1973 that would stimulate the natural gas flow by means of nuclear detonations in the Colorado fields. This scheme, however, was stalled by a conflict of interests between oil and gas companies. Since the proposed site for the detonations was close to oil shale deposits, the oil men were concerned that the explosions would render future oil shale mining impractical because of deposit disruption (1). In any event, the liberation of this gas would probably require a *minimum of 200 nuclear explosions*, certainly a procedure that would be severely frowned on, not only by environmental activists, but other sectors of the American public as well (25).

Oil Shales. According to *Resources and Man*, a scholarly report of the National Academy of Sciences, the shales of Colorado and the tar sands of northern Canada hold enough crude oil "to extend the total life time of the petroleum family of fuels as an important source of industrial energy to as much as a century from now. . . ." (18). These fields bear 80 billion barrels of recoverable oil, the richest shales yielding up to 1.5 barrels (65 gallons) per ton (18). However, their extraction has been strongly opposed by environmentalists. Even Hubbert foresees problems, "If you want to imagine one hell of a mess, imagine mining that shale and discharging the acid wastes into the Colorado River. I guarantee you'd kill the river . . ." (25). Certainly the use of Colorado River water for irrigation purposes would be at an end. Hoyte Hottle, a chemical engineer at the Massachusetts Institute of Technology, who has made comparative studies of new fuel resources, is pessimistic

Figure 17-21. *Oil shale hills. Oil deposits in Colorado shale and in Alberta tar sands could extend American industrial use of oil for at least a century.* [*Bureau of Mines, U.S. Department of Interior*]

Figure 17-22. *Drilling and loading operations in an oil shale demonstration project at Rifle, Colorado. [Bureau of Mines, U.S. Department of Interior]*

because of the excessive cost involved in heating the shale sufficiently to produce relatively meager amounts of oil. Says Hottle, "I'm for leaving it alone until we've made more use of our other resources . . ." (10).

Tar Sands. The so-called tar sands are impregnated with a heavy crude oil that is too viscous to permit removal by wells (18). In late 1967 a Canadian company, Great Canadian Oil Sands Limited, began large-scale exploitation of the tar fields in northern Alberta. Their plant has a design capacity of 45,000 barrels of oil daily. It is estimated that the Alberta tar sands hold at least 300 billion barrels of recoverable crude oil, fully ten times the amount of oil recently discovered in Alaska (18).

Future Use of Fossil Fuels as Energy Sources. We have seen therefore that although there do exist relatively large amounts of fossil fuels (coal, oil, natural gas) either on the North American continent or elsewhere in the world, their availability and actual use by the American people are fraught with problems—economic, political, technological, environmental, and moral. However, even if these fossil fuels were readily available, there has been considerable criticism directed at their continued intensive use as *energy* sources. Recently the prestigious National Academy of Sciences established a Committee on Resources and Man to evaluate the adequacy of America's resources. Composed of some of this nation's leading authorities, the committee strongly recommended "that the fossil fuels be conserved for uses which cannot be met by other sources. . . ." According to the committee:

> The fossil fuels are needed for petrochemicals, synthetic polymers, and essential liquid fuels, *for which suitable substitutes are as yet unknown.* (Italics added.) They might also play a part in synthetic or bacterial food production. They should not be spent in the generation of electricity, for heating, and for industrial purposes where substitutes can qualify. The Department of the Interior should be authorized and directed to develop and institute a practicable and effective hydrocarbon conservation program . . . (22).

Status of Energy Sources Other Than Fossil Fuels

Solar Energy. Sunlight is the ultimate source of the energy locked up in fossil fuels, the ultimate source of the energy powering the world's ecosystems, the ultimate source of the energy that permits you to read these words and for thoughts to flash through your mind concerning the energy crisis. However, as we learned in the earlier discussion of the second law of thermodynamics, fully 99 per cent of the radiant energy from the sun is "lost"; in other words, it is converted into heat energy that in turn dissipates from the earth's surface and becomes irretrievable by man. The possibility of harnessing this wasted solar energy has piqued the curiosity of man for ages. Solar power has in fact been harnessed at least since the 1860's, when a still was set up in Chile to provide 5,000 gallons of fresh water to thirsty miners. Then, too, in 1913 a solar-fired steam engine was developed by an American engineer for pumping irrigation water from the Nile. Solar-powered engines were also constructed in the nineteenth century by John Ericsson, better remembered as the builder of the *Monitor*, famed combat ship of the Civil War (16).

The amount of solar energy flooding the earth's surface on a cloudless day is roughly 100,000 *times greater than the world's presently installed total electric power capacity.* Unlike the hydrocarbon (fossil fuel) energy sources, solar energy will continue to be available at a uniform rate for millions of years—even long after the human species has become extinct. The world's largest solar furnace, near Odeillo in the French Pyrenees, provides us with an example of the awesome power of sunlight. This furnace is provided with mirror panels that swivel with the moving sun and focus rays on a 148-foot parabolic mirror. The mirror in turn focuses the sunlight on a furnace where temperatures reach 6,300° F, sufficiently hot to melt a 1-foot-wide hole in a three-eighths-inch-thick steel plate in only 60 seconds (28).

According to Farrington Daniels, of the University of Wisconsin, numerous small-scale practical uses could be made of solar energy, such as water distillation, cooking, and home heating. (Solar cells have been used, of course, on spaceships to convert solar energy into electrical energy. You will recall that the 1973 Skylab I Project was initially in jeopardy because of the faulty operation of its solar panels. The earth-bound world figuratively "held its breath" until the panels were properly realigned by some daredevil repair work on the part of the three astronauts.) Kenneth Hanson, head of General Electric's Space Power Programs at Valley Forge (Pennsylvania), states that the biggest drawback to using solar power for home heating is one of cost. Suppose, for example, that you wished to heat your home with solar-energy-derived electricity. One square foot of silicon solar cells would produce 21.9 kilowatt hours per year but would cost $2,500 each. At present you can get that much electricity from conventional sources for only $1. Besides you would require 350 square feet of such solar cell surface—which figures to a total cost of $875,000—and that's just the beginning. Batteries would be required for storing energy, since solar cells won't provide power at night or on cloudy days. Then, too, in order to catch the sun's rays with maximal efficiency, a specially designed tilt-table roof panel would be required, adding to the already prohibitive cost! However, it is always possible that a technological breakthrough and mass production might appreciably lower the cost (12).

Of the twenty solar homes currently operating in the United States, one of the most successful is the four-bedroom experimental home constructed by researchers at the University of Delaware. It derives 80 per cent of its heat and power from the sunshine beaming down on heat-collecting panels on its roof and front walls. All of the heat-collecting panels are relatively simple in basic design and include the following components:

1. A black metal plate that absorbs the sun's rays and gets hot.
2. Styrofoam insulation beneath the plate.
3. A glass cover to prevent radiation of heat to the atmosphere (greenhouse effect).
4. A system of channels (air ducts) for transporting heated air to other parts of the house.

The heat is stored in a six foot cube of special salts from which it may be withdrawn as needed by the home's residents. In addition, the house converts some solar energy directly to electrical energy by means of cadmium sulfide solar cells mounted on the collecting panels. (Cadmium sulfide cells are considerable less expensive than silicon cells.) The electrical power is stored in modified lead-acid auto batteries and can be used for lighting the home (11).

So much for the small-scale individualized home heating plant. Now what about the possibility of constructing a central heating plant, in the 1,000-megawatt range, comparable to major electrical plants now powered by coal oil or gas? Such a plant is indeed technologically possible. However, a plant capable of supplying the electrical needs of a city of 1.5 million people, such as Cleveland, would require the collection of solar energy from a 16-square-mile area, and that much space is in notoriously short supply, especially near urban centers (6).

Intensive research on such projects is nevertheless being conducted with enthusiasm and vigor. Two researchers at the University of Arizona, Arden B. Meinel and his wife, Marjorie, have proposed an ingenious scheme for trapping solar energy on a large-scale basis. They propose to spread out a system of silicon-and-silver-coated steel pipes under the relatively cloudless Arizona sky. The sun's rays would be directed into the pipes by means of many acres of tilt-table lenses that can follow the sun's path through the sky. The thin coatings of silicon and silver are excellent absorbers of sunlight but lose heat by radiation very slowly. This heat would then be transferred by nitrogen gas flowing through the pipes to tanks of molten salt. The heated salt could then be employed to generate electricity by means of a steam activated turbine-generator (28).

We are pouring billions of dollars into nuclear power research. On the other hand, we are spending ridiculously small amounts on the development of solar power. Solar energy is abundant, inexhaustible, and pollution-free. Nevertheless, of the $10 billion recently recommended by the AEC for energy research, an amazing 55 per cent would be channelled into nuclear power development, whereas only 2 per cent would be reserved for solar energy research. AEC's pessimistic view of solar power seems inexplicable in the light of a recent report by a distinguished panel of ten scientists headed by Alfred Eggers, Jr., of the National Science Foundation. The panel concluded that solar energy could be producing electrical power and heat on a commercial basis by 1979, if $1 billion were spent on solar power development over the five years beginning in 1975. When one considers that it costs much more than that amount for a single nuclear power plant, it is astonishing that the $1 billion has not been granted. It would seem that because the AEC is charged with the task of developing nuclear power, it probably is in a poor position to fairly evaluate the feasibility of developing alternative sources of power (solar energy, wind power, and so on). It is therefore imperative that a federal Department of Energy be established in the near future to bear the responsibility of appraising the overall energy situation on an impartial basis, and then make appropriate recommendations to Congress for research funding. Without such a neutral agency, the President and Congress will have to rely not only on the advice of the AEC, but on that of the various power and oil companies, all of which control pertinent information, and have vested interests in the development of certain specific energy sources (3).

Tidal Power. As Hubbert states, "tidal-electric power is obtained from the oscillatory flow of water in the filling and emptying of partially enclosed basins during the semi-diurnal rise and fall of the oceanic tides . . ." (18). The water flow is employed to drive hydraulic turbines propelling electric generators. The world's potential tidal power is 2.9 million megawatts, less than 1 per cent of the world's water power potential.

Tidal power has many advantages: It is inexpensive, produces no noxious wastes, and would be available long after the human species had become extinct. The big drawbacks—not enough of it and the massive machinery involved, including dams, dikes, levees, and so on.

Small tidal mills have been used for grinding grain since the twelfth century. However, the world's first major tidal-electric installation at La Rance estuary in France was not built until 1966. At present it is operating successfully, producing 240,000 kilowatts of power. Other plants have since been constructed in Russia. The United States and Canadian governments have been investigating the economic feasibility of a tidal electric plant in the Passamaquoddy Bay off the Bay of Fundy on the United States–Canadian border, where the average tidal range is 5.5 meters (18).

Geothermal Energy. In a few special geological situations volcanic activity will superheat underground water trapped in porous rock strata. If wells are drilled into such steam reservoirs, the steam that issues up the well shaft can be utilized by a conventional steam-electric plant as a power source. The first such use of *geothermal energy* was initiated at Larderello, Italy, in 1904. Other geothermal plants have been set up in New Zealand, Japan, Mexico, Iceland, and the Soviet Union. Almost all homes in the town of Hveragerdi, Iceland, and heated by geothermal steam (18). The world's third largest geothermal project, operated by the Pacific Gas and Electric Company, is located at the Geysers, in northern California, where production began in 1960. The plant supplies electricity to San Francisco. According to some authorities, the power needs of 20 million people could be satisfied with the steam that underlies the Imperial Valley in southern California (10). The San Diego Gas and Electric Company constructed a plant in this region in 1973.

Geothermal power is cheap and clean. Capital investment is minimal, costing only $150 per kilowatt, compared to $250 for a coal-fired plant and $500 for a nuclear power station. However, there are also drawbacks. For one thing, minerals dissolved in the steam tend to foul up machinery. Then, too, only negligible amounts of geothermal energy are available in populous eastern United States. Furthermore, land subsidence may occur after the sinking of a geothermal well. Nevertheless, despite the disadvantages, Joseph Barnes, United Nations director of resources, is quite optimistic and feels that geothermal energy is making a breakthrough. Another United Nations expert, Tsvi Meidav, has speculated that geothermal sources *could yield double the energy represented by the world's total deposits of oil, gas, and coal.* Leases have been granted for the development of geothermal energy in thirteen states embracing an area of 58 million acres. A panel of Interior Department experts have estimated that by the end of this century 395 million kilowatts could be supplied by geothermal sources—more electric power than is produced by all the generating capacity in the United States today.

Figure 17-23. *Commercial geothermal plant at "The Geysers," 75 miles north of San Francisco. The steam issuing from the earth's crust is used to drive a turbine and eventually generate electricity.* [U.S. Geological Survey]

Figure 17-24. *A commercial geothermal plant at "The Geysers," located 75 miles north of San Francisco.* [U.S. Geological Survey]

Hydropower. Ever since the Roman period in human history, water power has been employed by man to serve his needs. In the United States, hydropower has been extensively used in the nineteenth century for such purposes as grinding wheat and corn, sawing logs (whether white pine from Minnesota and Wisconsin or redwoods from California), and powering textile mills along the New England coast.

Hydropower has several advantages. It is relatively inexpensive, inflicts minimal environmental abuse, and certainly will never be exhausted during human survival on planet earth. Furthermore, it has been estimated that the global potential of hydropower is equivalent to all the energy derived from fossil fuels today. As a matter of fact, the installed hydropower capacity of the world is only about 8 per cent of its potential capacity.

One might suppose, therefore, that when the supply of fossil fuels is eventually exhausted, the world could simply shift over to full development of the hitherto unrealized hydropower potential. However, the situation isn't quite that simple. Several complexities cloud the picture. Thus:

1. The greatest hydropower potential exists in such underdeveloped continents as Africa and South America. For example, the potential in the United States is only 161,000 megawatts compared to 577,000 megawatts for South America and 780,000 for Africa (18). However, since the countries involved are poorly endowed with many other essential resources, and in any event are not highly industrialized, the prospect of actually developing this hydropower potential is not bright.

2. The massive, multimillion-dollar dams necessary in hydropower development would have an abbreviated life expectancy (as previously discussed in connection with water resources) because of as yet unsolved reservoir sedimentation problems. For example, even Egypt's Aswan Dam, the world's largest, probably will have a functional life of less than two centuries. In the United States, several California dams, such as the Mono Dam at Santa Barbara, have been "killed" by silt in less than twenty years!

3. Finally, there are aesthetic objections to converting some of the world's most lovely wilderness spectacles—wild, white-rushing streams cutting their way through craggy mountain gorges—into chains of drab, unexciting man-made reservoirs. In the event that we were eventually put in an increasingly tight energy squeeze, would we really be willing to trade off environmental grandeur for kilowatts? Or would we look elsewhere? The Colorado River is already closed to future dam projects by congressional mandate. Mounting public opposition has also blocked the development of dam sites on the Columbia and Snake rivers of the Northwest, as well as on the Eel and Mad rivers of California (25).

Other Possible Sources of Future Energy

Additional sources of energy that might be developed in the future include wind power, garbage, animal manure, and a system called magnetohydrodynamics (MHD).

Wind power has been used for centuries in areas such as Holland, which is relatively level and unobstructed. Furthermore, by means of huge towers, wind power could be obtained in any type of terrain, even in urban areas. However, such "skyscrapper" towers might be visually objectionable and pose a hazard to air traffic. Then, too, the technological problem of storing this power is rather formidable.

Experimental work has been conducted to explore the economic feasibility of generating power as a by-product of garbage incineration. In any event the heat generated from burning garbage is already being used in some localities to heat homes, thus substantially reducing the consumption of traditional heating fuels such as coal, oil, and gas. Federal researchers have been investigating the possibility of converting animal manure into oil. They have found it possible to accomplish this by combining animal manure with carbon monoxide under extreme heat and pressure. The technique yields three barrels of oil from every ton of manure. However, the process may not be useful on a widescale basis because of the costs involved in the manure collection and transport. It has been estimated that the 1.5 million tons of organic wastes (slaughter house refuse, corn stalks, household garbage, cannery and pulp mill waste, manure, and so on) could yield 300 trillion cubic feet of methane—50 per cent more than is consumed each year in the United States.

MHD is a novel electrical power production method that involves a perforated gas pipe containing imbedded electrodes. It is placed between the poles of a powerful electromagnet. Current is generated by magnetic lines of force when gas (heated to 2,500° C) is passed through the pipe under great pressure. The current is taken up by the electrodes and channeled into an electrical distribution system (27). MHD has been used in Japan, West Germany, and Russia with some success, using coal as a fuel source. Since combustion is highly efficient, stack effluents are reduced by 33 per cent. Moreover, 66 per cent more power is derived per pound of coal than in traditional coal-burning methods. Most particulate matter is removed from the effluent gases by a special recovery system. The U.S. Office of Science and Technology has estimated that, during the period 1985–2000 MHD would reduce coal expenditures by $11 billion. Arthur Kantrowitz, who has done much to develop MHD in the United States, regrets the lack of federal funding. With all the advantages of MHD, it does indeed seem surprising that the federal government budgeted only $3 million for MHD during 1972 (26). Kantrowitz states that in only nine years the Russians, with appropriate funding, were able to produce a large MHD generator that can deliver 25,000 kilowatts into the Moscow grid (28).

Conservation of Energy

In America's attempt to satisfy its prospective energy needs, most of the attention has been focused on methods of *producing* more hydrocarbon (fossil) fuels or on developing alternative, less conventional energy sources. Relatively little attention has been directed toward devising methods of *reducing* energy consumption. Nevertheless, the opportunities are great. For example, Wisconsin's Senator Gaylord Nelson has observed that the United States *wastes* more energy than is *consumed* by Japan—the world's third largest industrial nation. Allen L. Hammond, writing in *Science*, has emphasized that "five-sixths of the energy used in transportation, two-thirds of the fuel consumed to generate electricity, and nearly one-third of the remaining energy—amounting in all to more than 50 per cent of the energy consumed in the United States—is discarded as waste heat . . ." (14). Even if we saved only 1 per cent of the 63×10^{15} British Thermal Units our nation consumes each year, our annual energy gain would be equivalent to 100 million barrels of petroleum (14).

The fuel savings potential has been further underscored by the U.S. Office of Emergency Preparedness, which is of the opinion that we could cut energy consumption by 15 per cent through such stratagems as energy taxes, increased recycling and reuse, improved freight-handling systems, and expanded mass transit. The Office feels that such devices could save our nation 7.3 million barrels of oil daily by 1985.

Energy savings can be made in many sectors of American life—in home construction, in the design of factories and commercial buildings, in transportation, in industry, and in others. Let us examine just a few of these areas.

Home Construction. Americans have been notoriously mindless in building residences with minimal regard to the soundness of their architectural design in relation to climate. Today's homes consume twice as much energy as those built just a few years ago. The philosophy of the architect and home builder has been: if a home gets uncomfortably warm it can always be cooled off with energy-demanding air conditioning; if a house gets too chilly, it can always be warmed up with an energy-demanding heating plant. Architects can play an important role in energy conservation. S. David Freeman, director of a Ford Foundation study of

Figure 17-25. *View of the United Nations from the East River. The glass-walled Secretariat Building in the left-foreground, ironically, is a classic example of heat (and energy) wasting architectural design.* [*New York Convention and Visitors Bureau*]

national energy problems (and former director of the White House Office of Science and Technology), has had some revealing discussions with the American Institute of Architects. Freeman states:

> One architect told me that he looked over the plans for a building he'd just finished. He found that with a few small changes in the design—that would not have added a *penny* to the cost of the building—he could have cut down the energy consumption by 35 per cent *simply by replacing half the glass with walls.* . . . Glass is an excellent conductor and a poor insulator. Heat flows right through it. By cutting down on the area of glass you cut down the heat loss tremendously.

Ironically, the glass-walled United Nations building in New York City is a classic example of profligate energy waste caused by faulty architectural design!

A study of model homes in Atlanta, Minneapolis, and New York by John Moyers, of the Oak Ridge National Laboratory, has indicated that the use of more insulation, weather-stripping, and storm windows would reduce energy consumption for space heating purposes by 42 per cent. Solar hot water heaters could replace about half of the gas or electric heaters now employed, thus gaining an additional 1 per cent of energy. Deciduous tree plantings next to a house will shade the home in the summer, thus reducing the need for energy extravagant air conditioning, while permitting the sun's rays to warm the house during the winter. Architectural designs in modern commercial buildings often involve excessive use of mortar and steel, material whose manufacture is highly energy-consuming. A substantial saving

Figure 17-26. *Twin energy consumers: The towers of the new World Trade Center in New York, each 110 stories and one-quarter mile high. Each day the twin towers use as much energy as the entire city of Schenectady, New York. [New York Convention and Visitors Bureau]*

in electricity might be made in many department, clothing, and drug stores, whose managers apparently feel their places of business have to be "lit up like a Christmas tree" in order to attract customers. It has been estimated that the World Trade Center, the celebrated high-rise office building in New York City, consumes more energy than the entire city of Schenectady, New York, a community of over 100,000 inhabitants.

Transportation. The usual expansion pattern of the average American city is in the form of an irregular "doughnut," with many millions of people, the nation over, moving into the suburbs, the outer "rim" of the doughnut, even though their employment may be in the doughnut's "hole." Obviously much valuable fuel is consumed simply because these people must commute between home and work, some unfortunates easily driving a round trip of 60 miles per working day, or about 15,000 miles yearly. Since about 25 per cent of all energy consumed by Americans is used in transportation (either of men or materials), billions of dollars worth of energy could be saved annually if urban expansion patterns were changed. Moreover, if the commuter were willing to sacrifice a little privacy, comfort, and independence, substantial energy savings could be made by the formation of car pools

Figure 17-27. ". . . *Much valuable fuel is consumed simply because these people must commute between home and work, some unfortunate ones easily driving a round trip of 60 miles per working day, or about 15,000 miles yearly. . . .*" [Michigan Department of Natural Resources]

or by the increased use of mass transit systems, thus easing both the energy and air pollution problems simultaneously.

Industry.   Industry consumes about 40 per cent of all energy used in the United States. What is more, over 50 per cent of the energy used by industry is wasted as heat. It is apparent, therefore, that any large-scale saving in the industrial area would be very desirable. It is highly encouraging, therefore, that with fuel costs zooming, some American industrial corporations are beginning to make concerted efforts to reduce fuel wastage. Consider some items:

1. United States Steel is now capturing large amounts of natural gas emitted from its coke ovens and using this formerly wasted fuel in other plant operations (23).
2. The utility bill at one large General Motors plant was reduced by almost $1 million simply by cutting down on superfluous electric lighting during daytime hours (23).
3. United Air Lines is considering reducing jet flight speeds in an effort to conserve on fuel. For example, it could save at least 350 gallons on the New York–San Francisco 747 airliner flight simply by reducing the cruising speed from 588 to 574 miles per hour; moreover, the flight time would be extended only a negligible seven minutes (23).
4. It is most gratifying that at long last the car industry is showing signs of reducing the size of their giant gasoline-guzzling models. Thus Charles M. Heinen, Chrysler's chief engineer, announced at a recent California energy conference, "I've instructed my entire staff to concentrate on waste reduction right now. We're aiming for cuts of 500 to 700 pounds and that alone would save the consumer all

the extra gas consumption required as a result of new pollution control and safety measures . . ." (23).

5. Rather admirably, even the gasoline companies, who are in the business to *sell* gasoline, have stressed its conservation. The time when a motorist could blithely say "Fill 'er up!" are past. As of early 1974, Shell, Sohio, and other companies were limiting each customer to ten gallon purchases. Rather noteworthy is the following newspaper "advertisement" by Mobil, which appeared in the Minneapolis *Star*, May 31, 1973: "So we're trying to sell you *conservation* right now, instead of gasoline. We think it's the thing to do while shortages persist. We know, for instance, that if every driver in the United States used just a gallon less gasoline a week, the nation probably could get along without gasoline imports. This would save about $800 million yearly in foreign exchange payments. . . ."

Energy savings could also be effected were industry to produce more *durable* products. "Planned obsolescence" for many manufacturing corporations appears to be a "way of business life." Last Christmas season my wife and I bought at least a dozen plastic toys and mechanical gadgets for our youngsters, only to have them all wind up in the trashcan before New Year's. But that's small potatoes compared to the motor car business. If a Ford or Chevvie were built to last *ten* years instead of *five*, the amount of energy consumed in the car manufacturing process would be reduced by 50 per cent.

It is most encouraging that the automobile industry has finally shifted from the huge gas-guzzling models of the early 1970s to the compact, gas-conserving types. (Who needs the roar of a Cougar, Jaguar, or any of the other "metallic monsters" to bolster one's faded ego, anyway?) Why were cars built with a 450-horsepower engine when 95 per cent of the time the driver needs only one tenth as much power? One can only wonder, however, why the car industry persists in retaining the grossly inefficient, fuel-profligate internal combustion engine when alternative engines (steam, electric) would consume fuel in a much more economical fashion?

Project Independence

During the severe energy shortage of late 1973 President Nixon told Congress that America must extend every effort to become self-sufficient in energy by 1980. This massive undertaking, called Project Independence, was being blueprinted a short time later by 700 energy planners under the leadership of John C. Sawhill, head of the Federal Energy Administration (FEA). The estimated cost of the project is a staggering $600 billion—twenty times the cost of the entire Apollo Program that sent man to the moon. The FEA has estimated that the United States will have to increase oil and natural gas production 50 per cent, increase coal production 100 per cent, and increase nuclear power output 500 per cent—all within a ten year period—if Project Independence is to be considered a success (7).

As might be expected, the project has triggered heated controversy. On the one hand are the environmentalists who insist on a deliberate, carefully planned development of energy in which every effort will be made to prevent degradation of our soil, air, water, and scenic resources. On the other hand are the spokesmen for industry who complain that environmental "straitjackets" may well lead to electrical energy blackouts and economic chaos. The over-riding importance of Project Independence was underscored by Sawhill when he described energy as a "central social resource that determines where and how we live." Governor John Vanderhoof of Colorado, whose state hosted the initial public hearings on the project, went even further, suggesting that on the project's success depends "the survival of the United States" (7).

Prospect

The energy crisis is for real! It will be with us for several years. It can be resolved. But at a cost, measured in fuel price increases to the consumer, by possible fuel rationing, by a new energy-conserving rather than energy-spending life style on the part of the American people, and by some regrettable, but seemingly unavoidable, environmental damage. For the short term, until about 1985, the nation's accelerating energy demands can be met by a combination of such programs as energy conservation, coal gassification, Alaskan pipeline construction, the increased tempo of gas and oil exploration, and the import of foreign oil. In addition intensive development must be made of geothermal, solar, hydro, and tidal energy sources. However, unless the federal government launches a crash program in solar energy development, for the long term, beyond 1985 and into the twenty-first century, most authorities are agreed that America will be compelled to derive more and more of its energy from nuclear power plants. The production of nuclear power, which is highly controversial, and poses grave implications for environmental damage, will be discussed in the next chapter.

BIBLIOGRAPHY

1. Aaronson, Terri, and George Kohl. "Spectrum," *Environ.*, 14, No. 9 (1972), 24–26.
2. Alnes, Stephen. "Energy Cutbacks Not Likely to Be Voluntary," Minneapolis *Star* (April 25, 1973).
3. Ardman, Harvey. "How Far Should We Go with Nuclear Power?" *American Legion Magazine* 96, No. 6 (June 1974), 4–7, 42–46.
4. Bengelsdorf, Irvin. "Are We Running Out of Fuel?" *Nat. Wild.* (February–March, 1971).
5. Carlson, Dave. "Oil Shortage Gets Worse," Eau Claire *Leader Telegram* (January 11, 1973).
6. Ehrlich, Paul R., and Anne H. Ehrlich. *Population, Resources, Environment.* San Francisco: Freeman, 1970.
7. "Energy: A Question of Survival," *Newsweek* (Aug. 26, 1974), 65, 68.
8. "Energy Crisis: Are We Running Out?" *Time* (June 12, 1972).
9. Fay, James A., and James J. MacKenzie. "Cold Cargo," *Environ.*, 14, No. 9 (1972), 21–22, 27–29.
10. Gannon, Robert. "Special Report: Atomic Power—What Are Our Alternatives?" *Sci. Digest* (December 1971), 19–22.
11. Gilmore, C. P. "Can Sunshine Heat (and Cool) Your House?" *Popular Science* (March 1974), 78–81, 160.
12. Halacy, D. S., Jr. "The Solar Alternative to Atomic Power," *Sci. Digest* (March 1972), 45–46, 51–52.
13. Halmos, E. E., Jr. "Lots to Be Heard at the Trans-Alaskan Hearings," *Pipeline and Gas Jour.* (April 1971), p. 81.

14. Hammond, Allen L. "Conservation of Energy: The Potential for More Efficient Use," *Science* 178, No. 4065 (December 8, 1972), 1079–1081.
15. Hayes, Paul G. "As Power Cools Us, a Crisis Simmers On," Milwaukee *Journal* (August 20, 1972).
16. ———. "Power Crisis Brewing in U.S. for Long Time," Milwaukee *Journal* (August 22, 1972).
17. Heller, Jean. "U.S. Faces Ever-Increasing Shortage of Energy," *Wisconsin State Journal* (August 20, 1972).
18. Hubbert, M. King. "Energy Resources," in National Academy of Sciences, *Resources and Man*. San Francisco: Freeman, 1969.
19. Leith, C. K. "Conservation of Minerals," in Garry D. McKenzie and Russell O. Utgard, eds., *Man and His Physical Environment*. Minneapolis: Burgess, 1972.
20. Longworth, Richard C. "Scramble Looms Unless Nations Cooperate on Oil," Minneapolis *Tribune* (May 27, 1973).
21. Minneapolis *Tribune* (December 17, 1972).
22. National Academy of Sciences. *Resources and Man*. San Francisco: Freeman, 1969.
23. "Save a Watt," *Newsweek* (May 28, 1973), 90–91.
24. "There'll Be Enough Gas and Oil if People Pay the Price," *U.S. News and World Report* (June 4, 1973), 27–28.
25. O'Toole, Thomas. "United States Energy Crisis Called Incurable," Washington Post Service (April 30, 1972).
26. Sherrill, Robert, "The Industry's Fright Campaign," *The Nation* (June 26, 1972), 816–820.
27. Wagner, Richard H. *Environment and Man*. New York: Norton, 1971.
28. Weaver, Kenneth F., and Emory Kristof. "The Search for Tomorrow's Power," National Geographic, 142, No. 5 (November 1972), 650–681.

18.

Nuclear Energy, Radiation, and Man

The ordinary man knows that he must accept the dangers of his natural environment, but he sees no reason why he should endure hazards created by the human will, unless the benefit greatly exceeds the harm. He is at the mercy of a danger that is at the same time universal and insidious: it respects no frontiers, and man has no natural sense by which to know its presence. He cannot see it, he cannot smell it, he cannot taste it, he cannot hear it, he cannot touch it. He only knows it is always there, the invisible peril. He is an innocent in the hands of experts. . . . Surely he is entitled to ask that the process be brought under control before it is too late. He asks this, moreover, not only in his own name. He asks it on behalf of a child without a name, not to be born perhaps for a hundred years, who may be the victim of his indifference.

Robert Plant,
"The Dangerous Atom,"
World Health, January 1969

The world's first atom bomb hurtled earthward. Far below was Hiroshima. The blinding flash of light, awesome explosion, and mushroom-shaped cloud that followed not only brought World War II to an abrupt end, but ushered in the Nuclear Age. The development of nuclear power has become a two-edged technological "sword"—bearing vast potential for destruction on the one hand and holding bright promise for promoting human welfare on the other.

What Is Nuclear Energy?

Atomic Structure. All matter, whether a solid, liquid, or gas, is composed of submicroscopic particles called atoms. Each atom is composed of a central nucleus composed of positively charged *protons* and electrically neutral *neutrons*. Surrounding the nucleus are one or more rings of negatively charged *electrons*. Atoms combine with other atoms to form molecules. Thus an atom of *sodium* combines with an atom of *chlorine* to form one molecule of *sodium chloride*, or common table salt.

Nature of Radiation. In 1896 the famed scientist Henri Becquerel accidentally discovered that even though a photographic plate were carefully covered, it would nevertheless be exposed, even in total darkness, if radium were placed on top of the film. Later the French scientists Pierre and Marie Curi found that radium was also *radioactive*, or had the capacity of emitting radiation. It is now known that radium spontaneously disintegrates to give off three radiation types: *alpha* rays, which are positively charged protons; *beta* rays, which are negatively charged electrons; and *gamma* rays, which are electrically neutral and are similar to X-rays. If an atom of lithium (a silvery white metallic element) is hit by a proton, it will break up into two alpha particles; at the same time a certain amount of energy is released. The term *fission* is given to such a process in which an atom is split into fragments (13). The nuclear reactor used today generates energy as the result of the *fission* of radioactive fuel, such as uranium.

An *isotope* is a form of an element that is identical to the regular element except for a difference in *atomic weight* (weight resulting from the collective weight of the protons and neutrons). Isotopes may either be stable or unstable. A good example of a stable isotope is "heavy" hydrogen, or *deuterium*. Unstable isotopes are said to be *radioactive*. They undergo spontaneous disintegration, releasing large quantities of energy. The time required for 50 per cent of the radioisotope to disintegrate is known as its *half-life*. The half-life varies greatly among known radioisotopes. For example, iodine-131 has a half-life of eight days, cesium-137 27 years, strontium-90 28 years, carbon-14 5,600 years. With the aid of sensitive instruments, such as Geiger counters, which detect the emitted radiations, radioisotopes can be traced as they move through soil, air, water, and the bodies of living organisms.

Chain Reactions. The nucleus of uranium bears 146 neutrons. When bombarded by neutrons the uranium atom absorbs one neutron so that its nucleus has a total of 147 neutrons. The atom then disintegrates to form a *krypton* fragment with 47 neutrons and a *barium* fragment with 82. Forty-seven and 82 equal 129, meaning that *18 neutrons are left over*, in other words they are released into the environment (13). In the event that each of these neutrons in turn bombarded other uranium atoms, large quantities of additional neutrons could be released. This process could be repeated again and again as long as the uranium fuel supply remained, resulting in what is known as a *chain reaction*. The tremendous implications of nuclear chain reactions can be appreciated when one realizes that the explosive force resulting from the fissioning of only 1 *pound* of uranium, is equivalent to 10,000 tons of TNT; if this energy were gradually released it would provide 12 million kilowatt hours of power (13).

Background Radiation. In this discussion we are primarily concerned with the possible human health hazards resulting from man-induced radiation exposures, that is, exposures resulting from technological developments, such as the atomic bomb and nuclear power plants. In considering this problem, however, we should be aware that man is also exposed to *natural* or *background* radiation over which he has absolutely no control. Man eats, drinks, and breathes materials that, although radioactive, are part of the natural world around him. Man is exposed, for example, to cosmic rays from outer space. The crew of a supersonic transport plane, which averages about 480 hours flying time per year, receives a radiation dose just under the maximum dose permitted by the International Commission on Radiologic Protection (14). Radioactive gases are emitted from soil and rocks. Even coal contains radioactive material, which is emitted from the smokestacks of coal-fired power plants. Natural radiation sources may be internal as well as external. Thus Walter C. Patterson estimates that since the human body harbors about one-ten-thousand-millionth of a gram of radium, about four radium atoms are disintegrating inside the body every second, releasing destructive alpha particles to surrounding tissues. He further estimates that 4,000 beta particles per second emanate from the substantial number of radioactive potassium atoms found within the body (10). In essence, therefore, every man, woman, and child on earth is *naturally* radioactive. This radioactive dosage is an inescapable part of the ecological system to which man belongs.

Radioactive Fallout from Nuclear Bomb Blasts. When an atomic bomb is detonated, only 50 per cent of the energy released goes into the blast. Of the remainder 35 per cent is dissipated as heat, while only 15 per cent goes into radioactivity (13). The radioactive dust resulting from the explosion eventually becomes suspended at a height of 6 to 9 miles above the earth's surface and may ultimately be transported by air currents several times around the globe. Eventually, after several years, the bulk of the radioactive materials either settles to the earth or is scrubbed from the air by the cleansing action of rain or snow. Nuclear testing has added about 10 to 15 per cent to the world's background radiation.

Two major isotopes entering biological systems from such radioactive fallout are strontium-90 and cesium-137. Although both of these radioactive isotopes are extremely scarce, strontium-90 mimics the physiological characteristics of the much more abundant calcium in biological systems, while cesium-137 has physiological properties similar to potassium. As a result, therefore, both of these radioactive elements are transmitted eventually to animal tissues (including human tissues) via food chains. Plants require calcium as a component of calcium pectate, the cementive substance found between cell walls. The radioactive strontium is rapidly absorbed by the root systems, especially in calcium-deficient soils. Radioactive strontium tends to concentrate in herbivores such as rodents, deer, and cattle. Man gets radioactive strontium in his system by consuming contaminated cereals and

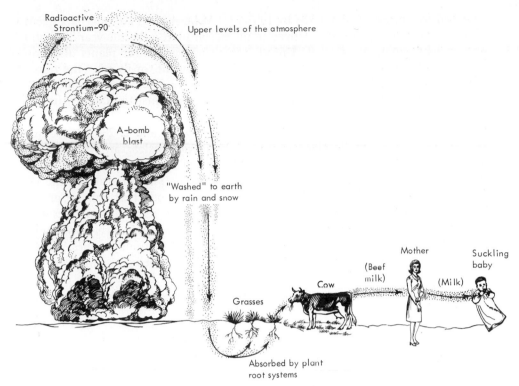

Figure 18-1. *Movement of radioactive strontium through the human ecosystem.*

milk. The radioactive strontium becomes concentrated in the milk of a lactating mother and is then ingested by the suckling baby. In either case, most of the radioactive strontium is deposited in the bones. Since all red blood cell and much white blood cell production eventually takes place in the bone marrow, the effects of marrow irradiation may be severely deleterious. Although any radiation is potentially harmful, the quantity of strontium-90 in the environment is still rather small. The total amount of strontium-90 in the 5 million acres of the Netherlands, for example, is only 1 gram, compared to the 1,000 grams of calcium carried around in a single human skeleton (13). Cesium-137 is not ordinarily absorbed by root systems because it is immobilized by the clay component of soil (13). However, it may be absorbed through plant leaves that have become dusted with fallout. Tundra food studies have shown that the amount of cesium-137 is *doubled* in each successive link in the lichen-caribou-Eskimo food chain.

The Nuclear Power Plant

Design and Operation of the Nuclear Reactor. It has been estimated that America's energy requirements will double every decade through the year 2000. Since fossil-fueled (coal, gas, and oil) power plants are prime sources of atmospheric contamination, more and more electrical power will be generated by nuclear plants. Although America had only 23 nuclear plants operating in 1972, the number is expected to increase to about 125 by 1982 (3). Whereas in 1970 only 2 per cent of America's electrical power was derived from nuclear sources, by the year 2000 almost 40 per cent will be so derived. Unfortunately, nuclear power plants also pose a contaminant threat, not with sulfur dioxide, benzopyrene, or fly ash (the principal pollutants from coal-fired plants), but with thermal and radioactive pollution. To understand the nature of this problem it will be necessary first to examine the design and operation of a nuclear-fired plant.

A typical nuclear reactor employs a mixture of U-235 and U-238 as a source of fuel. The fuel elements, in the form of uranium oxide pellets, are incorporated in long thin zirconium cartridges (13). Several hundred thousand pounds of uranium oxide may be contained in this so-called reactor *core*. The intensity of the chain reaction is controlled by neutron-absorbing cadmium rods that can be gradually inserted or withdrawn from the reactor core. The chain reaction generates a large quantity of heat that produces the steam required to drive the turbines to produce electrical power. As we recall from the second law of thermodynamics, whenever such an energy conversion occurs, whether inside a human being or a nuclear reactor, a certain amount is dissipated as heat. The core indeed becomes very hot, but is maintained at about 1,000° F by a water-cooling system.

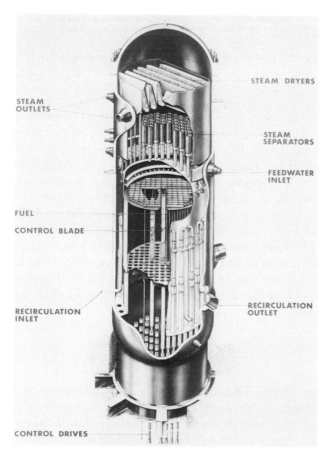

STEAM DRYERS

STEAM OUTLETS

STEAM SEPARATORS

FEEDWATER INLET

FUEL

CONTROL BLADE

RECIRCULATION OUTLET

RECIRCULATION INLET

CONTROL DRIVES

Figure 18-2. *Cutaway view of a reactor vessel showing the internal structure. At top of the diagram are the steam outlets, which deliver the steam to the turbines. Note the fuel rods, which are packed with uranium oxide pellets. Cooling water inlets are indicated.* [*Northern States Power Company*]

Figure 18-3. *Reactor vessel. This is the "heart" of the 500,000 kilowatt nuclear-fueled electric generating plant that the Northern States Power Company plans to build near Monticello, Minnesota. The uranium oxide pellets will be packed into the tubular structures seen in the picture. A reactor vessel such as this may receive over a hundred thousand pounds of uranium oxide. Cooling water keeps the heat generated by the vessel at about 1000° F. [Earl Chambers—Northern States Power Company]*

Thermal Pollution. Although nuclear plants are preferable to fossil fuel plants from the standpoint of atmospheric quality, they do pose a much more formidable threat with respect to thermal pollution, the nuclear plant generating 40 per cent more waste heat per kilowatt of power produced. The nuclear plant's cooling system is shown in Figure 18-4. The coolant water is ordinarily withdrawn from a stream, pumped to the plant's condenser system, and then, after absorbing heat from the primary coolant and being warmed up to 20° F above its original temperature, is pumped back into the stream. One disadvantage to this technique is that it adds to the already great demands on our nation's water resources. By the year 2030, for example, total water use in the United States will have increased six times above current usage. One nuclear plant, which was on the drawing boards for construction in Vermont, would have utilized two thirds of the Connecticut River's dry season flow!

Fossil fuel power plant

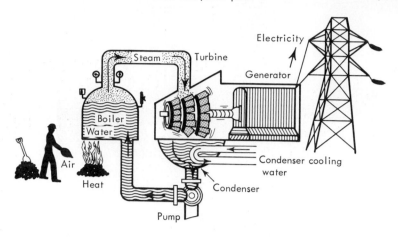

Nuclear power plant–
boiling water reactor (BWR)

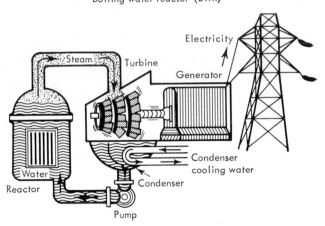

Figure 18-4.
Comparison of cooling systems for fossil fuel power plant and nuclear power plant (boiling water reactor). [*From:* Nuclear Power and the Environment. *American Nuclear Society, Hinsdale, Ill., 1973*]

Thermal pollution induces extensive, subtle, and complex changes in the delicate operation of aquatic ecosystems, which not only have adverse effects on plant (green algae) and animal life (crustaceans, insect larvae, game fish) by reducing levels of dissolved oxygen, but also reduce the aesthetic properties of the stream.

A classic example of a fish kill occurred at Consolidated Edison's Indian Point Nuclear Station at Peekskill, New York. Many thousands of valuable striped bass were destroyed, collected by utility employees, hauled by truck to a dump and "piled to a depth of several feet, covering an area encompassing more than a city lot . . ." (13). Partly because of this immense potential for ecosystem abuse, environmental activists recently (1972) blocked construction of two nuclear plants in the East—Philadelphia Electric's Limerick Plant and the Newbold Island plant of New Jersey Public Service Electric and Gas. Both plants were designed to use cooling water from the Delaware River, expected to be adequate as soon as the Tocks Island Dam

Figure 18-5.
*America's electrical
power needs are ex-
pected to double in the
next ten years. To meet
this demand, many new
nuclear plants are
under construction.
This is the Portland
General Electric
Nuclear Plant on the
shores of the Columbia
River at Rainier,
Oregon. The dome that
shields the reactor is a
characteristic feature
of nuclear plants. Note
the mammoth cooling
tower to the left.*
[Rollin R. Geppert]

Figure 18-6. *Nuclear
power plant at
Monticello, Minnesota.
Note the two
"batteries" of cooling
towers in the fore-
ground. Low-level
liquid wastes are
discharged into the
river to the right.*
[Northern States Power
Company]

was completed. However, when environmental considerations forced indefinite postponement of the dam, the Delaware River Basin Commission refused to approve construction of two nuclear plants because the volume of available cooling water was inadequate (1).

Radiation Emissions from the Nuclear Plant. Despite the alarms generated by the "scare tactics" of some environmental activists, the radiation emissions from a properly designed and operated modern nuclear power plant is negligible. The cumulative radiation dose after *six years* of operation is roughly equivalent to the radiation one would receive from a single dental X-ray (12)! For example, a 1971 survey by the Atomic Energy Commission showed that radioactivity in the effluent gases and liquids from the most recently constructed nuclear power plants was less than 1 per cent of the permissible levels (4). F. L. Parker, of Vanderbilt University, has estimated that even in the year 2000, when America will probably have about 200 nuclear plants in operation, the radiation emitted would be only 1 per cent of the natural background radiation (3).

Detailed studies have been conducted by various agencies of the amount of radiation (in addition to background radiation) to which residents were exposed who had been living in the vicinity of nuclear power plants that had been in operation for ten to twelve years. On the basis of its study of the Dresden Nuclear Power Station Unit I in Illinois, the Environmental Protection Agency concluded that "exposure to the surrounding population through consumption of food and water from radionuclides released at Dresden was not measurable . . ." (4). Since 1963 a research team from New York University's Laboratory for Environmental Medicine, headed by Merril Eisenbud, has conducted a similar study of the Indian Point Power Plant on the Hudson River. Eisenbud's comments on the investigation are most enlightening:

> The main route of human exposure from the Indian Point releases would be consumption of fish, and the bulk of the dose would be due to cesium-137 and cesium-134 . . . [The] dose received by an individual consuming 11 kilograms per year of Hudson River fish . . . would have been 0.08 millirem per year based on the 1971 data. To put these doses into perspective, it can be observed that the gamma radiation dose from igneous rock on the island of Manhattan exposes people to about 15 millirem per year more than they would receive from the sandy terrain of Brooklyn, another borough of the City of New York. A dose of 0.054 millirem per year from a steady diet of Hudson River fish would be equivalent to the additional dose a Brooklyn resident would receive if he visited Manhattan for a period of about 45 hours per year . . . (4).

Disposal of Radioactive Wastes. The biggest concern of environmentalists, as well as the Atomic Energy Commission, is not the radiation emissions from the nuclear plant itself, but how the high level radioactive fission products in the spent fuel can be safely disposed. After a reactor has been operating for one to two years, there is a tendency for these products to slow down the chain reaction. Because a large number of neutrons are absorbed the quantity available for continued nuclear bombardment is progressively reduced. Once this critical stage has been reached the used fuel cartridges are transported to a reprocessing plant. It is at this point that the wastes are most highly concentrated, most intensely radioactive, and of greatest potential threat to human safety (9). Recently the Atomic Energy Commission proposed to transport such radioactive wastes by truck from the Shoreham, Long Island, nuclear plant through New York City for reprocessing in upstate New York. Since the route would pass through areas where population density reaches 8,000 per square mile, the Environmental Protection Agency, quite concerned, suggested that the wastes be shipped instead by barge to reprocessing facilities in Illinois or South Carolina (1).

At the processing plant the uranium and plutonium are recovered and radioactive wastes are removed. The recovery of uranium for reuse is dictated by raw economics since it costs about $3,000 per pound. After the hot wastes have cooled off to some degree, they are concentrated in order to reduce volume. Roughly 100 gallons of highly radioactive waste must be disposed of for every ton of spent fuel (9).

One method of disposal involves placing the waste in stainless steel containers and giving them subterranean burial. As of 1969 8 million gallons, having radioactivity of up to 1,000 curies [1] per gallon, had already been stored in 200 subterranean tanks at four burial sites. Although this disposal method has been extensively employed in the past, there are several vexing problems associated with it. First, this disposal method requires 2 million cubic feet of storage space annually (9). Second, the precise location for such sites must be selected with extreme care and intensive planning. Apparently this was not the case during World War II when a subterranean dumping site was selected for the disposal of highly radioactive waste generated at the Hanford, Washington, reactor, for the burial site is located above a major geological fault. Possibly the poor choice of site was due to the urgency associated with the Manhattan Project—the development of the atomic bomb. However, were the tanks to be ruptured by an earthquake, the released radioactivity would have a severely detrimental effect on human health and life in the immediate area.

There is a third problem attending this disposal method. Thus, even were a geologically appropriate site selected, the wastes would continue to boil, because of the intensely generated internal heat, for many decades or even centuries, depending upon the half-life of the isotopes involved. The tanks holding these wastes, however, might have a longevity of only a hundred years at best, thus making it mandatory to maintain, repair, and ultimately replace them with new containers. It is apparent that such vigilance will have to be perpetuated by future generations of mankind as yet unborn. Because of these limitations to liquid waste burial, investigations are being made to determine the feasibility of disposal by *glassification*, concentrating the radioactive material and enclosing it in solid ceramic bricks. In the solid state the waste would not be as capable of escaping into the environment as a result of accident, sabotage, or some natural catastrophe. At one time the AEC proposed to store these bricks in abandoned salt mines, of which there are a considerable number in Kansas, New York, and the Gulf coast region. However, in 1972, after spending $25 million to develop a salt mine disposal site at Lyons, Kansas, the AEC finally decided to scrap this method because of technical problems. The preferred technique now appears to be above-ground burial in concrete bunkers (3).

---

[1] Curie = the amount of radioactive material that undergoes 3.7×10^{10} (37 billion) disintegrations per second.

Effects of Radiation on Human Health

The accelerating use of nuclear energy for electrical power production in the next few decades, as well as its increasing employment in agriculture, medicine, biological research, and spaceship propulsion, means that mankind will be subjected to ever-increasing levels of radiation. Although, as we have seen, the amount of radiation that would be emitted from a properly operating nuclear plant would be negligible, it nevertheless would be informative to consider the possible effects that chronic exposure to low-level ionizing radiation may have on the human body over a period of several years.

First of all it should be mentioned that fetuses and infants are much more sensitive to radiation than adults. Moreover, within the body of a single individual there is a considerable sensitivity differential among the various organs. Thus, *Preventive Medicine and Public Health* lists body tissues and organs in the following order of decreasing radiation sensitivity (11):

1. *lymphoid tissues* (bone marrow, blood lymphocytes, lymph nodes)
2. *white blood cells* (other than lymphocytes)
3. *epithelial cells* (smooth, membranous sheets of cells that occur in the ovaries, testes, salivary glands, skin)
4. *endothelial cells* (occurring in the lining of blood vessels and the smooth, moist lining (peritoneum) of the body cavity)
5. *connective tissue cells* (bone and cartilage)
6. *muscle cells*
7. *nerve cells* (brain, spinal cord, nerves)

The effects of low-level chronic radiation are highly varied. Hair loss and skin pigmentation changes are relatively minor effects that appear rather soon after exposure. However, after a period of five to ten years more serious effects develop such as sterility, anemia, cataract (clouding of the lens causing possible blindness), shortened life spans, and cancer.

Experiments on laboratory animals such as mice, rats, and rabbits have indicated that radiation can induce cancer in a variety of organs such as lymph glands, mammary glands, lungs, ovaries, and skin (11). Considerable evidence now exists which strongly suggests that ionizing radiation can cause cancer in man as well. Consider the following items:

1. A high incidence of skin cancer was found among radiologists during the early days of their profession when adequate safeguards were not as yet instituted; a high incidence of leukemia has been found among other workers who have been professionally exposed to radiation (11).
2. During World War I a number of women who painted radium on watch dials developed bone cancer; apparently they accidentally ingested the radioactive material when placing the brushes to their lips to draw them to a "point" (11).
3. Over a period of several years at least 5,000 miners who had been employed in a uranium mine in Joachimsthal, Czechoslovakia, eventually died from lung cancer (11).
4. Children who have been given X-ray treatment in the neck have shown a higher incidence of cancer than children not so treated.
5. Children irradiated within the mother's uterus during pelvic X-ray examinations (of the mother) have also shown a high cancer incidence.

Nevertheless, despite these disturbing facts, it must be emphasized that the radiation dosages to which these unfortunate people were exposed were considerably higher than the dosage to which the average human being would be exposed even were he to live in the immediate vicinity of a nuclear power plant in full operation. A study by the National Academy of Sciences has suggested that if a population of 1 million people were subjected to a dose of 1 rad [2] (a much higher dosage than they would get from normal nuclear power plant operations) a maximum of 20 leukemia cases and 145 other types of cancer would be produced during that population's lifetime (11). Eisenbud states that exposure from the nuclear power industry could produce a maximum of 12 cases of cancer per year in the United States population. ". . . Since the annual incidence of cancer in the United States is about 1600 cases per million persons, the 12 cases would occur against a background of nearly 500,000 cancers from other causes . . ." (4).

The Bombing of Hiroshima and Nagasaki. The day before writing this material on radiation effects I had an opportunity to be briefed by several power utility officials concerning the potential environmental effects of the operation of a mammoth nuclear power plant that the utility was planning to construct near Eau Claire, Wisconsin, and that would become operational about 1982. To allay the concern of the various professors at the meeting, one official stated that the chance of their power plant undergoing a major malfunction that would expose people in the vicinity to a massive radiation dose was virtually infinitesimal. He likened it to the probability that a person would get struck by lightning—one in many million! Perhaps the probability is that low; however, in the case of the lightning strike, only one person dies, and in the case of gross nuclear plant malfunction, literally thousands might die and many more would suffer in horrible fashion within a radius of probably 100 miles from the plant.

Such a catastrophe has not occurred and it is hoped that it never will. However, we can get a rough estimate of the type of damage such an episode would cause by examining the biological damage caused by the detonation of the nuclear bombs over Hiroshima and Nagasaki during World War II. The effects are summarized in *Health Effects of Environmental Pollutants*, by George L. Waldbott, of the Wayne State University Medical School:

> Similar to irradiation by X-ray, the atomic bomb had an immediate and delayed effect. Gastrointestinal injury, which in some cases were irreversible, occurred immediately. Plummer obtained a history of burns, loss of hair, fever, purpura (a disease characterized by tiny hemorrhages mainly on the skin), and gastrointestinal bleeding in 68 out of 250 pregnant women. . . . The second peak of illness involving the bone marrow gave rise to anemia, hemorrhages, purpura, leukemia, and infections. . . . Up to 1954, ten years after the bomb disaster, 92 cases of leukemia among 216,176 survivors of the atomic bomb were recorded. The first evidence of the disease appeared within one year following the bombing, but the peak did not occur until six to seven years later. A higher than normal incidence of radiation cataracts was also noted in survivors who had been in the vicinity of the bomb explosion . . . (14).

[2] Rad = a measure of radiation dosage, equivalent to the absorption of 100 ergs per gram of tissue.

Of course in addition to the radiation-induced illnesses described above, approximately 100,000 Japanese lost their lives.

Genetic Effects of Radiation. The heredity-determining material of the human body is composed of submicroscopic chemical units called *genes*, which in turn are borne in chromosomes. In interaction with the environment these genes, of which there are roughly 2,000 per chromosome, determine human body traits, such as nose shape, eye and hair color, blood type, presence or absence of limbs, number of fingers and toes, blood clotting ability, and mental development. A baby develops from a *zygote*, which in turn is formed by the union of a sperm and egg. The genes contained in the sperm (produced by the male testis) and in the egg (produced by the female ovary) may undergo *mutations*, "spontaneous" changes that can be inherited by future offspring. During the long 2-million-year history of human evolution many of the harmful mutations have been "weeded out" by natural selection, while the beneficial mutations have been incorporated into the human gene "pool." This means that if a gene in modern man undergoes a mutation, it probably will be a harmful one, resulting possibly in such defects as mental impairment or malformed limbs. Such mutations, caused possibly by natural or background radiation, occur spontaneously at the rate of about one per million sperm or eggs produced. However, since Herman Muller's Nobel prize-winning research on fruit flies, we have known that mutation rates can be artificially increased with the use of X-rays, a form of radiation similar to the gamma rays emitted from a nuclear reactor.

The radiation generated by the Hiroshima-Nagasaki bomb blasts which abruptly terminated World War II apparently induced the formation of a number of mutations. A follow-up survey, according to Waldbott, revealed that "children whose mothers while pregnant were within 1200 meters of the center of the explosion, developed *microcephaly*, an otherwise rare deformity of the skull associated with mental retardation . . ." (14). Other birth defects among such children exposed while in the uterus included mongoloid mental retardation, congenital dislocation of the hip, congenital heart disease, *hydrocele* (accumulation of fluid around the testes), clubfoot, glaucoma (resulting in blindness), partial albinism, and malformed chest and ears (14). We must emphasize, however, that barring nuclear war, or some massive malfunction of a nuclear reactor (which is highly unlikely), the American public will most certainly never be exposed to the high radiation levels that caused the defects described above. Nevertheless, James F. Crow, eminent University of Wisconsin geneticist and former president of the Genetics Society of America, suggests that *any* amount of radiation exposure, no matter how slight, is potentially damaging to genetic material. If so, it certainly behooves man to keep the radiation emissions generated by his technology down to an absolute minimum. Failure to exercise every precaution may eventually result in some genetic damage to the sex cells of people now living, at a cost which will be paid by generations of Americans yet unborn.

The Breeder Reactor

There is considerable concern that the proliferation of nuclear-fired power plants predicted within the next two decades will rapidly reduce America's supplies of high quality uranium-235 fuel. Faulkner estimates that by 1980 only about 210,000 tons of low cost uranium ore ($U_3 O_8$) can be produced. The solution to this potential scarcity of uranium fuel would be the ultimate replacement of the conventional uranium-235 "spending" reactor with a uranium-235 "conserving" *breeder* reactor. The *breeder reactor* utilizes a relatively small amount of uranium-235 as a "primer" to release energy from the much more abundant uranium-238, which in turn is converted into plutonium-239 from which the heat energy required to generate electrical power is ultimately derived.

The supply of fissionable uranium-235 is considered so limited that the development of a suitable commercial-type breeder reactor has assumed the earmarks of a crash program. Even though a breeder reactor (the Fermi plant in Michigan) had been in operation since 1955, the program proceeded at a casual, leisurely pace—only $12 million being budgeted annually (1948 to 1967) for the entire AEC breeder program (7). It is anticipated that the breeder reactors will eventually replace the nonbreeder type by the year 2000. When this occurs it will be possible to "tap" extensive uranium deposits that previously could not be used.

For example, uranium-bearing Chattanooga shale underlies a considerable portion of Ohio, Kentucky, Tennessee, Illinois, and Indiana (7). One part of the formation, which is 15 feet thick, embraces hundreds of square miles and bears many hundreds of thousands of tons of shale. Furthermore, every 100,000 pounds of shale yields about 6 pounds of uranium (7). We might well ask the question: If we were using the breeder reactor how much energy could be derived from this single shale formation? Hubbert estimates that "for each square meter of surface area there are five cubic meters of rock containing 750 grams of uranium . . . the fuel equivalent [of which] . . . would be 2,000 metric tons of coal or 10,000 barrels of crude oil . . ." (7). Hubbert further states that an area of Chattanooga shale *only 17 miles square* would provide us the energy equivalent of our country's 1,500 billion metric tons of mineable coal (7). Moreover, an area of shale of *less than 3 square miles* would yield as much energy as our nation's total supply of produceable crude oil amounting to *200 billion barrels*.

It is of utmost importance, therefore, that we shift from the uranium-235 "spending" nonbreeder reactor to the uranium-235 "conserving" breeder reactor before we exhaust our restricted supplies of this essential "trigger" to the release of the energy bounty. In Hubbert's words, "Failure to make this transition would constitute one of the major disasters in human history . . ." (7).

Prospect

Unless the federal government decides to launch a crash program to harness solar energy and convert it into electrical power, on the same scale, with the same fervor and dedication, with the same scientific and technical expertise, and with the same amount of financial support, as it channeled into the development of the atom bomb during World War II—a most unlikely event—then it would seem that industrialized societies the world over, and in America in particular, will be faced with the prospect of proliferating nuclear power plants, and hence unavoidable gradual increases in radiation exposure, well into the twenty-first century. This technological development promises unquestioned *material* benefit, such as relatively cheap, unlimited supplies of energy to power industry, illuminate and heat homes, schools, and office buildings, and to make it possible to save fossil fuels as raw materials in the chemical synthesis of dyes, plastics, and medicinal supplies. However, in the process of harnessing our affluence, life style, and the pursuit of the "American dream" to nuclear power, we are committing ourselves to a benefit-cost "trade-off" of gigantic proportions. Yale University professors Harte, Socolow, and Ginocchio have discussed it as follows:

> What seems certain is that there is some biological cost that cannot be escaped but must be "traded off" in exchange for the benefits of nuclear technology. Such trade-offs are implicit in the expansion of virtually every technology, not just nuclear technology. Excess deaths from cancer due to increases in ambient radiation have their non-nuclear analogs in excess deaths from emphysema due to air pollution. That some of the biological and psychological cost is borne by future generations is also not unique to nuclear technology: creating long-lived isotopes that will not decay for several generations is analagous to altering the level of carbon dioxide in the atmosphere in a way that may threaten injurious modifications in the future climate, and is also analagous to destroying the wilderness heritage by damming up river valleys . . . (6).

America has apparently committed herself to the trade-off, accepting the biological and ecological costs along with the power benefits. We must not become complacent, however. Remember that predictions are for 200 nuclear plants by the year 2000. Having all this nuclear power potential is somewhat akin to having an "energy-tiger by the tail." In the event of gross plant malfunction, admittedly a most unlikely event, the potential for human misery and loss of life, let alone property and environmental damage, boggles the imagination. Certainly the nuclear power industry, scientists, legislators, federal, state, and local governments, as well as the man on the street, must develop a moral responsibility to do everything possible to properly regulate the future generation and use of nuclear power.

BIBLIOGRAPHY

1. Aaronson, Terri, and George Kohl. "Spectrum," *Environ.* 14 (1972), 24–26.
2. Atomic Energy Commission. "Report on the Releases of Radioactivity in Effluents from Nuclear Power Plants for 1971," *Directorate of Regulatory Operations* (1972).
3. Benarde, Melvin A. *Our Precarious Habitat.* New York: Norton, 1970.
4. Eisenbud, Merril. "Health Hazards from Radioactive Emissions," paper presented at AMA Cong. Environ. Health, April 29–30, 1973, Chicago, Ill.
5. Gannon, Robert. "Special Report: Atomic Power—What are Our Alternatives?" *Sci. Digest* (December 1971), 19–22.
6. Harte, John, Robert H. Socolow, and Joseph N. Ginocchio. "Radiation," in John Harte and Robert H. Socolow, *Patient Earth.* New York: Holt, 1971.
7. Hubbert, M. King. "Energy Resources," in National Academy of Sciences, *Resources and Man.* San Francisco: Freeman, 1969.
8. National Academy of Sciences–National Research Council. "The Effects on Populations of Exposure to Low Levels of Ionizing Radiation," Report of Advisory Committee on the Biological Effects of Ionizing Radiation, Washington, D.C. (November 1972).
9. Odum, Eugene P. *Fundamentals of Ecology,* 3rd ed. Philadelphia: Saunders, 1971.
10. Patterson, Walter C. "Hazards of Radioactive Wastes," in Robert M. Chute, *Environmental Insight.* New York: Harper, 1971.

11. Sartwell, Philip E., Chapter 25, in *Preventive Medicine and Public Health*, 9th ed., ed. by K. F. Maxcy and M. J. Rosenau. New York: Appleton.
12. Turk, Amos, Jonathon Turk, and Janet T. Wittes. *Ecology, Pollution, Environment.* Philadelphia: Saunders, 1972.
13. Wagner, Richard H. *Environment and Man.* New York: Norton, 1971.
14. Waldbott, George L. *Health Effects of Environmental Pollutants.* St. Louis: Mosby, 1973.

19.

The Human Population Problem

Millions of people are going to starve to death, and soon. There is nothing that can be done to prevent it. They will die because of shortsighted governmental attitudes. They will die because some religious organizations have blocked attempts over the years to get governmental and United Nations action underway to control human birthrates. They will die because scientists have managed to persuade many influential people that a technological rabbit can always be pulled out of the hat to save mankind at the last moment. They will die because many people, like myself, who recognized the essential role of overpopulation in the increasing woes of Homo sapiens, could not bring themselves to leave the comforts of their daily routine to do something about it. Their blood will be distributed over many hands.

Paul R. Ehrlich,
"World Population: A Battle Lost?"
Stanford Today, Series 1, No. 22, Winter 1968

Population Increase

Phylogenists place man at the pinnacle of the animal kingdom because of his ability to assess a problem, to devise a solution, and to put that solution into operation. However, at this crucial period in human history, man has as yet not effectively applied his talents to solving the problem of his exploding population. If unresolved, this population increase may bring calamity to the human species.

Man is the most abundant mammalian species on earth. Already in 1961, according to Marston Bates, ecologist at the University of Michigan, 187 babies were born each minute. Although 142,000 people died each day, 270,000 were born daily; thus, there was a daily increment of 128,000 to the world population. To give each person in this daily increase a glass of milk would require milk from 9,600 cows; it would take 200 acres of wheat to give each a loaf of bread. At present the population is growing even more rapidly. Each year the world has to provide the necessary food, water, shelter, and living space to sustain 93 million additional people. Four billion pounds of human biomass are synthesized annually, a far greater increase than that for any other mammal.

Philip Hauser, director of the Population Research Training Center at the University of Chicago, has pointed out that an initial population of 100 people increasing at a rate of only 1 per cent per year for 5,000 years would produce a population density of 2.7 billion people per square foot of land on earth. But our global rate of annual increase is much greater than 1 per cent. In 1974 it was 2.0 per cent per year.

Figure 19-1. *Ten Centuries of World Population Growth. Note the slight population reduction caused by the European famine about 1140 A.D. and the Black Death (bubonic) plague about 1360. Industrial, transportation, medical, and agricultural revolutions all contributed significantly to the population "explosion" of the late twentieth century. Note that it took the human species two million years to attain a population of about .4 billion (in 1000 A.D.) but in only an additional thousand years, by 2000 A.D., the human population is expected to increase at least seventeen-fold. (Data from several sources.)*

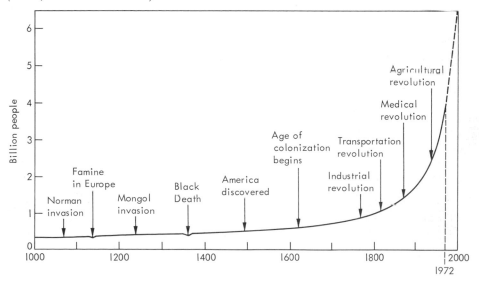

In 1968 the United States had a population of 200 million; by the year 2000 it is expected to reach 300 million. Examination of world population doubling rates can be quite informative. For example, it took early man almost 2 million years to build up to a population of a mere 0.25 billion by the year A.D. 1. However, in only 1,650 years man's population was doubled (to 0.50 billion), then doubled again (to 1 billion) in only 200 years, doubled again (to 2 billion) in only 90 years; the doubling (to 4 billion) being generated currently may be completed in only 35 years (15). Using 1957 as a benchmark, the population of Costa Rica doubled in 1973; Syria doubled its population in 1974. Libya's population will double by 1976, Vietnam by 1978, Mexico, Panama, and the Philippines by 1979, and Brazil by 1980. The annual population increase in China already equals the total 1963 population of the United States. Each day there is a population increment of 190,000, equal to another Madison, Wisconsin, or another Des Moines, Iowa; each year there is an increment of 90 million, equal to nine New York Cities or another France.

Some population experts believe the world will be jam-packed with 7 billion people by the year 2000. They are among the optimists. For example, George Wald, Nobel prize-winning Harvard biologist, believes not only that it would be impossible for the world's finite resources to sustain that number, but that the environmental degradation caused by this serious crush of people may well lead to man's extinction by the year 2000. Wayne H. Davis, population ecologist at the University of Kentucky, while not predicting human extinction, believes that the population surge will eventually overtax the carrying capacity of the earth's slender resources and cause a massive human die-off by the year 2000 (7).

Figure 19-2. *Population of 1900 compared with that of 1972, by areas. Note that the Asian population (other than China and Japan) has more than doubled since 1900. (Data from several sources.)*

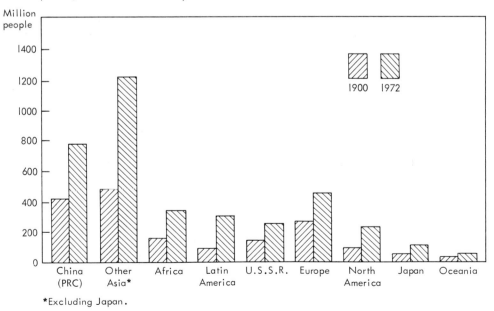

Comparative Impact of Populations in India and the United States on the Environment. It is true that roughly 85 per cent of the current population boom is being generated in the underdeveloped countries such as India, Pakistan, China, Guatemala, Nigeria, and Costa Rica. Annual population growth rates in some of these countries approach 3 per cent! The United States, on the other hand, has a growth rate, at present, of only 1 per cent. As a matter of fact in 1973 the average American couple was procreating at the replacement rate of about only 2.1 per family. How about those figures? Shouldn't they cause Americans to smugly congratulate themselves, that even if human civilization *is* coming to an end, at least the foresighted, intellectually superior, environmentally conscious, reproductive-instinct-restraining Americans will not have to shoulder the blame? Nothing could be further from the truth. To be sure, the population of India is edging toward 600 million, while the United States has only one third that number and its population is growing much less rapidly. However, sheer numbers alone do not begin to indicate the relative impact of the two nations on the environment.

As Wayne Davis so aptly writes in his article "Overpopulated America":

The average Indian eats his daily few cups of rice . . . , draws his bucket of water from the communal well and sleeps in a mud hut. In his daily rounds to gather cow dung to burn to cook his rice and warm his feet, his footsteps, along with those of millions of his countrymen, help bring about a slow deterioration of the ability of the land to support people. His contribution to the destruction of the land is minimal. . . . An American, on the other hand, can be expected to destroy a piece of land on

Figure 19-3. *Population by age groups in developed and less developed countries. Note the much larger number of people in the lower age groups in the less developed countries. This age distribution is most unfortunate, for it means that an increasingly large proportion of the population will be in the child-producing age groups within the next two decades.*

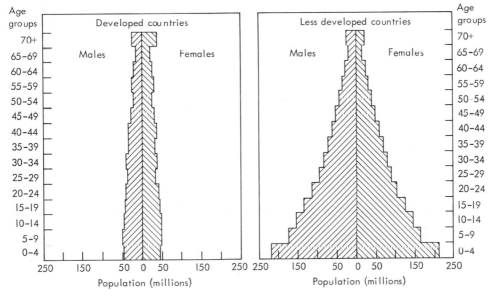

Figure 19-4. *Compare the life style of these Afghanistani with that maintained in New York, Chicago, or Los Angeles. Which life style would have the greatest impact on the environment? This is a village street in Afghanistan. The houses are windowless and lack sanitation. Gypsies are cooking in a "hole in the ground." (FAO photo by Jack Ling)*

which he builds a home, garage and driveway. He will contribute his share to the 142 million tons of smoke and fumes, seven million junked cars, 20 million tons of paper, 48 billion cans, 26 billion bottles the overburdened environment must absorb each year. To run his air conditioner we will stripmine a Kentucky hillside and burn coal in a power generator, whose smoke stack contributes to a plume of smoke massive enough to cause cloud-seeding and premature precipitation from Gulf winds which should be irrigating the wheat farms of Minnesota. In his life time he will personally pollute three million gallons of water, and industry and agriculture will use ten times this much water in his behalf. . . . He will use 21,000 gallons of leaded gasoline . . . , drink 28,000 pounds of milk and eat 10,000 pounds of meat. The latter is produced and squandered in a life pattern unknown to Asians. As steer on a Western range eats plants containing minerals necessary for life. Some of these are incorporated into the body of the steer which is later shipped for slaughter. After being eaten by man these nutrients are flushed down the toilet into the ocean. . . . The result is a continual drain on the productivity of rangeland. The average Indian citizen, whose fecal material goes back to the land, has but a minute fraction of the destructive effect on the land that the affluent American does (8).

Davis has suggested that, in terms of the average American's ability to reduce the earth's carrying capacity for human beings, *one American is equal to twenty-five Indians.* However, because America's per capita GNP is fully thirty-eight times that of India's, Davis' comparison should be considered rather conservative. During their life span, for example, a single year crop of American babies will consume 200 million pounds of steel, over 9 billion gallons of gasoline, and 25 billion pounds of beef. David Ehrenfeld, of Columbia University, has also addressed himself to the differential impact of America and India on the environment:

The idea that the "excess" in "population excess" is contributed primarily by the poor and underprivileged members of society is the most palpably and demonstrably untrue of the population clichés, particularly for the United States; yet it is the most stubbornly rooted idea in both conservative and liberal political philosophies (for different reasons). It is the privileged who are consuming living space at a frightening rate while the poor crowd more to one room; it is the privileged who can afford "throwaway" containers of all sorts and who discard a six-pound Sunday newspaper after one casual reading; it is the privileged who will not eat fish flour and who buy prime beef; it is the privileged who purchase the vast quantity of automobiles that spend their last days rusting in piles at the edges of highways or in once-productive salt marshes; it is the privileged who can attempt to shield themselves from the effects (rather than deal with the causes) of pollution and deforestation by means of zoning restrictions, resort vacations, and air conditioning . . . (11).

Because of the accelerating rate at which we are destroying our "life-support" system in the United States, it may be that the ultimate tragedy facing the United States will be greater than the mass starvation facing India. India may be able to "rise from her ashes," America may not. For, according to Wayne Davis, the United States

will be a desolate tangle of concrete and ticky-tacky, of strip-mined moonscape and silt-choked reservoirs. The land and water will be so contaminated with pesticides, herbicides, mercury fungicides, lead, boron, nickel, arsenic and hundreds of other toxic substances, which have been approaching critical levels of concentration in our environment . . . that it may be unable to sustain human life (8).

Factors Underlying Reduced Mortality

We regard today's medical technology as a wonder, a boon for man. However, this advanced medical technology is largely responsible for the present surge in human numbers. Before the advent of modern medicine human mortality rates were much higher. Aristotle once noted three centuries before Christ that "most babies die before the week is out." Man was at one time extremely vulnerable to the lethal attacks of infectious parasites, such as viruses, bacteria, and protozoa. Medieval lands were scourged with the horror of plague. It killed over 25 million people in Asia and Europe. Smallpox spread like wildfire and killed one out of every four afflicted until Jenner developed his vaccine at the close of the eighteenth century (1). A child born in 1550 had a life expectancy of only *eight and one-half years*. In 1900 the prime killer was tuberculosis, with pneumonia running a close second. As late as 1919 the influenza virus took a toll of 25 million people. The mortality picture has drastically changed. Largely because of modern medicine the mortality rate in the United States has been cut from 25 per thousand per year in 1900 to 9.4 in 1967. The world death rate of 25 per thousand in 1935 is expected to fall to 12.7 by 1980. Today, the primary fatal diseases are heart disease and cancer, in that order; both are primarily associated with the aging process.

Early in the twentieth century the mosquito-borne disease of malaria was either directly or indirectly responsible for 50 per cent of all human mortality. Today,

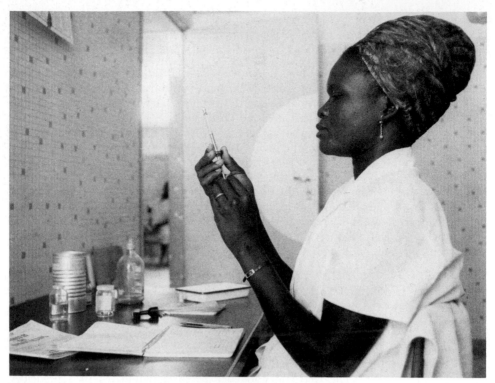

Figure 19-5. A young hospital technician prepares a hypodermic injection at an African tuberculosis center. In the process of saving lives, medical advances in the less developed countries, ironically, have contributed to the population problems in these areas. (PAN/FAO photo)

Figure 19-6. Note that in 1972 the undeveloped nations (UDC's) of Asia, Africa, and Latin America were responsible for 83.9 per cent of the world's births. (Based on United Nations data.)

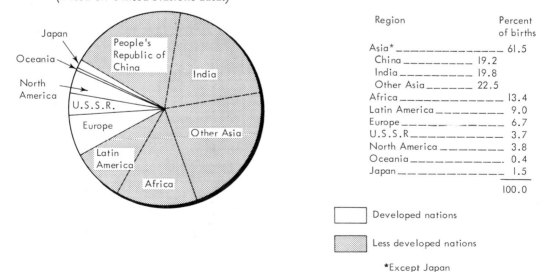

Region	Percent of births
Asia* _____	61.5
China _____	19.2
India _____	19.8
Other Asia _____	22.5
Africa _____	13.4
Latin America _____	9.0
Europe _____	6.7
U.S.S.R _____	3.7
North America _____	3.8
Oceania _____	0.4
Japan _____	1.5
	100.0

☐ Developed nations

▨ Less developed nations

*Except Japan

thanks to modern insecticides such as DDT and to superior drugs for killing the red-blood-cell-invading *Plasmodium* parasite, the malarial threat has greatly diminished. Consider Ceylon. Because of the intensive malarial control campaign launched there in 1946 the Ceylonese mortality rate was reduced from 22 to 13 per thousand within about six years. The elimination of malaria in many areas of Latin America caused the population growth rate to zoom to 4 per cent per year. Advances in medical and paramedical technology, then, have largely contributed to man's "golden" opportunity for growing old. Man is unique in his characteristic type of mortality today. He dies because of *senescence*. This is of course not the case in nature. There are few senile foxes or quail, very few aged deer or brook trout. Wild animals almost never live out their theoretical life span. Wild animal mortality invariably results from the pressures of environmental resistance.

In a nutshell, the reason for the present unprecedented increase in population growth is the introduction of death control without birth control. In the emerging nations it is now possible to cut the death rate in half within a period of five to ten years but with no reduction or even an increase in the birth rate. The result of these changes is that the advanced countries constituting one-third of the world's population are growing at a modest rate, where as the less developed and heavily populated areas of the world are showing fantastic population increments (15).

Multiple Effects of Overpopulation

In a brilliant article, "Prevalence of People," Roy Greep, of the Harvard Medical School, has aptly described the multiple sociological, economic, political, biological, and environmental consequences of the rapid population build-up. He writes:

1. *Marginal subsistence.* The world is replete with examples of overcrowded peoples suffering from chronic malnutrition and high infant mortality. Under such circumstances there can be no planning for the future, no human aspiration, only concern for day-to-day existence and degradation of the human spirit.

Figure 19-7. *Note that even though the global birth rate has gradually been declining since about 1951, the death rate has declined even more rapidly. As a result, therefore, the global population rate continued to rise from about 1951 to 1964. Note that in 1971 the global population growth rate was about 1.9., a rate that, if long sustained, would certainly result in the calamities of war, pestilence, and famine as predicted by Malthus. (Based in part on United Nations data.)*

2. *Failure of economic growth and development in the emerging nations.*
3. *Illiteracy.*
4. *Erosion of human rights and individual freedom.* Beyond a certain point in density the public interest becomes paramount. Mounting crime rates and group violence make greater regimentation necessary.
5. *Social unrest and political tension.* People enduring privation and with little to lose are easily stirred to action against neighbors or brothers by the prospect of bettering their lot.
6. *Threat to world peace.* Bertrand Russell concedes that "nothing is more likely to lead to an H-bomb war than the threat of universal destitution through overpopulation."
7. *Destruction or depletion of natural resources and pollution of the environment.*
8. *Impairment of the quality of life and living.* "Beyond a critical point in density man clearly suffers irritations, frustrations, and a serious decline in human dignity. We are even experiencing an alarming increase in the use of drugs: tranquilizers, pep pills, and the more dangerous varieties. More people are suffering from emotional anxieties and our mental institutions are overflowing. Crowding unquestionably nurtures man's baser instincts and predisposes him not only to violence and criminal behavior but to a callous inhumaneness. The shocking example of pedestrian indifference to murder on the streets of New York is a case in point. In India, starving beggars lie on the streets near death, but the throngs pass by or step over them with total lack of concern. Life cheapens in its own abundance" (15).

Malthusian Principle and Food Scarcity

Of all the adverse consequences of the current crush of people listed by Greep, undoubtedly the one with the greatest potential for human disaster is widespread hunger and malnutrition. This problem was predicted in 1798 by the British economist Robert Malthus. According to his thesis, because the human *population* tends to increase in *geometrical* progression (1, 2, 4, 8, 16) and *food supplies* increase at only an *arithmetical* rate (1, 2, 3, 4, 5) there would inevitably be more people to feed than food to feed them. Malthus argued that the only way this dilemma could ultimately be resolved was by pestilence, warfare, starvation, or other human calamities, which we would now sum up as "environmental resistance."

Two thirds of the world's population is suffering from either undernutrition, chronic malnutrition, or both. *Undernutrition* is a *quantitative* phenomenon characterized by an inadequate amount of food, resulting in half-empty stomachs and gnawing hunger pains. Nutritionists assume that the average person must have a minimum of 2,200 calories daily. Western Europeans and North Americans get 3,200 calories daily. They are among the fortunate. Certainly I have never gone to bed hungry. Have you? Most Americans are overfed. Compare our state to that of the average Indian who consume only 1,600 calories daily, only half of what we're getting. This 600 daily calorie deficit undermines strength, causes severe mental and physical lethargy, and weakens resistence to a broad spectrum of diseases. *Chronic malnutrition,* on the other hand, is a *qualitative* phenomenon, characterized by inferior food quality, notably a deficient supply of proteins and vitamins. Therefore, an African or Asiatic may suffer from chronic malnutrition despite a stomach bulging with high-calorie food. To write glibly about protein-hunger is one thing, but to actually witness it first hand is a distressing, shocking experience. T. A. Nash, a

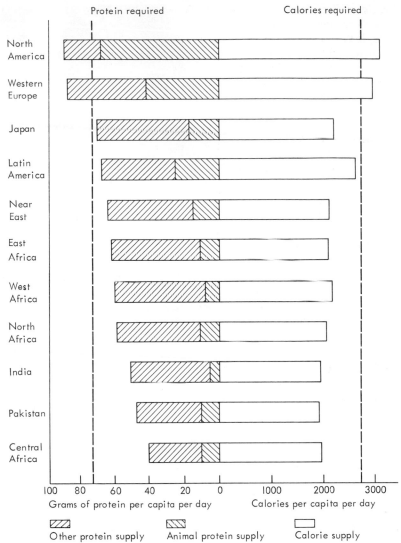

Figure 19-8. *Protein and caloric intake for major regions of the world. Daily protein and calorie requirements are not being supplied to most areas of the world. Inequalities of distribution exist not only among regions as shown here, but also within regions. According to the U. S. Food and Agriculture Organization, areas of greatest shortage include India, Pakistan, and central Africa.*

scientist who lived many years among the natives of West Africa, describes one of his experiences as follows:

Real "meat hunger" is something which should be seen to be believed. In Tanzania, I shot a large zebra near dusk and left two or three men to guard the carcass overnight. On returning next morning with porters, I was amazed to see how little meat was left; the men had eaten and vomited, eaten and vomited, throughout the night.

Figure 19-9. *Death from starvation. Parvati Pura, India. This village suffered from a local famine due to an extended drought. The two-year-old boy is almost dead from starvation (marasmus). (FAO photo by P. Pittet.)*

Millions of children (under six years of age) in the underdeveloped countries are suffering from the protein-deficiency disease known as *kwashiorkor*. Symptoms of this disease include malfunction of the digestive system, skin ulcers, swellings, wasting of the limbs, weakness, lethargy, and increasing susceptibility to infectious diseases (23). Most serious of all, however, in young children *kwashiorkor* tends to impede normal mental development, which cannot be rectified despite the assumption of a proper diet several years later. It is apparent that these countries—already poorly endowed in many natural resources—are also experiencing a lamentable erosion of their *human resource* as well.

Indian women have been known to abandon their infants along the roadside because they no longer have enough milk in their breasts to nourish them. Some years ago an American diplomat visiting in Siberia noticed that the bark of many riverside willows along the Volga appeared to have been stripped away as if by some giant rodent. When he questioned his Russian associates as to what animal was responsible, they replied "the human animal." The natives used willow bark as a basic ingredient in a soup that they regularly prepared. During the severe famine of 1974 many Africans and Indians stuffed their stomachs with grass, tree leaves, and even mud in a futile attempt to survive. As you read this very sentence another human being will die from starvation. Today, 25,000 people will die from hunger throughout the world; tomorrow, 25,000 more!

Solving the Food Shortage Problem

There are three basic methods for solving the food shortage problem—by increasing man's environmental resistance, by increasing his production of food, and, most important, by restricting his ability to reproduce.

Increasing Man's Environmental Resistance. As we have already learned, the population level of any species is dependent upon the interaction of two antagonistic forces, the positive force of the organism's biotic potential (BP) and the negative force of its environmental resistance (ER). Therefore, any sufficiently large increase in the ER would result in a population decrease and might conceivably bring the species within dynamic balance of its food supplies. Cannibalism, infanticide, and warfare are all examples of environmental resistance used by man against himself, with the result of reduced population.

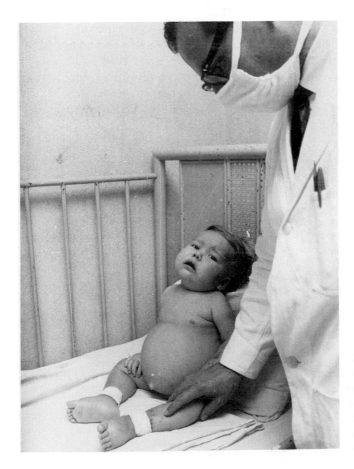

Figure 19-10. A Guatemalan child suffering from kwashiorkor (malnutrition). Note the extreme lethargy and protruding abdomen. (FAO photo)

Decreasing Man's Biotic Potential. It may be surprising to learn that man has been practicing various methods of birth control since long before Christ. Greep reports:

> Egyptian papyri dating to 5000 B.C. advocate contraception. Innumerable methods have been tried by ancient peoples, including vaginal barriers made of all manner of natural products such as wool or other fibers in combination with honey, vinegar, oils, alligator dung, etc. Animal membranes, especially bladders, have been used as condoms by males and females for centuries. Vile potions concocted from weeds, barks, and animal parts and often fortified with harmful ingredients were swallowed in the belief that they would prevent conception (15).

We shall discuss various methods of birth control such as sterilization, use of chemical and mechanical contraceptives, use of the rhythm method, delayed marriage, exercise of moral restraints, and legalization of abortion.

STERILIZATION. Either the man or the woman may be rendered incapable of procreation by the process of sterilization. However, neither the sexual drive nor the gratification from intercourse is diminished. In the male, sterilization simply involves cutting the muscular sperm ducts, which transfer the sperm from the testes to the penis during intercourse. This is a simple operation. (A man might walk into a doctor's office at 1:00 P.M. and walk out at 1:30 P.M. completely sterilized.) Sterilization of the female involves opening the abdominal cavity and cutting the oviducts, or egg tubes, which convey the mature eggs from the ovary to the uterus.

There exists today a small but dedicated group of people, known as *eugenicists*, who would like to "improve" the quality of the human species by the simple technique of making sterilization mandatory for "inferior" individuals (cripples, the mentally slow, criminals, the lazy, and so on). The eugenicists believe that by this simple technique the "quality" of human beings would increase in a few generations. This theory seems sound on the surface, and it would aid in restricting the human

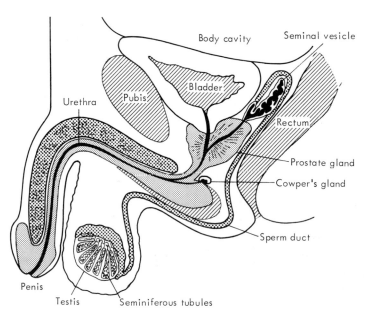

Figure 19-11. *Male reproductive system. (From: Paul R. Ehrlich and Anne H. Ehrlich,* Population, Resources, Environment, *San Francisco: Freeman, 1970).*

BP. However, geneticists inform us that such a program of compulsory sterilization would have to operate for many centuries before any substantial "improvement" in the human species could be discerned. There are obviously powerful ethical, moral, and religious arguments against the establishment of such a program.

To be a successful birth control method, sterilization would require an intensive and extensive education campaign to allay the fears of both sexes concerning reduced abilities during intercourse. Among underdeveloped countries only the governments of Taiwan, Korea, Pakistan, and India have initiated official sterilization programs. It is the only method to date that has been effective in India. The State of Madras launched a voluntary sterilization program in 1957, which included incentives for participants, such as a free operation, the equivalent of a $7.50 cash bonus, and a three-to-six-day holiday for government employees (21). Other Indian states quickly followed suit. Despite the considerable handicap imposed by the doctor shortage, the New Delhi government has achieved about 5 million male sterilizations annually.

CHEMICAL CONTRACEPTIVES. Considerable progress has been made by the technologically advanced nations of the West in the use of the chemical contraceptive. The chemical contraceptive most widely employed is taken in pill form and contains both of the steroid hormones, *estrogen* and *progestin*. Progestin is similar to the hormone *progesterone* secreted by the ovary's corpus luteum. Since the estrogen component exerts a negative feedback on the pituitary gland, the latter is prevented from secreting the follicle-stimulating hormone (FSH) necessary for the maturation of the ovum (6). No eggs, no conception! There are certain drawbacks, however, to the use of chemical contraceptives. It has some undesirable side effects. For example, the estrogen component has caused bleeding, nausea, weight loss, and irritability, all symptoms associated with pregnancy. More seriously, three out of every 100,000 users of the pill have died as a result of these side effects (23). The long-term effect on the emotional life of the woman is still unknown. In addition, it

Figure 19-12.
Female reproductive system. (From: Paul R. Ehrlich and Anne H. Ehrlich, Population, Resources, Environment, *San Francisco: Freeman, 1970).*

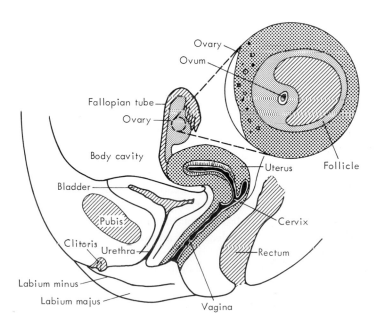

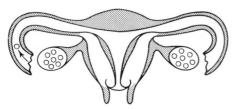

(1) Egg released from ovary into Fallopian tube

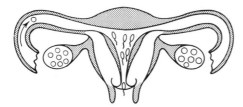

(2) Sperm enter uterus and move toward tube

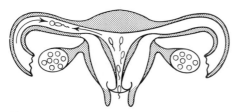

(3) Sperm fertilizes egg in tube

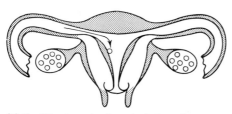

(4) Fertilized egg implants in lining of uterus

Figure 19-13. *Fertilization of the egg and implantation of the embryo in the uterus.*

demands a high degree of self-discipline, because a woman must remember to take twenty pills monthly at the right time. Then, too, because the pills are expensive, they do not lend themselves to use among the impoverished nations, where the need for them is most acute. A second type of chemical contraceptive is being marketed that contains only progestin. Although this hormone does not prevent ovulation, it apparently prevents conception because of its destructive effect on sperm. The chemical is incorporated in a plastic ring that is inserted into the vagina. It works on the time-release principle, small amounts of the hormone gradually being released into the blood stream. The ring must be replaced after each menstruation (23). Currently, intensive research is being conducted to develop a pill that need be taken only once each month, and a retroactive, "morning after" pill may even be in the offing (21).

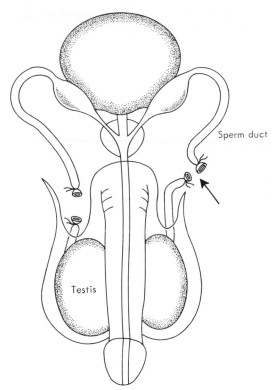

Figure 19-14. *Vasectomy. Sperm ducts are cut and tied.*

Figure 19-15. *Different types of IUD's.*

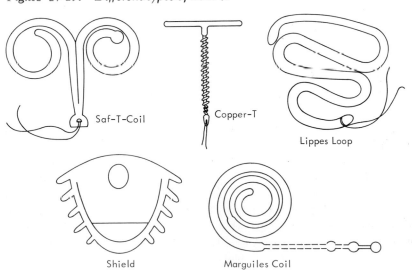

Saf–T–Coil

Copper–T

Lippes Loop

Shield

Marguiles Coil

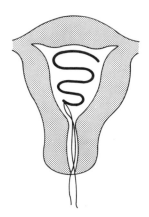

Figure 19-16. *An IUD in place within the uterus. Threads attached to IUD permit easy removal.*

MECHANICAL CONTRACEPTIVES. Some population experts hope that the intra-uterine device (IUD) will prove effective in the underdeveloped countries. Factories are even being built to produce them cheaply in these nations on a mass basis. The IUD is a plastic or nylon coil that is inserted in the womb to prevent implantation of the embryo. Although the IUD's mode of action is unknown, it has been suggested that it may inhibit the muscular contractions which normally propel the egg through the egg tube to the uterus. (Some progressive women have even worn the coiled IUD's as earrings in order to emphasize their position on birth control.)

RHYTHM METHOD. The rhythm method of birth control alone has the full sanction of the Catholic church. (Pope Paul VI has denounced birth control as an attempt by the wealthy to prevent hunger by "forbidding the poor to be born.") Rhythm, of course, is practiced extensively by non-Catholics as well. It is based upon the fact that the viability of egg and sperm extends for only two days after they have entered the oviduct and vagina, respectively. After this period the gametes perish and are incapable of reproducing. The average human female has a 28-day menstrual cycle and ovulates on the fourteenth day. If she abstains from intercourse, therefore, from days 11 through 17, she probably would not be able to conceive. Although this method is not completely reliable from the individual's standpoint, for the population as a whole it may serve to reduce birth rates appreciably. It has been advocated, in conjunction with other methods, for developing nations.

DELAYED MARRIAGE. In Ireland a considerable proportion of engaged couples delay marriage for several years. For example, the average age for Irish brides and bridegrooms is twenty-six and thirty-two, respectively. This is in marked contrast to the average ages of nineteen and twenty-one for their American counterparts. Ireland is not endowed with rich mineral wealth, an abundance of fertile soil, a long growing season, or many other natural prerequisites for a prosperous economy. Thus, because they cannot afford it, many Irish couples postpone marriage. This effectively restricts the ultimate size of their families.

MORAL RESTRAINTS. Currently, according to Donald Bogue, of the University of Chicago, there appears to be a trend toward smaller families, not only in America, but in Europe, Canada, Great Britain, Australia, and New Zealand as well. Where it was once considered most desirable to have three children, it is now becoming

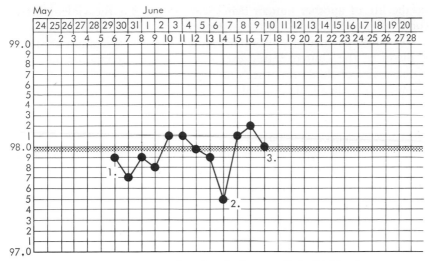

Figure 19-17. *Temperature chart for rhythm method: (1) Temperature readings begin when the "period" terminates; (2) Dip indicates onset of ovulation; (3) "Safe" period begins following three successive days in which the temperature is .6 degrees above the temperature at time of ovulation (2).*

stylish in the United States and Europe to have a two-child family. This permits a higher standard of living in which the color TV or second car takes the place of the third child (1). Many other families, however, have restricted their size because of a feeling of moral responsibility to a population-beseiged world.

LEGALIZATION OF ABORTION. The expulsion of the fetus from the uterus before full term is known as an *abortion* if it causes fetal death. Some abortions occur naturally, and fortunately so, for almost 40 per cent of these fetuses would otherwise develop into physically and mentally impaired offspring. Some abortions, on the other hand, are caused by human intervention and result in death of a fetus that probably would have developed into a normal, healthy baby. The legalization of artificial abortions may become an effective method of population control. After World War II, Japan, with its expansionist dreams shattered and with only 0.166 acre per capita, was faced with the vexing problem of a zooming population. The government acted quickly and boldly. Abortions were legalized in 1948. By 1955 over 1.2 million abortions were being performed annually. In 1949 Japan had a birth rate of 32 per thousand, whereas by 1967 the birth rate had been reduced to a mere 19.4 per thousand. This desperate bid on the part of the Japanese government to restrict its population surge has been celebratedly successful. It had to be. The alternative was certainly a severely depressed economy and grinding poverty for thousands. Contributing to Japan's remarkable success, however, was a low illiteracy rate of only 1.1 per cent and an extensive and sophisticated medical profession. It is quite doubtful that her success with legalized abortion could be duplicated in any of the developing nations.

There are obviously strong ethical, moral, and religious arguments against the legalization of abortions. What right does a man who happens to be living today have to take the life of another human being who, except for the violent act of abortion, would be alive tomorrow? In the eyes of many eminent in law, medicine, and religion, the willful practice of abortion is murder. This interpretation has made the practice illegal in the United States, except in the case of rape or incest, or where either the health of child or mother would be in severe jeopardy.

However, since 1967, when Colorado led the way, thirteen states have liberalized their abortion laws. (These states include Arkansas, California, Delaware, Georgia, Hawaii, Kansas, Maryland, New Mexico, New York, North Carolina, Oregon, and South Carolina.) New York's law, passed in April, 1970, is the most liberal, permitting abortions for any reason. However, since abortions are relatively expensive (averaging $600 in California), and since psychiatric consultations are often a prerequisite, illegal abortions are still frequent. Thus, in California there were only 14,000 legal abortions in 1969 compared to 80,000 illegal ones. Nevertheless, it would appear that the trend toward more relaxed abortion laws will eventually serve to dampen our nation's population surge.

GOVERNMENT PERMITS. In addition to the birth control techniques listed above, which would be initiated by the individual, there are others that could be initiated by the government. Walter E. Howard, vertebrate ecologist at the University of California (Davis), believes that the population problem is so serious that "we can no longer be prophets and philosophers. We must act. The biomagnification of births must be brought to an abrupt halt. Procreation must come under governmental control if no other way can be found. Perhaps what is needed is a system of permits for the privilege of conceiving" (17). The supply of permits, of course, could be quite restricted. For example, permits might be granted, for a fee, only to childless couples. In the event a couple had a baby without the proper permit, they would be liable to a fine.

Increasing Food Production. We shall now consider some methods by which food production might be increased in a hungry world. They include hydroponics, algae culture, yeast culture, food synthesis, extension of agriculture into new regions, drainage, increased use of fertilizers, pest control, and agricultural breeding programs. As we examine these methods, however, we must not delude ourselves into believing that hunger will eventually be erased from the face of the earth. The best these methods can do is buy time, time to get our runaway global population under control.

HYDROPONICS OR NUTRICULTURE. *Hydroponics* is the technique of growing crops in an aqueous nutrient solution without soil. It has certain advantages to more conventional crop production. Food tonnage per acre may be six to eight times higher. Problems of soil sterility and soil-borne pests are obviated. It is economical of water because it can be continuously recirculated as long as it is replenished with appropriate nutrients. It may temporarily alleviate an acute fresh vegetable shortage. It was employed during World War II to feed our military personnel on the volcanic ash of Ascension Island and the wasteland of Labrador. Hydroponics has provided fresh foods for manganese miners isolated in the Amazonian wilderness. It has many disadvantages, however. There are problems attending the air- and water-borne molds and bacteria. Hydroponics requires a heavy capital investment in tanks, pumps, and other equipment. All nutrients must be supplied, rather expensively, by man, and balanced according to a precise prescription for each type of crop. Although the United States has had at least 100 nutriculture farms in commercial operation, it would appear to be a prohibitively costly operation in less technologically advanced countries.

ALGAL CULTURE. About 0.1 to 0.5 per cent of the solar radiation reaching the earth is converted by crops into chemical energy. Only 1 calorie of human food is derived for every 1 million calories of sunshine received by this planet. It takes roughly 100,000 pounds of algae to produce 1 pound of fish. These facts are explicable in terms of the second law of thermodynamics, as noted earlier. It would seem, therefore, that if man shortened his food chains and consumed algae directly, a much larger food base would be available to nourish a food-deficient world.

Algal culture has been conducted in the United States, England, Germany, Venezuela, Japan, Israel, and the Netherlands. The alga *Chlorella* can be grown in huge tanks; it is rich in proteins, fats, and vitamins and apparently contains all the essential amino acids. Each acre devoted to algal culture can produce up to 40 tons, dry weight, of algae. This is 40 times the protein yield per acre of soybeans and 160 times the per acre yield of beef protein. Algal food may be used as a supplement in soups and meat dishes and as livestock feed. From the foregoing, one might suppose that algal culture would show great promise. Not so, however, according to Georg Borgstrom, food expert at Michigan State University, "Rarely ever has so much been written about so little." In his opinion the final product is not nearly as nutritious as some would claim; moreover, it has poor keeping qualities. Even the astronauts engaged in long-distance spaceship flights will not have the dubious privilege of feeding on algae directly, as was originally planned. Instead, they will consume algae-fed fish and quail, grown and processed aboard the spaceship. According to Borgstrom, in most cases mass algae culture would be prohibitively expensive. The one exception might be in large urban areas where large quantities of sewage would be available as a nutrient source. Even then, the final product would best serve as food for livestock rather than human beings. In any event algal culture would not appear to be a feasible food production method in the underdeveloped countries for decades to come (4).

FOOD SYNTHESIS. The technology is available for the laboratory synthesis of the basic sugars, fats, amino acids, vitamins, and minerals of the human diet. This is an extremely complicated and expensive process, however. The major attempt so far to synthesize human diet calories was conducted by Germans during the edible fat scarcity imposed by World War II. By the Fischer-Tropsch process, beginning with the hydrogenation of coal, the Germans managed to produce 2,000 tons of synthetic fats annually, much of which was then converted into margarine. It is probable that the bulk of our food calories will always be produced by conventional agricultural methods. A few of our amino acids and vitamins, on the other hand, may be synthesized. Synthetic sources today may provide all the vitamins necessary for vigorous health at a modest annual cost of 25¢ to $1 to the consumer. The people of the underdeveloped countries, who rely heavily on cereal foods, frequently incur a dietary deficiency of such important amino acids as lysine, tryptophane, and methionine. Although these can all be synthetically produced, a year's requirement of these three amino acids would cost about $40, and hence would be prohibitively expensive. United States food manufacturers have succeeded in producing substitute meats, high-protein breakfast foods, and beverages simply by fortifying basic cereals with protein. This process requires an astonishingly small amount of protein. For example, the protein content of a ton of wheat can be raised to a level close to that of milk casein with the addition of a few pounds of lysine. Indians by the thousands are now consuming lysine-fortified bread marketed by Indian government bakeries in Bombay and Madras. Looking far into the future, Harrison Brown, of the California Institute of Technology, suggests that some day our food technology might be in a position to synthesize some pretty good steaks from vegetables; he even goes so far as to provide them with plastic sinews to make them chewy (5).

YEAST CULTURE. Much interest has been shown recently in the prospects of yeast culture for alleviating protein-deficient diets. Yeast can be grown on organic substrates such as coal, petroleum, citrus-cannery waste, grain hulls, straw, beet and cane sugar molasses, and the black liquor derived from paper-pulp manufacture. One French researcher suggests that yeasts could synthesize the equivalent of all the animal protein consumed globally today by using only 3 per cent of our petroleum output as a yeast substrate (21). Yeast culture provides a method by which the hitherto inedible crop residues such as corn cobs, stalks, stems, and woody fibers can be converted into protein-rich food. In the United States, for example, where a man consumes 0.37 tons of food annually, but where each year 1.75 tons per capita of inedible corn and wheat residues accumulate, it would be theoretically possible to increase food supplies from 50 to 100 per cent. Moreover, yeasts are 65 per cent efficient in the conversion of carbohydrate to protein; this compares with the 4 to 20 per cent efficiency of livestock. Yeast food has been produced in Africa, Jamaica, Puerto Rico, Australia, Florida, Hawaii, and Wisconsin. A new factory in Taiwan produces 73,000 tons of yeast annually, most of which, ironically, is shipped to the United States. Four thousand tons of yeast are produced annually in Green Bay, Wisconsin, as a by-product of the pulp industry. The yeast may be used as a supplement in rice dishes, casseroles, soups, and stews (20). To date, however, yeast has been cultured on only a limited scale and is expensive to produce. Extensive use of yeast in the underdeveloped countries would require the construction of plants, distribution systems, and, above all, acceptance by the people. Many of the very people in greatest need of protein food supplements are least likely to use them because of their extremely conservative food habits (13).

EXTENSION OF AGRICULTURE INTO NEW AREAS. According to the Woytinskys, in order to be productive, land must embrace the proper combination of soil texture, soil chemistry, temperature, rainfall, growing season, and topography (24). Of the 12.5 acres of the world's land available per capita, only 1.1 are being cultivated. However, according to a United Nations document *Statistics of Hunger*, a minimum of 2.65 additional acres per capita have food production potential. A U.S. Department of Agriculture report states that the world's farmers are now tilling only 30 per cent of the potentially productive land. Note that the key word is *potential*. In the context of the technology, and the social, economic, and political patterns existing in the underdeveloped countries; to believe that the farmers in these countries can actually *realize* this food production potential is somewhat of a delusion. For example, most of the potentially productive land in Asia requires irrigation, an almost prohibitively costly proposition.

Figure 19-18. *Fish, fish meal, and flour, stages in the production of fish protein concentrate. (Bureau of Commercial Fisheries, U. S. Department of the Interior)*

Figure 19-19. *Farm consolidation makes practical the use of heavy, expensive equipment such as this modern grain combine moving through a Washington wheat field. Use of such equipment will aid in boosting world food production. (U. S. Department of Agriculture)*

Tropical Rain Forests. Much publicity has centered around the possible establishment of agriculture in the tropical rain forest regions of South America, Africa, and Asia. Would such schemes have much chance for success? These areas are indeed blessed with an abundance of rainfall, intense sunlight, and a long growing season. These regions have supported dense forest cover for many centuries; they should be able to produce crops. Unfortunately, there are unexpected problems: one deals with the pattern of nutrient cycling, and the other relates to the nature of the soil.

If you were standing in a beech-maple woods during a Michigan summer, the forest floor would be covered with a thick, spongy layer of decomposing leaves, several inches in thickness. Nutrients from those leaves are gradually released to the soil, making the latter a nutrient reservoir. It was this type of soil that was tilled by the colonists of early America and yielded reasonably good harvests. In Amazonia, and many other rain forest tropics, however, the majority of nutrients are "locked up" in the tissues of forest vegetation, a minimum being retained by the soil. When leaves and branches fall to the forest floor, the organic matter is rapidly decomposed by the abundant bacteria fungi, insects, and earthworms. The nutrients then are immediately absorbed by root systems to be incorporated into new plant tissue. If the Brazilian settlers would bulldoze or chop down the forest, release of nutrients would be so rapid that the planted crop plants would not be able to absorb them quickly enough to prevent massive nutrient loss caused by the leaching action of torrential rain storms during the wet season. Moreover, after several seasons of cropping, the reddish, iron-rich *laterite soil* would bake "brick-hard" in the "kiln" of the hot equatorial sun. Such bricks were used by the ancient Khmer civilization of Cambodia to construct the magnificent temples at Angkor Wat; they still stand many centuries later. Modern buildings in Thailand are being built today in part from lateritic bricks. (Such hardness and durability may be good for buildings but certainly does not facilitate penetration by crop roots.) In fact, some historians implicate laterization in the decay not only of the Khmer civilization, but also that of the Mayas in Mexico.

Mary McNeil, a field geologist who has made an intensive study of laterization in South America and Africa, describes the ill-starred attempt of the Brazilian government to establish an agricultural colony at Iata in the heart of the Amazon basin:

> Earthmoving machinery wrenched a clearing from the forest and crops were planted. From the beginning there were ominous signs of the presence of laterite. Blocks of ironstone stood out on the surface in some places; in others nodules of the laterite lay just below a thin layer of soil. What had appeared to be a rich soil, with a promising cover of humus, disintegrated after the first or second planting. Under the equatorial sun the iron-rich soil began to bake into brick. In less than five years the cleared fields became virtually pavements of rock. Today Iata is a drab, despairing colony that testifies eloquently to the formidable problem laterite presents throughout the Tropics . . . (18).

It has been suggested that by subjugating the podzols of the wet and cold regions, as well as the laterites of the warm and wet tropics, we could increase cultivated land in North and South America by 50 to 60 per cent and in Asia by 30 per cent. If we brought these newly subjugated areas, as well as the currently cultivated regions, to the productive level of western Europe today, we could adequately feed 4 to 5 billion additional people. But this increase in food production would be predicated on a corresponding increase in the development of research, education, fertilizer plants, crop and livestock breeding programs, credit institutions, marketing services, transportation facilities, storage accommodations, and farm extension programs of global scope. Moreover, it would require two to three decades to complete at an estimated overall cost of $500 billion.

Tundra. Crop production in the tundra is severely limited by the abbreviated growing season of 75 to 85 days, the continuous summer sunlight (many crops require a period of darkness), and the scant precipitation of less than 10 inches annually. Perhaps geneticists of the future may develop short-season crops with accelerated growth rates that can mature before the onset of the Arctic frost. Russian scientists have discovered that the growing season can be extended a month by scattering coal dust on the snow to accelerate melt. Moreover, crop growing time can be shortened by *vernalization,* the technique of inducing seed germination artificially and then retaining the seedlings temporarily in cold storage.

Arid Regions. There are rosy-visioned optimists who claim that some day agriculture may even be possible in the Sahara Desert. In 1960 an area of fertile land was discovered in the central Sahara that was equal to the total area of Great Britain. Water might be secured from underground aquifers. For example, in 1950 the Albienne Nappe, a nodular sandstone aquifer, was found. One thousand feet thick in some places, this aquifer now supplies water for an oil town of 30,000 people, for the extension of oases, and for the survival of 50,000 trees planted in 1960. In 1961 the wells in the area were yielding 90 million cubic meters of water annually.

However, many irrigation projects are not so encouraging. For example, salinization and waterlogging as a result of irrigation has virtually destroyed the crop producing capability of 5 million acres in West Pakistan alone, an acre dropping out of production every 5 minutes (13). Schemes to make the desert "bloom" will never boost world food production to any significant degree. Most of these schemes are either prohibitively costly (about $400 per acre), of too small a dimension, or simply could not become operational until *after* global famine had become an accomplished fact. Take the colossal North American Water and Power Alliance project. Its potential for alleviating world hunger is described by Ehrlich and Holdren as follows:

> The most ambitious water project yet conceived in this country is the North American Water and Power Alliance, which proposes to distribute water from the great rivers of Canada to thirsty locations all over the United States. Formidable political problems aside, this project would involve the expenditure of $100 billion in construction costs over a 20 year completion period. . . . This monumental undertaking would provide for an increase of only 21 per cent in the water consumption of the United States, during a period in which the population is expected to increase by between 25 and 43 per cent. To assess the possible contribution to the *world* food situation, we assume that all this water would be devoted to agriculture. Then using the rather optimistic figure of 500 gal. per day to grow the food to feed one person, we find that this project could feed 126 million additional people. Since this is less than 8 per cent of the projected world population growth during the construction period (say 1980 to 2000), it should be clear that even the most massive water projects can make but a token contribution to the solution of the world food problem in the long term. And in the crucial short term—the years preceding 1980—*no* additional people will be fed by projects still on the drawing board today (14).

Wetlands. Man has achieved notable success as well as a few infamous failures

Figure 19-20. *Irrigation made possible in Egypt by the Aswan Dam. An area of one million acres formerly dependent on the annual Nile floods for irrigation is now cultivated under a system of perennial irrigation based mainly on lifting water. The new irrigation system makes possible a 40 per cent increase in crop production in Upper Egypt, because at least one additional crop can be grown per year. Photo shows a mechanized irrigation pump at Habu which has replaced the laborious methods of lifting water by hand-operated or animal-driven water wheel. Unfortunately, the increased food production can barely keep up with Egypt's population increase. (FAO photo)*

through drainage schemes. The agriculturally productive fen land of Britain was once a swamp. Flourishing Israeli settlements now occupy the site of the former waterlogged Huleh marshes. Grain is now abundantly produced in Canada's prairie provinces in areas once dominated by muskeg. Arable land may even be reclaimed to a limited extent from shallow seas; in Holland the ingenious Dutch have increased their agricultural area 1 million acres by draining the Zyder Zee! Many additional millions of acres might be reclaimed by lowering the water table. A considerable area could be brought into cultivation in the lowlands of the Sudan simply by redirecting the wasted waters northward to the Nile.

(We must emphasize, however, that marshland habitat, already dwindling throughout the world, is an intrinsically valuable resource in its own right. It provides a unique type of scenic beauty, serves as a natural mechanism for minimizing water level fluctuations, and represents excellent wildlife habitat.)

INCREASED USE OF FERTILIZER. Japan has only 0.166 acre of arable land per capita, only one thirteenth that of the United States. Only with the most intensive agricultural methods is Japan able to feed her 100 million people. She has achieved amazing success, producing 13,200 calories per cultivated acre, almost three times the per acre calorie production of American farmers, and 350 per cent higher than the world average of 3,800 calories per acre per day. One key to Japan's agricultural accomplishments is the large amounts of fertilizer applied to her farms. A great variety of fertilizers are employed, from sardine-soybean-cottonseed cakes to compost, and from green manure to human dung; in addition, the standard commercial preparations are used (20). It has been shown that Japan's success with soil enrichment can be repeated in many underdeveloped countries, even though it be on a smaller scale. By adding double superphosphate to the soil the Institute for Soil Research in Indonesia increased rice production 308 pounds per acre. In northern Nigeria an extra 300 pounds per acre of guinea corn resulted from the per acre use of 50 pounds of superphosphate. Manuring of impoverished farmland in Southern Rhodesia has boosted maize production over 200 per cent (20). FAO-sponsored fertilizer trials in Turkey raised wheat production 52 per cent. Fertilizer increased Guatemalan cabbage production 140 per cent, with each fertilizer dollar resulting in a $63.90 increase in harvest value. Even without modifying any farm method 9,500 fertilizer field trials conducted by the FAO in fourteen countries have shown an overall average yield increase of 74 per cent (21).

The preceding data show what can be done in the developing nations on an *experimental* basis. The sobering truth is that fertilizer application in these countries must be greatly increased to ensure the necessary food increments. Even though hungry nations have 55 per cent of the world's arable land and 70 per cent of the world's population, as recently as 1962 they were utilizing only 10 per cent of the world's fertilizer production (21). Age-old superstitions and social practices may hinder acceptance of fertilizers. For example, in East Africa, the Bantu of North Kavirondo are reluctant to employ cattle dung for manuring because they associate its use with evil magic. The size of the dung heap in the cattle-kraal is also a status symbol and indicates the owner's wealth in numbers of cattle. Partly because of these factors, the entire African continent uses no more fertilizer than Italy. Incredibly, all of South America, where the population is doubling every 35 years, uses about as much fertilizer as Holland. Moreover, most of this fertilizer is used to grow cash crops such as coffee, cocoa, and bananas, which, ironically, are largely shipped to the well-fed Western nations (4). Although India has twenty-five times the cultivated area of Japan, until very recently she used only 1 per cent as much fertilizer (21). One reason for this disparity is the almost prohibitive cost. Because most fertilizer must be imported from abroad, Indian rice farmers pay three to four times as much as the Japanese in terms of the price they get for their crops.

The problem may not finally be solved until the governments of the developing nations launch an aggressive program of fertilizer plant construction. This will require technical assistance, considerable amounts of raw materials, and capital (5). It will require a great deal of energy for nitrogen fixation and the processing of

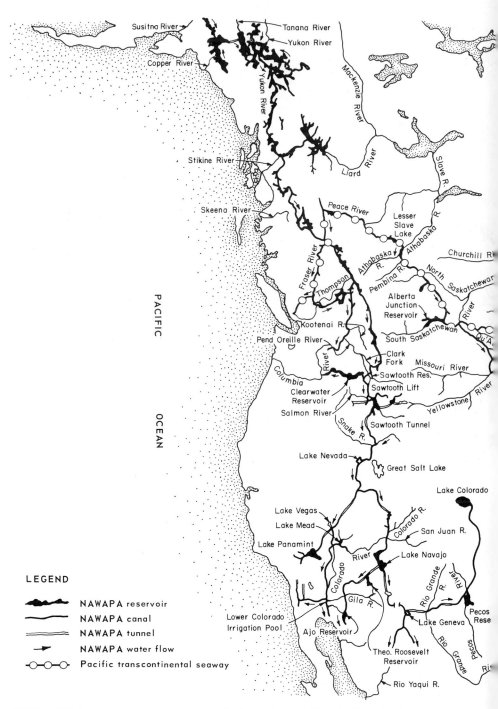

Figure 19-21. *Water sources, reservoirs, canals, tunnels, and flow pattern in the North American Water and Power Alliance Plan. (Adapted from Guy-Harold Smith,* Conservation of Natural Resources *(New York: John Wiley & Sons, Inc., 1965).)*

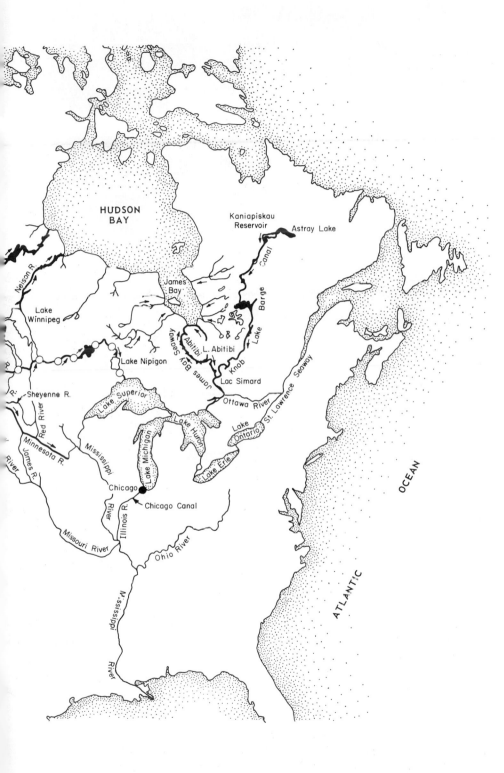

HUDSON
BAY

Kaniapiskau
Reservoir

Astray Lake

Nelson R.

James
Bay

Lake
Winnipeg

Lake Barge Canal

Lake Nipigon

Abitibi

L. Abitibi

James Bay Seaway

Sheyenne R.

Knob

R.

Lac Simard

Red River

Lake Superior

Ottawa River

St. Lawrence Seaway

Minnesota R.

Mississippi

Lake Huron

Lake Ontario

James River

Lake Michigan

Lake Erie

OCEAN

Chicago

Chicago Canal

Illinois R.

River

Missouri River

Ohio River

Mississippi

ATLANTIC

River

Figure 19-22. *Shifting type of cultivation in Central Sumatra. Agricultural land is opened up by cutting and burning the forests. The cleared area will then be intensively cropped for a few years until the fertility has been exhausted, at which time it will be abandoned and left exposed to erosion by wind and water. (FAO photo)*

phosphates. In addition, it will be necessary to construct an extensive transportation system to get the fertilizer to the farmer. It is a tremendous job and one that has to be done soon. The prospects are not bright. As Borgstrom states, "The needs are, in the overpopulated parts of the world, so enormous that it is highly unlikely the fertilizer industry will ever catch up with them. . . . India alone would have to invest something in the order of twenty billion dollars in fertilizer factories to achieve parity and balance. On top of that, two additional gigantic factories would be needed each year" merely to feed an annual addition of 15 million stomachs. The rapidly increasing cost of oil compounds the problem because oil is required in the manufacture of nitrate fertilizer. Thus, India's bill for oil in 1974 was $2 billion, twice what she paid in 1973, and equal to what she earns from all her exports.

CONTROL OF AGRICULTURAL PESTS. On a global scale insects alone cause $21 billion of agricultural damage yearly (4). Rats, insects, and fungi annually destroy 33 million tons throughout the world, sufficient to feed all the people in the United States. One of every fourteen people in the world will starve because of food deprivation imposed by agricultural pests (6). A fungus disease, which caused 90 per cent rice crop destruction in some areas, contributed significantly to the appalling Indian famine of 1943. The rat is one of man's greatest competitors, each one being capable of consuming 40 pounds of potential human food yearly. The 120 million rats in the United States alone inflict $1 billion damage yearly (4). The crop volume destroyed annually by rats in India would fill a 3,000-mile-long train. And yet, India spends 800 times as much money on fertilizer as she does on rat control (5). In India, where rats may outnumber people ten to one, up to 30 per cent of the crops are ravaged by rodents. Rats destroyed 35 to 40 per cent of Vietnamese farm produce in 1962. Insects are equally destructive. Food destruction by insects in India alone would feed Michigan's entire population of 9 million people. The U.S. Department of Agriculture estimates that insects inflict up to $5 billion damage in the United States yearly and that 155 million additional acres would have to be cropped in order to compensate for the loss (4). Even in the United States as recently as 1943 the European corn borer (*Pyrausta nubilalis*) chewed its way into 120,648 million bushels of corn. Recently the golden nematode (*Heterodera rostochiensis*) devastated so much of Europe's prime potato country that this basic food crop has been restricted to a four-year rotation. The microscopic malarial parasite *Plasmodium* has been a scourge to the farmers of Southeast Asia. It incapacitates millions of rice farmers at the critical periods of transplanting and harvesting. In an attempt to escape the malarial season in northern Thailand farmers are prevented from raising a second rice crop, one that could be used to great advantage in alleviating hunger elsewhere.

The effective control of agricultural pests in the developing nations would markedly boost food output. The United States and western Europe have developed sophisticated techniques of pest control. Their control experts now wage war against agricultural pests with a veritable arsenal of weapons, including chemo-sterilants, gamma radiation, sound waves, sex attractants, resistant mutants, natural predators, and microbial agents in addition to the more conventional pesticides. The USDA's Agency for International Development is currently disseminating some of this know-how to the rural regions of South America, Africa, and Asia.

In equatorial Africa, twenty-three varieties of tsetse fly, vector of the trypanosome that causes the dread sleeping sickness in man and an equally serious disease in livestock, have effectively prevented livestock production *in an area larger than the entire United States*. The AID and the Agricultural Research Council of Central Africa have sponsored a research team of USDA, British, and African scientists that has attempted to eradicate the tsetse fly with the use of chemosterilants. The objective has been to sterilize great numbers of male flies and release them to mate with normal wild females, thus rendering the latter incapable of producing young, a technique first employed with dramatic success against the screw worm fly in the southeastern United States.

LOCUSTS. By the very extension of his cultivation programs, man has unwittingly improved breeding conditions for locusts. Their migratory hordes have decimated man's grain fields since the time of Moses and are continuing this devastation to the present, as 109 major infestations in India in a single year would testify (4). Examples of locust "nurseries" provided by man are the alfalfa fields of Libya and the crop "islands" in Saudi Arabia, Yemen, and the plains of the Red Sea. Because of their great mobility, adult locusts may destroy crops over a thousand miles and several nations away from their hatching sites. International cooperation, therefore, is frequently required to control an extensive outbreak. Piecemeal attempts are doomed to fail. Farmers of hungry nations are at a disadvantage because of their lack of pesticides and ignorance concerning their use. Aid may come from half a world away. For example, the USDA sends scientists and technologists to critical areas to collaborate with the Desert Locust Control Organization for East Africa. In the spring of 1951 locusts threatened Persia with the worst plague in eight decades. They were breeding primarily in a remote, inaccessible 2,000-square-mile area. Prompt action by the United States, which rushed spray planes and insecticides to the region, quickly brought the outbreak under control. Of course, the use of insecticides must be employed only when absolutely necessary to prevent massive food destruction, lest the widespread ecosystem contamination experienced by the industrialized nations be repeated in the developing countries.

Figure 19-23. *Fighting a locust outbreak in East Africa. In July 1968, more than 40 countries in East Africa were threatened with the most serious locust plague since 1959, a record plague year. International efforts to control the locust swarms were coordinated by the Food and Agriculture Organization of the United Nations. Photo shows field worker dusting crops with benzene hexachloride. (FAO photo by G. Tortoli)*

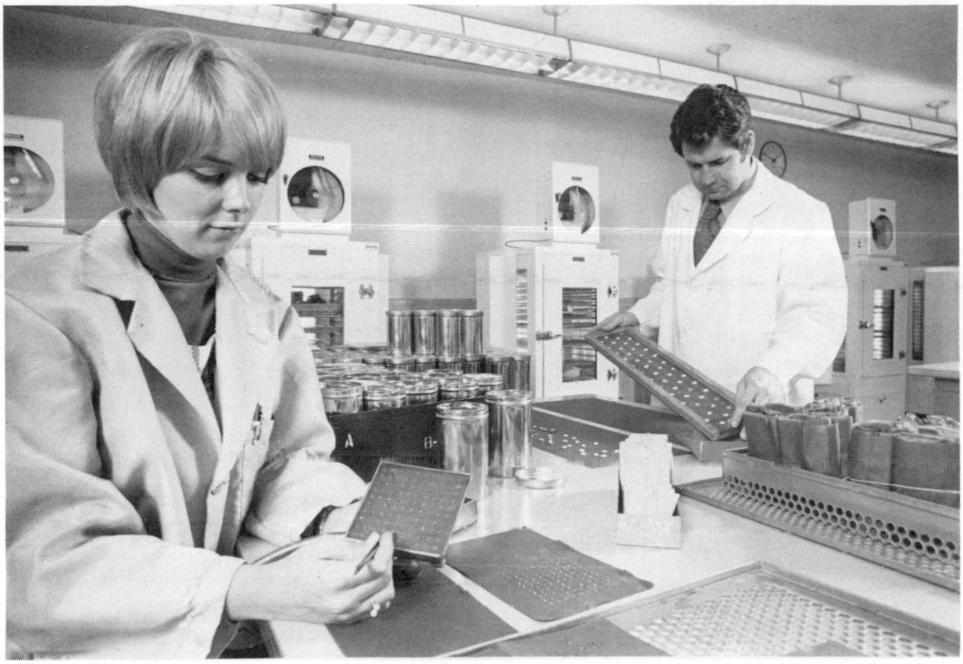

Figure 19-24. *A seed bank to fight global starvation. Scientists at the National Seed Storage Laboratory in Ft. Collins, Colorado, preserve germ plasm to aid the world's plant breeders in improving old crops. This facility also tries to save from extinction seeds of wild and primitive plants that are endowed with irreplaceable traits such as disease resistance or high protein content. Here technicians are planting seeds on special paper for germination tests. The laboratory stores over 80,000 different kinds of seeds—a living reserve of germ plasm for tomorrow. (U.S. Department of Agriculture photo by Murray Lemmon)*

PLANT BREEDING PROGRAMS. Since the dawn of the human species more than 2 million years ago, man has succeeded in domesticating only about 80 species of food plants. The "big three" among food plants are wheat, rice, and corn, over 50 per cent of the world's croplands being devoted to them. It is only natural, therefore, that plant geneticists have channeled much of their research into developing superior strains of the "big three." Within the last decade great strides made hold considerable promise for partially closing the gap between food supply and demand in the underdeveloped countries. Plant geneticists have been able to develop sugar beets with a higher sugar content, soybeans with greater protein. They have developed insect- and disease-resistant grains. They have developed high yield grains with up to 13 per cent protein content (14). They have produced wheat that will develop in shorter growing seasons and that are hence adaptable to more northern latitudes. They have developed crops with a larger proportion of edible parts or with a greater ability to use fertilizer. At the University of Washington, plant geneticists have developed a wheat variety that yield 152 bushels per acre on one experimental plot, fully 750 per cent more than the 20-bushels-per-acre yield considered good some years ago. Varieties of corn have been developed that will utilize 200 pounds of nitrogen per acre compared to the 90 pounds utilized per acre only a few years ago. Crops have been developed that are resistant to heat, cold, and drought. A variety of grain has been secured that will tolerate the continuous sunlight of the brief Arctic summer.

The introduction of improved strains of sweet potatoes into China by the Food and Agricultural Organization of the United Nations increased food output 37 per cent. In 1933 the corn yield per acre in the United States, when only 0.1 per cent of the crop was in hybrids, was 22.6 bushels: by 1963, when 95 per cent of the crop was in hybrids, the per acre yield had tripled to 67.6 bushels (19). A five-year testing program for hybrid corn sponsored by the FAO in twenty-one European countries showed that the superior North American hybrids yielded 60 per cent more than the best local open-pollinated varieties (21). In a single year the European planting of hybrid corn resulted in a yield increase of 640,000 tons. An American-African research team crossed an African strain of maize with one from Central America; the resultant hybrid gave 100 per cent greater yields than local African types (22). Although only 3,000 acres were planted in 1963, the year of its introduction, by 1966 farmers were so pleased they increased plantings to 100,000 acres.

Recently scientists at Purdue University, as a result of the mutant opaque-2 gene, have developed a strain of corn bearing large quantities of lysine and

Figure 19-25.
Introduction of new plant strains increases wool and mutton production in the Punitaqui Valley of Chile. Scientist (right) and local farmer (left) inspect the hardy, tall-growing atriplex plant in the region of El Espinal. Atriplex can thrive in an arid climate and has so successfully increased sheep forage that many other villages will soon be using it. (FAO photo)

Figure 19-26. *Women planting rice in paddies of the Solo River Basin, Java. (FAO photo by H. Null)*

tryptophane (22). Because these amino acids are essential for normal human growth, nutrition experts agree that this mutant corn may represent a practical approach to solving the severe protein deficiencies in the diets of Africa, South America, and Asia, where meat, fish, eggs, and poultry are prohibitively costly or short in supply.

It is of interest that although 40 per cent of the global corn production comes from the eastern United States, very little is used directly as human food. It is fed to pigs and cattle instead, which in turn are ultimately consumed as pork chops and beef steaks by overfed Americans. As noted in our discussion of energy pyramids, much plant food energy is squandered when man channels it through livestock instead of consuming it directly. In a world where two of three stomachs are only partly filled or empty, it would seem almost immoral for Americans to continue to live "high on the hog" (and the food chain).

The International Maize and Wheat Improvement Center, sponsored by the Rockefeller and Ford foundations, was established in Mexico in 1943 at a time when that country was experiencing a critical food scarcity. After twenty-five years of intensive research a huge "bank" of seed varieties has been established. When aid is sought by a developing nation this bank can provide a seed variety that will be adapted to that nation's particular combination of soil chemistry, soil structure, climate, rainfall, and growing season. The center has developed strains of rust-resistant beans that have increased yield from 150,000 to 600,000 tons annually. It has produced blight-resistant potatoes that have shown a 500 per cent yield increase. Partly as a result of the Improvement Center's work, grain production in Mexico has soared from 700 pounds to 4,200 pounds per acre. In 1962 the International Rice Institute was set up by the Rockefeller and Ford foundations in the Philippine Islands. Because rice is a staple in the diet of 60 per cent of mankind, it was of

Figure 19-27. *Fish ponds and rice fields go together in Southeast Asia. The Indonesian government is making great efforts to produce fish in order to supplement the traditional starchy diet of its people with protein. Here a native fish culturist has set nets in a pond for sorting fish and holding fish fingerlings temporarily. (FAO photo by Jack Ling)*

considerable moment when, in 1966, the institute developed a new rice called IR8. Among its outstanding features was a capacity to respond to high levels of fertilization (whereas other varieties might "burn up") and an insensitivity to day length. As a result, IR8 is adaptable to a wide spectrum of soil and climatic conditions (24). IR8 has already made a dramatic impact on rice production in the underdeveloped countries. It has transformed the Philippine Islands from a rice-import to a rice-export nation and has enhanced the economy of southeastern Asia by $300 million.

LIVESTOCK BREEDING PROGRAM. Of the 24 species of domesticated livestock, only nine (cattle, pigs, sheep, goats, water buffalo, chickens, ducks, geese, and turkeys) provide almost 100 per cent of man's animal protein. America has been foremost in the development of superior livestock strains. In the 1920's the King Ranch of Texas crossed the shorthorn with the Brahman to develop the Santa Gertrudis. In the 1930's the Brangus strain was produced by Oklahoma breeders by crossing the shorthorn with the Black Angus. Both Santa Gertrudis and Brangus are meaty, tick and heat resistant, and both form the basis of livestock production in several tropical countries. The recent development of *artificial insemination* has made possible greatly accelerated improvement of livestock. For example, although in natural

Figure 19-28. A new rice strain for hungry India: IR5 (left), a new high-yielding variety of rice under test at a research station in Aduthurai. The smaller plant to the right is the traditional variety. (FAO photo by D. Mason)

service a New York bull might inseminate only thirty-five cows in the immediate locality, in artificial insemination stud that same animal may be "mated" to 2,000 cows. Because refrigerated bull sperm may retain viability for at least five years, ranches in Brazil, Southern Rhodesia, Vietnam, or India may have contemporaneous access to germ plasm of, say, an Oklahoma Black Angus or a Wisconsin Holstein. In the near future it may even be possible for breeders to predetermine sex of progeny resulting from artificial insemination programs, an obvious advantage to dairy farmers.

Through Western methods of selection and crossbreeding, a rancher can rapidly develop cattle with meatier carcasses or swine with larger litters and faster growing rates. Cows have been produced with milk flow vastly superior to dairy cattle of undeveloped nations. For example, American test breeds of Holsteins produce up to 2,000 pounds of milk annually, compared to the 300-pound annual flow from the yellow cattle of China. Chickens with greater egg-laying capacity and more efficient feed-biomass conversions have been developed by American researchers. With the assistance of the United Nations' FAO, ranchers from underdeveloped countries will gradually acquire the technical assistance required for greatly improving the quality of their livestock.

WILD GAME RANCHES. Several years ago wildlife biologists Pearsall and Dasmann compared the meat (protein) production value of domesticated livestock raised in Africa, with an herbivorous wild game population (antelope, zebras, giraffes, elephants) maintained in a wild state. Their conclusions, as related by Richard Wagner in his book *Environment and Man*, are most illuminating:

1. Wild game were much more efficient in exploiting the available plant food base. While cattle were found to be very selective, consuming only certain grasses of high palatability, other potentially nutritious, though apparently less tasty forage was neglected. Such a differential feeding response could quickly result in over-grazing in some areas and undergrazing in others, effectively limiting the carrying capacity of a given range acre. On the other hand, a mixed-species population of wild game showed a broad spectrum utilization of available plant foods—antelopes feeding on grasses and low-level foliage, giraffes consuming foliage on the higher branches, and the elephants selecting bark and roots (23).

2. Wild game were much better adapted to drought than domesticated livestock.

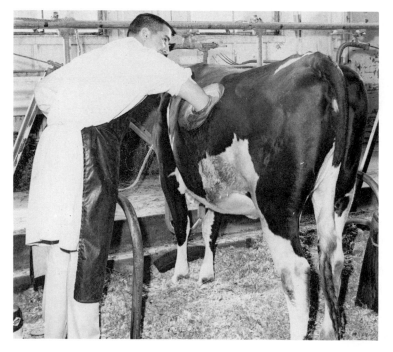

Figure 19-29. *Recent research conducted at the University of Wisconsin has made it clear that wood will play an increasingly important dual role for livestock feeding—both as roughage and as a source of carbohydrate. (U.S. Forest Products Laboratory, Forest Service, U. S. Department of Agriculture)*

Figure 19-30. *Giraffes and zebras in Southern Rhodesia. Such animals could be raised on large game ranches more profitably and efficiently than traditional livestock such as cattle and goats. (FAO photo)*

For example, when a given water hole dries out, wild game will move for miles to another water source to satisfy their requirements. Furthermore, they require much less water per pound of biomass than livestock. Thus, a zebra can get along without water for a period of three days, while the gemsbok (like the kangaroo rat of the southwestern American desert) does not require drinking water at all, but depends on metabolic water and the water occurring in its plant foods to satisfy its requirements (23).

3. Wild game are immune to the potentially lethal sleeping sickness transmitted by the tsetse fly. On the other hand, introduced livestock are highly susceptible (23).

4. Wild game ranches can expect a profit margin fully six times that of the traditional livestock rancher (23).

One might suppose that the widespread practice of wild game ranching would severely deplete and endanger the survival of African game populations. It must be emphasized, however, that, in any event, the use of a given range for livestock would pre-empt its use by wild game.

DONATIONS FROM FOOD-RICH NATIONS. One might suppose that the impending starvation in "have-not" countries might be alleviated, at least temporarily by food gifts from the "nutrient-rich" countries such as the United States and Canada. It certainly would seem that the United States would have a moral obligation to donate food. After all, with only 6 per cent of the world population, she is consuming about 40 per cent of the world's resources. Better to fill the empty stomachs of Asia, Africa, and South America than to sit by and watch surplus corn and wheat get moldy in storage bins. However, things aren't quite that simple; they are complicated by the laws of raw economics. Let us cite an example.

In 1969 the world experienced the greatest wheat glut in history. Several factors contributed to the record breaking harvests—optimal weather, improved agricultural techniques, and the use of superior wheat strains in Mexico, India, and

Figure 19-31. *Modern grain storage in India. During recent years the United States has been sending large quantities of food grains to India under Public Law 480, to help alleviate India's chronic shortage of food. Proper storage of food grains in India is essential for the most efficient use of the available stock. To help India overcome this problem, the U. S. Agency for International Development (AID) assisted in building silos and godowns. This is India's first grain storage elevator situated at Hapur, near India's capitol, New Delhi. In addition to the elevators, AID has made available the services of U. S. technicians to advise on construction and operation of the facility. (U. S. Department of Agriculture)*

Pakistan. Consider the economic plight of the Canadian wheat farmer. Canada's storage bins, already crammed with a record 850 million bushels, now received an additional 650 million bushels, at a time when the price of wheat was falling to bedrock levels. Canadian farmers simply could not afford to give the wheat to Nigeria, Guatemala, Costa Rica, or any other country where the jutting ribs and lethargic behavior of half-starved youngsters was an every day fact of life. Wheat farmers still owed the Canadian government $65 million in past loans. The government paid out cash advances of $6,000 per farm to compensate for unsold wheat.

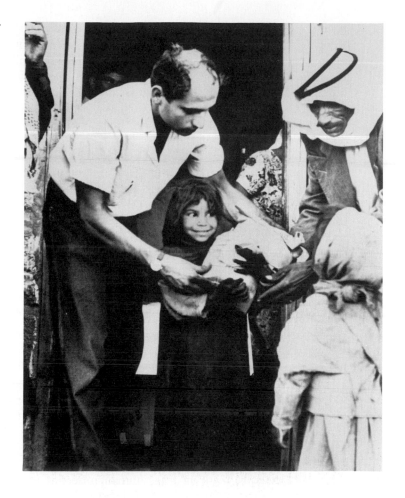

Figure 19-32. *Food for a hungry Jordanian youngster. She is being given dried milk and wheat flour under the CARE Food Crusade Program. This food will provide supplementary rations for her family for one month. (U.S. Department of Agriculture)*

The Canadians were forced into a financial squeeze—they simply had to get as much money for their wheat as possible. Ironically, and perhaps immorally, the wheat eventually was used, not to assuage the hunger pangs of the malnourished peoples of the world, but to produce more pork chops and beef steaks for those who were already overfed—the affluent people of America and Europe (9).

What of the Future?

Future historians may well speak of 1975 as the first year of The Great Hunger. Norman Borlaug himself, who earned the Nobel Prize for developing superior strains of wheat, has predicted that 20 million people in Africa, Asia, and South America will starve to death each year, beginning in 1975. Considering the finite resources, of planet Earth, in terms of arable land, water, and soil fertility, man certainly has the innate capacity to breed himself into starvation—despite the most advanced agricultural technology, despite food synthesis, yeast, and algal culture, drainage schemes, the most effective pest control programs, and the development of superior plant and animal breeds. You recall that when the Kaibab deer population increased precipitously, the environment eventually deteriorated so severely as to decimate the herd. Men are not deer but they are subject to the same basic ecological laws. It could well be that in man's intensive efforts to save himself, he may destroy himself. Perhaps in the long run, it would be more humanitarian to permit a relatively small-scale starvation now than to ensure an overwhelming catastrophic food crisis, say, within fifty years. Were you to ask your neighbor this very day what he thought of the possibilities of global famine within a century, he might answer, "Somehow, science and technology will see to that." But that is just the point. Despite all the wonders science and technology have wrought for twentieth-century man, "the population problem cannot be solved in a technical way, any more than can the problem of winning the game of tick-tack-toe" (16). A recognized authority on global food problems, Lester R. Brown, of the Overseas Development Council, was once highly optimistic that global food production, with the impetus provided by the green revolution, would catch up with the demands of a burgeoning world population. It is of considerable interest, therefore, that within the past five years his mood has changed to one of considerable pessimism. For example, in 1974 Brown commented: "We are seeing food riots in a number of countries now: Bolivia, Ethiopia, India. We may well see 10 or 15 governments toppled around the world . . . as a result." Even without a drought Brown believes Americans now have the choice of either eating less meat [so that more grain will be available for export] "or watch people starve to death on the TV news."

Take another glance at the human population growth curve shown in Figure 19-1. Do you see on what part of the curve our population is right now? On the exponential part, where the curve is zooming almost straight up! If the world population continues to increase at its present rate, the world's surface will eventually be saturated with people, at which point population increase will end. As Garrett Hardin, eminent professor of biology at the University of California, states, "It is clear that we will greatly increase human misery if we do not, in the immediate future, assume that the world available to the terrestrial human population is finite. Space is no escape" (16).

Is this what man wants? To maximize his population on earth? It took the human population 1 million years before Christ to double from 2.5 to 5 million. Today, we have a global population of about 4 billion; at the current rate of increase it will double in thirty-seven years. As Paul Ehrlich states, "If growth continued at that rate for about 900 years there would be some 60,000,000,000,000,000 people on the face of the earth. Sixty million billion people. This is about 100 persons for each square yard of the earth's surface, land and sea . . ." (12).

Sometimes it is difficult to grasp the significance of such a rapid build-up in human bodies. Let us examine a telling example right here in the United States, as described by Wayne Davis:

> In the United States and Canada is a small religious sect called the Hutterites on which good demographic data are available. Since they are fanatically opposed to birth control, are never killed in auto accidents or wars, and take advantage of the best in modern medicine, they should be the most rapidly growing human population on earth. . . . The average completed family size of the Hutterite family is 10.4 children. Thus the average couple has 108 grandchildren, 1125 great-grand children, and *lives to see the first few of their 11,703 great-great-grandchildren arrive.* (Italics added.)

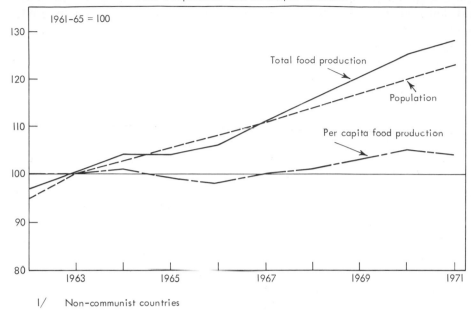

1961-65 = 100

Total food production

Population

Per capita food production

1963   1965   1967   1969   1971

1/   Non-communist countries

Figure 19-33.   *Note that even though food production in the less developed countries is progressively rising, it is barely keeping pace with the population increases. The available food per capita since 1970 is actually decreasing.*

Crude birth rates and death rates for the Hutterites are 45.9 and 4.4 per thousand respectively. . . . However, there are 34 hungry nations which have birth rates higher than the Hutterites. These include some larger nations such as Nigeria with a population of 54 million and a birth rate of 50, and Pakistan with 131 million people and a birth rate of 52 (9).

Unfortunately (or should we say fortunately?) both Nigeria and Pakistan have a higher mortality rate, which tends to restrain their population build-up. Let us suppose, however, that we send medical missionaries to these countries with antibiotics, antiseptics, vaccines, and the latest surgical know-how, so that their mortality rate can be reduced to the Hutterite level. Let us further suppose that now, because of the green revolution and/or because of the food gratuities of the food-rich nations (and the United States *did* send $15 billion dollars worth of food to hungry nations under Public Law 480), all the men, women, and children in Nigeria and Pakistan eventually will go to bed with a full stomach. What then? The respite from hunger would be brief to say the least. When you consider that within a single century Nigeria's population would increase to 3.6 billion (which almost equals the global population today) and the Pakistan population to 13 billion—it is obvious that these people ultimately would have bred themselves back to their originally wretched condition, or even one infinitely worse.

In fact, this phenomenon is the basis for the curious paradox: *Man causes starvation by feeding the hungry*. The editors of *Bioscience* recognized this dilemma when they wrote, "Because it creates a vicious cycle that compounds human suffering at a high rate, the provision of food to the malnourished populations of the world that cannot or will not take very substantial measures to control their own reproductive rates is inhuman, immoral and irresponsible" (10).

Nobel prize-winning Norman Borlaug, himself one of the main architects of the "green revolution," admits that the recent developments in plant breeding, including high-protein strains of rice and wheat, *are merely stopgap devices.* They serve only to buy time against the inevitable catastrophe of global famine, unless the world's nations mount a massive attempt to silence the ominous ticking of the population bomb. A step in the right direction was the United Nations-sponsored World Population Conference held at Bucharest, Romania, in August 1974. The largest international conference ever conducted behind the Iron Curtain, it was attended by 3,200 delegates from 130 nations. Although no unified global program of population control was achieved, the conference nevertheless was of considerable value in stimulating world-wide discussions on methods of restraining the current population surge.

Family planning will not prevent the ultimate crisis. As Kingsley Davis states, contemporary planning continues "to treat population growth as something to be planned *for,* not something to be *itself planned*" (7). There is a solution to this dilemma. But the solution depends neither on science nor on technology; it depends on a re-evaluation of values; it involves a new type of *morality*; it is a "simple" matter of the great majority of people reaching a decision either not to procreate or to restrict their families to one or two children and abiding by that decision.

Indeed, is it morally right for *any* couple to bring children into the world at a time when ecological systems are being strained to the point of collapse? If truly significant population control is to be achieved over the long term, it is essential that the world's prospective parents demonstrate the same kind of sensitivity, concern, and thoughtfulness that was recently shown by Dave, a 27-year-old man from Rosslyn, Virginia (just across the Potomac River from crowded downtown Washington, D.C.). After his wife Cindy announced that they were going to have their first baby, Dave tried to express his feelings in a letter to his unborn child:

> . . . Your mother and I are looking forward to seeing you with a love that we have never had the opportunity to feel before. . . . But, every once in a while, when I look out the window or walk down the street, I sense an apology in the recesses of my mind when I think of you. When I stand at a bus stop in a cloud of exhaust that lingers around me so I smell the city when I go home or try to shield my eyes against the flying debris that litters the streets I wonder how your eyes and lungs will react to it. When I think of showing you this land of ours, I think of trash-lined highways, littered beaches and no-fishing signs warning of polluted waters. When I think of your mother taking you for a stroll in the fresh air, I wonder how far she will have to go to find that fresh air. How long will you be able to sleep with the jets overhead and the trucks below?
>
> And if you should survive the earth, sea and sky, will you survive your fellow man? I must apologize for what the past generation has left and what some of the present generation is creating.
>
> It is a selfish love that welcomes a new born child into the world. We hope you don't suffer because of it.[1]

[1] From "Expectant Father Composes Letter to His Unborn Child," a newspaper article by UPI Senior Editor Louis Cassels.

BIBLIOGRAPHY

1. Asimov, Isaac. *A Short History of Biology*. Garden City, N.Y.: Natural History Press, 1964.
2. Bogue, Donald J. "End of Population Explosion?" *U.S. News and World Report* (March 11, 1968), pp. 59–61.
3. Borgstrom, Georg. *The Hungry Planet*. New York: Macmillan, 1965.
4. Borgstrom, Georg. *World Food Resources*. New York: Intext, 1973.
5. Brown, Harrison. "If World Population Doubles by the Year 2000," *U.S. News and World Report* (January 9, 1967), pp. 51–54.
6. Calder, Ritchie. *Common Sense About a Starving World*. New York: Macmillan, 1962.
7. Davis, Kingsley. "The Urbanization of the Human Population," *Scient. Amer.*, 213, No. 3 (1965), 53.
8. Davis, Wayne H. "Overpopulated America," *New Republic*, 162, No. 2 (January 10, 1970), 13–15.
9. ———. "Thoughts on Feeding the Hungry: More or Less People?" *New Republic*, 162, No. 25 (June 20, 1970), 19–21.
10. Editorial, *Biosci.* (February 1969).
11. Ehrenfeld, David. *Biological Conservation*. New York: Holt, 1970.
12. Ehrlich, Paul R. *The Population Bomb*. New York: Ballantine Books, 1968.
13. ———, Anne H. Ehrlich, and John P. Holdren. *Human Ecology: Problems and Solutions*. San Francisco: Freeman, 1973.
14. Ehrlich, Paul R., and John P. Holdren. "Population and Panaceas: A Technological Perspective," *Biosci.* 19 (December 1969), 1065–1071.
15. Greep, Roy O. "Prevalence of People," *Perspect. in Biol. and Med.*, 12 (Spring 1969), 332–343.
16. Hardin, Garrett. "The Tragedy of the Commons," *Science*, 162 (1968), 1243–1248.
17. Howard, Walter E. "The Population Crisis is Here Now," *Biosci.*, 19 (September 1969), 779–784.
18. McNeil, Mary. "Lateritic Soils," *Scient. Amer.*, 211, No. 5 (November 1964), 96–102.
19. National Academy of Sciences. *Resources and Man*. San Francisco: Freeman, 1969.
20. Oser, Jacob. *Must Men Starve?* New York: Abelard-Schuman, 1957.
21. Paddock, William, and Paul Paddock. *Famine—1975!* Boston: Little, Brown, 1967.
22. U.S. Department of Agriculture. *Annual Summary 1966. International Agricultural Development*. Washington, D.C.: 1968.
23. Wagner, Richard H. *Environment and Man*. New York: Norton, 1971.
24. Woodham-Smith, Cecil. *The Great Hunger*. New York: Harper, 1962.
25. Woytinsky, W. S., and E. S. Woytinsky. *World Population and Production*. New York: Twentieth Century Fund, 1953.

20.

Economics and the Environment

Economists as a group have been guiltier than most in perpetuating the most dangerous myths of this troubled age. Agricultural economists have given us the fiction that seven billion mouths in the year 2000 can be easily fed, in spite of the miserable failure of agriculture to feed half that number today. Mineral economists rely on the cornucopian dream, in which advancing technology conjures up ever cheaper minerals while consuming ever increasing amounts of energy and the earth's crust to do it. And economists of the Presidential-advisor variety continue to assure our lawmakers that the "magic" trillion dollar GNP is a milestone worth striving for. The fallacy in every case lies in what has been left out of the accounting: the ecological costs of food production; the facts of mineral distribution and diminishing returns; the conversion of resources and amenities into pollutants and eyesores; the massive expenditures for junk and planned obsolescence while social needs go begging.

John P. Holdren and Paul R. Ehrlich,
Global Ecology,
New York, Harcourt Brace Jovanovich, Inc., 1971

The "Cowboy" Versus the "Spaceman" Economy

Several years ago the noted economist Kenneth E. Boulding, in a paper entitled "The Economics of the Coming Spaceship Earth," described and analyzed two basic types of economic systems, that of the "cowboy" and that of the "spaceman" (1).

Our Present "Cowboy" Economy. In Boulding's opinion America is presently maintaining a "cowboy" type of economy. He employs the term *cowboy* because it seems symbolic of the violent, exploitative, brash, romantic era of nineteenth-century America. This was a period when the word *frontier* was almost an everyday household word. It was a time when the population was relatively sparse and the amount of "open spaces" was relatively great. If a farmer's land became impoverished because of his ignorance of soil conservation techniques or if he was simply loath to check erosion and fertility depletion, he could always "pull up stakes" and move further west. Somewhere out there, beyond the western horizon, vast acreages of relatively fertile land were virtually awaiting the touch of his plow. What was true of the farmer was also true of the nineteenth-century rancher. When his range began to deteriorate, and his cattle began to get scrawny, there was always a "sea of grass" somewhere out west, possibly just over the next ridge, where cattle could "put meat on the bones." Unscrupulous land companies, backed with capital from the East, Scotland, and England, publicized the prairie as a "green gold" paradise, where a settler could grow wealthy almost as fast as a buffalo grass seedling could grow to maturity. A considerable promotional literature had wide circulation. One book, excessive in its claims for the prairie country's economic possibilities, was known as *Brisbane's Beef Bonanza* (8). One chapter of this book, "Millions in Beef," described in detail how an initial investment of $25,000 would yield a net profit of $51,378 in only six years.

Much of the adventurous development of the frontier was fostered by federal policy. Thus, under the provisions of the Homestead Act, the federal government encouraged settlement by offering 160 acres of land to every settler who would in good faith occupy and develop the site for a period of at least five years. After this five-year period, the rancher was free to move once again. Certainly the prevailing feeling of both the government and the people was that America's natural resources, whether productive soil, lush range grass, high quality water, coal and oil deposits, timber, or wildlife, were virtually limitless. And if any one ever suggested that good air itself might some day be limited in supply he probably would have been considered a candidate for the "nuthouse." Since resources seemed inexhaustible, and since human well-being could be promoted by using them, it seemed to be only "common sense" to exploit them. And exploited they were, with a speed and thoroughness that perhaps has been unparalleled in human history.

A second characteristic of the "cowboy" economy, according to Boulding, was the notion that somehow the natural environment, whether soil, air, stream, or ocean, could serve as unlimited reservoirs of the "waste products" of society. Thus both human and livestock excrement, as well as factory wastes, could be discharged into a stream or lake, day after day, without any deterioration of water quality. For example, I remember my granddad telling me that "a stream would purify itself every ten miles." Industrial smokestacks belched massive quantities of black smoke and other materials into the air so that cities such as Chicago and Pittsburgh became shrouded in haze, and dusk seemed to come prematurely. Solid waste, such as rusting auto "carcasses," tin cans, bottles, rubber tires, and oil drums, were discarded on vacant land at the edge of town, in rock quarries, swamps, or any convenient "wasteland" that happened to be nearby. As long as there was so much "space," why not fill it up and get rid of the stuff?

Of course, as Boulding points out, the "cowboy" economy is still operating in America today, long after the last frontier vanished, long after her "inexhaustible" resources were close to the exhaustion point, and long after her natural reservoirs (soil, air, and water) were becoming overwhelmed with society's wastes. In summary, the cowboy economy is characterized by (1) rapid depletion of resource; (2) a huge stock of capital goods, produced from those resources; (3) a short "life span" for these goods; and hence (4) a rapid accumulation of waste. In Boulding's viewpoint, such an "open" type of economy simply cannot be maintained for very long before the resource exhaustion and massive pollution, as well as the depletion of energy supplies, will force it to come to an end, with disastrous effects on both societal well-being and the environment.

We all know, of course, that "big business" continues to espouse the "cowboy" type of economy, regardless of the implications for eventual human suffering. Many

Figure 20-1. *The bankers, stock brokers, industrialists, and economists housed in these Manhattan skyscrapers are very sensitive to the slightest fluctuations of the GNP. But what does GNP mean to the misery-ridden of a New York ghetto? Or for the millions in America's human ant hill for whom life has somehow lost its meaning? (New York Convention and Vistors Bureau)*

economists are sure that the "cowboy" economy cannot continue indefinitely but are not sure when it should be terminated. Or else, along with industry, they resort to some "fuzzy-minded" rationalizing that permits them to procrastinate. The "cowboy" economy's "health" is frequently measured by the GNP (gross national product). The GNP may be defined as "the sum total of expenditures by governments and by individuals for goods, services, or investments." Bankers, stockbrokers, industrialists, and economists are very sensitive to the fluctuations of the GNP from year to year. When the GNP is up they are happy; when it is down they are concerned. It must be remembered, however, that even though the GNP may be useful in assessing the rate of the "flow" of goods through the economic system, it nevertheless is not a valid measure of the *quality* of life, and therefore of human happiness. What does GNP mean to the wretched, poorly educated, semi-starved people crowded in squalid shacks in strip-mined Appalachia? What does the GNP mean to the misery-ridden of the New York ghetto? Or to the Detroit suburbanite who tried to kill himself because he felt like just another ant in the human ant hill and life had lost all meaning? Or for the night worker who shot and killed a kid playing nearby because he was so noisy? Or to the construction worker

Figure 20-2. *The wasteful "cowboy" economy compared with the efficient "spaceship" economy with its emphasis on recycling and production of durable goods.*

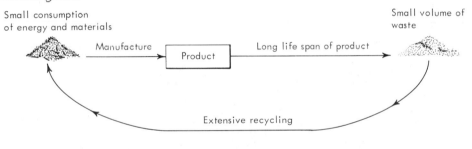

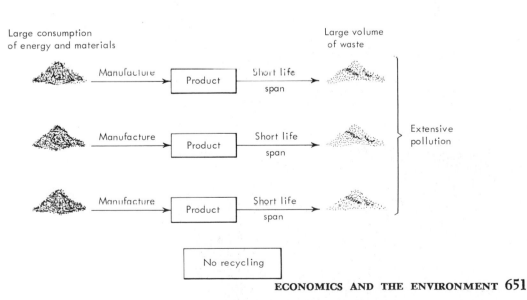

dying from asbestos particles in his lungs? Or to Colorado cattle ranchers who saw their rolling grass and sagebrush hills converted to a strip-mined desert?

The fallacy of equating GNP with the quality of human life was emphasized by the late Robert Kennedy:

> . . . the Gross National Product includes air pollution and advertising for cigarettes, and ambulances to clear our highways of carnage. It counts special locks for our doors, and jails for the people who break them. The GNP includes the destruction of the redwoods and the death of Lake Superior. It grows with the production of napalm and missiles and nuclear warheads, and it even includes research on the improved dissemination of bubonic plague. The GNP swells with equipment for the police to put down riots in our cities; and though it is not diminished by the damage these riots do, still it goes up as slums are rebuilt on their ashes.[1]

Changing to a "Spaceman" Economy. According to Boulding, America can no longer afford to enjoy the "cowboy" type of economy, in which success is based on the amount of production and consumption, or "throughput." Instead, he suggests that we shift to a "spaceman" economy, which would be in harmony with the limited resource reservoirs and pollution reservoirs available on "spaceship" earth. In order to appreciate better the nature of this type of economy, let us briefly consider how it would operate on an actual spaceship headed to some far-off planet such as Mars. Because it would take many months to get to Mars, it would obviously be impossible to cram all the food necessary to sustain the space crew for the trip to and back from Mars. Instead the food supply would have to be continuously replenished. It has been suggested, for example, that the nitrogen- and phosphorus-containing wastes of the astronauts could be used to fertilize an aqueous medium in which crops of algae would be grown. The astronauts could then either consume the algae directly, or could eat fish, snails, or quail that had fed upon the algae. Note that in this system the nutrient phosphorus and nitrogen could be continuously recycled through the bodies of spacemen, algae, fish, and spacemen once again. Theoretically none of these nutrients would be lost or discarded. Not only would the algae be used as a food source but during the photosynthetic process oxygen would be released that would be inhaled by the astronauts to sustain their respiratory processes. Furthermore, the carbon dioxide exhaled by the astronauts in turn would be used by the algae as a raw material in the process of photosynthesis.

Of course, as we have learned from our study of the laws of thermodynamics even though elements theoretically may be continuously recycled, energy may not. In other words there would have to be a continuous input of energy to compensate for the energy that would be continuously escaping (from the otherwise completely "closed" system) in the form of heat. The energy "input" would be provided by solar energy. Not only would solar energy be utilized to power the process of photosynthesis and hence serve as the basic energy source for all the organisms, in the spaceship from algae to astronauts, but, with the aid of solar cell batteries, the solar energy would be continuously converted into the electrical energy required for lighting systems and for powering the electronic equipment aboard the space vehicle. And even though all of the solar energy input eventually would be degraded to heat, the heat energy could ovbiously be employed to good purpose in a vehicle

---

[1] Quoted in David B. Van Vleck, *The Crucial Generation.* Charlotte, Vt.: Optimum Population Incorporated, 1971.

Figure 20-3. *Kennedy Space Center, Fla. The Apollo 16 Saturn V space vehicle carrying Astronauts John W. Young, Thomas K. Mattingly II, and Charles M. Duke, Jr., streaks skyward past Florida landscape at the start of NASA's eighth manned voyage to the moon. Liftoff was recorded at 12:54 P.M. EST April 16, 1972 (NASA)*

speeding through an interplanetary environment where temperatures are about −300° F! The point to emphasize, then, about the "spaceman economy" is that the reservoirs of resources (food, oxygen, nutrients, and so on) are *extremely limited*, as are the available reservoirs that might accommodate waste (pollution).

Now, it is true, that planet earth is not quite yet so stripped of resource and pollution reservoirs that such "tight" recycling would have to be initiated at once. Certainly, the spaceship analogy would not really apply until after the people now alive would long since have died. Certainly Spaceship Earth will be here in some future "tomorrow." But not now. But listen to economist Boulding:

I would argue . . . that tomorrow is not only very close, but in many respects is already here. *The shadow of the future spaceship, indeed, is already falling over our spendthrift merriment.* (Italics added.) Oddly enough it seems to be in pollution rather than in exhaustion that the problem is first becoming salient. Los Angeles has run out of air, Lake Erie has become a cesspool, the oceans are getting full of lead and DDT. . . .

One big distinction between the "cowboy" and "spaceman" economies is the yardstick used to measure the system's success. In the "cowboy" economy, success is based upon the amount of *throughput*—the amount of production (using up of resources) and *consumption* (the conversion of goods into polluting wastes). On the other hand, in the closed "spaceman" economy production and consumption are considered "bad"—something to be avoided as much as possible. (Tell that to most present-day economists and they would consider you soft in the head.) If the "spaceship" economy visualized by Boulding is going to have a chance of success, it is apparent that the earth's current population surge must be brought under control. If it were to continuously increase production, consumption would at least temporarily increase in proportion. However, if our global population eventually is stabilized, then scientists and technologists could concentrate on *improving the quality and durability of our capital stock of goods* rather than in placing major emphasis on accelerating their movement through the system only to eventually be converted into wastes with a high pollution potential. Human well-being does not really de-

Figure 20-4. *Spaceship Earth. ". . . The shadow of the future spaceship, indeed, is already falling over our spendthrift merriment. . . ."* (NASA)

pend on the volume and rapidity of "throughput" but on the *quality of the goods that are being used by the consumer*. Thus, as Paul Ehrlich has observed, "Most people would rather own *one* Rolls Royce than a *succession* of Fords" (3). One aspect of commodity improvement would be an increase in its durability. From the plastic toys, with life spans of only a few days, you buy for your youngsters, to the motor car, with a life span of only four or five years, you buy for yourself, lack of durability is a common denominator. The obsolescence that Detroit builds into its motor cars might be a good sales technique (and help accelerate "throughput"), but it is highly wasteful of energy and resource supplies that are already in scarce supply. Moreover, planned obsolescence is rapidly overwhelming our junked car "grave-yards" as even a brief survey of backyards, alleys, old fields, and city junkyards will reveal. Housing construction is another example. Homes built today are actually less durable, despite our sophisticated architectural and engineering "know-how," than those that were built 700 years ago.

Ehrlich feels that once the basic material requirements of food and suitable living conditions are provided, the quality of one's life and hence one's happiness will depend on the *services* and the *options of life style* available to him. Services would include such things as health and medical facilities, educational opportunities, a good judicial system, effective police and fire protection, and opportunities for recreation and entertainment (3). The life style options might include the choice of friends, environments, cultural pursuits, and professional careers. The quality of a young man's life would be just a bit richer, for example, if he had the knowledge that he *could* study to become a medical doctor, or a musician, if he so decided even though he was now "pumping gas"; or if he knew that he *could* live in Wisconsin north woods country, even though he was in fact living in a Manhattan apartment!

Methods of Pollution Control

In the earlier sections of this book we learned that serious contamination of our country's land, water, and air was an accomplished fact. Whether it is smog in Los Angeles, blazing oil on the Cuyahoga River (Ohio), or DDT-contaminated sediment on the bottom of Long Island Sound, the situation is grave and demands the attention of environmental agencies at all levels of government. We shall now explore the pros and cons of three basic methods of pollution control: *direct regulation*, *subsidization*, and *putting a price tag on pollution*.

Direct Regulation. The traditional approach to pollution control has been the establishment of laws that prohibit the acts of contamination. Unfortunately there are many drawbacks to this approach. Let us suppose that the owner of a paper mill has been cited by the state environmental protection agency to reduce the level of pulp waste being discharged into a stream. Noncompliance would result in a $500 per day fine. The owner of the plant may weigh the cumulative costs of the daily fines against the costs of equipment that would remove the wastes from the effluent. For example, the plant theoretically might "tie in" which the municipal sewage treatment system—for a price, let's say $10,000 per year. Now, the paper mill owner might decide to take the risk of a *possible* fine, or many fines, rather than *certainly* pay the annual fee of $10,000 charged by the municipality for sewage treatment services. Influencing his decision might be the fact that since the state environmental control agency is rather understaffed, monitoring of pulp waste levels in the river is sporadic; and even if he were fined ten times during a given year, and were forced to pay an annual total of $5,000 in fines, he still would be saving $5,000 per year. He might rationalize his fine payments as part of his overhead costs, such as those for heating the plant, repairing machinery, and buying fire insurance. Moreover, since the plant employs several hundred employees, and is a source of considerable tax revenue for the town, the plant owner may try to rely on his economic and political clout to successfully avoid any punitive action on the part of the control agency.

Note, then, that at least in this hypothetical case, and many others like it, direct regulation of pollution by establishing standards and then levying fines quite often does not actually result in the desired goal of pollution abatement. In the absence of effective inspection and policing (which frequently is the case because of limited state funds) compliance with regulations is quite often dependent upon whether such compliance will result in an overall benefit to the polluter, certainly not upon ethics or a well-developed social conscience. As Marshall I. Goldman states, "When policemen are not around, traffic laws are usually observed even though this means a delay, because failure to do so may lead to automobile accidents. In contrast, the Volstead Act (Prohibition Act) could not be enforced because too many citizens felt that the consequence of alcohol was pleasure rather than pain" (4).

If pollution-restricting laws are to be effective they must be backed by public support. Without the backing of overwhelming citizen sentiment even the most economically and environmentally appropriate laws will not be very well observed by industry or the general public. For example, it was not until almost every citizen of Los Angeles was aware that the city's smog was primarily generated by automobile exhaust that it was possible to formulate and effectively enforce a strict emission control law.

Subsidization. In some instances an industry may find it prohibitively costly to comply with pollution-control laws because of huge expenditures on sewage-processing or air-filtering equipment. (A large electrostatic precipitator or a cooling tower, for example, might cost a power plant at least $1 million.) Under these circumstances, even though the industry would like to comply, the board of directors may decide to move the plant's operation to another city or state. The net result of the pollution law, therefore, might mean a severe economic setback not only for the workers who are laid off, but for the entire town—especially in a small town whose economic life blood was "pumped" by that single industrial plant. In such a situation both environmental and economic goals might best be served were the municipal, state, or federal government to *subsidize* the industry so that it would be able to purchase and operate suitable pollution control equipment. The subsidy may be made in the form of *tax credits* (7). Thus an agreement would be negotiated between the industry and the appropriate government whereby a certain percentage of the cost of the control equipment (say, 10 per cent of a $1 million precipitator or $100,000) would be "given" to the industry in the form of an income tax reduction. Subsidization may also take the form of low-interest *loans* or even outright *grants*. In economically depressed areas the federal government, for example, might pay up to 80 per cent of the cost of pollution control facilities. Thus, in poverty-stricken Appalachia the federal coffers might "cough up" $400,000 to help defray the costs of a half-million dollar project to rehabilitate strip-mine spoil banks and control acid mine drainage. The goals for this "gratuity" would obviously be economic and social, as well as environmental.

Putting a Price Tag on Pollution. A third, more novel method of pollution control would be to assess an industrial corporation, a municipality, or private citizen a certain fee A for releasing B pounds of pollutant C into the nation's land-water-air pollution reservoirs. Since *all* polluters would be assessed, and the assessment would be on a standardized basis, such an assessment would ultimately be accepted, even though initially there might be a few heated complaints. Each polluter would be charged on the basis of the *poundage* of the contaminant he discharges—the *greater the poundage, the higher the charge.* In other words, the pollution control board (federal, state, or municipal) would add the *social cost* of dumping cannery waste (fish kills, odorous air, defilement of scenic beauty) to the routine costs (raw materials, labor, marketing, fuel, power, insurance, and so on) that the plant has traditionally assumed in order to operate.

It is apparent, however, that there would be a number of variables to be considered in such a "pay by the pound" system. First, *not all contaminants are equally destructive* to the environment. Thus, an industrial plant would certainly be assessed more for dumping a pound of mercury or arsenic into the water than for discharging a pound of pulp fibers. Similarly, a motorist who spews lead from his exhaust should be charged more than the driver who consumes lead-free gasoline.

Second, the *locality of the pollution act* might be a variable. For example, at the time of this writing the Reserve Mining Company has been brought to court by the federal Environmental Protection Agency for dumping 67,000 tons of "tailings" (residue left over after the processing of taconite, a low-grade iron ore) daily into relatively uncontaminated Lake Superior. In the "pay by the pound" system Reserve Mining probably would be assessed higher charges at its present site than if it were located on the shores of Lake Erie and was merely adding to the contamination of an ecosystem that was already badly defiled.

Third, the *season of the year* may be a variable. For example the discharge of a ton of untreated human excrement into the Sacramento River during the dry season should involve a higher assessment than if it were released during the wet season, when stream volume is much greater and sewage dilution would be maximal.

Obviously not all industrial corporations would be content to pay the pollution assessments indefinitely. Instead, they would most certainly explore every possible avenue for reducing the amount of their pollution discharge. They probably would install an adequate number of pollution control devices so that the assessments (and incidentally the amount of pollution!) would be substantially reduced. It may well be, for example, that it would be economical for a coal-fired power plant to reduce particulate emissions by 95 per cent; however, to make *further* reductions would actually cost more (in terms of, say, electrostatic precipitators) than the fees assessed on the remaining 5 per cent of the pollution discharged. Therefore the power company would accept the pollution fee as part of the "cost of doing business." This "pay by the pound" method of pollution control might even induce several factories and/or municipalities to pool their resources and build a communal pollution treatment plant that could not have been financed by any of the parties acting by themselves. This is the action that was taken by several industries along the Ruhr River in Germany. Although the Ruhr serves as a "sewer" for almost 40 per cent of German industry, the assessment system has stimulated the development of a number of communal sewage disposal systems. As a result, despite the mammoth discharges, parts of the Ruhr river system are actually of sufficiently high quality *to permit fish to survive* and *to enable people to swim in the water* without ill effect.

O.K. So putting a price tag on pollution will work for industrial discharges, but would it be any good in reducing smog—over 50 per cent of which apparently is traceable to the internal combustion engine? Larry E. Ruff, of the federal Environmental Protection Agency, is of the opinion that it would work very well, despite the seeming difficulties. He writes:

> Suppose, then, that a price is put on the emissions of automobiles. Obviously, continuous metering of such emissions is impossible. But it should be easy to determine the average output of pollution for cars of different makes, models, and years, having different types of control devices and using different types of fuel. Through graduated registration fees and fuel taxes, each car owner would be assessed roughly the social cost of his car's pollution, adjusted for whatever control devices he has chosen to install and for his driving habits. If the cost of installing a device, driving a different car, or finding alternative means of transportation is less than the price he must pay to continue his pollution, he will presumably take the necessary steps. But each individual remains free to find the best adjustment to his particular situation (7).

Environmental Impact of Economic Growth

It has been difficult for both economists and environmentalists to broaden the "tunnel vision" that they have used during the early years of the environmental crisis.[1] Wrapped up in their preoccupation with such things as "throughput," GNP, and GWP (gross world product), economists have shown deplorable insensitivity and appalling ignorance concerning the cause-and-effect relationship between "increased production" and "environmental abuse." On the other hand, for their part, the environmentalists seem often afflicted with a dreamy sort of idealism that refuses to recognize that pollution control must somehow be harmoniously integrated with the basic laws of economics if it is to be effective (2).

Commoner defines *economic growth* as "the increase in output of goods and services generated by economic activity." He defines *environmental deterioration* as "the degradative changes in the ecosystems which are the habitat for all life on the planet." If any economic system is to survive, it must operate in a manner that is compatible for the continued stability of the ecosystems from which it derives its natural resources. In other words, a "sick" ecosystem will inevitably result in a "sick" economy.

Human productive activities, whether the construction of a highway or the operation of a nuclear power plant, will always exert some sort of *environmental impact* on the ecosystem. According to Commoner, the environmental impact "represents the amount of an agency *external* to the ecosystem, which, by intruding upon it, tends to degrade its capacity for self adjustment." Such environmental impacts may be generated in three different ways.

---

[1] Much of the material in this section is drawn from Barry Commoner's paper "The Environmental Costs of Economic Growth," which he presented at a Resources for the Future Forum on "Energy, Economic Growth, and the Environment," in Washington, D.C. a few years ago.

1. *The stress may be caused because the biological productivity of the ecosystem is being exploited.* A familiar example would be the depletion of timber or game because of continued exploitation without reforestation or re-stocking of game. A classic example, of course, would be the ultimate extinction of the passenger pigeon caused by excessive market-hunting.
2. *The stress may be caused when some component of the ecosystem has been artificially augmented because of intrusion from outside the ecosystem.* The accelerated use of commercial nitrate fertilizer to increase crop production is a familiar example. The resultant chain of events leading to such phenomena as lake eutrophication and the blood disease methemoglobinemia has been described earlier in this text.
3. *The environmental stress may be caused when an "exotic" substance, completely foreign to the ecosystem, is imposed on it from the "outside."* Good examples would be the dissemination of synthetic pesticides and plastics into the natural land-water-air reservoirs.

America has polluted her environment almost since the first Pilgrim set foot on Plymouth Rock. However, it has largely been since World War II with the development of new technologies (and hence new types of stresses) that the United States has virtually "overwhelmed" her ecosystems with unprecedented volumes of contaminants. It has been during the post–World War II period, for example, that such pollutants as synthetic pesticides, plastics, herbicides, radioactive materials, and detergents have been dispersed into the environment. To get an idea of the tremendous increase in pollution rates since World War II, consider these statistics: During the period 1950–1967 production of synthetic organic pesticides increased 267 per cent; during the period 1950–1967 beer bottle production increased 595 per cent; the emissions of tetraethyl lead increased 415 per cent from 1946 to 1967; inorganic nitrogen fertilizer production increased 648 per cent from 1949 to 1968. Most startling, however, is that during the period 1946–1968 the *production* of detergent phosphorus increased 1,845 per cent.

We accept the fact, then, of vastly increased pollution rates since World War II. However, to what can this increase be attributed? To increase in population growth? To increase in per capita use of goods? Or to technology itself? In other words, have technological changes taken place since World War II that have exerted a more adverse environmental effect than the technologies they replaced? These obviously important questions must be accurately answered before an efficient pollution clean-up can be completed. Fortunately, the answer is readily secured. For example, since the population growth of the United States between 1946 and 1968 was only 42 per cent, and the GNP per capita increased only about 59 per cent, the only way we can explain emission increases of up to 1,845 per cent (in the case of detergent phosphate) is to attribute it to a shift from a less-polluting technology (manufacture of low-phosporus detergents) to a more-polluting technology (manufacture of high-phosphorus detergents). Analysis of data of this type indicates that *changing technology*, rather than *population growth* or *increase in per capita GNP*, is the main cause of the postwar environmental pollution problems in the United States.

Textile Industry. Take the textile industry, for example. Since 1946 the fiber production per capita has remained at a fairly constant level. However, natural fibers such as cotton and wool have rapidly been displaced by the artificial fibers of nylon. This technological shift has had two deleterious effects. First, it required the use of much greater supplies of *energy*. Thus, the synthesis of the cellulose in cotton fibers is accomplished in the plant with the use of solar energy that bathes the leaves of the cotton plant each cloudless day without generating the slightest bit of pollution. On the other hand, the synthesis of the polyamides in the nylon is a complex process requiring up to ten steps, which can not be effected without huge expenditures of both thermal and electrical energy. (Of course, the generation of this energy by a power plant, as we already know, results in substantial quantities of thermal, particulate, and chemical (sulfur dioxide, benzopyrenes) pollution. A second adverse feature of the change in textile technology is that it has caused the accumulation of nonbiodegradable nylon fibers in the land-water-air reservoirs. The cotton and wool fibers are readily degraded by fungi and bacteria into harmless water and carbon dioxide. On the other hand, since the synthetic nylon fibers are foreign "intruders" to the natural ecosystems, no bacterial or fungal enzyme has evolved that is capable of effecting their decomposition. As a result the nylon fibers and similar synthetic polymers such as plastics tend to accumulate in the environment. As Commoner states, "microscopic fragments of plastic fibers, often red, blue or orange, *have now become common in certain marine waters.*" (Italics added.)

Motor Vehicles. Let us now examine the technology-environmental impact relationship with reference to the motor car. One major change in the automobile engine since World War II has been the increase in the compression ratio from 5.9 to 9.5. This has resulted in a 400 per cent increase in the use of tetraethyl lead, a gasoline additive that tends to reduce the engine "knock" that otherwise would develop with the modern high compression engine. Almost all of the lead is dispersed into the atmosphere via the car's exhaust. Now, since lead is not an element required for the normal healthy functioning of any living organism, it represents a "foreign" intrusion to the ecosystem. As we know, the effects on man range from kidney malfunction and anemia to nervous disorders and even deterioration of the brain. With reference to tetraethyl lead, Commoner observes that "the largest increase in impact is in vehicle-miles travelled per capita (due to expansion of the suburbs) (100 percent), followed by the technological factors (83 percent) and the population factor (41 per cent)" (2).

Another pollutant that has been increased greatly in the human environment since the advent of the high-compression engine is nitrogen dioxide. Engine temperature increases proportionately with compression. At the high temperatures generated in the high-compression engine the nitrogen and oxygen present in the air (which is mixed with the gasoline in the carburetor) combine to form nitrogen dioxide. As mentioned earlier, this gas is the catalyst that triggers the production of *photochemical smog.* This type of smog was first observed in Los Angeles in 1942 and since has become a common component of the urban scene throughout the United States. Since the population has increased only 41 per cent, and the vehicle-miles traveled per capita only 100 per cent, we can explain a 630 per cent increase in the environmental impact of nitrogen oxides only by attributing the major cause to the technological shift from the low compression to the high compression engine.

It must be apparent from Commoner's superb analysis of the causal factors contributing to our environmental crisis that although the increasing population, and the increased production (consumption) of goods per capita are important, the over-riding cause is the shift from a pre–World War II technology that generated modest amounts of environmental contaminants to the massively polluting technology of today. Not only does this situation threaten the environment. *It also threatens the vigor of the American economy itself.* For the vitality of America's *economic system* is ultimately dependent on that of her *ecological systems.* The two are inextricably inter-related. If this is true, what economic-ecological guide lines should America follow for the future? What changes must be made? And how quickly? Commoner makes an emphatic response to these questions:

> If we are to survive economically as well as biologically, much of the technological transformation of the United States economy since 1946 will need to be, so to speak, redone in order to bring the nation's productive technology much more closely into harmony with the inescapable demands of the ecosystem. This will require the development of massive new technologies, including: systems to return sewage and garbage directly to the soil; the replacement of synthetic materials by natural ones; the reversal of the present trend to retire soil from agriculture and to elevate the yield per acre; the development of land transport that operates with maximal fuel efficiency at low combustion temperatures; the sharp curtailment of the use of biologically active synthetic organic agents. In effect, *what is required is a new period of technological transformation of the economy which will reverse the counter-ecological trends developed since 1946.* (Italics added.) The cost of the new transformation might represent a capital investment of hundreds of billions of dollars. To this must be added the cost of repairing the ecological damage which has already been incurred, such as the eutrophication of Lake Erie, again a bill to be reckoned in the hundreds of billions of dollars (2).

Let's Get Down to Earth

Astronaut Frank Borman has described the moon as a "vast, lonely forbidding type of existence, a great expanse of nothing, that looms rather like clouds and clouds of pumice stone. It certainly would not appear to be a very inviting place to live or work." During the the close-up view of the moon astronaut Jim Lovell commented, "The vast loneliness of the moon . . . makes you realize just what you have back there on earth. . . ."

The federal government spent $21 billion during the decade of the 1960's to put *four* men on the lunar wasteland for a few hours. Now it is time to spend much greater sums to repair an earth on which almost 4 *billion* people will spend the rest of their lives. Recently Charles A. Lindbergh, the renowned avaiator, remarked, "The cost of adequate conservation is small in relation to what we spend on space exploration, aviation, and so forth; yet the natural resources we neglect offer far more to us and to our children, than do all such enterprises combined." Joseph Wood Krutch, one of America's foremost naturalists, has put space exploration and other technological feats in proper perspective:

> Science and technology can point to achievements as spectacular as any in their previous history. The physicists and mathematicians have sent men around the moon and brought them back safely to earth. . . . But despite these achievements ours is, even more conspicuously than it was years ago, an age of anxiety. Three of the threats we are most aware of—overpopulation, epidemic crime, and the increasing pollution of our environment—were threats many of us didn't worry about a decade ago. And they are not likely to be solved by the so-called conquest of space . . . (5).

Nevertheless, in September, 1969, President Nixon's Space Task Group recommended that our national space effort be directed toward a manned Mars landing in

Figure 20-5. *Astronaut Frank Borman has described the moon as a "vast, lonely, forbidding type of existence, a great expanse of nothing, that looms rather like clouds and clouds of pumice stone. It certainly would not appear to be a very inviting place to live or work." According to Astronaut Jim Lovell: "The vast loneliness of the moon . . . makes you realize just what you have back there on earth. . . ."* (NASA)

Figure 20-6. *". . . The physicists and mathematicians have sent men around the moon and brought them back safely to earth. . . . But despite these achievements, ours is, even more than it was years ago, an age of anxiety. . . ."* (NASA)

Figure 20-7. *Hurricane Doria is shown here in the National Aeronautics and Space Administration's Numbus II weather satellite APT picture (upper center) off the northeast coast of the United States. The dark outline of Chesapeake Bay can be seen to the west (left) of the hurricane and also the coastal outline of southeastern United States (left center). Diligent "tracking" of such potentially destructive storms permits the alerting of coastal residents so that loss of life and property damage are minimized. (NASA)*

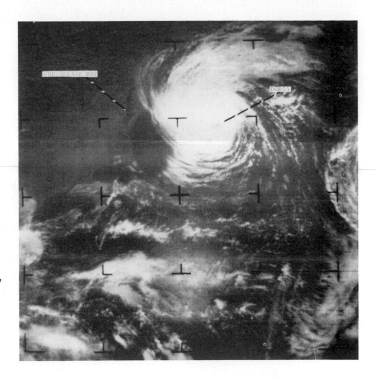

Figure 20-8. *Glacial sediment spotted from space. Image from first experimental Earth Resources Technology Satellite reveals sediment plumes from coastal glaciers of Alaska. The plumes can be clearly identified, extending more than 30 miles into the Pacific Ocean. U. S. Geological Survey glaciologists point out that although it had been known that large amounts of sediments are carried to sea from glaciers, the over-all view that the satellite images give are the first to visually show the extent. (NASA)*

Figure 20-9. *Space satellite photo showing portions of Germany, Holland, and Denmark under heavy air pollution, July 19, 1973. (NASA)*

1986! The overall cost of such a program, including the development of space stations and vehicles that can be reused, would be more than $100 billion. This would be the *ultimate ecological absurdity*. We certainly are in no position to afford the luxury of sending spaceships to the moon, Mars, or anywhere. There might be no habitable Earth to which the spacemen could return. As Senator Nelson admonished in a recent message to Congress, "Just to control pollution, it will take $275 billion by the year 2000." It would seem much wiser, from the standpoint of human well-being to cancel the Martian adventure and use the $100 billion to clean up the earth.

This is not to suggest that we abandon all of the sophisticated technology that made our lunar explorations possible; quite the contrary. But we should apply these developments to earthly objectives. Walter Orr Roberts, former president of the American Association for the Advancement of Science, has suggested that future space research be earth-oriented. A high-priority future item in space research would be manned space stations with earth-directed instrumentation. Roberts visualized the eventual development of a world monitoring network "with teams of skilled observers studying hurricanes, tropical ocean-atmosphere energy transformations, ocean current flow patterns for fish migration analysis, air pollution drift, and spread of insect pests and plant diseases, assessing water reserves in the world's watersheds, and making a host of other terrestrial studies . . ." (6).

BIBLIOGRAPHY

1. Boulding, Kenneth E. "The Economics of the Coming Spaceship Earth," in Henry Jarrett, ed., *Environmental Quality in a Growing Economy*. Baltimore: Johns Hopkins, 1966.
2. Commoner, Barry. "The Environmental Costs of Economic Growth," in Robert Dorfman and Nancy S. Dorfman, *Economics of the Environment*. Norton, 1971.
3. Ehrlich, Paul R., Anne H. Ehrlich, and John P. Holdren. *Human Ecology: Problems and Solutions*. San Francisco: Freeman, 1973.
4. Goldman, Marshall I. *Controlling Pollution: The Economics of a Cleaner America*. Englewood Cliffs, N.J.: Prentice-Hall, 1967.
5. Krutch, Joseph Wood. "Dropouts, Do-gooders, and the Two Cultures," *Amer. Forests* (August 1969), pp. 34, 35, 41.
6. Roberts, Walter Orr. "After the Moon, the Earth!" *Science* 167 (January 2, 1970), 11–16.
7. Ruff, Larry E. "The Economic Common Sense of Pollution," *Public Interest*, No. 19 (Spring 1970), 69–85.
8. Stewart, George. "History of Range Use," *The Western Range*. Senate Document No. 199 (1936), 119–133.

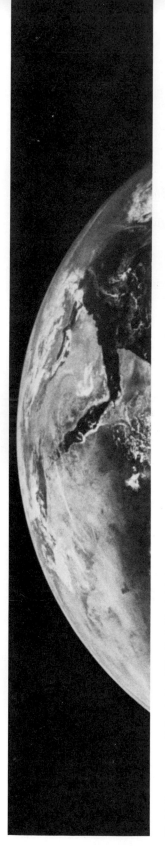

21.

The Future of Planet Earth

I do not wish to seem overdramatic, but I can only conclude from the information that is available to me as Secretary-General, that the Members of the United Nations have perhaps ten years left in which to subordinate their ancient quarrels and launch a global partnership to curb the arms race, to improve the human environment, to defuse the population explosion, and to supply the required momentum to development efforts. If such a global partnership is not forged within the next decade, then I very much fear that the problems I have mentioned will have reached such staggering proportions that they will be beyond our capacity to control.

U Thant, 1969

The task of ensuring that planet Earth will still be capable of supporting *Homo sapiens* by the year 2000, 2050, or 2100 is exceedingly complex and, quite frankly, may be impossible to achieve. The problem is that there are so many interacting variables, such as population levels, resource availability, industrial production, pollution levels, social attitudes, political institutions, changing patterns of war and peace, new technological developments, and so on. In fact, the task of maintaining a reasonably high quality of human existence for even several decades into the future is much more formidable and challenging than was the development of the atomic bomb, or the fabrication of the rockets that sent man to the moon.

In an extremely important book entitled "*Limits to Growth,*" published in 1972, a research team at the Massachusetts Institute of Technology reported on the results of a study in which the available statistical data for the major environmental variables (population, industrial production, pollution levels, resource depletion, food production, and so on) were fed into a computer (3). In this way an attempt was made to ascertain the gradual changes in the quality of the human environment that will occur through the year 2100, assuming that industrial and population growth continues at the current exponential rates. The graphed projections that appeared on the computer printouts (Figure 21-1.) are most illuminating—and highly disturbing. Notice that until about 2030, even though the population continues to increase sharply, the expanded industrial output occurring simultaneously will make possible more food production per capita. However, the industrial and food production gains, unfortunately, will be made only at considerable environmental expense —accelerating resource decrements and pollution increments. Thus, by the year 2030, the world's stomachs will have a bit more food in them, but the quality of life for the human organism in most other respects will be rapidly deteriorating. Several decades later, such resources as pure water, fertile soil, clean air, minerals, fossil fuels, and so on will be so badly depleted that both food and industrial production will drop off sharply. Aggravating the problem at this time will be a continuing upsurge in the global population. By 2050, pollution rates will sharply subside, the

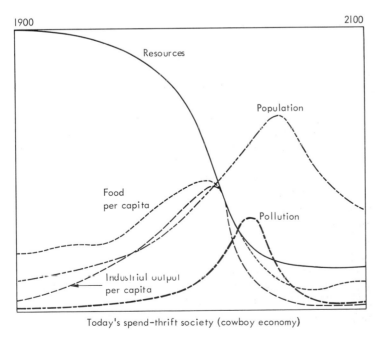

Figure 21-1. *Computer predictions of various variables (food, population, industrial output, pollution, resources) if current trends continue (After David Van Vleck,* The Crucial Generation, *Charlotte, Vt.: Optimum Population Incorporated, 1971. Source: Donella H. Meadows et al.,* The Limits to Growth, *New York: Universe Books, 1972)*

logical result of severely depressed levels of industrial and agricultural output. Ultimately, and predictably, by about 2070, the world population will begin a precipitous decline or "crash," caused by a combination of starvation, reduced fertility, belated family planning, extensively employed contraceptive measures, and, possibly, delayed marriage. Certainly, during this period, a catastrophic one in human history, the Malthusian prophecy of massive starvation would seem to be fulfilled. Even though continuing a decline, the global population will still be about seven billion by 2100 (compared to the 1975 figure of about 3.9 billion). By 2100, both industrial output and pollution rates will have become negligible. The prospects for survival beyond 2100 would appear rather grim, because the stock of natural resources will have reached the point of exhaustion (3).

This, then, is the prospect for planet Earth through the year 2100, as concluded by a group of respected scientists, assuming that both industrial and population growth will continue at the current exponential rates. However, there is a much more desirable alternative, based upon the spaceship economy (described in the chapter "Economics and the Environment"), in which every attempt is made to bring about a slowdown of both economic and population growth. Ideally, this would ultimately bring about a "steady state" type of society. Examination of Figure 21-2 reveals that if the world's industrialized nations made a concerted attempt *now* to convert to a "no-growth" system (and such a conversion is certainly possible, even though it would indeed cause certain dislocations of the economy), the "steady state" might be achieved in less than fifty years. Of course food production per capita must continue to increase; after all, two thirds of the present world population are suffering from malnutrition or undernourishment. Such food increase might be accomplished with the aid of recent advances in agricultural genetics, the development of higher yielding strains of corn, wheat, and rice, the construction of improved grain storage and distribution facilities, and the dissemination of technical "know-how" to the

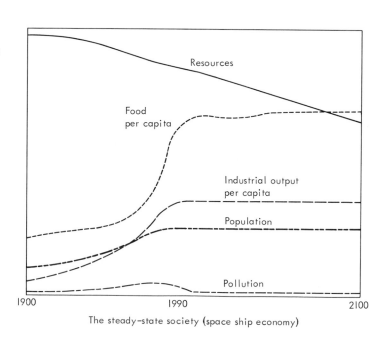

Figure 21-2. *Note that if strenuous attempts are made now (1975–1980) the steady-state society might be achieved by 2025. (After David B. Van Vleck, The Crucial Generation, Charlotte, Vt.: Optimum Population, Inc., 1971. Source: Donella E. Meadows et al., The Limits to Growth. New York: Universe Book, 1972.)*

Resources

Food per capita

Industrial output per capita

Population

Pollution

1900   1990   2100

The steady-state society (space ship economy)

undeveloped countries. It will be noted, however (Figure 21-2), that because many resources (e.g., oil, coal, natural gas, copper, iron) are non-renewable, the global stock of resources will unavoidably continue to decline. Nevertheless, with much greater emphasis on efficient utilization, and with the development of sophisticated new recycling technologies that would convert "waste" into the "great new resource," the rate of natural resource depletion would be reduced to a minimum (3).

Life styles in the "steady-state" society, envisaged for the year 2025, would be much simpler than those of today. The average American or European would have to make do without some of the traditional status-and-affluence symbols, such as the color TV, second family car, lake cottage, and snowmobile, but he would be able to maintain a life style that would be ecologically *sound* rather than ecologically *suicidal,* and would have a genuine chance of finding real happiness. In today's "growth-mania" society, happiness might be a "jet flight to Vegas," "a Christmas holiday in Spain," or "watching the Indy 500," but in the no-growth society of 2025 happiness might be "a canoe trip down the Apple River," "growing melons in one's own back yard," or even "learning the stars in the Big Dipper on a warm summer's night."

Many authorities in the areas of political science, sociology, economics, and science are of the firm opinion that eventually some sort of "simple life" will be man's fate, one way or another (Figure 21-3). It could be "simple life A," such as we have been describing, characterized by much real human happiness, with emphasis on spiritual and cultural values rather than on material wealth. A prerequisite for "simple life A" might well be a massive redistribution of the global resources, in which many of the "have" nations, such as the United States, Canada, West Germany, and Japan would make outright donations of food, technical knowledge, machinery, and money to the "have-not's," such as India, Pakistan, Liberia, Nigeria, Costa Rica, and Guatemala. This thesis has been strongly supported by a recent computer study conducted by Mihail Mesarovic of Case Western Reserve University and Eduard Pestel of the University of Hannover, Germany. Their data indicated that there would be massive, chronic starvation in South Asia and Africa, beginning in 1985, unless the industrialized nations provide a minimum of $700 billion of investment aid over the next fifty years. If such redistribution is not effected, the frustrated aspirations of the multitudinous wretched, representing 66 per cent of mankind, inevitably would lead to political unrest, violence, revolution, and, quite possibly, nuclear war. Bertrand Russell, for one, has observed that "nothing is more likely to lead to an H-bomb war than the threat of universal destitution through overpopulation." Syndicated columnist Smith Hempstone makes the following grim prediction: "Neither democracy nor peace will survive in areas where the roots of both are weak. Governments will fall like ten-pins and hungry nations will go to war in an effort to seize what they cannot produce." A nuclear exchange could conceivably impose a different kind of "simple life" (Type B) on mankind, one characterized not by basic human happiness, but by a primitive level of existence, with remnant populations literally scratching for survival in the moon-scape rubble of what was once planet Earth (9).

These somber predictions have been ridiculed by those who believe that somehow technology will solve all problems. After all, we have had crises before, and have eventually prospered from the technology that developed as a result. History is replete with examples that "necessity is the mother of invention." These optimists would suggest that the western world is on the brink of another technological revolu-

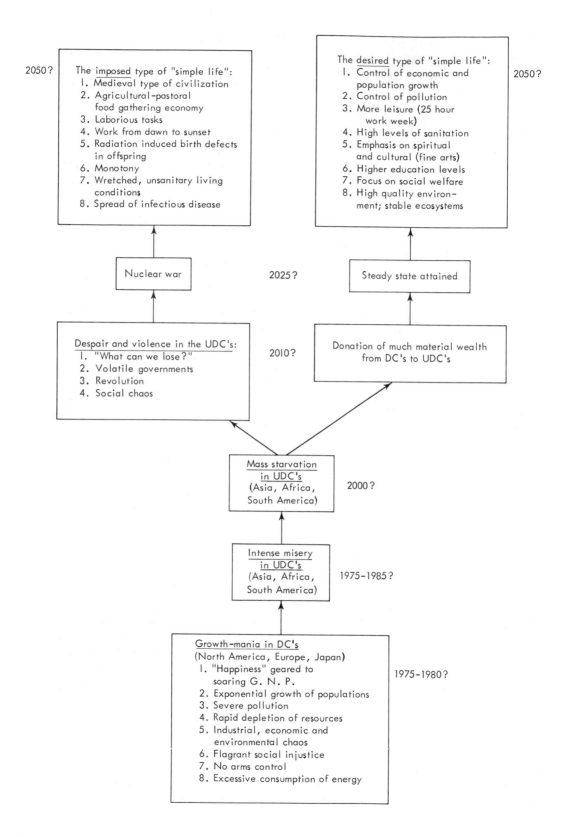

2050?

The imposed type of "simple life":
1. Medieval type of civilization
2. Agricultural-pastoral food gathering economy
3. Laborious tasks
4. Work from dawn to sunset
5. Radiation induced birth defects in offspring
6. Monotony
7. Wretched, unsanitary living conditions
8. Spread of infectious disease

The desired type of "simple life":
1. Control of economic and population growth
2. Control of pollution
3. More leisure (25 hour work week)
4. High levels of sanitation
5. Emphasis on spiritual and cultural (fine arts)
6. Higher education levels
7. Focus on social welfare
8. High quality environment; stable ecosystems

2050?

Nuclear war

2025?

Steady state attained

Despair and violence in the UDC's:
1. "What can we lose?"
2. Volatile governments
3. Revolution
4. Social chaos

2010?

Donation of much material wealth from DC's to UDC's

Mass starvation in UDC's (Asia, Africa, South America)

2000?

Intense misery in UDC's (Asia, Africa, South America)

1975-1985?

Growth-mania in DC's (North America, Europe, Japan)
1. "Happiness" geared to soaring G. N. P.
2. Exponential growth of populations
3. Severe pollution
4. Rapid depletion of resources
5. Industrial, economic and environmental chaos
6. Flagrant social injustice
7. No arms control
8. Excessive consumption of energy

1975-1980?

670

tion. After all, isn't the current crisis the greatest in human history? If small crises precipitate small innovations, then certainly today's global population-resource-environment dilemma may be the stimulus for the greatest technological breakthroughs of all time. Where there is a need, science and technology will find an answer. Athelstan Spilhaus, a leading spokesman for the technological optimists has suggested that "energy is the ultimate currency of civilization"—in other words, if enough energy is available, all things can be accomplished—pollution will be controlled, the world's stomachs will be filled, clothing and shelter for the needy millions will be provided, and so on. Indeed, the nuclear power enthusiasts are predicting unlimited energy once the breeder reactor has been perfected. As an editor of *Skeptic* magazine recently observed: "With limitless energy we can plumb the depths of the earth and the ocean bed, or colonize the moon in our search for resources. We can sink mines to far greater depth economically, refine ores that do not now yield enough to interest us, transform old resources into new, reclaim resources already used. We can farm the sea, . . . melt the ice caps, level the mountains to make arable land" (4). To increase food production we could perhaps employ a variety of schemes from hydroponics to food synthesis, from yeast and algal culture to the irrigation of the Sahara, from swampland drainage to the development of superior strains of corn, rice, and cattle. We can derive oil from old auto tires, methane gas from cow manure, and obtain construction materials from broken bottles and fly ash. Yes, we can always depend upon human skill and ingenuity to bring another rabbit out of man's technological hat. After all, Robert Malthus made similar dire predictions way back in 1798. And didn't technology make a fool out of him? And it will make liars out of the neo-Malthusians of today.

Could these optimists be right after all? It would indeed be highly reassuring to millions of the world's wretched. It is regrettable, however, that there is one big fly in this technological ointment that is supposed to heal this planet's wounds. And that is the matter of *time*. There simply isn't enough left for a technology-mediated salvation. And why not? The key word to the answer is *exponential*. Perhaps the metaphor employed by the authors of *Limits to Growth* will help explain its significance. Imagine a pond. Then imagine a special kind of water lily that grows *exponentially*, one that doubles its spread over the pond each day. Assume now that in 30 days the water lilies will have completely covered the pond. Suppose that you were a fisheries biologist assigned to the task of keeping the pond open for fishing. You examine the pond on the twenty-ninth day. How much of the pond will be covered with vegetation at this time? Only half! Now, if you were unfamiliar with the dynamics of exponential growth you certainly would guess that perhaps you had ample time to check water lily encroachment before the entire pond is choked with vegetation. Wrong. You would actually have just one day. In this metaphor the rapid growth of the water lilies represents both the surging global population and accelerating environmental pollution (as well as the earth's sharply declining stock

Figure 21-3. *Flow chart for events on planet Earth leading either to a desired or imposed type of "simple life." (Modified after David B. Van Vleck, The Crucial Generation, Charlotte, Vt.: Optimum Population Incorporated, 1971.)*

of resources). And even though technologists may attempt to push back the boundaries of our global "pond," it would be to no avail. For this is day 29. *And there is only one day left* (3)!

International Commission on Environmental Quality

"No man is an island" wrote Thomas Merton—and neither is a nation in this twentieth century world. Whether it be in the cultural, political, economic, or ecological sense, nations are interdependent, or at least interacting. Certainly very few would question the fact of economic interdependency. Witness the Middle Eastern oil embargo of 1973–1974, in which a handful of tiny Arab states disrupted the industrial tempo and life style of the mightiest nation on earth. Nations are "one" in an ecological sense as well, a point we tried to emphasize from time to time in this text. Take pollution. It recognizes no national boundaries. Insecticides sprayed on a Georgia cotton field are eventually washed into the ocean and carried by the Gulf Stream to the coast of Europe, eventually winding up in a fish some French housewife has prepared for supper. The detonation of a nuclear bomb over Siberia could generate radioactive strontium that might circle the globe at stratospheric levels for several years before a spring rain "scrubs" it to earth in some Michigan cow pasture. The generation of sulfur dioxide by coal-fired power plants in Germany may contribute to the formation of a strongly acid, fish-killing rainfall in Sweden. Salty run-off water from an improperly irrigated ranch in Arizona might be carried by the Colorado River into Mexico and cause the Mexican president to complain that the salt is sabotaging his country's valiant food-producing efforts. The construction of the Aswan Dam in Egypt substantially curtails the commercial fish harvest of adjacent coastal nations because fertility of the Mediterranean has been reduced. In a very real sense, pollution, resource exhaustion, and almost every other form of environmental degradation have international and even global implications, though at first glance it might appear to be a local or regional phenomenon.

Because time is of the essence (we have about one decade in which to get our environmental house in order, according to former United Nations Secretary-General U. Thant), uncoordinated, piecemeal attempts at "patching up" by either the United States, Russia, or Japan acting as "island states" simply must give way to a unified program directed and coordinated by an International Commission on Environmental Quality. Ideally, this agency would represent all nations, large and small, developed and undeveloped, Communist and non-Communist. Such an agency may or may not operate within the administrative framework of the United Nations. (The establishment of the United Nations Environmental Center at Nairobi, Southern Rhodesia, in 1973, was a step in the right direction.) It would have the responsibility of analyzing and integrating global environmental data made available from national resource agencies (America's Environmental Protection Agency), university research centers (e.g., University of Moscow, Cornell University) and from environmental satellites and space laboratories. Then, on the basis of the data available, the Commission would be able to make computerized projections (as in the case of the MIT study) of long-term trends and consequences. Typical problems to which the Commission might address itself come to mind:

1. How many degrees warmer (or colder) will the average global air temperature be by the year 2000? Will the polar ice caps start melting? If so, what coastal areas would probably be inundated?
2. What will be the average concentration of chlorinated hydrocarbons in the body fat of an Indian or South African if pesticide use in the UDC's continues to increase in tempo? Just what are the chronic effects of these chemicals in *any* human body over the long run?
3. Will the long-term effects of the pesticides now being used in the UDC's eventually outweigh the short-term gains?
4. What effect will the warm water discharges into coastal waters off the American and European coasts have in disrupting the breeding migrations of valuable food fishes such as the tuna and herring?
5. What will be the long-term effect of the use of commercial fertilizers on impairing soil structure to the point where crop production will no longer be possible? Are Ukranian soils more susceptible than the black soils of Iowa and Illinois?
6. How can the thousands of varieties of crop plants represented in American "seed banks" most effectively become integrated in the agricultural patterns of those nations having compatible soils and climates?
7. Should the International Environmental Commission outlaw all whaling operations indefinitely so that endangered species, such as the blue whale, will have a chance to escape extinction?
8. What effect will the release of soot and other particulates from smokestacks in the industrial Ruhr have on lung cancer rates in Scandinavia?
9. Are pollutants bringing about a change in climatic patterns? If so, which nations will be most adversely affected? Should provisions be made, for example, to facilitate the transition of, say, Iowa from an agricultural economy with heavy emphasis on corn to an economy based on sheep grazing?
10. Should an international effort be launched to explore the fish-farming potential of shallow coastal regions?
11. Could the oceanic currents be affected by thermal pollution? If so, what would be the long-term effect on climate, the photosynthetic rates of marine algae, and biome modification?
12. What is the long-range effect of oil pollution on marine productivity? Should oil tanker traffic be restricted to special corridors where the potentially damaging effects of the inevitable oil spills on waterfowl and marine fish will be minimized? Should the International Commission have representatives aboard oil tankers so that regulations relative to oil pollution can be strictly enforced?
13. Precisely what *is* the carrying capacity of the Earth in terms of human beings? Eight billion? Five billion? Or have we already, with a population of 3.9 billion, exceeded the ability of planet Earth to sustain so many people over the long term? Would the translocation of people from over-populated regions to under-populated regions be ecologically feasible?

Even with the scientific expertise available to the Commission, it of course would degenerate into nothing more than a sort of super "think-and-dream" tank unless it were vested with legislative, inspection, and enforcement authority as well. Severe penalties, in the form of economic sanctions (possibly an embargo on oil, copper, or fertilizer, for example), could be assessed against any member nation guilty of violating the regulations formulated by the Commission.

This concept sounds visionary, unattainable, and almost ludicrous in the cold light of an everyday world in which individuals, states, and nations operate primarily on a selfish "What's in it for me?" philosophy. However, the urgency of the environmental posture of planet Earth demands nothing less.

Can Man Survive?

Will man eventually, because of environmental mismanagement, blunder his way to extinction? Will *Homo sapiens* follow the path of the passenger pigeon and saber-toothed cat? The distinguished ecologist, Barry Commoner, has voiced this opinion:

". . . We are in a crisis of *survival;* for environmental pollution is a signal that the ecological systems on which we depend for our life and our livelihood have begun to break down and are approaching the point of no return. My own estimate is that if we are to avoid environmental catastrophe by the 1980's we will need to begin the vast process of connecting the fundamental incompatabilities of major technologies with the demands of the ecosystem. This means that we will need to put into operation essentially emissionless versions of automotive vehicles, power plants, refineries, steel mills, and chemical plants. Agricultural technology will need to find ways of sustaining productivity without breaking down the natural soil cycle, or disrupting the natural control of destructive insects. Sewage and garbage treatment plants will need to be designed to return organic waste to the soil, where, in nature, it belongs. Vegetation will need to be massively reintroduced into urban areas. Housing and urban sanitary facilities will need to be drastically improved. All of these will demand serious economic adjustments, and our economic and social system will need to be prepared to meet them. . . . I believe that we have, as of now (1970), a single decade in which to design the fundamental changes in technology that we must put into effect in the 1980's—if we are to survive. We will need to seize on the decade of the 1970's as a period of grace—a decade which must be used for a vast pilot program to guide the coming reconstruction of the nation's system of productivity. This, I believe, is the urgency of the environmental crisis—we must determine, now, to develop, in the next decade, the new means of our salvation" (1).

The Washington-based headquarters of the Environmental Teach-In of April 22, 1970, has eloquently described America's plight and the essential commitments which society must make:

A disease has infected our country. It has brought smog to Yosemite, dumped garbage in the Hudson, sprayed DDT on our food, and left our cities in decay. Its carrier is man.

The weak are already dying. Trees by the Pacific. Fish in our streams and lakes. Birds and crops and sheep. And people.

We must act *now* to reclaim the environment we have wrecked.

Earth Day is a commitment to make life better, not just bigger and faster; to provide real rather than rhetorical solutions.

It is a day to examine the ethic of individual progress at mankind's expense.

It is a day to challenge the corporate and governmental leaders who promise change, but who short-change the necessary programs.

It is a day for looking beyond tomorrow.

Earth Day seeks a future worth living.

Earth Day seeks a future period.

Americans must make every day an Earth Day. We must make these commitments and act on them, for every day of our natural lives. In this crucial period it is imperative that we elect responsible leaders in government at all levels who "recognize and act upon the fact that time is running out, that only the resolute rejection of war, profits as usual, procreation as usual, comforts as usual, and politics as usual will prevent our planet from sliding to disaster" (7).

J. Mayone Stycos of Cornell University states that all major social (and environmental) changes are not finally realized until they have passed through four phases:

1. No Talk—No do.
2. Talk—No do.
3. Talk—Do.
4. No-talk—Do.

America has barely entered phase three. Time for the completion of phases three and four is limited. Knowledgeable men have made predictions concerning man's fate if the trend of deterioration continues at its present pace. After noting that land and resources are finite, Martin Litton, a director of the Sierra Club, sounds a note of pessimism: "We are prospecting for the very last of our resources and using up the nonrenewable things many times faster than we are finding new ones. . . . We've already run out of earth and nothing we can do will keep mankind in existence for as long as another two centuries" (2).

Slightly more optimistic is Gardner D. Stout, president of the American Museum of Natural History: "That man will survive is likely. When the chips are down he is astonishingly adaptable, cunningly expert. But the concept of survival by itself is a minimal and chilling one. Survival can be appallingly rudimentary . . ." (5).

America is in crisis—and time is running out. Were the rising voice of concern to be muffled, the American Dream may yet turn to a nightmare. As Lowell Sumner has written, ". . . the human population explosion, and its declining spiral of natural resources, is . . . the greatest threat of all. The time is ripe, even dangerously over-ripe, as far as the population control problem is concerned. We shall have to face up or ultimately perish, and what a dreary, *stupid*, unlovely way to perish, on a ruined globe stripped of its primeval beauty" (6).

BIBLIOGRAPHY

1. Commoner, Barry. "Salvation: It's Possible," *The Progressive* (April 1970), 12–18.
2. Litton, Martin. Quoted in *Time*, February 2, 1970, p. 62.
3. Meadows, Donella H., et al. *The Limits to Growth*. New York: Universe, 1972.
4. *Skeptic*, "Can Technology Come to Our Rescue?" (Editorial), Special Issue No. 2 (1974). The Forum for Contemporary History, Santa Barbara, Calif.
5. Stout, Gardner D. Quoted in Creighton Peet, "Can Man Survive?" *American Forests* (August 1969), 5–7, 41–42.
6. Sumner, Lowell. Quoted in Paul Ehrlich, *The Population Bomb*. New York: Ballantine, 1968.
7. *The Progressive*, "Action for Survival," (Editorial), Madison, Wis., April 1970, 3–6.
8. Toynbee, Arnold. "After the Age of Affluence," *The London Observer*, April 14, 1974.
9. Van Vleck, David B. *The Crucial Generation*. Charlotte, Vt.: Optimum Population, Inc., 1971.

Glossary

Abortion.   The premature expulsion of the fetus from the uterus.

Abyssal Zone.   The bottom zone of the ocean; characterized by darkness, close to freezing temperatures, and high water pressures.

Accelerated Erosion.   A rapid type of soil erosion that is induced by human activities, in contrast to the relatively slow processes of geologic erosion.

Activated Sludge.   In a secondary or tertiary sewage treatment plant, the solid organic waste that has been intensively aerated and "seeded" with bacteria so as to promote rapid bacterial decomposition.

Aggregate.   A grouping of soil particles. Soil aeration, moisture content, fertility, and erosion resistance are in part dependent on aggregate patterns.

Alluvial Soil.   A type of soil that develops from waterborne sediment; frequently very fertile.

Alpha Particle. A positively charged particle (proton) that is emitted from the nucleus of a radioactive atom.

Altitudinal Migration. Seasonal movement of birds (grosbeaks, finches, juncos) and mammals (elk, bighorn sheep) up and down mountain slopes.

Ammocoetes Larva. The immature stage of the sea lamprey.

Ammonification. The process by which the bacteria of decay convert complex nitrogenous compounds occurring in animal carcasses and their excreta, as well as in the dead bodies of plants, into relatively simple ammonia (NH_3) compounds.

Anadromous Fish. A fish, such as the Pacific salmon, that spawns and spends its early life in fresh water but moves into the ocean where it attains sexual maturity and spends most of its life span.

Annular Ring. A concentric ring visible in a cross section of a tree trunk because the xylem cells which form the ring lay down thick walls during periods of abundant moisture, but produce thinner walls when moisture is less abundant; in the north temperate zone where a moisture-abundant spring and summer alternate with a relatively dry fall and winter the rings may be useful in determining the age of the tree.

Antimycin. A toxic substance that has been rather extensively used by fisheries biologists to eradicate carp, effective at extremely low concentrations.

Aquifer. A subterranean stratum of porous water-bearing rock such as sandstone and limestone.

Artificial Insemination. In cattle breeding the technique by which sperm from a bull of one breed (Hereford) might be refrigerated and over a period of several years be used to fertilize the eggs of the same or other breeds in widely separated localities.

Artificial Reef. A reef constructed of housing debris, rubble, junked automobiles, tires, and so on; frequently placed in relatively shallow water near the coast; a method of increasing breeding sites and shelter for marine fish.

Bathyal Zone. The oceanic zone located between the euphotic and abyssal zones; occurs at a depth between 200 and 2,000 meters.

Beta Particle. A negatively charged particle (electron) that is emitted from a radioactive atom.

Biodegradable Material. Material, such as human waste, that may be decomposed by bacterial activity.

Biological Control. The control of pests (insects, rodents, and so on) by means of biological agents—for example, the control of rabbits by means of a virus or the control of screwworm flies by sterilizing large numbers of males by cobalt radiation and then releasing them into the wild population.

Biological Magnifier. An organism that increases the concentration of a particular insecticide (DDT, dieldrin, and so on) above the level occurring in the plants or animals it consumes.

Biological Oxygen Demand (BOD). The amount of oxygen required by aquatic bacteria to decompose a given load of organic waste, such as human waste or residues from canneries.

Biomass. The total mass of living substance (protoplasm); for example, the biomass of a lake or an oak woodlot.

Biome. The largest community easily distinguished by an ecologist; for example, the grassland biome, deciduous forest biome, or desert biome.

Biotic Potential (BP). The theoretical reproductive capacity of a species.

Blister Rust.   A fungus-caused disease of the white pine; characterized by the appearance of orange "blisters" on the bark.

Botulism.   A disease of waterfowl caused by a bacterium and characterized by eventual respiratory paralysis and death.

Breeder Reactor.   A nuclear reactor that uses a relatively small amount of uranium-235 as a "primer" to release energy from the much more abundant uranium-238.

Broadcasting.   A method of reseeding range or forest; seeds are dispersed broadly by hand, machine, or plane.

Browse Line.   A line delimiting browsed and unbrowsed portions of shrubs and trees in an area where the deer population exceeds the carrying capacity of the range.

Cambium.   The layer of rapidly dividing cells located between the phloem and xylem in the trunk of a tree; permits growth in diameter of the trunk.

Carbon Dioxide Fixation.   The incorporation of carbon dioxide into glucose molecules by the process of photosynthesis.

Carrying Capacity.   The capacity of a given habitat to sustain a population of animals for an indefinite period of time.

Catadromous Fish.   A type of fish that grows to sexual maturity in fresh water but migrates to the ocean for spawning purposes; for example, the American eel.

Chain Reaction.   The sequence of events in which neutrons that have been emitted from a radioactive atom bombard another atom and cause it to emit neutrons that in turn bombard yet another atom, and so on.

Channelization.   The process by which a natural stream is converted into a ditch for the ostensible purpose of flood control; attendant environmental abuse is severe.

Chernozem.   The type of soil developing under a mixed-grass prairie; characterized by a fertile, thick, blackish-brown topsoil and a grayish subsoil.

Chlorinated Hydrocarbon.   A "family" of nonbiodegradable pesticides such as DDT, dieldrin, and endrin; may have a harmful effect on nontarget organisms such as fish and birds; accumulate in the environment and in the tissues of organisms.

Chlorosis.   An abnormal condition in plants characterized by a chlorophyll deficiency.

Clearcutting.   A method of harvesting timber in which *all* trees are removed from a given patch or block of forest; the method of choice when applied to a single-species-stand composed of uniformly aged trees.

Climax Community.   The stable, terminal stage of an ecological succession.

Cochlea.   The snail-shell-like portion of the inner ear that is concerned with hearing.

Coliform Bacteria.   A type of bacterium occurring in the human gut; used as an index of the degree to which waters have been contaminated with human waste.

Community.   The total number of organisms of all species living in a given area; for example, the community of an oak woods, abandoned field, or cattail marsh.

Compensation Depth.   The depth in a lake at which photosynthesis balances respiration; this level delimits the upper limnetic zone from the lower profundal zone.

Compost.   Partially decomposed organic material (garbage) that can be used as a soil conditioner and fertilizer.

Consumer.   A term used for any animal link in a food chain.

Contour Farming.   Plowing, cultivating, and harvesting crops along the contour of the land rather than up and down the slope; an effective technique for controlling soil erosion.

Crown Fire.   The most destructive type of forest fire; that is, one that consumes the entire tree, including the canopy.

Cyclic Population. A population that peaks and troughs at regular intervals, e.g., the four-year cycle of the lemming, and the ten-year cycle of the ruffed grouse.

Cyclohexamide. An antibiotic used to control blister rust on white pine seedlings.

Cyclone Filter. A type of air pollution control device that removes particulate matter (dust) with the aid of gravity and a downward spiraling air stream.

Decibel. A unit of measurement of the intensity of sound.

Decreaser. A highly nutritious, highly palatable species of the climax grassland community that generally decreases under heavy grazing pressure.

Deferred Grazing. A range management technique in which a range is divided into several pastures, with the pastures being grazed on a rotation basis, so that all pastures will have an opportunity to reach maturity and produce seeds; the system prevents overgrazing and eventual rangeland deterioration.

Denitrification. The decomposition of ammonia compounds, nitrites, and nitrates by bacteria which results in the eventual release of nitrogen into the atmosphere.

Density-Dependent Factor. A population regulating factor, such as storms, drought, floods, or volcanic eruptions, whose effect is independent of the population density.

Density-Independent Factor. A population regulating factor, such as predation or infectious disease, whose effect on a population is dependent upon the population density.

Desalination. The removal of salt from sea water in order to make it potable.

Desert Pavement. The stony surface of some deserts caused by excessive erosion of the thin topsoil from the occasional heavy rainfall.

Dioxin. An extremely toxic impurity occurring in the herbicide 2,4,5–T, which is suspected of causing birth defects in South Vietnam.

Ecology. The study of the inter-relationships that exist between organisms and their environment.

Ecosystem. A contraction for "ecological system."

Edge. The interspersion of various habitat types; densities of game animals tend to be greater in areas that have a substantial amount of edge.

Electron. A negatively charged particle occurring in the orbit of an atom.

Electrostatic Precipitator. A pollution control device that removes solid particles from smokestacks by providing them with a negative charge and then attracting them to a positively charged plate.

Elemental Cycle. The "circular" movement of an element (nitrogen, carbon, and so on) from the nonliving environment (air, water, soil) into the bodies of living organisms and then back into the nonliving environment once again.

Emphysema. A potentially lethal disease characterized by a reduction in the number of alveoli in the lungs as well as a reduction in total respiratory membrane area.

Environmental Resistance (ER). Any factor in the environment of an organism that tends to limit its numbers.

Epilimnion. The upper stratum of a lake that is characterized by a temperature gradient of less than 1° C per meter of depth.

Estrogen. The female sex hormone, produced by the egg follicle in the ovary, which is responsible for many of the female characteristics such as the development of the vagina, uterus, and oviducts, the growth of pubic and armpit hair, the widening of the hips, and the sexual urge.

Eugenicists. A dedicated group of people who would like to "improve" the quality of the human species by making sterilization mandatory for "inferior" individuals such as cripples, criminals, and the mentally retarded.

Euphotic Zone. The open water zone of the ocean characterized by sufficient sunlight penetration to support photosynthesis; located just above the bathyal zone.

Euryphagous. Refers to an animal with a highly varied diet, such as a pheasant or opossum, in contrast to an animal having a narrow or stenophagous diet, such as an ivory-billed woodpecker.

Eutrophication. The enrichment of a lake, river, marsh, or ocean with nutrients (nitrates, phosphates) that promote biological productivity (algae, weeds, and so on).

Fabric Filter Baghouse. An air pollution control device that operates somewhat like a giant vacuum cleaner in removing solid particles from industrial smokestacks.

Fall Overturn. The thorough mixing of lake waters during autumn, which occurs at this time because the water temperature and density is uniform from top to bottom.

Fenuron. A herbicide that has been used extensively to control rangeland pests such as the mesquite bush. Use of fenuron should be held to a minimum.

Fibrous Root System. A complex root system, such as that of grass plants, in which there are several major roots and a great number of primary, secondary, and tertiary branches; useful in "binding" soil in place and preventing erosion.

Field Capacity. The amount of water that remains in the soil after the excess has drained away from soil that had been water saturated.

Fluorosis. A disease in animals caused by fluoride poisoning; symptoms in livestock include thickened bones and stiff joints.

Flyway. One of the major migration pathways used by waterfowl, e.g., Atlantic Flyway, Pacific Flyway, and so on.

Food Chain. The flow of nutrients and energy from one organism to another by means of a series of eating processes.

Food Web. An interconnected series of food chains.

Furunculosis. A serious bacterial disease occurring in fish.

Gamma Radiation. An intense type of radiation, similar to X-rays, which is easily capable of penetrating the human body.

Glassification. A method of disposing of radioactive waste, by concentrating it and enclosing it in solid ceramic bricks.

Glasphalt. A type of road surfacing material that employs crushed glass in its manufacture rather than sand; more durable than ordinary asphalt.

Green Manure. The bodies of green plants (alfalfa, vetch, and so on) that have been plowed under to increase soil fertility.

Green Revolution. The increased food production capability made possible in recent years because of selective breeding, increased use of fertilizer, development of "seed banks," more intensive use of herbicides and insecticides, and so on.

Gross National Product (GNP). The sum total of expenditures by governments and individuals for goods, services, or investments.

Ground Water. Water that has infiltrated the ground, in contrast to runoff water, which flows over the ground surface.

Gully Reclamation. The "mending" of a gully by either physical methods (check dams of boulders or cement) or vegetational means (planting of rapidly growing shrubs on the slopes).

Gyptol. The sex attractant produced by the female gypsy moth, which serves to attract the male moth from considerable distances.

Habitat. The immediate environment in which an organism lives; it includes such components as cover, food, shelter, water, and breeding sites.

Hair Cells. Sensory cells in the inner ear (cochlea) that are concerned with the sensation of hearing.

Half-life. The time required for one-half of the radioactivity of a given radioactive isotope (uranium, strontium, and so on) to be dissipated.

Hardwood. A species of tree such as oak, hickory, and maple, that has relatively hard wood in contrast to the soft woods of the conifers such as spruce and pine; synonymous with "deciduous."

Heartwood. The dark, central portion of a tree trunk characterized by the presence of dead, xylem cells that have become filled with gums and resins.

Home Range. The total area occupied by an animal during its life cycle; that is, the area required for feeding, breeding, loafing, and securing refuge from the weather and from predators.

Horizon. One of the horizontal layers (A, B, C, and D) visible in a cross section of soil.

Hybrid. The offspring that results from a cross of two different species or strains of animals or plants; for example, the Santa Gertrudis cattle resulted from a series of crosses involving two parental types, the Brahmin cattle and the shorthorn.

Hydrocoele. A type of radiation-induced birth defect characterized by the accumulation of fluid around the testes.

Hydrologic Cycle. The "circular" movement of water from the ocean reservoir to the air (clouds), to the earth in the form of rain and snow, and finally back to the ocean reservoir via streams and estuaries.

Hydrolysis. A type of chemical reaction in which a compound is broken down into simpler components by the action of water.

Hydroponics. The technique of growing crops in an aqueous nutrient solution without soil.

Hydroseeder. A machine employed to disperse grass seed, water, and fertilizer on steep banks.

Hypolimnion. The bottom layer of water in a lake characterized by a temperature gradient of less than $1°$ C per meter of depth.

Increaser. In the context of range management, a moderately palatable, highly nutritious climax species that tends to increase in number, at least temporarily, when a range is heavily grazed.

Integrated Pest Control. A method of pest control that judiciously employs chemical, biological, and other methods (cultural), depending upon the specific problem; the use of chemicals is minimized to avoid environmental damage.

Introduction. The bringing in of an exotic plant or animal to a new region, e.g., the introduction of the European carp into the United States, and the introduction of the coho salmon from the Pacific Coast to Lake Michigan.

Invader. A term employed in rangeland management which refers to the establishment of a pioneer species of plant, usually a noxious weed, in an overgrazed pasture.

Irruption. A sudden increase in the population of an organism, which is followed by a precipitous decline (crash); frequently the carrying capacity of the habitat is reduced for many years thereafter—for example, the Kaibab deer irruption.

Isotope. A form of an element identical to the regular element except for a difference in atomic weight. Thus, deuterium is an isotope of hydrogen.

Juvenile Dispersal. The dispersal of young animals (bald eagles, ruffed grouse, muskrats, and so on) from the general region of their hatching site or birth site; the presumed function is to prevent overpopulation in the parental area.

Krill. The crustaceans and other small marine organisms that are used as food by the whalebone whales.

Landfill. A method of solid waste disposal in which the waste is dumped, compacted, and then covered with a layer of soil.

Latitudinal Migration. The north-south type of migration characteristic of caribou, gray whale, and waterfowl.

Levee. A dike composed of earth, stone, or concrete that is erected along the margin of a river for purposes of flood control.

Limiting Factors. Any factor in the environment of an organism, such as radiation, excessive heat, floods, drought, disease, lack of micronutrients, that tends to reduce the population of that organism.

Limnetic Zone. The region of open water in a lake, beyond the littoral zone, down to the maximal depth at which there is sufficient sunlight for photosynthesis.

Littoral Zone. The shallow, marginal region of a lake characterized by rooted vegetation.

Loam. The most desirable type of soil from an agricultural viewpoint; composed of a mixture of sand, silt, and clay.

Macronutrient. Mineral nutrient used by organisms in relatively large quantities (calcium, nitrogen, potassium, phosphorus).

Macropores. A large space that occurs between the individual soil particles.

Mass Emigration. The mass movement of a species from a given area; for example, the mass movement of the snowy owl from the tundra to the United States during periods of lemming scarcity.

Metabolic Reserve. The lower 50 per cent of a grass shoot that is required by a grazed plant for survival; contains the minimum amount of photosynthetic equipment needed for food production purposes.

Microcephaly. A birth defect characterized by an abnormally small brain; associated with mental retardation; may be induced by radiation.

Microhabitat. The immediate, localized environment of an organism.

Micronutrient. A mineral nutrient required by organisms in only minute quantities (iodine, zinc, copper, iron, and so on).

Millirem. One thousandth of a *rem*, which is a unit for measuring the effect of radiation on the body of a living organism.

Mulch. Dead plant material that accumulates on the ground surface; is a reliable indicator of range condition.

Mycelia. The branching "root system" of a fungus.

Mycorrhiza. An intimate relationship between the root systems of trees and soil fungi.

Myxomatosis Virus. The virus that was used to control the rabbit outbreak in Australia; animals become infected when they consume contaminated forage.

Natural Resource. Any component of the natural environment, such as soil, water, rangeland, forest, wildlife, minerals, that man can use to promote his welfare.

Nematode. An extremely abundant and ubiquitous type of worm (roundworm) that occurs in soil, water, and the bodies of plants and animals; some are free-living, others are parasitic.

Neritic Zone. The relatively warm, nutrient-rich, shallow water zone of the ocean that overlies the continental shelf; valuable zone in terms of fish production.

Net Production. The total energy incorporated into the body of a plant as a result of photosynthesis *minus* the energy required for respiration.

Neutron. The electrically neutral particle in the nucleus of an atom.

Nitrate Bacteria. Bacteria that have the ability to convert nitrites into nitrates; essential bacteria in the cycling of nitrogen.

Nonbiodegradable Material. Material not readily susceptible to being decomposed by bacteria; for example, DDT, dieldrin, and other chlorinated hydrocarbon pesticides.

North American Water and Power Alliance (NAWAPA). Scheme for transferring water from the water-rich, lowly populous areas of northwestern Canada to the water-deficient areas of the United States and Mexico.

Oak Wilt. A fungus-caused disease that has threatened extensive oak forests in the southern Appalachians and the upper Mississippi valley.

Oligotrophic Lake. A nutrient-poor lake occurring in the northern states and in high mountain areas, characterized by great depth, sandy or gravelly bottom, sparse amount of rooted vegetation, low production of plankton and fish; for example, Lake Superior, Finger Lakes of New York.

Organic Phosphorus Pesticides. A group of pesticides (malathion, parathion, and so on) which are lethal to insects because they reduce the supply of cholinesterase at the junction (synapse) between two nerve cells in a nerve cell chain.

Oxidation. The chemical union of oxygen with metals (iron, aluminum) or organic compounds (sugars); the former process is an important factor in soil formation; the latter process permits the release of energy from cellular fuels (sugars, fats, and so on).

Ozone. A gaseous component of the atmosphere; normally occurs at elevations of about 20 miles; important to man because it shields him from the ultraviolet radiation of the sun; also represents one of the products resulting from the action of sunlight on the hydrocarbons emitted from the internal combustion engine.

Particulate Matter. Minute solid and liquid particles in the atmosphere, e.g., soot.

Permafrost. The permanently frozen soil in the tundra that occurs at a depth of about 1 foot.

Phloem. The elongate food-conducting cells of the trunk and branches of a tree; these cells convey food from the leaves downward to the root system.

Photochemical Smog. The type of smog that has plagued Los Angeles and other California towns, as well as other areas in the United States; formed as a result of the action of sunlight on the hydrocarbon emissions from motor cars and other sources; at nightfall the production of this type of smog ceases.

Photolysis. A phase of photosynthesis in which solar energy splits water molecules into hydrogen and oxygen.

Photosynthesis. The process occurring in green plants by which solar energy is utilized in the conversion of carbon dioxide and water into sugar.

Phreatophyte. A type of plant, such as cattail, willow, and saltcedar, that uses unusually large quantities of water to the disadvantage of more desirable species of plants such as range grasses.

Phytoactin. A type of antibiotic that has been used successfully to control the blister rust disease on western white pine.

Phytoplankton. Minute plants, such as algae, living in lakes, streams, and oceans, which are passively transported by water currents or wave action.

Pioneer Community. The initial community in an ecological succession; such a community (weeds, lichens, and so on) is frequently capable of surviving under severe conditions such as drought, extreme heat, or cold.

Pistil. The female sexual part of a flower, composed of a stigma, a style, and an ovary.

Plankton. Tiny plants (algae) and animals (protozoa, small crustaceans, fish embryos, insect larvae, and so on) that live in aquatic ecosystems and are moved about by water currents and wave action.

Podzol Soil. A soil group that develops under forest cover; characterized by a relatively infertile, thin, grayish topsoil and a dark brown subsoil; because this soil is rather acid in nature, it must be limed if it is to be used for crop production.

Population. The total number of individuals of a species occurring in a given area; for example, the population of deer in a cedar swamp, the population of black bass in a lake.

Prescribed Burning. A type of surface burning (used by foresters, wildlife biologists, ranchers, and so on) in which the utmost precaution is taken in terms of dryness of fuel, wind velocity, relative humidity, and so on; prescribed burning attempts to improve the quality of forest, range, or wildlife habitat.

Primary Production. The *total* amount of sugar produced by photosynthesis; on a global basis it amounts to about 270 billion tons annually.

Primary Succession. An ecological succession that develops in an area not previously occupied by a community; for example, a succession that develops on a granite outcrop or on lava.

Primary Sewage Treatment. A rudimentary sewage treatment that removes a substantial amount of the settleable solids and about 90 per cent of the biological oxygen demand (BOD).

Producer. A plant that can carry on photosynthesis and thus produce food for itself and indirectly for other organisms in the food chain of which it is a part.

Profundal Zone. The bottom zone of a lake, which extends from the lake bottom upward to the limnetic zone; characterized by insufficient sunlight for photosynthesis.

Progesterone. A hormone produced by the corpus luteum of the ovary, which is responsible for preparing the uterus to receive the fertilized egg.

Proton. A positively charged particle in the nucleus of an atom.

Purse Seine. A seine used by commercial fishermen that closes to entrap fish somewhat as a drawstring purse closes to "trap" money.

Pyramid of Energy. The graphic expression of the second law of thermodynamics as applied to the energy transfer in food chains; i.e., a certain amount of energy is lost in the form of heat as it moves through the links of a food chain, the greatest amount being present in the basal link (producer) and the least amount being present in the terminal link (carnivore).

Pyramid of Biomass. The graphical expression of the fact that there is a progressive reduction in total biomass (protoplasm) with each successive level in a food chain.

Pyramid of Numbers. The graphic expression of the fact that the number of individuals in a given food chain is greatest at the producer level, less at the herbivore level, and least at the carnivore level.

Pyrolysis. The destructive distillation of solid waste.

Quercitin. A substance derived from tree bark that is useful in checking bleeding.

RAD. A unit devised to measure the amount of radiation absorbed by living tissue; a rad is 100 ergs (unit of energy) absorbed by one gram of tissue; about 1 roentgen, which is about the amount of radioactivity received from a single dental x-ray.

Range of Tolerance.   The tolerance range of a species for certain factors in its environment such as moisture, temperature, radiation, micronutrients, oxygen.

REM.   A unit of absorbed radiation dose taking into account the relative biological effect of various types of radiation; about 1 roentgen, which is roughly the amount of radiation received from a single dental x-ray.

Respiration.   The process by means of which cellular fuels are "burned" with the aid of oxygen so as to permit the release of the energy required to sustain life; during respiration oxygen is used up and carbon dioxide is given off.

Rhizobium.   One of a genus of nitrogen-fixing bacteria that lives in the root nodules of legumes (alfalfa, clover, and so on).

Rhizome.   An underground stem; occurs in grasses; permits vegetative reproduction, since the tip of the rhizome may develop a bud that can develop into a new plant.

Rhizosphere.   The soil in the immediate vicinity of a plant root system

Rotenone.   A poisonous substance derived from the roots of an Asiatic legume; has been extensively used to control rough fish populations.

Rough Fish.   Undesirable trash fish such as garpike and carp.

Runoff Water.   The water that flows over the land surface after rainfall or snowmelt to eventually form streams, lakes, marshes, and the like.

Salinization.   An adverse aftereffect of irrigating land that has poor drainage properties; as a result, especially in the arid western states, evaporation of the salty water leaves a salt accumulation on the land, which renders the soil unsuitable for crop production.

Salt Water Intrusion.   The contamination of freshwater aquifers with salt water as the result of excessive exploitation of those aquifers in coastal regions near the ocean.

Sapwood.   The lighter, moist, more porous layer of xylem tissue immediately ensheathing the heartwood; composed of water and nutrient-transporting xylem cells.

Secondary Sewage Treatment.   An advanced type of sewage treatment that involves both mechanical and biological (bacterial action) phases; although superior to primary treatment much of the phosphates and nitrates remain in the effluent.

Secondary Succession.   An ecological succession that occurs in an area that had at one time already supported living organisms; for example, a succession developing in a burned-over forest or in an abandoned field.

Septic Tank.   A part of a rudimentary type of sewage treatment system used commonly by families who are located in rural areas; the sewage flows into the subterranean septic tank and is gradually decomposed by bacterial action.

Shade-Tolerant Plant.   A species of plant, such as the sugar maple, that reproduces well under conditions of reduced light intensity.

Sheet Irrigation.   A type of irrigation in which water flows slowly over the land in the form of a "sheet."

Shelter Belt.   Rows of trees and shrubs arranged at right angles to the prevalent wind for the purpose of diminishing the desiccating and eroding effects of the wind on crop and range land; commonly employed in the Great Plains.

Sigmoid Growth Curve.   The S-shaped curve commonly followed by the population of an animal (deer, grouse, rabbit, and so on) when it has been newly introduced into a habitat with good carrying capacity.

Siltation.   The filling up of a stream or reservoir with water-borne sediment.

Softwood.   A species of tree such as spruce, pine, and fir, that has softer wood than hardwoods such as oak and hickory; usually synonymous with *conifer.*

Soil Fire. A slowly burning fire that consumes the organic material in the earth; characterized by little flame but considerable smoke.

Soil Profile. A cross-sectional view of a particular soil type in which the characteristic layers or horizons are well represented.

Soil Structure. The arrangement or grouping of the soil's primary particles into granules or aggregates; a soil with good structure has a spongy or crumbly quality with an abundance of pores through which water and oxygen can move.

Soil Texture. The size of the individual soil particles; the four textural categories ranging from the smallest to the largest sized particles are *clay, silt, sand,* and *gravel.*

Solar Energy. The radiant energy generated by the sun, which "powers" all energy-consuming processes on earth, whether biological or non-biological.

Spoil Bank. The mounds of overburden that accumulate during a strip-mining operation; unless properly limed and then vegetated these spoil banks may be an important source of acid mine drainage and erosion.

Spring Overturn. The complete top-to-bottom mixing of water in a lake during the spring of the year when all the water is of about the same temperature and density.

Stamen. The club-shaped, pollen-producing part of a flower.

Stenophagous. Having a very specialized diet; for example, the ivory-billed woodpecker, which consumes beetle larvae secured only from *recently* dead trees, or the Everglade kite, which feeds almost exclusively on the snail *Pomacea caliginosa.*

Sterilization. A method of human population control involving the cutting and tying of the sperm ducts in the male and the oviducts (egg tubes) in the female.

Stolon. A horizontal stem or runner that passes over the surface of the ground.

Strip Cropping. An agricultural practice in which an open row crop (potatoes, corn, cotton) is alternated with a cover crop (alfalfa, clover) to minimize soil erosion.

Strip Mining. The type of mining in which coal or iron, for example, is scooped from the earth by giant earth-moving machines; the results are frequently a badly scarred landscape, soil erosion, and acid mine drainage.

Succession. The replacement of one community by another in an orderly and predictable manner. The succession begins with a pioneer community and terminates with a climax community.

Surface Fire. A type of forest fire that moves along the surface of the forest floor; it consumes litter, herbs, shrubs, and tree seedlings.

Sustained Yield. The concept that a forest or wildlife resource can be managed in such a way that a modest crop can be harvested year after year without depletion of the resource as long as annual decrements are counterbalanced by annual growth increments.

Synergistic Effect. A condition in which the toxic effect of two or more pollutants (copper, zinc, heat, and so on) is much greater than the sum of the effects of the pollutants when operating individually.

Taiga. The northern coniferous forest biome, which is typically composed of spruce, fir, and pine.

Tannin. A substance derived from tree bark that is employed in tanning leather.

Taproot. The type of root system characterized by one large main root; for example, that of a beet or carrot.

Telemetry. The electronic technique involving a transmitter-receiver system in which the movements and behavior of animals (deer, elk, grizzly bear, salmon, etc.) are monitored from a distance.

Terracing. A soil conservation technique in which steep slopes are converted into a series of broad-based "steps"; the velocity of runoff water is thus retarded and soil erosion is arrested.

Territory. An area that is defended by a member of one species against other members of that same species.

Tertiary Sewage Treatment. The most advanced type of sewage treatment, which not only removes the BOD and the solids but also the phosphates and nitrates; the installation of such a plant at Lake Tahoe has arrested eutrophication of the lake.

Thermal Inversion. An abnormal temperature stratification of the lower atmosphere in which a layer of warm air overlies a layer of cooler air. Such an inversion frequently occurs at heights from 100 to 3,000 feet, resulting in stagnation of the air mass below the inversion; it contributes to air pollution problems, especially in industrial areas.

Thermocline. The middle layer of water in a lake in summer characterized by a temperature gradient of more than 1° C per meter of depth.

Throughput. An economics term that relates to the amount of materials being produced and consumed in a given society.

Transpiration. The evaporation of water from the breathing pores (stomata) of a plant leaf; an oak tree may transpire 100 gallons per day, almost 40,000 gallons per year.

Tundra. The type of biome occurring in northern Canada and Eurasia north of the timberline; it is characterized by less than ten inches of annual rainfall, sub-zero weather in winter, a low-lying vegetation composed of grasses, lichens, mosses, and dwarf willows, a fauna composed of lemmings, Arctic foxes, caribou, and snowy owls, and an abbreviated growing season of six or seven weeks.

2,4–D. A herbicide that kills a weed because it mimics the plant's growth hormones, causing it to grow more rapidly than can be sustained by its supply of oxygen and food materials.

2,4,5–T. An herbicide that operates on the same principle as 2 ,4–D above.

Upwelling. The movement of nutrient-rich cold water from the ocean bottom to higher levels by means of vertically moving currents.

Vessel Element. The elongate xylem cell in a tree trunk or branch that has water-transportation as a major function.

Watershed. The total area drained by a particular stream; may range from a few square miles in the case of a small stream to thousands of square miles in the case of the Mississippi River.

Water Table. The upper level of water-saturated ground.

Wet Scrubber. An air pollution control device that washes contaminants from the outgoing air stream by means of a water spray.

Xerophytes. Specialized plants that are well adapted to survive in arid regions because of such water-conserving features as reduced leaves, recessed stomata, thick cuticles, accelerated life cycles, periodic dormancy and the presence of water-storing (succulent) tissues.

Xylem. A type of tissue occurring in the trunks and branches of trees (and other plants) that serves to transport water and nutrients from the roots to the leaves, and also provides support.

Zooplankton. Minute animals (protozoans, crustaceans, fish embryos, insect larvae, and so on) that live in a lake, stream, or ocean and are moved aimlessly by water currents and wave action.

Index

ABS (alkyl-benzene-sulfonate) detergents, 148
Abyssal zone of ocean, 382–83
Acidity, of soil, 55
Agassiz Wildlife Refuge, 325
Air pollution, 457–503
  as cause of cancer in man, 485
  emissions in the United States, 462
  equipment for controlling, 492
  human eyes and, 465
  laboratory research and, 5, 488
  lung damage and, 486
  oil refineries and, 468
  satellite photo of, 664
Aircraft noise, reduction of, 511–12
Algal blooms, 143–45
Alluvial soils, 60
Alpha rays, 589

* Bold numbers refer to illustrations.

Aluminum cans, recycling of, 522–23
American eel, introduction of, 362
Ammonification, 24
Animal manure, use of, 95
Annular rings, in trees, 222
Artificial propagation of fish, 356–61
Artificial reefs, 532
Artificial selection of fish, 374
Asbestos, 546–49
    as cause of cancer, 548–49
    cyanosis, 548
    human lungs and, 546–48
    dispersal of, 546
    industrial use of, 546
    mesothelioma, 548–49
Astronaut on moon, **2, 662**
Aswan Dam
    controversy over, 128–30
    irrigation of, 628
Atlantic Salmon, 375
Atomic bomb, 590
Atomic Energy Commission, 573, 597
Atomic structure, 589
Atomic weight, 589
Automobile
    emissions, **502**
    junked, 525–27
    noise, reduction of, 510–11

Background radiation, 590, 596
Bacteria
    nitrogen-fixing, 56
    in soil, 57
Banding Canada goose, **328**
Bark beetles, as forest pests, 255–57
Bass nest, **343**
Bear River Wildlife Refuge, 291
Beta rays, 589
Big Bend Gambusia, 375–76
Big blue-stem, **188**
Biological control of pests, 444–49
    synthetic hormones and, 448–49
    use of with rabbits, 447–48
    use of with St. John's wort, 445–47
Biological succession, 38–40
Biomass, pyramid of, 29–30
Biomes of North America, 41–46
Biotic potential, 34
    of fish, 342–43
    of marine fish, 387

of wildlife, 283–86
Bird banding, 325–28
Birth control, rhythm method of, 621
Births in underdeveloped countries, **610**
Bison, depletion of, 274–76
Black lung disease, 484
Blister rust
    dissemination of spores, **251**
    fungicides and, **252**
Blue-green algae, 143
BOD (biological oxygen demand), 150–53
Boreal forest biome, 41–43
Botulism, waterfowl mortality and, 290–92
Bottles, as solid waste, 523–25
Brackish water regions, **179**
Breeder reactor, 600–601
Bristlecone pine in California, 223
Brown trout, introduction of, 362–63
Browse improvement, for deer, 317–18
Browse line, of deer, 292
Brush fire in California, 123
Buffalo grass, 202
Buffalo suckling calf, **275**

California Aqueduct, **185**
California condor, 279
California Water Plain, **182, 184**
California Water Project, 181–85
Canada goose, 323, 520
Cancer
    asbestos and, 548–49
    radiation and, 598–99
Cannibalism, 615
Cannon net, 326–27
Cans
    recycling of, 522–23
    as solid waste, 519–23
Carbon cycle, 24–26
Carbon dioxide fixation, 19
Carbon monoxide, effect of on man, **488**
CARE Food Crusade Program, **643**
Carolina parakeet, 279
Carp
    introduction of, 363
    seining operation, **372**
    spearing, **364**
    waterfowl depletion and, 287–88
Carrying capacity, 34
Catalytic converter, **501**
Cattle breed selection, 203–205

Hereford, 203
Santa Gertrudis, 205
Cattle feed lot, **147**
Central Valley, California, **132**
Chain reactions, 589–90
Channel catfish
introduction of, 362
stocking of, **357**
Channelization, of streams, 130–31
Chernozem soils, 65–67
Chestnut blight, 249–50
Chickadee, black-capped, **305**
Chlorinated hydrocarbons, 426
Chlorophyll, 19
Civilian Conservation Corps, 7
Classification of natural resources, 13–14
Clearcutting controversy, 235–37
Clostridium botulism, 291
Clutch size in birds, 283–84
Coal, 560, 562–64
discovery of, 560
formation of, 25, 560, 562–64
gasification of, 563–64
shaft mining of, **561**
strip mining of, 562–63
United States production of, 561
Coho salmon, introduction of, 361
Coliform bacteria, 159
Collection of solid waste, 529–30
Community
defined, 20
pioneer, 38
Compensation depth, 336
Composting, solid waste disposal and, 531–32
Conflicts in government, 10–11
Coniferous forest biome, 41, 43
Conservation
citizen involvement and, 11–12
education, 11
history of in United States, 5–10
principles, 15–16
Contour farming, 84
Contour plowing, 83
Cooling towers, **156, 556, 595**
Cotton boll weevil, **428**
Crisis, environmental, 1–2
Croaker, life cycle of, 384–86
Crop rotation, 97–98
Cropland requirements in United States, 99–101

Cyclic populations, 298–99

Dams
Aswan Dam controversy, 128–30
disadvantages of, 125–30
flood control and, 125–30
reservoir evaporation losses, 127–28
siltation, 127
Decibel scale, 505–506
Deciduous forest biome, 43
DDT, 3, 426, 428, 430, 431, 432, 433, 434, 436, 437, 440, 441, 442, 443, 444, 449, 451, 452
Deer
aerial census of, 316
browse cutting for, 292, 317–18
irruption on the Kaibab Plateau, **298**
management, 316–20
mortality factors, 292–97
accidents, 260, 294–95
irruptions, 297, 298
predation, 295–97
starvation, 292–94
population, 37, **319**
problems in forest management and, 244–45
regulation of harvest, 2, 318–20
Deferred grazing system, 198–99
Denitrifying bacteria, 24
Density-dependent factors, 35–36, 37
Density-independent factors, 35–36
Desalination methods, 178–80
Desert
animal adaptations and, 46
biome, 43–44, **45**
plant adaptations, 44–46
soils, 65–67
Detergents, 148–49
Diet, 31–32, 300–301
Disease organisms
coliform bacteria, 159
Salmonella, 160
viruses, 160
Disposal, solid waste, 530–34
Dissolved oxygen, polluted water and, 151
Drainage, waterfowl depletion and, 286–87
Drought, 114–16
effect on reservoir, **115**
range grasses and, 193–94

Dumps
  open burning at, **528**
  solid waste disposal and, 530–31
Dust Bowl, 7–8, 75, **76, 77**
Dust storm, **74, 76, 77**
Dutch elm disease
  control of, 434–37
  elm bark beetle and, **437, 438**
  fungus, **436**

Eagle, golden, **304**
Ear, structure of human, **508**
Earth Day, 674
Earthworms, soil formation and, 59
Ecological pyramids, 26–30
Ecology, organizational levels and, **21**
Economy, environment and, 649–61
Ecosystem
  balanced and unbalanced, **22**
  defined, 20
Egg shell thinning, 440–41
Electric car, **499**
Elemental cycle, 22–26
Energy
  conservation of, 581–85
  conversions, 27–28
  pyramid of, 30–32
  sources, future prospect, 586
Energy crisis
  America's high living standard and,
    558–59
  causes of, 554–59
  economic incentive, 556
  environmentalist obstruction, 556–57
  fuel import restrictions, 554
  high sulfur fuel restrictions, 558
  oil embargo, 554
  pollution control and, 558
  poor estimate of needs, 555
Engelmann spruce bark beetle larvae, **256**
Environmental impact of economic growth,
    658–61
Environmental Protection Agency, 10
Environmental Teach-In of 1970, 13
Epilimnion, 336
Erosion, geological, **50**
Estrogen, contraception and, 617
Estuarine ecosystem, 383–86
Estuary of San Joaquin River, 383
Euphotic zone of ocean, 382

Euryphagous animal, 300
Eutrophication, 142–49, 168
  algal blooms and, 143–45
  at Lake Tahoe, **144, 168**
  eutrophic lake, 142–43
  oligotrophic lake, 142–43
  rooted weeds, 145
  sources of nutrients, 146–49
  survey, **144**
Everglade kite, 279–80
Exotics, introduction of, 309, 362–63
Extinction of wildlife, 278–83

Fall overturn, 340
Federal Energy Office, 554
Fermi nuclear reactor, 601
Fertilization, in humans, **618**
Fertilization of water for fish production,
    367–68
Fertilizers
  harmful effects of, 98
  inorganic, use of, 97–98
  use of in increasing food production, 629
Fire, range management of, 199–200
Fire Scan, **266**
Fish
  culture in Asia and, **638**
  effect of pesticides on, 442
  effect of toxic materials on, **172**
  habitat of, 364, 366, 367
  mortality rate of, 343–53
Fish kill, **5, 150, 153, 345, 347, 348, 349,
    350, 392**
Fisheries management, 354–76
  artificial propagation and, 356–61
  endangered species and, 375
  habitat improvement, 363–74
  introduction of, 361–63
  legislation of, 354–55
  selection of superior fish, 374
Fishery resource, **408**
Fishing pressure, 353
Fission, nuclear, 589
Floods, 116–21
Flurosis, in cow, **481**
Flyways, waterfowl, 327–29
Food chains, 28
Food donations, 641–43
Food production
  methods of, 623–41

new strains of rice and, **639**
selective plant breeding and, **636**
underdeveloped countries and, **645**
wild game ranches and, **641**
Food synthesis, 623–24
Food web, 28–29
Ford motor car, *Model T*, **497**
Forests
   destructive agents of, 247
   economic value of, 216–17
   exploitation of, 227–31
   management of, 233, 268
   multiple uses of, **245**
   prescribed burning of, **267**
   products of, **217**
   resources, 216–72
   types of in the United States, 227
   use of as recreational area, **246**
Forest fire
   chemical control of, 265
   control of, 257–67
   damage and, **259**
   danger meter, **261**
   smokejumpers, and control of, **264**
   tower lookout, **262**
Forest Service (United States), 231–32
Forestry
   clear cutting of Douglas fir, **234**
   sustained yield plan, 233
Fossil fuels, future use of, 575
Four Corners power plant, 562
Fox, red, 310
FPC (fish protein concentrate), **625**
FSH (follicle stimulating hormone), 617
Fungicides, 426
Furunculosis, in fish, 351

Gallinaceous guzzler, **301**
Game laws, 308–309
Gamma rays, 589
Gasoline shortage, 552–54, **566**
Genetic damage, radiation and, 600
Geothermal energy, 577–79
Glacial drift, 51
Glacial sediment, **663**
Glaciers, erosion and, **110**
Glasphalt, 525–26
Glass, recycling of, **525**
Glassification, nuclear waste and, 597
Glen Canyon Dam, 126

Globigerina ooze, 24–25
Gnat control, 439
Grand Canyon, influence of geological
   erosion on, **78**
Grass plant biology, 192–93
Grasshopper, **210**, 211–12
Grassland biome, 43
Gray whale, 417
Grazing districts, 191
Great Barrier Reef, 24
Green manure, use of, 95–96
Green house effect, **474**
GNP (Gross National Product), 554,
   650–54
Ground water
   hydrologic cycle and, 112
   industrial use of, **170**
Grouse
   drumming on log, **303**
   newly hatched young, **442**
   ruffed, young newly hatched, **306**
Gullies, 79, 86, 102
Gully reclamation, 85
Gypsy moth
   as forest pest, 253–55
   trap, **254, 446**
Gypsy moth caterpillars, **253**

Habitat development
   for fish, 363–74
   for water fowl, 320–25
   for wildlife, 299–305, 311–15
Hardpan soil, 60
Hare, population cycles of, 299
Heat island, 473
Hepatitis, polluted water and, 160
Herbicides, 453
Hereford cattle, **204**
Herring catch, dominance of age class and,
   393
Hiroshima, bombing of, 599–600
Home range, of wildlife, 302–303
Homestead Act, 649
Human survival, 674–75
Humus, 60
Hunting animals, novel uses and, 281
Hunting regulations, waterfowl and,
   329–30
Hurricane, satellite photo of, **663**
Hutterites, population growth among, 644

Hybridization, of fish, 374
Hydrocoele, 600
Hydrologic cycle, 109
Hydropower, 579
Hypolimnion, 336

Ibex, extinction of, 281
Imperial Valley, 132–33
Incineration, of solid waste, 532–33
India, environmental impact of population, 607–609
Indian Point Nuclear Power Plant, 596
Insect infestation of timber, **253**
Integrated control of pests, 449–50
Interdependence, on environmental matters, 672–73
International Commission on Environmental Quality, 672–73
International Commission on Radiologic Protection, 590
Intrauterine device, **619, 620**
Inventories of resources, 16
Irish potato famine, 29
Irrigation, 131–38
    canal, 129, 135
    consumptive use of water, 138
    dams and, 133, 135
    ground water depletion, 137–38
    history of, 132
    Imperial Valley, 132–33
    salinization, 136–37
    water loss during transit, 135–36
Irruptions, of deer, **297**
Isotopes, 589

James River, North Dakota, 149
Juvenile dispersal, 305

Kaibab National Forest, **297**
Kangaroo rats, as range pests, 212
Kirtland's Warbler, 278–79
Klamath Basin Wildlife Refuge, 325
Kwashiorkor, 614

Lake ecosystem
    discussion of, 335
    distribution of oxygen and temperature and, 338–39
spring and fall overturn in, **339**
stereo view, **337**
Lake Erie, pollution and, 9
Lake Mattamuskeet Wildlife Refuge, 316–17
Lake Mead, 127
Lake Tahoe, 168–69
Laminated beams, testing strength of, **269**
Lamprey
    adult, **369**
    control of, 368–71
    larvae, 370
Land
    abuse of, 70–72, 73–78
    ethic, deterioration of, 5
Landfills, solid waste disposal and, 531
LAS (linear-alkylate-sulfonate) detergents, 148–49
Laterization, 626
Law of tolerance, **33**
Lead, 541–46
    poisoning by, 289–90, 542–46
    source of in human environment, 542–43
    use of leaded gasoline, 543
Lemming, population cycles, 298
Levees, in flood control, 124
Limiting factors, 32–33
Limits to Growth, 667–68
Limnetic zone, 336
Litter, highways and, **219**
Litter size in mammals, 285
Littoral zone, 336
Livestock
    breeding programs, 638–40
    feeding, **640**
Locust outbreaks, control of, 634
Logging, **229, 239**
Los Angeles, smog and, **472**
Lynx, population cycles of, 299

Magnetohydrodynamics, 580–81
Malaria control, in Ceylon, 611
Malathion
    insect spray, **424**
    used in grasshopper control, **211**
Malthusian theory, 668
Management
    of fish, 375
    of waterfowl, 320–30

Man-Environment Communications
    Center, 12
Manure, use of, 95–96
Marine ecosystem
    major features of, 380
    zonation of, 381
Marine fish, 387–409
    competition for food among, 392–93
    distribution and water temperature,
      389–91
    mortality of, 391–98
Marine fisheries management, 402–409
    artificial reef construction, 403
    introduction of upwelling, 403
    introduction of, 402
    regulation of fishing pressure, 403–408
    transplantations, 402–403
Marine food chains, 386
Marine mammals, 414–19
    Alaskan fur seal, 414–16
    whales, 416–19
Marine shellfish, 409–414
    oyster fishery, 410–14
    shrimp fishery, 409–10
Marsh drainage, food production and, 627
Mass emigration, 306
Meat shortage, in United States, 187–88
Menhaden fishermen, 379
Mercury, 536–41
    in fish food chains, 540–41
    industrial use of, 536, 540, 541
    inorganic, 537
    Minamata Bay episode, 537
    movement through ecosystem, 536–38
    poisoning by, 536–41
    restrictions on use of, 541
    seed grain treated with, 539
    use of in chlor-alkali industry, 540–41
Mesothelioma, 548–49
Mesquite, 207, 209
Microcephaly, 600
Microhabitat, 38
Migration
    of golden plover, 307
    of marine fish, 387–89
    of wildlife, 306–308
Milorganite, 166
Milwaukee, power shortage, 552
Mono Dam, siltation of, 580
Mono Reservoir, 127
Moon, surface of, 662

Motor vehicles, environmental impact of,
    660–61
Movements of animals, 305–308
    altitudinal migration, 308
    dispersal of young, 305
    latitudinal migration, 306–308
    mass emigration, 306
Multiflora rose, use in hedges, 313
Multiple use of resources, 15
Muskrats, improving habitat for, 315
Mutations, induced by radiation, 600
Myxomatosis virus, use of in rabbit
    control, 447–48

Nagasaki, bombing of, 599–600
National Seed Storage Laboratory, 635
Natural gas, 568–73
Neritic zone of ocean, 382
Nests, artificial for waterfowl, 323–25
Newspapers, use of as cattle food, 520
Nitrification, 24
Nitrogen
    cycle, 22–24
    intoxication, in salmon, 352
Nitrogen-fixing bacteria, 56
Nitrogen-fixing legumes, 25
Nixon conservation program, 9
Noise
    levels, 506
    pollution, 504–16
North American Water and Power
    Alliance, 627, 630
North American Wildlife and Resources
    Conference, 8
NTA (nitrilo-triacetic acid), 149
Nuclear bomb, 590
Nuclear fission, 589
Nuclear power plants, 591–97
    design and operation of, 591–92
    proliferation of, 602
    prospect for, 601–602
    radioactive emissions, 596
    radioactive waste disposal, 596–97
    reactor core, 592
    thermal pollution, 593–96
Nuclear reactor
    cooling system, thermal pollution and,
      154
    cooling towers for, 595
    core, 592

Oak wilt, 248
Ocean
  major characteristics of, 380
  as part of hydrologic cycle, 109
  pollution of, 378–80, **663**
  value to man, 379–80
  zonation of, 380–83
Oil, 564–74
  consumption rate in United States,
    564–65
  discovery of, 565
  exploration, Arabian desert, 567
  imports, 565
  pollution, 395–401
    as cause of waterfowl depletion,
      288–89
    control of, 398–401
    marine fish mortality and, 395–98
  production in the United States, 566
  shales, 573–74
  spills, **395, 397, 398, 399, 400, 401**
  wells, Titusville, Pennsylvania, 565
Optimum yield, 35
Organic phosphate pesticides, 425–26
Organizational levels, studied in ecology,
  20–21
Osprey, **441**
Overgrazing, rabbits and, 448
Overpopulation, multiple effects of, 611
Owl pellets, analysis of contents, 311
Oxygen control, fish habitats and, 373
Oxygen-demanding organic waste
  BOD test, 150–51
  effect of on stream life, 151
  fish mortality and, 346
Oyster
  culture, **413, 414, 415**
  fishery, 410–14
  shells, **411**
Ozone, tobacco damage and, **478**

Passenger pigeon, 281–83
Patuxent Research Center, 324–26
Peccary
  in desert biome, 214
  exonerated as range pest, 213–14
Pelicans, removal of oil from, **396**
Percolation test, 105
Peregrine falcon (duck hawk), 452
Pest control, use of airplane in, **430**

Pesticides, 422–55
  benefits derived from, 428
  causes of pests, 423
  classification of, 425–27
  cycling of, 434–39
  effect of, 427, 439–44
  manufacture and use of, 423
  negative features of, 428–34
  pest control, 454
  survey of accumulations of, **432**
  suspected cause of pheasant mortality,
    439
  testing soil for, **431**
Pet trade, wildlife extinction and, 280
Petrochemicals, fossil fuels and, 575
Petroleum, world reserves of, 567
Photosynthesis, 19, 21, 32
Phreatophytes, 180
Phytoplankton, 336
Pine beetle, **255**
Pine seedling, **238**
Pintail, long distance flights of, 326–27
Pioneer community, 38
Planet Earth, future of, 671
Plant breeding programs, 635
Plastic, as solid waste, 528–29
Precipitation, hydrologic cycle and,
  110–11
Predation on fish, 351–53, 391
Predator control, 310–11
Prescribed burning, 266–68, 279, **314**
Primary production, 32
Primary succession, 38–40
Principles of conservation, 15–16
Producer, 28
Profundal zone, 336
Progesterone, birth control and, 617
Protein, caloric intake and, 613
Pulp chipper machine, **269**
Pulp logs at New York mill, **218**
Purse seining, 406
Podzol soils, 63–65
Poison, human environment and, 536–49
Pollution control, 655–58
Population
  by age groups in developed and less
    developed countries, 607
  cycle, of hare and lynx, **299**
  defined, 20
  growth
    curves, 34–35

rate of, 611
since 1900, **606**
human, increase of, 2
methods of controlling human rate, 616–22
regulations of, 35
ten centuries of global growth, 605
Potato famine, in Ireland, 29
Potholes, 286–87, 321–22
Pyramid
of biomass, 29–30
of energy, 30–32
of numbers, 29–30
Pyramids, ecological, 26–30
Pyrolysis, solid waste and, 533–34

Quail, population fluctuations of, 311

Rabbit
cottontail, 312
explosion in Australia, **447**
Radiation, 589–96
background, 590, 596
human health and, 598–600
Radioactive material
fallout, 590–91
isotopes, 589
pollution of water by, 161–62
strontium, 590–91
Rainmaking, 181
Range management, 194–214
nutrition of livestock, 205–206
pest control and, 206–14
of range grasses, 194–203
selection of cattle breeds, 203–205
Range of tolerance, 33–34
Range pest control, 206–14
grasshoppers, 210–12
jackrabbits, 212
kangaroo rats, 212
mesquite, 206–208
poisonous plants, 208–10
predators, 213
Rangelands, 189–214
burning of, **199**
depletion and abuse of, 189–91
drought, 193–94
fire control on, **200**
grass plant biology, 192–93

range management, 194–214
reseeding of, 201
Taylor Grazing Control Act, 191–92
Recreational use of forests, 245–47
Red tide, 391–92
Redwoods of California, **222**
Reforestation, 238–41
Refuge, for waterfowl, 325
Reproductive system
female, **617**
male, **615**
Reserve Mining Company, 657
Reservoir evaporation losses, 127–28
Resources
classification of, 13–14
consumption of, 3
exhaustion of, 667
inventories, 16
Respiration, 24 25, 32
Rice paddies in Java, **637**
Rice weevil, **429**
Rodenticides, 426
Root systems, compared, **190**
Rough fish, 350–51
chemical control of, **371**
removal of, 371–73

Salinization, result of irrigation, **136**
Salmon
coho salmon, **362**
hatchery, 355, **359**
leaping falls, **353**
mortality, 352–53
nitrogen intoxification of, 352
purse seining, **406**
Salt mines, radioactive waste disposal and, 597
Salvage, of junked cars, 525–26
Sanitary landfill, 531
Santa Barbara oil spill, 400–401
Santa Gertrudis cattle, **205**
Schistosomiasis, 128
Sea lamprey control, 368–71
Seal, Alaskan fur, 414–16
Sediment
control basin, **103**
pollution, 160–61
Sedimentation, cause of, **161**
Selective cutting, in forest, 237–38
Septic tank problems, 105

Sewage discharge, stream life and, 152
Sewage treatment and disposal, 162–69
  plant, 165–66
  primary, 165–67
  secondary, 167–68
  sludge digester, 165–66
  sludge disposal, 165–67
  tertiary, 168–69
Shale
  of Chattanooga, 601
  oil hills, 573
Shelterbelt
  influence on wind velocity, **88**
  in Kansas, **88**
  in North Dakota, **87**
Shifting stocking levels, **196**
Shortage, power, 552
Shrimp fishery, 409–10
Silt
  pollution, by satellite photo, **385**
  transport by river, **50**
Siltation
  of dam reservoirs, **127**
  fish mortality and, 344
Slash pine plantation, **236**
Sludge disposal, 165–67
Smelt
  haul of, **363**
  introduction of, 362
Smog
  over New York City, **466**
  over San Francisco, **464**
  over St. Louis, **476**
Snail fever, 128
Snow surveyors, **124**
Snowmobile, noise pollution and, **507**
Soil Conservation Service program, 89–93
Soil
  erosion, 78–89
    control of in rural environment,
      83–89
    influence of cover, 82
    nature of, 78–83
  fertility, restoration of, 95–99
  formation, 48–51
  groups, 62–67
  maps, **62**
  nutrients, 92–99
    depletion of, 93–95
    and human health, 99
    macronutrients, 92–93

    micronutrients, 93
    movement of, 53
  profile, 59–61
  problems in urban-suburban environ-
    ment, 101–105
  properties of, 51–59
    biotic composition, 57–59
    gaseous content, 55–56
    moisture content, 55
    structure, 53–55
    texture, 51–52
  role of fungi and bacteria in, **58**
  slide, **104**
  structure, 54
  textural classes, **52**
  water content of, **56**
Soil Erosion Service, 7–8, 77
Solar energy, 30, 575–77
Solid waste, 518–34
  collection methods, 529–30
  disposal methods, 530–34
  types of, 518–29
Space exploration, 661, 664
Space vehicle blast-off, 653
Spaceship Earth, **654**
Spawning sites for fish, 365, 367
Spring overturn, 336
Sprinkler irrigation, **134**
Starling, introduction of, 309
Steady state society, 668
Stenophagous diet, 300
Stock manipulation, range management
  and, 197
Stomata, 19
Stone Age Man, 518
Stream
  channelization, 130–31
  ecosystem, 340–42
  longitudinal zonation of, **342**
Strip cropping, 83–84
Strip mining
  coal mining, 80
  mine operation, **562**
  mined area, revegetation of, **563**
  mines and reforestation, 241
Stubble mulch tillage, **90**
Submarine disposal of waste, 532
Subsoil, 60
Succession
  in abandoned field, **39**
  biological, 38–40

in pond, **40**
primary, 38–40
Sulphur, use of in pest control, **427**
Summerkill of fish, 348–49
Surface water, hydrologic cycle and, 112
Sustained yield, of timber, 232
Swimming beach, pollution and, **141**

Taiga (biome), 43
Tar sands, 574
Taylor Grazing Control Act, 191–92
Temperature inversion, **470**, 472
Terracing, erosion and, 85
Texas longhorn, **183, 209**
Textile industry, environmental impact of, 659–60
Territories, wildlife habitat and, 303–305
Thermal pollution, 153–58, 593–96
    adverse effects, 155–56
    abatement of, 157–58
    benefits derived from, 158
    fish mortality and, 344–46, 394
Thermocline, 336
Thermodynamics, laws of, 27–28
Third Wave, conservation movement and, 8
Tidal power, 577
Tilapia, importance of in weed control, 365
Timber growth, effect of thinning on, **237**
Timgad, northern Africa, 72
Tires, as solid waste, 527–28
Tolerance ranges, 33–34
Topsoil, 60
Toxic industrial waste, mortality and, 346
Transmission lines, 555
Tree, 217–26
    anatomy and physiology of, 217–26
    annular rings of, **221**
    biology of, 219
    cross section of trunk, **221**
    reproductive organs of, 224–25
Trout
    season opening, **361**
    stocking of, **360**
Tse-tse fly, control of, 633
Tubifex worms, polluted water and, 151
Tuna catch, **388, 404, 407**
Tundra (biome), 41–43
Tundra food chain, 591

TVA (Tennessee Valley Authority), 8, **122, 563**
2, 4, -D, 453–55
2, 4, 5-T herbicide, 453–55
Typhoid fever, source in polluted water, 160

Undernutrition, 612
United Nations, 666
United States Forest Service, 231–32
United States, impact of population in, 607–609
Uranium, source of, 601

Vasectomy, **619**
Vernalization, 627
Viet Nam, defoliation program in, 454–55

Wastepaper, 518–19
Water, new sources of, 175–85
    asphalt coatings in desert, 177–78
    California Water Project, 181–85
    desalination, 178–80
    eradication of moisture-wasting plants, 180
    forest removal, 180
    ground water development, 177
    rainmaking, 181
    reclamation of sewage water, 176–77
Water pollution, 140–85
    categories of, 142–70
        detergents, **148**
        disease organisms, 159–60
        human waste, **163**
        industrial waste, **171**
        municipal sewage, **145**
        nutrients and eutrophication, 142–49
        oxygen-demanding organic waste, 150–51
        radioactive materials, 161–62
        sediments, 160–61
        thermal pollution, 153–58, 593–96
    industry and, 170–73
Water problems, 114–31
    drought, 114–16
    floods, 116–21
    flood control, 121–30

Waterfowl
  depletion of, 286–92
  early hunting of, 276
  flyways, **329**
  habitat improvement of, **321**
  management of, 320–30
    banding studies, 325–28
    flyway administration, 327–29
    habitat development, 320–25
    hunting regulations, 329–30
    refuge establishment, 325
  mortality, botulism and, 291–92
Watershed protection, flood control and, 121
Weather satellite, **663**
Weed control, fisheries management and, 365
Whales, preservation of, 416–19
Whaling industry, 417–19
White House Conference of 1962, 8
White House Conference on Natural Resources, 6
White pine blister rust, 250
Whooping cranes, 277–78
Wild game ranches, 640–41
Wildlife
  management, 244, 308–15
  resources, 273–333
    abuse and depletion, 274–83

biotic potential, 283–86
cyclic populations, 298–99
deer herd depletion, 393–97
extinction, 278–83
habitat requirements, 299–305
movements, 305–308
values of, 274
waterfowl depletion, 286–92
Wildlife Restoration Act of 1937, 8
Wind power, 580
Winterkill of fish, 346–49
Wisconsin Electric Company, 552
Wisconsin Institute of Environmental Studies, 557
Wisconsin Petroleum Institute, 557
Wood duck nest box, 323–24
Woodpecker, red-headed, 279
World Trade Center, use of energy by, 583

Xerophytes, 65

Yellowstone National Park, littering in, 5

Zooplankton, 336